the structure of matter

Robert W. Christy / Agnar Pytte
Dartmouth College

the structure of matter: an introduction to modern physics

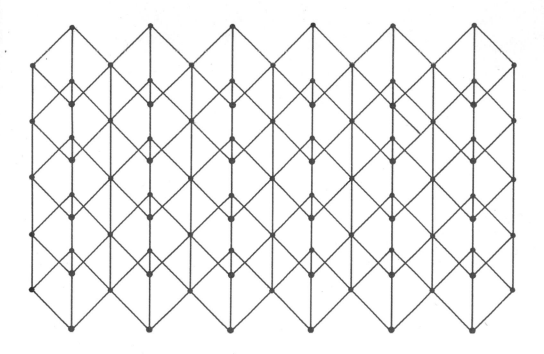

W. A. BENJAMIN, INC. 1965   NEW YORK / AMSTERDAM

THE STRUCTURE OF MATTER: AN INTRODUCTION TO MODERN PHYSICS

Library of Congress Catalog Card Number 65–10938
Manufactured in the United States of America

*The manuscript was put into production on July 2, 1964;
this volume was published on July 15, 1965*

W. A. BENJAMIN, INC.
New York, New York 10016

preface

This book is primarily designed for a two-semester course in contemporary physics, following a standard general physics course. It could also, with some omissions, be used for a one-semester course. The mathematical preparation which is assumed is a good grounding in calculus. The Dartmouth course for which the book was written has developed over the past ten years. It is required of all physics and engineering science majors in the sophomore year. Many chemistry and some mathematics and geology majors take it in their sophomore, junior, or senior year. It is a prerequisite for all junior and senior physics courses.

This is, of course, not the first book to present modern physics at an elementary level. The trend in such books over the past few decades has been a gradual increase in the level of sophistication, in response to corresponding advances in the introductory physics courses. Our book is intended to represent another step in this progress away from a descriptive and phenomenological approach. It is to this end that we have allowed two terms for the course and included an unusually large amount of background material on classical mechanics and kinetic theory in Parts I and II. Greater rigor is made possible by bringing the student farther along in these areas than the normal elementary course. (On the other hand, our intention is not to replace existing junior courses in classical physics; the result, however, is that such courses can be upgraded.)

Perhaps a more significant difference in viewpoint is in our reading of the term "modern." In the usage employed in the titles of textbooks, "modern" refers primarily to those great revolutions of half a century ago, quantum mechanics and relativity, especially as embodied in atomic and nuclear physics. On the other hand, in common parlance, "modern" means "contemporary," and much of contemporary physics, particularly in plasma and solid-state physics, is neither relativistic nor quantal. It seems to us that what really distinguishes contemporary physics and chemistry (and, to a growing extent, engineering) is its preoccupation with the *microscopic*. Therefore, we have taken as our organizing principle the *structure of matter*. Our aim is to understand the observable properties of matter in terms of the interactions of its microscopic constituents. Roughly the first half of the book is classical, in the sense of nonquantal. The separation of what *can* be explained by classical mechanics from what cannot is motivated, not by a die-hard loyalty but, by recognition of the practical importance of classical concepts and arguments in those cases where they apply. Furthermore, the limitations of the classical theory, as an approximation to the relativistic and quantum mechanical theories, are illuminated by the cases where it does apply as well as by the cases where it does not apply.

Our plan is to begin with the interactions of entire atoms in Part II, after the classical groundwork of Part I. On a smaller scale of microscopic distance, subatomic phenomena are treated in Parts IV and V, following the introduction to quantum mechanics of Part III. This arrangement is advantageous from the pedagogic point of view: In the first half, the treatment can be almost entirely classical, whereas the subatomic electronic and nuclear structure is essentially quantum mechanical. We therefore postpone as long as possible quantum mechanics, with its inherently greater conceptual difficulty and mathematical sophistication. Some initiation into partial differential equations is unavoidable in connection with the three-dimensional Schrödinger equation, but this is delayed until the students have had one more term of mathematics. For the same mathematical reason, the emphasis of the book is on mechanics and particles, in contrast to a relative neglect of electromagnetism and fields. The mathematical preparation of the students, which is assumed to include no previous acquaintance with partial differential equations, leads us to postpone any field-theoretical approach to physics.

Representative problems at the ends of the chapters have been carefully devised to exercise or develop each major point in the text. A special feature of the problems is that in some cases necessary numerical data have been intentionally omitted. The students are expected to look up the data in other references, in order to introduce them to the very important techniques of information retrieval. The necessary data can be found without going beyond the *Handbook of Chemistry and Physics* (Chemical Rubber Publishing Company). Other data not so easily located, especially in the areas of nuclear and elementary-particle physics, are included in extensive tables in the text. In addition, references to a small number of other books, a number which the student might reasonably be expected to use, are given at the end of each chapter.

A distinctive feature of this book is that its emphasis is on theoretical understanding and the agreement of theories with experimentally observed results. The instruments and machines by which the experiments are actually carried out are de-emphasized. We believe that it is the function of laboratory work to impart appreciation and familiarity with the techniques and attitudes involved in actual experimental observation.

In order to present this material in one semester to a class with superior preparation, some omissions would probably have to be made. To aid in planning an abbreviated coverage of the material, we may point out that, although in general our aim has been toward coherence and interdependence, some early chapters or sections can be skipped without serious loss of continuity. These sections, while not necessarily inherently less important, are not referred to in an essential way in later sections. (Other sections may of course be already familiar to certain students.) We suggest that omissions in the first half be chosen from the following: Chapter 2; Sections 4–2, 4–3, 5–4, 9–5, 9–7, 10–1, 10–4; Chapter 11; Chapter 12; Sections 13–3, 13–4, 13–8, 14–4, 14–7; and Chapter 15.

We feel that it is extremely important to introduce students to contemporary microscopic physics as early in the curriculum as this can be done without limiting the introduction to a purely descriptive approach. Contact with areas of current research interest is essential for the appreciation of physics as a vital and creative intellectual activity. For prospective physics students, this contact should, if possible, precede the final choosing of their major field of study. For many engineering and chemistry students, this course is their last course in physics; for them it gives a rigorous foundation for material which will underlie much of their future work. To both groups we hope to convey what makes physics exciting for contemporary physicists.

We wish to thank Professor Peter Roll of Princeton University for a critical reading of the manuscript and for useful suggestions.

ROBERT W. CHRISTY

AGNAR PYTTE

Hanover, New Hampshire
March 1965

contents

introduction

Man has described, in contemporary science, a fascinating microscopic world, populated by molecules, nuclei, mesons, and the like, which obey strange laws, not always the same as those which describe familiar events like the motion of billiard balls and the falling of stones. The inhabitants of this world of conduction electrons, nucleic acids, and so on, will never be directly perceived by human senses (although they may come close if you feel that what has been seen through a microscope has really been "seen"). Nevertheless, nearly all of the articles published in current physics journals refer, directly or indirectly, to this microscopic world. Even those developments which belong to applied science or engineering will in the last analysis be "understood" in terms of constructs like macromolecules, conjugated bonds, or the band theory of solids. The main purpose of this book is to introduce you to that microscopic world.

The introduction will not take the form of a concerted attempt to convince you that these basic particles must exist. The chronology of the discoveries and insights that motivated men to invent the concepts belongs to the history of science, and the logical analysis of the relation of the concepts to experimentally observable "meter readings" belongs to the philosophy of science. These fascinating fields deserve your attention, but they are distinct from physics. Therefore, considerations of historical or philosophical justification will not claim very much of our attention, but we will adopt the viewpoint of the working physicist, to whom the concept "electron" is as real as, for example, the concept "star." One can undeniably see the light emitted by a star, but one cannot handle the star, and the concept that it is an extremely hot gas of nuclei and electrons, with a complex structure, rather than, say, a hole pricked in the sky, requires a very involved collection of interpretive inferences; indeed, under certain circumstances, one can undeniably see the light emitted by an electron too. Therefore, while bearing in mind that our present notion of an electron has evolved from the ingenious models invented by certain imaginative physicists in order to explain uncomprehended experiments, we shall not try faithfully to recapitulate these events. Instead, we shall try to learn the properties of the particles, the laws which describe their behavior, and the methods by which one can deduce conclusions that can be compared with experimental observations made on real matter in the macroscopic sense. (The experimental methods by which the observations are actually made will not receive much attention, although hopefully some appreciation of these will be gained in laboratory work.)

The authoritative tone of the preceding paragraph is not meant to stamp out your healthy skepticism. On the contrary, the inclination to doubt and to reexamine is an essential ingredient of every scientist and, in a somewhat different way, of every engineer. The recommendation embodied in our approach is merely that temporarily, as an heuristic program, your critical faculties can most profitably be employed in trying to catch the mistakes of your teachers and textbook writers. Constructive skepticism requires a great intellectual effort—greater than learning. Ultimately, the fundamental ideas of physics are not immune to criticism. Since 1900 the foundations of physics have been changed in two very far-reaching respects. The creation of relativity theory by Einstein and the formulation of quantum mechanics by Schrödinger and Heisenberg have had effects which extend far beyond physics, not only to the technology of what we make, but even to man's philosophical conception of himself and his relation to the world. (It may be noted that such sweeping and profound revisions as these have been rather rare events in history. Whether their frequency will increase with the general acceleration of scientific effort, or whether they are the creation of really rare individuals, is an open question.)

In developing our model of the microscopic structure of matter, the subject falls into two big divisions. In the first, in which the atomic constitution of matter—gases, liquids, and solids—is studied, classical mechanics suffices for the most part. Atoms and molecules are sufficiently massive objects that, except at very low temperatures, it is unnecessary to use the new quantum mechanics. (Of course, one *could* use quantum mechanics: as it is a more complete theory, it gives the same answer as classical mechanics in those cases where the classical theory is applicable; but its use would be more cumbersome.) Therefore, some methods of classical mechanics are developed in Part I, which probably contains no fundamental ideas which are new to you. In Part II, these analytical techniques are applied to matter consisting of aggregations of large numbers of molecules. Here a new fundamental principle is introduced. Boltzmann's statistical principle is essential for discussing assemblies of very large numbers of objects, where it is futile to inquire about the exact behavior of any individual one of them. The principle manifests itself through "temperature," a concept which does not arise in the mechanics of a single particle, and it carries over intact when we take up quantum mechanics.

In the second major division, we investigate the internal structure of an atom itself, and here quantum mechanics is essential—in that classical mechanics usually gives a wrong, even nonsensical, answer. We therefore begin with a study of the laws and techniques of quantum mechanics in Part III. The theory is applied to the electronic structure of atoms in Part IV, either isolated atoms or in interaction with each other. In Part V a roughly analogous theory of the structure of the atomic nucleus is sketched.

We have not yet mentioned the other great twentieth-century revolution in physics, the theory of relativity. It is discussed in two parts. In Chapters 1 and 3 we introduce the mechanical effects of the relativistic change of mass with velocity, especially as they influence collisions of particles, and these will be used as needed. In Chapter 2 we analyze the revision of our notions of space and time made necessary by the theory and their mathematical formulation. This material is the most profound aspect of relativity, and it provides the real basis for the formalism of most fundamental physical theory, but we shall not make much further use of it. The combination of special relativity with quantum mechanics led to the prediction of the existence of antimatter. Our study of particles and antiparticles will be confined, however, to the phenomenological level. Relativistic quantum mechanics, because of its mathematical complexity, will not be treated. Incidentally, the term "classical" is often used in the sense of "nonrelativistic" rather than "nonquantum." To avoid confusion, only the second usage is adopted here; thus, every description is either relativistic or nonrelativistic and also either quantum or classical.

The mathematical preparation we have assumed is a good grounding in the calculus of functions of one variable, plus some acquaintance with probability, vector algebra, and the calculus of functions of several variables. Differential equations will be formulated and solved on numerous occasions, but it will not be assumed that you know much about them. One of the aims of this book is to afford an opportunity to exercise the mathematical ability you have acquired, to appreciate its usefulness and power in applications, and even to extend your mathematical knowledge—in short, to teach you to make sophisticated, careful, and accurate calculations.

A second and perhaps more important aim, however, is to teach you to make simple, rough, and unprecise calculations. These seemingly contradictory aims are actually complementary: if you do not know at all what to expect in a given physical situation, it is usually worthwhile to try to make a very crude estimate of the order of magnitude of the effect first. You really get much more information from this step than you do from a subsequent accurate but laborious calculation of a precise result. For example, if you have no idea whether the power output of a certain device will be a microwatt or a megawatt, it is immensely informative to estimate that it will be of the order of magnitude of 100 watts (i.e., not 10 and not 1,000).

For some purposes it may then be interesting to ascertain the detailed result that it is 60 watts rather than 75, but this difference is very pale compared to the difference between 100 watts and 100 megawatts. The concern with actual (but not necessarily precise) numbers is the core of physics.

We cannot close this introduction without referring to a rather trivial point—namely, the units in which the numbers are expressed. The choice of units is for most purposes a matter of convenience, although there are purists who adopt a stricter approach to the subject. The most convenient choice for atomic and electronic physics is the cgs (Gaussian) system, and that is the choice we shall usually make. The mks (Giorgi) system is more convenient for ac circuit analysis, since the electrical units coincide with those in technological use. For this reason, it has been favored by engineers, as has the English system for mechanical calculations. The mechanical equations are the same no matter what units are used, but it is conventional to write electromagnetic equations with slightly different constants depending on whether cgs or mks units are used. (There are no English electrical units.) For example, Coulomb's law of electric force is written $F = q_1 q_2 / r^2$ in cgs units and $F = q_1 q_2 / 4\pi\epsilon_0 r^2$ in mks units. This difference is the primary reason for the preference of physicists for the cgs system: the intuitively meaningful constant c, the velocity of light, enters many formulas when cgs units are used, in place of the less natural ϵ_0 and μ_0. At the end of a calculation using the cgs equations, the electrical units must be converted to volts and amperes; on the other hand, at the end of a calculation using the mks equations, the magnetic units must be converted to the commonly used gauss and oersteds. In any case, these conversion problems should be no more alarming than the conversion of centimeters to inches. (The conversion factors are listed in Appendix A.) There are also many other units in common use—angstroms, light years, calories, electron volts, etc.—which do not belong to any "system" but continue to be used because they are convenient. We hope you will acquire a flexibility in the use of units, become multilingual so to speak, in order to facilitate communication between people with diverging special interests.

I
CLASSICAL MECHANICS

The purpose of this text is to introduce you to the microscopic structure of matter. In doing so we build on what you have already learned in an introductory physics course, particularly the mechanics part of it. In fact, we shall find that the study of the atomic constitution of matter—gases, liquids, and solids—can largely be carried out within the context of classical particle mechanics. When we come to the study of the internal structure of the atom itself— the electronic structure of matter—a new mechanics, quantum mechanics, is needed. Even the quantum theory, however, leans heavily on the concepts of classical mechanics.

A knowledge of classical mechanics is therefore a prerequisite to the study of the structure of matter. An introductory physics course does not always give a sufficient background for the topics covered here. For this reason those aspects of the classical (as opposed to quantum) mechanics which are particularly relevant to our inquiry into the structure of matter are the subject of Part I of this book.

1/vectors and the equation of motion

The concepts of position, velocity, acceleration, and force are already familiar. It will be useful, however, to reconsider these notions from a somewhat more precise and elegant mathematical standpoint before introducing any new physical concepts. Accordingly, we shall in this chapter define vectors and some of the mathematical operations which can be carried out with them, and then summarize some of the most important kinds of force (a vector).

1-1 VECTOR ALGEBRA

Because our world is three dimensional, we must be able to symbolize events which occur in a three-dimensional space in order to describe it adequately. If we choose a particular Cartesian coordinate system, a point (for example, the point where a particular particle is located) is specified by the *triple of numbers* (x,y,z), where x, y, and z are the coordinates of the particle. (See Fig. 1–1.) We abbreviate the notation for the point using the *vector*

$$\mathbf{r} \equiv (x,y,z)$$

The vector $\mathbf{r}$, called the *position vector,* simply represents the ordered triple of numbers which are the three coordinates of the particle. We shall see that other vectors can be defined, so that not every vector represents the position of a particle, but all vectors are ordered triples of numbers. A vector is therefore a very different kind of mathematical entity from a single number. In order to emphasize the difference between a vector and a number, in this context a single number is called a *scalar*. Vectors will always be represented in **boldface type** and scalars in *italics*. We shall see shortly that a vector as defined here coincides with the more elementary description of it as a kind of "arrow," but the general mathematical theory develops most conveniently from its definition as a triple of numbers.

Our definition of the position vector appears to depend on the prior choice of a coordinate system, but actually the definition can be made *invariant* (i.e., independent of any particular coordinate system) by specifying the transformation of coordinates when the coordinate system is changed; this problem, although fundamental, need not concern us now. Nevertheless, it is worth noting that not every ordered triple of numbers constitutes a vector. For example, the pressure, volume, and temperature of a certain mass of gas (P,V,T) form a triple of numbers, but it is not a vector because, unlike the coordinates of a particle, the numbers P, V, and T do not depend on the choice of any coordinate system and so are unchanged in a coordinate transformation. We can ignore this problem here because all the vectors which we treat can be defined ultimately in terms of the position vector of a particle, and so the position vector can be taken as a prototype of vectors. A number of properties of vectors and operations on them will be defined, formally at first, and then we shall see that these have useful physical interpretations.

The *length* of the vector **r** is defined as

$$|\mathbf{r}| \equiv \sqrt{x^2 + y^2 + z^2}$$

and often it is written as $|\mathbf{r}| = r$ (the same letter but not in boldface). The length of a vector is not a vector, but just an ordinary number—a scalar. Geometrically, the vector can be represented by an arrow from the origin of the coordinate system to the point in question, and then the "length" of the vector is just the length of the line from the origin to the point (Fig. 1–1). The length is also called the *magnitude* of the vector.

The *product* of a scalar a and a vector **r** is defined as another vector,

$$a\mathbf{r} \equiv (ax, ay, az)$$

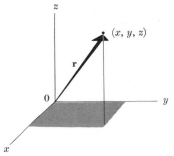

Fig. 1–1. Position vector **r**.

Geometrically, this is an arrow pointing in the same direction as **r**, but with a length a times as long, i.e. another vector. The *sum* of two vectors is also another vector, defined by

$$\mathbf{r}_1 + \mathbf{r}_2 \equiv (x_1 + x_2, \, y_1 + y_2, \, z_1 + z_2)$$

Geometrically, the sum of $\mathbf{r}_1$ and $\mathbf{r}_2$ is a vector which is the diagonal of the parallelogram formed by $\mathbf{r}_1$ and $\mathbf{r}_2$, or alternatively the third side of the triangle formed by laying $\mathbf{r}_1$ and $\mathbf{r}_2$ head to tail (Fig. 1–2(a)).

These rules of scalar multiplication and addition define an *algebra* of vectors. The vector algebra can be considered as an abstract mathematical theory, of which we have a particular concrete representation, or merely as an abbreviation for the geometrical relationships which have been described. The mathematical interpretation will not be emphasized here, but note that the addition is associative and commutative, and the scalar multiplication is distributive, according to the definitions given. For example,

$$\mathbf{r}_1 + (\mathbf{r}_2 + \mathbf{r}_3) = (\mathbf{r}_1 + \mathbf{r}_2) + \mathbf{r}_3$$
$$\mathbf{r}_1 + \mathbf{r}_2 = \mathbf{r}_2 + \mathbf{r}_1$$
$$a(\mathbf{r}_1 + \mathbf{r}_2) = a\mathbf{r}_1 + a\mathbf{r}_2$$
$$(a_1 + a_2)\mathbf{r} = a_1\mathbf{r} + a_2\mathbf{r}$$

Subtraction of two vectors can be defined in terms of addition (see Fig. 1–2(b)):

$$\mathbf{r}_1 - \mathbf{r}_2 = \mathbf{r}_3 \quad \text{if and only if} \quad \mathbf{r}_1 = \mathbf{r}_2 + \mathbf{r}_3$$

Consequently,

$$\mathbf{r}_1 - \mathbf{r}_2 = (x_1 - x_2, \, y_1 - y_2, \, z_1 - z_2)$$

The usefulness of the addition operation is apparent if $\mathbf{r}_1$ and $\mathbf{r}_2$ represent the positions of two different particles; then $\mathbf{r}_1 - \mathbf{r}_2$ is a vector which de-

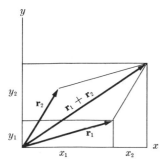

Fig. 1–2(a). *Sum of two vectors lying in the* xy-*plane.*

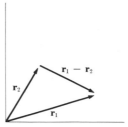

Fig. 1–2(b). *Difference of two vectors.*

scribes their relative separation. Or if $\mathbf{r}_1$ and $\mathbf{r}_2$ represent successive positions of the same particle, $\mathbf{r}_2 - \mathbf{r}_1$ represents the *displacement* between the two positions. The usefulness of multiplication by a scalar will be clear shortly.

Another useful operation is the *scalar product* (also called the dot product, from its notation) of two vectors:

$$\mathbf{r}_1 \cdot \mathbf{r}_2 \equiv x_1 x_2 + y_1 y_2 + z_1 z_2$$

The scalar product is commutative, i.e. $\mathbf{r}_1 \cdot \mathbf{r}_2 = \mathbf{r}_2 \cdot \mathbf{r}_1$. It is a scalar (a number) which is a function of (i.e., depends on) the two vectors $\mathbf{r}_1$ and $\mathbf{r}_2$. The scalar product is a *scalar function of two vectors*. It can be shown geometrically that an alternative expression for the dot product is

$$\mathbf{r}_1 \cdot \mathbf{r}_2 = r_1 r_2 \cos \theta$$

where θ is the angle between the vectors $\mathbf{r}_1$ and $\mathbf{r}_2$ (Fig. 1–3). Note that the length of a vector is the square root of the scalar product of the vector with itself, $r = (\mathbf{r} \cdot \mathbf{r})^{1/2}$.

A differently defined product of two vectors is also useful in physics. This is the *vector product* (or cross product, from its notation):

$$\mathbf{r}_1 \times \mathbf{r}_2 \equiv (y_1 z_2 - z_1 y_2,\ z_1 x_2 - x_1 z_2,\ x_1 y_2 - y_1 x_2)$$

This product is not commutative. In fact, $\mathbf{r}_2 \times \mathbf{r}_1 = -\,\mathbf{r}_1 \times \mathbf{r}_2$, so it is sometimes called *anticommutative*. The vector product is a *vector function of two vectors*, in that for every choice of $\mathbf{r}_1$ and $\mathbf{r}_2$ there is associated another vector $\mathbf{r}_1 \times \mathbf{r}_2$. It can be shown that an alternative expression for the cross product is given by

$$|\mathbf{r}_1 \times \mathbf{r}_2| = r_1 r_2 \sin \theta$$

together with the specification of the direction of $\mathbf{r}_1 \times \mathbf{r}_2$ as perpendicular to $\mathbf{r}_1$ and $\mathbf{r}_2$, in such a way that $\mathbf{r}_1$, $\mathbf{r}_2$, and $\mathbf{r}_1 \times \mathbf{r}_2$ form a right-handed system (Fig. 1–4). Note that the cross product of two parallel vectors is zero.

In the manipulation of vectors, it proves to be especially convenient to express all vectors as linear combinations of three particular vectors, called *basis vectors*. The three basis vectors point in the direction of the coordinate axes:

$$\mathbf{e}_x \equiv (1,0,0) \qquad \mathbf{e}_y \equiv (0,1,0) \qquad \mathbf{e}_z \equiv (0,0,1)$$

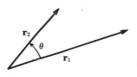

Fig. 1–3

Then, using the above-defined rules for vector addition and multiplication of scalars and vectors, clearly

$$\mathbf{r} = x\mathbf{e}_x + y\mathbf{e}_y + z\mathbf{e}_z$$

The scalars x, y, and z which multiply the basis vectors are called the *components* of $\mathbf{r}$. The basis vectors themselves are *unit vectors*, because their length is 1:

$$\mathbf{e}_x \cdot \mathbf{e}_x = \mathbf{e}_y \cdot \mathbf{e}_y = \mathbf{e}_z \cdot \mathbf{e}_z = 1 \tag{1-1}$$

Furthermore, they are mutually perpendicular, or *orthogonal*

$$\mathbf{e}_x \cdot \mathbf{e}_y = \mathbf{e}_y \cdot \mathbf{e}_z = \mathbf{e}_z \cdot \mathbf{e}_x = 0 \tag{1-2}$$

Unit vectors which are orthogonal are called *orthonormal*. Another useful relation between the orthonormal basis vectors, which follows easily from the rule for cross product, is

$$\mathbf{e}_x \times \mathbf{e}_y = \mathbf{e}_z \qquad \mathbf{e}_y \times \mathbf{e}_z = \mathbf{e}_x \qquad \mathbf{e}_z \times \mathbf{e}_x = \mathbf{e}_y \tag{1-3}$$

Henceforth, when we wish to refer vectors to a particular coordinate system, we shall always express them as a linear combination of the basis vectors, rather than as a triple of numbers. Indeed, if the relations between the basis vectors in Eqs. 1–1, 1–2, and 1–3 are memorized, it is not even necessary to remember the definitions of the vector operations in terms of triples of numbers. All calculations could be made using the associative and commutative relations for addition, the distributive law for multiplication of a scalar and vector, and the commutation relations for the two types of products of vectors. For example, if

$$\mathbf{r}_1 = x_1\mathbf{e}_x + y_1\mathbf{e}_y + z_1\mathbf{e}_z \qquad \mathbf{r}_2 = x_2\mathbf{e}_x + y_2\mathbf{e}_y + z_2\mathbf{e}_z$$

then

$$\begin{aligned}
\mathbf{r}_1 \cdot \mathbf{r}_2 &= (x_1\mathbf{e}_x + y_1\mathbf{e}_y + z_1\mathbf{e}_z) \cdot (x_2\mathbf{e}_x + y_2\mathbf{e}_y + z_2\mathbf{e}_z) \\
&= x_1 x_2 \mathbf{e}_x \cdot \mathbf{e}_x + x_1 y_2 \mathbf{e}_x \cdot \mathbf{e}_y + x_1 z_2 \mathbf{e}_x \cdot \mathbf{e}_z \\
&\quad + y_1 x_2 \mathbf{e}_y \cdot \mathbf{e}_x + y_1 y_2 \mathbf{e}_y \cdot \mathbf{e}_y + y_1 z_2 \mathbf{e}_y \cdot \mathbf{e}_z \\
&\quad + z_1 x_2 \mathbf{e}_z \cdot \mathbf{e}_x + z_1 y_2 \mathbf{e}_z \cdot \mathbf{e}_y + z_1 z_2 \mathbf{e}_z \cdot \mathbf{e}_z \\
&= x_1 x_2 + y_1 y_2 + z_1 z_2
\end{aligned}$$

Note also that two vectors are equal if and only if their components are equal.

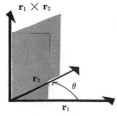

Fig. 1–4. *Vector cross product.*

1-2 VECTOR CALCULUS

We will next introduce some other vector functions and a calculus of vectors. Again, these can be regarded simply as abbreviated notations for expressions which could be written out in the ordinary way. Suppose the coordinates of the particle are functions of time t, a scalar, so that the particle moves:

$$x = x(t) \qquad y = y(t) \qquad z = z(t)$$

Then the position is a *vector function of a scalar:*

$$\mathbf{r}(t) = x(t)\ \mathbf{e}_x + y(t)\ \mathbf{e}_y + z(t)\ \mathbf{e}_z$$

Now the *derivative* of $\mathbf{r}$ with respect to t is defined as (Fig. 1–5)

$$\frac{d\mathbf{r}}{dt} \equiv \lim_{\Delta t \to 0} \frac{\mathbf{r}(t + \Delta t) - \mathbf{r}(t)}{\Delta t} = \frac{dx}{dt}\mathbf{e}_x + \frac{dy}{dt}\mathbf{e}_y + \frac{dz}{dt}\mathbf{e}_z$$

It is assumed that our coordinate system is fixed, so that the unit vectors $\mathbf{e}$ are independent of time. A useful notation (which we owe to Isaac Newton) for the time derivative is

$$\frac{d\mathbf{r}}{dt} = \dot{\mathbf{r}} \qquad \frac{dx}{dt} = \dot{x},\ \text{etc.}$$

The time derivative of the position vector $\mathbf{r}$ is another vector called the *velocity*. The magnitude of the velocity vector is called the *speed*. The components of the velocity are the time rates of change of the three coordinates:

$$\mathbf{v} \equiv \dot{\mathbf{r}} \qquad v_x = \dot{x},\ \text{etc.}$$

The velocity is a vector function of t, and its time derivative is another vector called the *acceleration*.

$$\mathbf{a} \equiv \dot{\mathbf{v}}$$

also written

$$\mathbf{a} = \ddot{\mathbf{r}} = \frac{d^2\mathbf{r}}{dt^2}$$

These definitions provide for the geometrical description of the motion of a particle in three dimensions, or *kinematics*. Having developed the descrip-

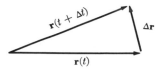

Fig. 1–5

tive apparatus that we need, we are now ready to introduce the physics, or *kinetics*, by defining forces and other physical quantities in terms of the position, velocity, and acceleration vectors already defined.

1-3 VECTOR OPERATORS

Before leaving the formal manipulation of vector functions, we shall digress for a moment to discuss derivatives with respect to the spatial coordinates as well as with respect to the time coordinate, since we shall eventually need to use them also. Consider a function $f = f(x,y,z)$. This function can be considered a *scalar function of a vector* $f = f(\mathbf{r})$, because specifying $\mathbf{r}$ means specifying the numerical values of x, y, and z, which in turn determines a specific numerical value of f. A simple example is the length of the vector $\mathbf{r}$:

$$f(\mathbf{r}) = |\mathbf{r}| \quad \text{or} \quad f(x,y,z) = (x^2 + y^2 + z^2)^{1/2}$$

Since $f(x,y,z)$ is a function of x, it can be differentiated with respect to x, treating y and z as if they were constants. This derivative is the *partial derivative with respect to x*, denoted

$$\frac{\partial f}{\partial x}$$

In the above example,

$$\frac{\partial f}{\partial x} = x/(x^2 + y^2 + z^2)^{1/2}$$

The partial derivatives with respect to y and z are defined and calculated in an analogous way. Now the quantity which we shall later have occasion to use is

$$\frac{\partial f}{\partial x}\mathbf{e}_x + \frac{\partial f}{\partial y}\mathbf{e}_y + \frac{\partial f}{\partial z}\mathbf{e}_z$$

It is a *vector function of position*, whose components are the three possible partial derivatives of the original scalar function f.

Because such vector functions arise so often in physics, it is convenient to define an operator ∇, which transforms the scalar function f into a vector function ∇f:

$$\nabla f \equiv \frac{\partial f}{\partial x}\mathbf{e}_x + \frac{\partial f}{\partial y}\mathbf{e}_y + \frac{\partial f}{\partial z}\mathbf{e}_z \tag{1-4}$$

The function ∇f is called the *gradient* of f. The operator ∇ is a *vector differential operator*, because it transforms the operand into a vector and at the same time it differentiates it. The gradient of f has some interesting geometrical properties which are responsible for the name "gradient," but we must forego a discussion of these properties. We may note, however, that

$$\nabla f \cdot d\mathbf{r} = \frac{\partial f}{\partial x}dx + \frac{\partial f}{\partial y}dy + \frac{\partial f}{\partial z}dz$$

This expression is called the *total differential* of $f(x,y,z)$,

$$df \equiv \frac{\partial f}{\partial x}dx + \frac{\partial f}{\partial y}dy + \frac{\partial f}{\partial z}dz$$

The differential df is an approximation for the change produced in f when simultaneously x is changed by dx, y by dy, and z by dz.

The gradient operator ∇ is sufficiently like a vector that two other operators suggest themselves, based on the dot- and cross-products of vectors. If

$$\mathbf{f} = f_x\mathbf{e}_x + f_y\mathbf{e}_y + f_z\mathbf{e}_z$$

is a *vector function of a vector*, the position vector $\mathbf{r}$, so that

$$f_x = f_x(x,y,z) \qquad f_y = f_y(x,y,z) \qquad f_z = f_z(x,y,z)$$

then we may define $\nabla{\cdot}\mathbf{f}$ and $\nabla \times \mathbf{f}$. Representing the operator ∇ as

$$\nabla \equiv \mathbf{e}_x\frac{\partial}{\partial x} + \mathbf{e}_y\frac{\partial}{\partial y} + \mathbf{e}_z\frac{\partial}{\partial z}$$

an obvious extension of the rules for multiplication of vectors leads to the definitions

$$\nabla{\cdot}\mathbf{f} \equiv \frac{\partial f_x}{\partial x} + \frac{\partial f_y}{\partial y} + \frac{\partial f_z}{\partial z}$$

$$\nabla \times \mathbf{f} \equiv \left(\frac{\partial f_z}{\partial y} - \frac{\partial f_y}{\partial z}\right)\mathbf{e}_x + \left(\frac{\partial f_x}{\partial z} - \frac{\partial f_z}{\partial x}\right)\mathbf{e}_y + \left(\frac{\partial f_y}{\partial x} - \frac{\partial f_x}{\partial y}\right)\mathbf{e}_z \qquad (1-5)$$

The first of these is called the *divergence* of $\mathbf{f}$, and the second is called the *curl* of $\mathbf{f}$. They are most important in describing the flow of fluids and electromagnetic fields, but we shall make little use of them in this book.

1-4   FORCE AND MASS

To introduce the actual physical content, in contrast to a mere geometrical description of motion, we shall make a fundamental definition—of "force." Then we shall write down a few general laws concerning some particular forces. With this simple basis, we will be able to develop an enormous amount of theory, although eventually we will see that modifications and additions are necessary in order to understand some aspects of the microscopic structure of matter.

In order to define force, we first imagine that we have defined *mass*. By mass, we shall mean the mass of a body at rest, or moving very slowly. Skirting a number of interesting philosophical problems, we may say, with sufficient (actually complete) rigor, that mass is what is measured by a balance. In the logical development of physics, the various concepts are precisely defined in terms of previously introduced concepts. In this logical structure, one can work back to the starting point, where a few concepts must be encountered that cannot be reduced to others (since the structure is finite and non-circular). These primitive concepts, such as "length," "time," and "mass," must be specified by an *operational definition* like the one just indicated for "mass." An operational definition explains exactly how the quantity in question should be measured. In the present case, the balance yields a single number for the mass of a body, so that "mass" is a scalar.

In order to get at the definition of force, we shall make a preliminary definition of *momentum*. The momentum **p** of a particle of mass m which is moving slowly is defined by

$$\mathbf{p} \equiv m\mathbf{v} \qquad (1\text{--}6)$$

The momentum is a vector by definition, since it is equal to a scalar times a vector. The momentum of a particle is then simply proportional to its velocity, but it proves to be a more useful quantity for some purposes, as we shall see in Chapters 3 and 6. Now we can define the *force* acting on a particle as the time derivative of its momentum:

$$\mathbf{F} \equiv d\mathbf{p}/dt \qquad (1\text{--}7)$$

The force is also a vector by definition, since it is the derivative of a vector with respect to a scalar. When the mass m is independent of time (as it is in most ordinary cases),

$$d\mathbf{p}/dt = d(m\mathbf{v})/dt = m\,d\mathbf{v}/dt = m\mathbf{a}$$

so that Eq. 1–7 reduces to the more familiar form,

$$\mathbf{F} = m\mathbf{a} \qquad (1\text{--}8)$$

According to Eq. 1–7 or 1–8, the force vector acting on a particle at any time can be measured by observing the kinematical behavior of the particle (its acceleration), provided that its mass is known. This definition of force is also called *Newton's Second Law*. Why is a mere definition regarded as one of man's greatest insights and noblest achievements? The answer is that this particular definition of force is extremely *useful*, because we find that, with this definition of force, the forces acting on a particle in a particular situation can be very simply described. With some other definition of force, we might find that the force acting on a particle depended on the time of day, the weather, the observer's mood, etc. But with this definition we can abstract from all such "extraneous" factors and write down the required force if we know a few simple facts about the physical environment of the particle. We will mention several examples in Section 1–5 and examine a few of them in more detail in the following chapters.

The first form of Newton's law, Eq. 1–7, is more fundamental than Eq. 1–8, because Eq. 1–7 is valid even when the mass is not constant. An example is the powered flight of a *rocket*, when the mass continually decreases as the fuel is exhausted. A much more profound example of the superiority of the formulation $\mathbf{F} = d\mathbf{p}/dt$ stated in Eq. 1–7, which could not have been anticipated by Newton, occurs when any particle is moving at very high speed, where "high" in this context means comparable with the speed of light c. Such a case is called *relativistic*, for reasons which are explained below. In the relativistic case, the relation

$$\mathbf{F} = d\mathbf{p}/dt \tag{1-7}$$

is still valid, but, experimentally, it is necessary to define *relativistic momentum* by

$$\mathbf{p} \equiv m\mathbf{v}/\sqrt{1 - v^2/c^2} \tag{1-9}$$

instead of by Eq. 1–6. (See Fig. 1–6.) The form $\mathbf{F} = m\mathbf{a}$ given by Eq. 1–8 is now quite wrong, because the denominator of Eq. 1–9 must be differentiated with respect to time, as well as $\mathbf{v}$. In fact, the vectors $\mathbf{F}$ and $\mathbf{a}$ even point in different directions in general.

It is worthwhile to spell out more carefully what is meant by saying that it is *experimentally necessary* to define the relativistic momentum by Eq. 1–9 instead of 1–6. We have not prescribed any operational method for directly measuring the momentum of a particle of mass m and velocity $\mathbf{v}$. What is really meant is that if one makes the definitions of Eq. 1–9 and 1–7, one can make theoretical calculations which correctly agree with experimental results. In particular, one can use the same force laws (to be described in Section 1–5), no matter whether the particle on which the force acts is moving at low speed or high speed. Thus, a simple description of a particular force in terms of the physical environment can still be maintained, regardless of the speed of a particle which may be moving under the influence of that force. Alternatively, the definition of force in Eq. 1–8 could be preserved, and the empirical force laws could be modified to depend in a complicated way on the velocity of a particle, but this ap-

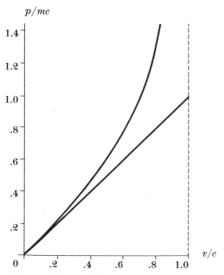

Fig. 1–6. *Relativistic momentum function (curved line) and nonrelativistic momentum function (straight line).*

proach would involve a much more complex statement of the theory. More importantly, the present approach coincides in a natural way with Einstein's theory of relativity, a fundamental re-examination of our notions of space and time, which is described in Chapter 2. It is this connection which dictates the term "relativistic."

Formally, one can salvage a little more of the nonrelativistic theory by defining a *"relativistic mass,"* m_r, by

$$m_r \equiv m/\sqrt{1 - v^2/c^2} \qquad (1\text{--}10)$$

(See Fig. 1–7.) The relativistic mass depends on the speed v (relative to the speed of light c) in a way which permits us to write the correct relativistic momentum

$$\mathbf{p} = m_r\mathbf{v} \qquad (1\text{--}11)$$

in analogy to Eq. 1–6. The definition in Eq. 1–11 is deceptively similar to Eq. 1 6; the relativistic momentum is a rather complicated function of velocity for particles which are moving at high speed (Fig. 1–6). We note that the relativistic mass m_r reduces to the previously defined mass m when $v = 0$. By contrast with the relativistic mass, m is called the *rest mass* of the particle. The rest mass is what would be measured by a balance, and is an invariant property of the particle. When a physicist speaks of "mass," he almost always means rest mass, and henceforth that is what we shall mean, unless specifically stated otherwise. Since

$$c = 3 \times 10^{10} \text{ cm/sec} = 3 \times 10^5 \text{ km/sec} = 186,000 \text{ mi/sec}$$

m_r differs negligibly from m even at speeds which are normally considered rather high. Probably the highest speed ever imparted to a man-made ob-

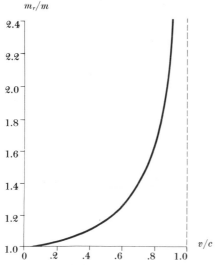

Fig. 1–7. Relativistic mass as a function of velocity.

ject is the launch velocity of an interplanetary probe; for this case, v^2/c^2 is only about 10^{-9}. On the other hand, when v gets close to c, m_r approaches infinity (Fig. 1–7), and the correction to the rest mass becomes very important. Such speeds commonly occur in the case of particles like electrons, protons, etc., which have been accelerated to high energy.

1–5   FORCE LAWS

We now examine the problem of writing down the expression for $\mathbf{F}$ which is to be inserted into Eq. 1–7 in any particular physical situation. After this has been done, it is merely a mathematical problem to find the resulting motion of the particle.

The most fundamental force laws are quite simple. For example, the *gravitational force* can be written in vector form as

$$\mathbf{F} = -\, Gm'm\frac{1}{r^2}\mathbf{e}_r \tag{1–12}$$

where $\mathbf{e}_r = \mathbf{r}/r$ is the *unit vector in the direction of* $\mathbf{r}$ (Fig. 1–8). The vector $\mathbf{r}$ is the position vector of the particle of mass m, on which the force $\mathbf{F}$ is acting. The origin is taken at the attracting particle of mass m'; usually we will consider this particle to be fixed in space. (The condition under which this is a good approximation is $m' >> m$.) The value of the *gravitational constant* is

$$G = 6.67 \times 10^{-8} \text{ dyne-cm}^2/\text{g}^2 = 6.67 \times 10^{-11} \text{ newton-m}^2/\text{kg}^2$$

The above expression describes a force which is always directed toward the origin, and whose magnitude is proportional to $1/r^2$. For every point in space, it tells what would be the force acting on the particle of mass m if the particle were at that point—even if the particle does not happen to be there. Such an expression is more than just a single force vector; it is called a *force field*. A force field is an example of a *vector function of a vector*. Both its domain and its range are vectors, and we can write it

$$\mathbf{F} = \mathbf{F}(\mathbf{r})$$

When the above vector function is written out fully in Cartesian components, we appreciate the usefulness of the vector notation as an abbreviation:

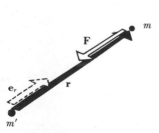

Fig. 1–8. Gravitational attraction.

$$F_x(x,y,z) = - Gm'm \; x/(x^2 + y^2 + z^2)^{3/2}$$
$$F_y(x,y,z) = - Gm'm \; y/(x^2 + y^2 + z^2)^{3/2}$$
$$F_z(x,y,z) = - Gm'm \; z/(x^2 + y^2 + z^2)^{3/2} \qquad (1\text{-}12')$$

The *coulomb force* has exactly the same functional form as the gravitational force—only the proportionality constant is different. It is

$$\mathbf{F} = q'q\frac{1}{r^2}\mathbf{e}_r \qquad (1\text{-}13)$$

where q' and q are the charges of the interacting particles. This force may be either toward or away from the origin, depending on whether the signs of q' and q are different or alike. (If mks units are used, a proportionality constant $1/4\pi\epsilon_0$ must be added.)

There is also a *magnetic force* which acts on a charged particle,

$$\mathbf{F} = q\frac{\mathbf{v}}{c} \times \mathbf{B} \qquad (1\text{-}14)$$

where $\mathbf{v} \times \mathbf{B}$ designates a vector whose magnitude is $vB \sin \theta$, θ being the angle between the velocity $\mathbf{v}$ and the magnetic field $\mathbf{B}$, and whose direction is perpendicular to both $\mathbf{v}$ and $\mathbf{B}$, using the right-hand rule (Fig. 1–4), and where c is the velocity of light. This force differs from the two preceding forces in that it depends not only on the particle's position, but also on its velocity. Forces dependent on velocity are somewhat harder to handle, but this one is not too troublesome because the force is always perpendicular to the velocity, so that it never does any work (Chapter 3). Actually, according to the theory of relativity, the magnetic force is just another manifestation of the coulomb force when the particle is moving. That is why the ratio v/c comes in. (In mks units, c does not occur in the formula.)

The relation between the magnetic force and the coulomb force is made clearer if Eq. 1–13 is rewritten in terms of the *electric field* $\mathbf{E}$, which is the analog of the magnetic field $\mathbf{B}$. Writing

$$\mathbf{E} = (q'/r^2)\mathbf{e}_r$$

the force is

$$\mathbf{F} = q\mathbf{E}$$

This expression can be combined with Eq. 1–14 into a single electromagnetic force law,

$$\mathbf{F} = q[\mathbf{E} + (\mathbf{v}/c) \times \mathbf{B}]$$

This force law, the so-called Lorentz force, unites the electric and magnetic force laws into just one general force law.

Besides these forces, the only other fundamental forces are *nuclear forces*. There are several kinds, belonging to two general classes, called the strong interactions and weak interactions. They cannot be written down in an elementary way (some are not even known), and so we will not consider them now. They will be described at least in an approximate way in Chapter 28.

In theory, this list of forces would provide all the laws we would need to deduce all of the infinitely various possible natural phenomena, but in practice it does not work out just that way. Especially when dealing with "macroscopic particles" (i.e., bodies of ordinary size—not atoms—in whose internal motions we are nevertheless not interested), it is convenient to introduce other approximate force laws. These could, at least in principle, be derived from the above fundamental laws, but one would not want to try to do that each time. Even in the case of atoms, it is often advantageous to apply an approximate force law, in order to simplify the problem mathematically to the point where we can actually solve it. A few examples of what is meant may be listed at this point.

There are *constant forces* (i.e., forces independent of position), for example, the uniform gravitational force

$$\mathbf{F} = -K\mathbf{e}_z \quad K = mg \tag{1-15}$$

There are *elastic forces*,

$$\mathbf{F} = -K\mathbf{r} \quad \text{or} \quad F = -Kx \quad \text{(in one dimension)} \tag{1-16}$$

such as are exerted by a spring. There are velocity dependent *frictional forces*,

$$\mathbf{F} = -K\mathbf{v}/v \quad \text{(sliding)} \tag{1-17}$$

$$\mathbf{F} = -K\mathbf{v} \quad \text{(air resistance)} \tag{1-18}$$

These are always directed opposite to the direction of motion ($\mathbf{v}$). There are even *contact forces*, for which no general expression can be written down, because they depend on internal stresses in the body and the examination of these is not consistent with the treatment of the body as a "particle." Such forces will be used in the following pages, but ultimately we will be interested in relating them to the fundamental force laws. The uniform gravitational force, Eq. 1–15, can be seen intuitively to be an approximation to Eq. 1–12, the approximation being valid over short distances—for example, over distances above the surface of the earth small compared to the earth's radius. In Chapter 14 we show in detail how the elastic force, Eq. 1–16, arises from the forces acting between the atoms of the material, which in turn depend ultimately on the coulomb force between the electrons and nuclei which make up the atoms. Frictional forces, Eqs. 1–17 and 1–18, are less easily analyzed, but clearly they too arise from the interatomic forces between atoms on the surface of the body, and thus finally reduce to the coulomb force. The central purpose of this book is to show how ordinary macroscopic phenomena can be understood in terms of microscopic systems whose behavior is derived from the fundamental force laws.

PROBLEMS

1-1.   Consider the two vectors $\mathbf{a} = 3\mathbf{e}_x - \mathbf{e}_y + 4\mathbf{e}_z$, $\mathbf{b} = 2\mathbf{e}_x + 6\mathbf{e}_y + 4\mathbf{e}_z$
Calculate their sum; difference; dot product; vector product. What is the cosine of the angle between them? Which has the greater length?

1-2.   Show that $\mathbf{a \cdot b} \times \mathbf{c} = \mathbf{a} \times \mathbf{b \cdot c}$ (i.e., one may interchange the $\cdot$ and $\times$).

1-3.   Using vector dot products, prove that the diagonals of a rhombus are perpendicular.

1-4.   Using vector dot products, prove the Law of Cosines for a triangle.

1-5.   Find the angle between the diagonal of a cube and one of its edges. (*Hint:* Let the diagonal be a vector which makes equal angles with the three coordinate axes.)

1-6.   Prove the Law of Sines for a triangle, using the vector cross product.

1-7.   Prove that the dot- and cross-products are distributive:

$$\mathbf{a \cdot (b + c)} = \mathbf{a \cdot b} + \mathbf{a \cdot c}$$
$$\mathbf{a} \times \mathbf{(b + c)} = \mathbf{a} \times \mathbf{b} + \mathbf{a} \times \mathbf{c}$$

1-8.   Show that $\mathbf{a} \times \mathbf{b}$ can be expressed by the determinants

$$\mathbf{a} \times \mathbf{b} = \begin{vmatrix} \mathbf{e}_x & \mathbf{e}_y & \mathbf{e}_z \\ a_x & a_y & a_z \\ b_x & b_y & b_z \end{vmatrix} = \begin{vmatrix} a_x & a_y & a_z \\ b_x & b_y & b_z \\ \mathbf{e}_x & \mathbf{e}_y & \mathbf{e}_z \end{vmatrix}$$

1-9.   Show that $\mathbf{a} \times \mathbf{b \cdot c}$ can be expressed by the determinant

$$\mathbf{a} \times \mathbf{b \cdot c} = \begin{vmatrix} a_x & a_y & a_z \\ b_x & b_y & b_z \\ c_x & c_y & c_z \end{vmatrix}$$

1-10. Prove that $\mathbf{a} \times \mathbf{b}$ is orthogonal to $\mathbf{a}$ and $\mathbf{b}$. (*Hint:* Take the dot product with $\mathbf{a}$ and $\mathbf{b}$.)

1-11. Prove that $\mathbf{a \cdot b} = ab \cos \theta$.

1-12. Prove that $|\mathbf{a} \times \mathbf{b}| = ab \sin \theta$. (*Hint:* Choose coordinate axes so that $\mathbf{a} = a_x\mathbf{e}_x$, $\mathbf{b} = b_x\mathbf{e}_x + b_y\mathbf{e}_y$.)

1-13. Suppose the position vector of a particle is

$$\mathbf{r} = at^3\mathbf{e}_x + bt\mathbf{e}_y - ct^2\mathbf{e}_z$$

Find the velocity and acceleration as a function of time.

1-14. Does $|\dot{\mathbf{r}}| = \dot{r}$?

1-15. Suppose $f(x,y,z) = (x^2 + y^2 + z^2)^{1/2}$. Calculate $\dfrac{\partial f}{\partial y}$ and $\dfrac{\partial f}{\partial z}$.

1-16. If $f(x,y,z) = x^2 + y^2 + z^2$, calculate $\dfrac{\partial f}{\partial x}$, $\dfrac{\partial f}{\partial y}$, and $\dfrac{\partial f}{\partial z}$.

1-17. Suppose $f(\mathbf{r}) = r$. Show that $\nabla f = \mathbf{e}_r$.

1–18.   If $f(\mathbf{r}) = \mathbf{r}$, find $\nabla \cdot \mathbf{f}$.

1–19.   Suppose the position x of a particle as a function of time is

$$x = \frac{m^2 g}{b^2} \left(1 - \frac{bt}{m} - e^{-bt/m} \right)$$

Calculate its velocity and acceleration, and the force acting on it. Express the force in terms of the speed.

1–20.   Suppose the position vector of a particle is

$$\mathbf{r} = A \sin \omega t \ \mathbf{e}_x + B \cos \omega t \ \mathbf{e}_y$$

Find its velocity and acceleration, and the force acting on it. Express the force in terms of the position $\mathbf{r}$.

1–21.   Suppose a rocket loses mass (fuel) at a constant rate, so that its mass is $m = m_0 - bt$. If the rocket's motion is in a straight line, show that $ma = F + bv$.

1–22.   Suppose an electron has a velocity 99.99% of the velocity of light. What is the ratio of the relativistic mass to the rest mass?

1–23.   At relativistic speeds, $\mathbf{F} \neq m_r \ \mathbf{a}$. Find the correction term from Eq. 1–9.

1–24.   Suppose two protons are 1 Å apart. Calculate the electrostatic force between them, the gravitational force between them, and the ratio of the two forces.

1–25.   What percentage error is introduced if one uses Eq. 1–15 instead of Eq 1–12 for the gravitational force law, assuming the particle remains within 10 km of the surface of the earth?

REFERENCES

B. Hague, *An Introduction to Vector Analysis* (Methuen, 1964, 3rd ed.), Ch. I–III.

K. R. Symon, *Mechanics* (Addison-Wesley, 1960, 2nd ed.), Ch. 1.

R. A. Becker, *Introduction to Theoretical Mechanics* (McGraw-Hill, 1954), Ch. 1.

2/the lorentz transformation

In Chapter 1 we considered the position vector of a particle as a vector function of time in a suitable coordinate system, without inquiring further into what is meant by time or a suitable coordinate system. In this chapter we will examine these concepts more closely.

This re-examination stems primarily from the work of one man, Albert Einstein (1905), and goes under the name of the special theory of relativity. *(The reason for this name will be understood later in this chapter.) Special relativity is very useful in formulating problems connected with electromagnetic fields. It is also important in problems of astronautics and in certain problems in high-energy physics. Of far greater significance, however, are the implications of relativity theory with respect to our most fundamental notions of length and time. Thus, even though we shall have few occasions to use the results of this chapter later in the book, it is nevertheless worthwhile to sketch the basic ideas of special relativity theory here.*

The development of relativity begins with operational definitions of length and time—quantities which, like "mass," are "primitive concepts" and can be defined only in this operational way. (See Section 1–4.) As is already suggested by the role of velocity in relativistic expressions, for example Eq. 1–9, motion is the central idea in relativity. Relativity grows from an attempt to formulate an operational definition of the length *of a moving object, and of the* time *measured by a moving observer. Stating the problem in this way already shows the profoundly revolutionary nature of relativity theory, since it seemed obvious to everyone that the length of a moving object has to be the same as when it is at rest and that time is independent of the motion of an observer. Yet these intuitive ideas were in conflict with the results of the epoch-making experiment of Michel-*

son and Morley in 1887 (Section 2–3), a conflict which was satisfactorily resolved by Einstein's new ideas.

The resolution consists in stating the transformations of length and time measurements which are entailed when the observers making the measurements are moving relative to each other. The transformation equations had actually been written down formally by Lorentz in an earlier attempt to understand the Michelson-Morley experiment, but with a different interpretation. Einstein's contribution lay in the simplicity inherent in recognizing the relative nature ("relativity") of length and time measurements. In this chapter, we shall see that the Lorentz transformation can be derived from operational definitions of length and time which are in harmony with the Michelson-Morley experiment.

2–1 MEASUREMENT OF LENGTH AND TIME AND THE PRINCIPLE OF RELATIVITY

We all have an intuitive feeling for what is meant by time. Our experiences are ordered in a series of *events*, the ordering of two events being decided by which occurred "earlier" and which occurred "later." Conventionally the later event is associated with the larger value of the time coordinate. This fixes the "direction of time" for each of us. In order to assign actual numbers to the time coordinate of events, we need a time measuring apparatus or a *clock*.

The operational definition of time is that which is measured by a clock. A "clock" is defined by some repetitive phenomenon, and equal intervals of time are given by the successive repetitions (periods) of the phenomenon. Since 1957, the most accurate clocks have been based on the period of the electromagnetic waves emitted by certain atoms. The atomic vibrations of these "atomic clocks" can be counted, by sophisticated instruments, to within one part in 10^{11}! The unit of time natural to an atomic clock (i.e., its period of vibration) is very small by normal standards—about 10^{-10} sec— and so they are not too useful for measuring very long time intervals. The most accurate working standards presently depend on the vibrations of quartz-crystal oscillators in carefully regulated environments; their period is about 10^{-6} sec. An old fashioned mechanical clock depends on the oscillation of a physical pendulum, with a period of about 1 sec. All of these kinds of clocks are useful for measuring time intervals, because they can be constructed anywhere in the world according to exact specifications, and measurements based on them can be expected to be comparable, even though they are made in different parts of the world.

Although all the above types of clocks are useful for measuring *intervals* on the time scale, they are less useful in practice for specifying a common *origin* of the time scale. For this purpose the repetitive motions of astronomical bodies are commonly utilized, because the same event can be observed by all men. For example the day (about 10^5 sec) is determined by one rotation of the earth on its axis, and the year (about 3×10^7 sec) by one revolution of the earth about the sun. Unfortunately, the repetition of these events is not perfectly periodic, according to an atomic clock, because of eccentricity of the earth's orbit and other such effects. Of course, if the day were *defined* as the unit of time, then all days would be equal by definition, and one would have to say that the vibrational frequencies of atoms varied according to the season of the year. In order to avoid this uncongenial complication of physical laws, the astronomical unit of time is based on the *mean* solar day. The actual determination of this mean is an exceedingly complex task, which is entrusted to special governmental laboratories. These laboratories maintain standard atomic and quartz-crystal clocks which are synchronized with solar time; other clocks are synchronized with the standard clocks, in most cases indirectly.

Once we have a clock we can define time operationally as the number which we read on our clocks. When I say, for example, that a touchdown was scored at 2 o'clock, what I mean is that the scoring of the touchdown and the pointing of the little hand on the clock to the number 2 were *simultaneous events*, neither one occurring earlier or later than the other. Before 1900, it was always assumed that the temporal ordering and the simultaneity of events would be agreed on by all observers, so that if all the clocks had once been perfectly synchronized, all the observers would assign the same time coordinate to any given event. Thus if a given event is observed by you to take place exactly 1000 seconds after another event, this would not be just your personal time, but the time agreed on by everybody. We will find that this assumption is in fact false and that observers in relative motion must necessarily assign different numbers to the time interval between events.

The concepts of *length* and three-dimensional *space* are as familiar to us as that of time. An operational definition of length is easy to come by. Length is what is measured by a ruler, or meter stick. A standard meter stick—two fiducial marks on a platinum-iridium bar—is kept in the International Bureau of Weights and Measures in France. Two other points (e.g., the two ends of a certain object) are separated by 1 m if they can be brought into *coincidence* with the two fiducial marks, *simultaneously*. The lengths of other objects (or the separations of other pairs of points) are measured by determining whether they can simultaneously be made to coincide with multiples or submultiples of a meter stick. The most precise submultiple of the meter, now used as a standard, is the wavelength of the red light emitted by krypton atoms of atomic weight 86. The comparison between this wavelength and the meter stick requires a high precision device (Michelson interferometer), since the wavelength used is less than 10^{-6} m. Various governments maintain secondary standards of length which have been compared with the primary standard, and ordinary meter sticks are calibrated against these, usually indirectly.

The distance between two points at rest may be measured by bringing up a meter stick and reading the numbers on the meter stick, also at rest, directly opposite the two points. The absolute value of the difference between the two numbers is then defined as the distance between the two points.

All observers with identical meter sticks should then agree on this distance. (When the distance is very large or very small one necessarily resorts to less direct measurements, but for now let us assume that we can proceed as above). When both of the points are in motion with respect to the meter stick, however, we would have to insist that the two readings be taken *simultaneously* at some common time t in order to measure the distance at that time. If, as we shall find, observers in relative motion disagree on whether or not two events are simultaneous, then it would be expected that they would disagree on distance measurements as well.

Time and distance measurements are always carried out in a definite *coordinate system*, the system in which the clock and the meter stick are at rest. Special significance is attached to the so-called *inertial* coordinate systems. An inertial system is defined as a frame of reference in which Newton's first law holds. In an inertial frame a body will therefore move with constant velocity in the absence of an external force. (An example of a non-inertial frame would be a coordinate system rotating with respect to an inertial frame: a particle at rest in the inertial frame, with no force acting on it, would appear to move in a circle in the rotating system. On the other hand, a particle could remain at rest in the rotating system only under the influence of a centripetal force, since it would be moving in a circle in the inertial frame. Thus Newton's first law does not hold in the rotating frame.)

The principle of *relativity* pertains to the form of the laws of physics in inertial frames. It is basic to the old Newtonian mechanics, as well as the new Einsteinian mechanics, i.e., the theory of "special relativity." The principle of relativity may be stated very simply: *in all inertial systems the laws of physics take the same mathematical form.* We will first examine this principle in the context of Newtonian mechanics.

2–2 THE GALILEAN TRANSFORMATION

We now turn to the equations which relate the time and space coordinates of a body in two coordinate systems in relative uniform motion. In Newtonian mechanics these equations are named after Galileo. The Galilean transformation equations can be read directly from Fig. 2–1. Here S_1 denotes one inertial coordinate system, while S_2 is a coordinate system whose origin moves with constant speed v in the x-direction with respect to S_1. Let

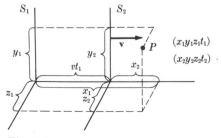

Fig. 2–1

us assume that the clocks at rest in S_1 and S_2 were synchronized and set to read zero at the instant the origins of S_1 and S_2 coincided. Assume also that distance scales have been layed off on the coordinate axis of each system, using a standard meter stick.

As seen by an observer at rest in S_1, the origin of S_2, at a later time t_1, will be located at $(vt_1, 0, 0)$. Let P be a point with space coordinates (x_1,y_1,z_1) in S_1 and (x_2,y_2,z_2) in S_2. The latter coordinates (Fig. 2-1) are then related to the former by:

$$x_2 = x_1 - vt_1$$
$$y_2 = y_1$$
$$z_2 = z_1 \qquad (2\text{-}1)$$

(The apparent lack of symmetry in these equations is due to the fact that the x-axes are taken to lie along the direction of motion.) One further assumes that the clocks in S_1 and S_2, when synchronized initially, will continue to run at the same speed so that the observers will always read the same number for the time coordinate:

$$t_2 = t_1 \qquad (2\text{-}2)$$

Equation 2-2 embodies the classical concept of *absolute time*. Similarly Eq. 2-1 yields an *absolute length* between two points P and P' at the time $t_1(=t_2)$, since the length L_2 in S_2 is equal to

$$L_2 \equiv \sqrt{(x_2' - x_2)^2 + (y_2' - y_2)^2 + (z_2' - z_2)^2}$$
$$= \sqrt{[(x_1' - vt_1) - (x_1 - vt_1)]^2 + (y_1' - y_1)^2 + (z_1' - z_1)^2}$$
$$= \sqrt{(x_1' - x_1)^2 + (y_1' - y_1)^2 + (z_1' - z_1)^2} \equiv L_1$$

where L_1 is the length in S_1. Equations 2-1 and 2-2 constitute the Galilean transformation, which up to Einstein's time was regarded as self-evident.

If we accept the Galilean transformation equations, it is easy to show that Newton's equation of motion satisfies the principle of relativity. Differentiating the right-hand side of Eq. 2-1 with respect to t_1 and the left-hand side with respect to t_2, and noting that $dt_1 = dt_2$ (Eq. 2-2), we arrive at the following velocity transformations:

$$\dot{x}_2 = \dot{x}_1 - v$$
$$\dot{y}_2 = \dot{y}_1$$
$$\dot{z}_2 = \dot{z}_1 \qquad (2\text{-}3)$$

or

$$\dot{\mathbf{r}}_2 = \dot{\mathbf{r}}_1 - \mathbf{v}$$

It is clear that a body moving with a constant velocity in S_1 will also have a constant velocity in S_2 (i.e., $\dot{x}_1$, $\dot{y}_1$, and $\dot{z}_1$ constant implies $\dot{x}_2$, $\dot{y}_2$, and $\dot{z}_2$ constant). Since S_1 is an inertial frame, therefore so is S_2. This conclusion would hold for any system in uniform motion with respect to S_1 but for no other. A frame accelerated with respect to S_1 ($\mathbf{v}$ not constant) would *not* be an inertial frame.

Differentiating once more, we find the transformation equations for acceleration:

$$\ddot{x}_2 = \ddot{x}_1$$
$$\ddot{y}_2 = \ddot{y}_1$$
$$\ddot{z}_2 = \ddot{z}_1$$

or

$$\ddot{\mathbf{r}}_2 = \ddot{\mathbf{r}}_1 \tag{2-4}$$

The acceleration is the *same*, in either frame.

Suppose a body at point P has a mass m and is acted upon by a force $\mathbf{F}$. Newton's second law in the nonrelativistic form (Eq. 1–8) would be expressed in the S_1 frame as follows:

$$\mathbf{F} = m\ddot{\mathbf{r}}_1$$

By Eq. 2–4, this equation may equally well be written in terms of the S_2 coordinates,

$$\mathbf{F} = m\ddot{\mathbf{r}}_2$$

The important consequence is that the mathematical form of the equation of motion is the same in both inertial frames S_1 and S_2. Newton's second law, within the context of the Galilean transformation, satisfies the principle of relativity. We say that the nonrelativistic form of Newton's law is *invariant* under a Galilean transformation. Since Newton's second law of motion is invariant, it is clear that the nonrelativistic conservation laws of momentum and energy, which follow from this law (Chapter 3) must also be invariant under Galilean transformations. Indeed all the laws of Newtonian (nonrelativistic) mechanics take the same form in all inertial frames (all frames in uniform motion with respect to S_1), i.e., they satisfy the principle of relativity.

While the laws of Newtonian mechanics are invariant under the Galilean transformations, Maxwell's equations for the *electromagnetic field*, which successfully explain light as an electromagnetic wave, are not. Since Maxwell's equations are thought to be equally as fundamental as Newton's, this difference presented a very serious problem. The dilemma confronted physicists with three possibilities: (a) Maxwell's equations were wrong, (b) the principle of relativity should be given up, or (c) the Galilean transformation equations were incorrect. The latter possibility turned out to be the acceptable one. The new transformation equations (Section 2–3) leave electromagnetic theory as well as the principle of relativity intact.

The requirement that the laws of mechanics should also be invariant under the new transformation equations must then lead to a modification of Newtonian mechanics. The necessary modification was discussed in Section 1–4, and will be further elaborated in Chapter 3. The changes in the mechanical theory which are required in order to make it invariant become apparent only at very high (relative) velocities, comparable with the velocity of light. Then Eq. 1–8 is not invariant under the correct Lorentz transformation, Eq. 2–5.

2–3 THE LORENTZ TRANSFORMATION

The Lorentz transformation equations can be derived from the principle of relativity together with a second postulate: *the speed of light in vacuum is the same when measured in any inertial frame.* The constancy of the speed of light would follow from the invariance of Maxwell's equations when we transform to a moving frame: since the equations describe the propagation of an electromagnetic light wave with speed c, if the equations are valid in both frames, then the speed of light must be c in both frames. This postulate is therefore a simple way of expressing the validity and invariance of Maxwell's equations.

The above postulated constancy of the speed of light is clearly at odds with the Galilean transformation: if the velocity of light equals c in the S_1 system (Fig. 2–1), it should equal $c - v$ in the S_2 system (Eq. 2–3). The constancy of the speed of light has been firmly established by a series of experiments, however, in contradiction with this seemingly intuitive notion. The most famous of these experiments are those carried out by Michelson and Morley in 1887.

At the time of the Michelson and Morley experiments, it was assumed that light (or electromagnetic waves) propagated through a medium called the *ether*, at rest in some particular inertial frame, the *ether frame.* If light propagated with a constant speed c in all directions in this ether frame, the speed of light in any other inertial frame would in general differ from c by Eq. 2–3. If we assume that the Michelson-Morley laboratory moves with a velocity **v** relative to the ether frame, then the times required for two light waves to travel equal distances along paths oriented parallel to and perpendicular to **v**, respectively, would differ.

The details of the Michelson-Morley experiment will not concern us here. Suffice it to say that the velocity of light was found to be the same ($= c$) in all directions in their laboratory. According to the Galilean equations, this could happen only if the laboratory were at rest in the ether. Half a year later, however, when the velocity of Earth with respect to the Sun was reversed and the laboratory was momentarily in quite a *different* inertial frame, the experiment was repeated with the same result. The only sensible, but revolutionary, conclusion to draw was that *the velocity of light is the same ($= c$) in all directions in every inertial frame.*

Let us accept the principle of relativity and the invariance of the speed of light. Let us then try to find a transformation between the two inertial frames S_1 and S_2 in relative motion (Fig. 2–2) which satisfies these two postulates. Let S_2 move in the x-direction with a velocity **v** as seen in the S_1 frame. With no relative motion in the y and z directions, we would again expect (Eq. 2–1)

$$y_2 = y_1$$
$$z_2 = z_1$$

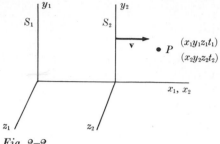

Fig. 2-2

The transformation of the x-coordinate must differ from the Galilean transformation, however, or else the speed of light will not be the same in the two frames. What form should the transformation take?

We must first require that the transformation should reduce to Eq. 2–1 for small velocities, where the Galilean transformation agrees with experiments. We must also require the transformation equations to be *linear* (rather than quadratic, say), in order that an event in S_1, (x_1,y_1,z_1,t_1), should correspond to a single event in S_2. (A quadratic relation would have two solutions.) Let us try a linear transformation of the x-coordinate which does not involve y or z:

$$x_2 = \gamma(x_1 - vt_1)$$

where γ is a factor which depends on v in such a way that it approaches unity as v approaches zero (Eq. 2–1). Similarly we try the following linear transformation for the time coordinate:

$$ct_2 = \alpha(ct_1 - \beta x_1)$$

where (Eq. 2–1) $\alpha \to 1$, $\beta \to 0$, as $v \to 0$.

If we assume that a spherical light pulse leaves the common origin at the common initial time $t_1 = t_2 = 0$, the constancy of the speed of light c in the two systems requires that at any later time

$$c = \sqrt{x_1^2 + y_1^2 + z_1^2}/t_1 = \sqrt{x_2^2 + y_2^2 + z_2^2}/t_2$$

That is, the equation for the spherical wave front of the pulse will be the same in the two coordinate systems. Squaring this equation, one finds

$$0 = x_1^2 + y_1^2 + z_1^2 - c^2t_1^2 = x_2^2 + y_2^2 + z_2^2 - c^2t_2^2$$

Now employing the transformation equations, we obtain,

$$x_1^2 - c^2t_1^2 = \gamma^2(x_1 - vt_1)^2 - \alpha^2(ct_1 - \beta x_1)^2$$

or

$$x_1^2(1 - \gamma^2 + \alpha^2\beta^2) - t_1^2(c^2 + v^2\gamma^2 - c^2\alpha^2) - 2x_1t_1(c\alpha^2\beta - v\gamma^2) = 0$$

For this equation to be satisfied in general we must require that the coefficients of x_1^2, t_1^2 and x_1t_1 vanish.

$$1 - \gamma^2 + \alpha^2\beta^2 = 0$$
$$c^2 + v^2\gamma^2 - c^2\alpha^2 = 0$$
$$c\alpha^2\beta - v\gamma^2 = 0$$

This set of three equations in three unknowns is readily solved:

$$\alpha = \gamma = 1/(1 - (v/c)^2)^{1/2}$$
$$\beta = v/c$$

Substituting these values back into the assumed transformation equations, we obtain the so-called *Lorentz transformation*:

$$x_2 = (x_1 - vt_1)/\sqrt{1 - (v/c)^2}$$
$$y_2 = y_1$$
$$z_2 = z_1$$
$$t_2 = (t_1 - vx_1/c^2)/\sqrt{1 - (v/c)^2} \tag{2-5}$$

Note that if we set v/c equal to zero, the Lorentz transformation reduces to the Galilean transformation. Only when v/c becomes appreciable is there a measurable quantitative difference between the two transformations.

The conceptual difference between the Galilean and the Lorentz transformations is enormous, however. In the former case we find that distances and time intervals are *absolute* (agreed on by all observers in inertial frames) while in the latter case distances and time intervals are *relative* to the coordinate system in which they are measured (different values assigned by observers in relative motion). These ideas will be explored further in the following sections.

2-4 SPACE CONTRACTION AND TIME DILATATION

Suppose that an object is at rest in the S_2 frame (Fig. 2-2), and that an observer in S_2 measures its length to be L_2. What is the length, as seen by an observer in S_1, of the object (moving with velocity v in S_1)? Let the two end points of the object be labeled x_2' and x_2 in the S_2 frame and x_1' and x_1 in the S_1 frame. Then $x_2' - x_2 \equiv L_2$ is the length as seen in S_2. By the Lorentz transformation Eq. 2-5 we can relate these coordinates to the corresponding ones in S_1:

$$L_2 \equiv x_2' - x_2 = \frac{(x_1' - vt_1') - (x_1 - vt_1)}{\sqrt{1 - v^2/c^2}}$$

where t_1' and t_1 are the times at which the observer in S_1 measures the end point coordinates. To measure the length $L_1 \equiv x_1' - x_1$ in the S_1 frame correctly, it is essential that these end point coordinates x_1', x_1 be measured *simultaneously* in S_1: $t_1' = t_1$. Then the above equation reduces to

$$L_2 = \frac{x_1' - x_1}{\sqrt{1 - v^2/c^2}} = \frac{L_1}{\sqrt{1 - v^2/c^2}}$$

or

$$L_1 = L_2\sqrt{1 - v^2/c^2} \tag{2-6}$$

The observer in S_1 finds the moving object to be *shorter*, by the factor $\sqrt{1 - v^2/c^2}$, than the length L_2 measured in S_2, where the object is at rest. The length of an object is *not* absolute, but depends on the relative velocity of the object and the observer. The largest value for the length (the "rest length") of an object will be recorded by an observer at rest with respect to it. All observers moving with respect to the object (or with respect to whom the object is moving) will find its length to be shorter than the rest length. This effect is usually referred to as *space contraction*, or the Lorentz-Fitzgerald contraction.

Next we turn to measurements of time. Let us assume that two clocks have been synchronized while at rest with respect to each other. Subsequently one clock, at rest in S_2, moves relative to S_1 in the x-direction with a constant velocity $\mathbf{v}$ (Fig. 2-2). The other clock, at rest in S_1, is located at a fixed point x_1. Let $T_1 \equiv t_1' - t_1$ be the time interval between two events as measured by the observer in the S_1 frame using the clock at rest in S_1. The observer in S_2 will record the time interval between the same two events on his clock at rest in S_2 as (using Eq. 2-5)

$$T_2 \equiv t_2' - t_2 = \frac{(t_1' - t_1) - \dfrac{v}{c^2}(x_1' - x_1)}{\sqrt{1 - v^2/c^2}}$$

where x_1 and x_1' are the positions in S_1 where the two events occur. Let us assume that in S_1 the events occur at the same point ("at rest"), so that we have $x_1' = x_1$. Then

$$T_2 = \frac{T_1}{\sqrt{1 - v^2/c^2}} \tag{2-7}$$

The time interval as recorded by an observer in S_2 between the two "moving" events in S_1 is *longer* than the time interval recorded by the observer in S_1 on a clock at rest with respect to where the events occur. The smallest value for the time interval (the "proper time") between two events is measured in the frame where they occur at the same location. All observers moving with respect to this frame will measure the time interval to be longer than the proper time interval between the events. This relativistic effect is known as *time dilatation*. If the observer in S_1 asserts that the events took place 1 minute apart, the observer in S_2, if for example $1/\sqrt{1 - v^2/c^2}$ equals 2, would assert that the events took place 2 minutes apart. (The observer in S_2, unless he knew the theory of relativity, would argue that the observer in S_1 read a clock that was running too slowly.)

2-5   RELATIVITY OF LENGTH AND TIME INTERVALS

In the preceding section, we have seen formally that the Lorentz transformation, between length and time coordinates measured in reference frames which are in uniform motion relative to each other, leads to conclusions which are in direct contradiction to the intuitive results of the Galilean transformation (Section 2–2). Since these conclusions are so counter-intuitive, it is worth dwelling on them at greater length. The application of the Lorentz transformation in place of the Galilean transformation is necessitated by the principle of relativity, in conjunction with preserving the validity of Maxwell's equations in all inertial coordinate systems (or alternatively, with the observed constancy of the speed of light). As a consequence of the Lorentz transformation, however, we are not only compelled to abandon the simple form of Newtonian mechanics, but we are also led to some very curious conclusions about the relative nature of length and time intervals.

In deriving Eqs. 2–6 and 2–7, for reasons of formal convenience we assumed in one case that S_1 was the "moving" frame and in the other case S_2 was the "moving" frame. That is, in the first case we assumed that the measured object was at rest in S_2 and in the second case that the timed events were "at rest" (occurred at the same point) in S_1. In order to eliminate this difference in notation for the rest frame, let us rewrite Eqs. 2–6 and 2–7 in a more neutral form and try to clarify their meaning further.

In order to express the space contraction, suppose that L_0 is the length of an object (the rest length) measured in the coordinate frame in which the object is at rest (the rest frame). Then if the length L of the object is measured in another coordinate system, moving with the speed v with respect to the rest frame,

$$L = L_0\sqrt{1 - v^2/c^2} \qquad (2\text{–}6')$$

according to Eq. 2–6. Likewise, to express the time dilatation, suppose T_0 is the time interval between two events (the proper time) measured in the coordinate frame in which the two events occur at the same point. (For example, if the two events are the turning on and off of a light bulb, this is the rest frame of the light bulb.) Then according to Eq. 2–7 the time interval T between the two events measured in another frame moving with speed v relative to the rest frame is

$$T = T_0/\sqrt{1 - v^2/c^2} \qquad (2\text{–}7')$$

These two equations summarize much of the content of relativity theory with regard to space and time, and it would not be wrong to memorize their meaning.

In a certain sense, a given object or sequence of two events does single out a preferred reference frame—namely its rest frame. In this frame the length of the object is greatest or the time interval between the events is least. In any other frame than this, the measured length would be shorter or the time interval greater, conversely. (Relativity may seem odd but it does not violate logic: if one thing is greater than another, then the other is less than the one.) Even though a particular object or sequence of events may suggest a coordinate frame singularly adapted to its description (the rest frame), nevertheless the physics of space and time is completely in accord with the relativity principle. That is, the Lorentz transformation itself is symmetric, in that the inverse transformation to Eq. 2–5, expressing (x_1,y_1,z_1,t_1) as a function of (x_2,y_2,z_2,t_2), would be found to have exactly the same form as Eq. 2–5, except with v replaced by $-v$ (Prob. 2–1).

What this means is the following. Suppose an object is at rest in the frame S_2. Then an observer who is at rest in a (relatively) moving frame S_1 would obtain a smaller value for the length of the object than an observer at rest in the frame S_2. Conversely (or in other words), the observer in S_2 would measure a greater length of the object than the observer in S_1. The length measured by the observer in S_2 is absolutely (not relatively) greater than the length measured by the observer in S_1. *However*, if the same object were instead at rest in the frame S_1 (a different physical situation), then an observer at rest in the moving (this time) frame S_2 would obtain a smaller value for the length of the object than an observer in the rest frame S_1. This is the symmetric aspect of the two physical situations. In both cases the observer who happens to be in the rest frame of the object measures the greater value of its length—but also in both cases the two observers are able to agree on which has observed the greater length. In both cases the observer for whom the object is moving records a smaller (contracted) length than the observer for whom it is at rest; and in both cases the observers agree with each other. Exactly analogous statements could be made about time dilatation. The shortest time interval between two events will be measured in the coordinate frame in which they occur at the same point (the rest frame). If the same phenomenon occurs instead in a different frame, then the proper time is measured in that frame. In neither case do the observers argue over which has recorded the smaller time interval.

In order to avoid confusion in thinking about relativistic problems, in which ordinary intuition and common sense are of so little use, it is extremely important to specify carefully the coordinate system in which the observations are made, and the rest frame in which the measured object is fixed or events take place. Relativistic effects can sometimes be phrased in other terms. For example, at the end of the last section, we remarked parenthetically that an observer in S_2 would assume that a clock in the moving (with respect to him) frame S_1 was running too slowly. Such statements are often made about what one observer thinks about another observer's clock or meter stick. They are not really helpful, however, and they can lead to confusion. Each observer is using good instruments in his own coordinate frame (the one which is natural to him, where *he* is at rest). They arrive at different answers simply because of the curious nature of space and time. Therefore we prefer to avoid such explanations, and re-emphasize the content of Eqs. 2–6' and 2–7'.

In deriving the expressions for the length of an object which would be measured by observers in its rest frame and in a moving frame, we noted that for the observer in the "moving" frame, from his point of view, the *object* was moving, and so it was essential that he measure the positions of the two ends of the moving object *simultaneously*. The observer in the rest frame of the object ought also to make his measurements of the ends simultaneously, but since they are fixed in his frame, this constraint does not make any difference. Now, according to our description in Section 2–4, the observer in the frame with respect to which the object is moving does make his measurements simultaneously (at the same instant, according to his time), but he gets a different answer from the observer in the rest frame. Basically, the reason the observer in the rest frame would ascribe for this difference is that the other's measurements were *not* made simultaneously, according to *his* time. The basic reason for the relativity of length measurements can therefore be reduced to the operational definition of simultaneity, and this turns out to be dependent on the reference frame. It is connected with the result of the Michelson-Morley experiment, since a judgment of the simultaneity of two distant events depends on the transmission of a light signal between the two distant points. This connection has never been explained better than by Einstein himself; every one ought to read his explanation, and we therefore refer you to it. (See references at end of chapter.)

The notions of space contraction and time dilatation will perhaps become clearer if we consider a specific example. The time dilatation is strikingly confirmed in the decay of high energy unstable nuclear particles, such as π-mesons (Chapter 31). An average charged π-meson at rest (or moving slowly with $v \ll c$) is known to have a mean life τ_0 of 2.6×10^{-8} seconds. In nonrelativistic physics a high energy π-meson with a velocity $v \approx c$ would then be expected to travel a mean distance of $\sim c\tau_0 = 3 \times 10^8 \, \dfrac{\text{m}}{\text{sec}} \times 2.6 \times 10^{-8}$ sec $= 7.8$ meters.

Let us first think about the path of the meson from the viewpoint of an observer in a reference frame fixed to the laboratory. With respect to this frame, the meson is moving at a high speed, nearly c. The distance it travels, measured in the laboratory frame, is its speed $v \approx c$, times its lifetime τ, both measured in the laboratory. The lifetime τ is the interval between two events—the creation of the meson and its decay. In the meson's rest frame, the two events occur at the same point and are separated by a time interval $\tau_0 = 2.6 \times 10^{-8}$ sec, the proper time. As measured in the laboratory, however, the lifetime is

$$ \tau = \frac{\tau_0}{\sqrt{1 - v^2/c^2}} $$

using Eq. 2–7′ for the time dilatation. In this time, it travels a distance

$$ v\tau \approx \frac{c\tau_0}{\sqrt{1 - v^2/c^2}} $$

in the laboratory. Since $1/\sqrt{1 - v^2/c^2}$ is often as large as 10, the length of a π-meson beam in the laboratory may be 78 meters rather than 7.8 meters.

We have studied this example of π-meson decay in the laboratory frame, but the same physical result would be obtained in the rest frame moving with the π-meson: if the laboratory were 78 meters long as measured in the laboratory frame, the meson would see the length of the laboratory space-contracted (Eq. 2–6′) to $78 \sqrt{1 - v^2/c^2} \approx 7.8$ meters, a distance which the meson could cover in the time $\tau_0 = 2.6 \times 10^{-8}$ seconds. In either frame we therefore reach the conclusion that the π-meson beam will travel the length of the laboratory rather than 1/10 this distance as expected in Newtonian physics. The relativistic results are found to be in complete accord with the experiments.

2-6   VELOCITY TRANSFORMATION AND THE RELATIVISTIC MOMENTUM

From the Lorentz transformation Eq. 2–5, we may calculate the following relations between the differentials of the space and time coordinates in the two relatively moving systems S_1 and S_2:

$$dx_2 = \frac{dx_1 - vdt_1}{\sqrt{1 - v^2/c^2}}$$

$$dy_2 = dy_1$$
$$dz_2 = dz_1$$
$$dt_2 = \frac{dt_1 - vdx_1/c^2}{\sqrt{1 - v^2/c^2}}$$

The velocity in the S_1 system is $\dot{\mathbf{r}}_1 = \dfrac{d\mathbf{r}_1}{dt_1}$ (i.e., $\dot{x}_1 = \dfrac{dx_1}{dt_1}$, etc.), while the velocity in the S_2 system is $\dot{\mathbf{r}}_2 = \dfrac{d\mathbf{r}_2}{dt_2}$. After some algebra (Prob. 2–9) the above equations for the coordinate differentials can be cast in the following form:

$$\dot{x}_2 = \frac{\dot{x}_1 - v}{1 - vx_1/c^2}$$

$$\dot{y}_2 = \dot{y}_1 \frac{\sqrt{1 - v^2/c^2}}{1 - v\dot{x}_1/c^2}$$

$$\dot{z}_2 = \dot{z}_1 \frac{\sqrt{1 - v^2/c^2}}{1 - v\dot{x}_1/c^2} \tag{2–8}$$

The non-trivial transformations of $\dot{y}$ and $\dot{z}$ arise from the non-trivial time transformation.

We see that if v/c is set equal to zero, this velocity transformation reduces to the Galilean one, Eq. 2–3. At high speed the Lorentz velocity transformation, Eq. 2–8, is very different from Eq. 2–3. In particular, it follows from Eq. 2–8 that the speed of an object can never exceed the constant speed of light c. To see this result, consider the following simple example: let a particle travel in the $-x_1$ direction in frame S_1 with a velocity $\dot{x}_1 = -kc$, where k is an arbitrary positive constant. Let us further assume that the S_2 frame travels in the $+x_1$ direction with a speed v which is also equal to kc

(Fig. 2–3). According to the "common sense" Galilean transformation, Eq. 2–3, the velocity $\dot{x}_2$ of the particle in the S_2 frame would be $-2kc$; i.e., $|\dot{x}_2|$ would exceed c for $k > \frac{1}{2}$. By the relativistic velocity transformation, Eq. 2–8, however, we find $\dot{x}_2$ to be:

$$x_2 = \frac{-kc - kc}{1 - kc(-kc)/c^2} = -\frac{2k}{1 + k^2}c \qquad (2\text{–}9)$$

Since $\dfrac{2k}{1 + k^2}$ has a maximum value equal to unity (for $k = 1$), it follows that $|\dot{x}_2|$ can never exceed c for any value of k.

In Chapter 1 (Eq. 1–9) we mentioned that the relativistic expression for momentum differs from the Newtonian expression $\mathbf{p} = m\dot{\mathbf{r}}$ (Eq. 1–6). We will now show that with the relativistic transformation equations, Eq. 2–8, the nonrelativistic momentum (Eq. 1–6) is not conserved in a collision, while the relativistic momentum (Eq. 1–9) is. We are faced with a choice, therefore, of modifying our old Newtonian expression for the momentum or giving up conservation of momentum altogether. Because of the physical importance of conserved quantities (Chapter 3), we choose the former alternative.

Consider the following simple experiment: two balls of equal rest mass m and with velocities $\dot{x}_1 = u$ and $\dot{x}_1' = -u$ in the S_1 system (Fig. 2–2), and velocities $\dot{x}_2$ and $\dot{x}_2'$ in the S_2 frame, collide and stick together. In the S_1 frame the momenta are equal and opposite whether we use the nonrelativistic (Eq. 1–6) or the relativistic (Eq. 1–9) expression for the momentum. With the total momentum in S_1 equal to zero before the collision, the two balls must be at rest in S_1 after the collision in order to conserve momentum. Therefore they move with a velocity $\dot{x}_2 = -v$ in the S_2 frame (Fig. 2–2). With the velocities of the balls before the collision equal to (Eq. 2–8),

$$x_2 = \frac{u - v}{1 - vu/c^2}$$

$$\dot{x}_2' = \frac{-u - v}{1 + vu/c^2} \qquad (2\text{–}10)$$

the total nonrelativistic momentum (in S_2) before the collision, $m(\dot{x}_2 + \dot{x}_2')$, is clearly *not* equal to its value, $2m(-v)$, after the collision. Only in the

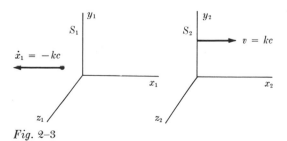

$\dot{x}_1 = -kc$

$v = kc$

Fig. 2–3

limit $v/c \to 0$, with $\dot{x}_2 = u - v$ and $\dot{x}_2' = -u - v$, is the nonrelativistic momentum conserved in S_2.

Let the relativistic masses, Eq. 1–10, of the two balls in S_2 be m_r and m_r' respectively. The relativistic momentum, Eq. 1–11, of the balls in S_2 before the collision is then

$$m_r \dot{x}_2 + m_r' \dot{x}_2' \qquad (2\text{--}11)$$

The total relativistic mass of an isolated system is also conserved however, since it is equal to the total energy of the system divided by c^2, as we shall see in Eq. 3–18. Thus the relativistic momentum in S_2 after the collision is equal to

$$(m_r + m_r')(-v) \qquad (2\text{--}12)$$

Using Eq. 2–10 (Prob. 2–10) we can show that the expressions in Eqs. 2–11 and 2–12 are equal, proving the conservation of the relativistic momentum in the inelastic collision considered here, as seen from S_2 as well as S_1. The general conservation laws of mechanics, both relativistic and nonrelativistic, will be discussed more fully in the chapter which follows.

To summarize the contents of this chapter, we have defined an inertial coordinate system as one in which the ordinary laws of physics hold—in particular Newton's first law, that a particle's momentum (or speed) is constant when no force is acting on it. Any coordinate system which is moving uniformly with respect to an inertial one is itself an inertial system, according to this definition. The principle of relativity postulated that *all* the fundamental laws of physics should take the same form in every inertial coordinate frame. This principle is suggested by the conclusion from the Michelson-Morley experiment, that the speed of light always has the same value c in every coordinate system. (The propagation of light with speed c is described by Maxwell's equations, and so they must be invariant when we transform to another inertial frame.) In order to leave the speed of light invariant, we are forced to adopt the Lorentz transformation equations, instead of the intuitive Galilean ones, to describe the coordinates of a point in one system in terms of its coordinates in the other system. The most striking feature of the Lorentz transformation is that the time variable is also transformed to a new value. The bizarre consequence of the Lorentz transformation is that length and time measurements are *relative* to the coordinate frame in which they are carried out, not absolute. The length of an object is greatest when measured in its rest frame; when measured in a moving frame (or in other words, a frame in which the object is moving) it is contracted. Likewise the time interval between two events is shortest when measured in their rest frame; when measured in a moving frame (a frame in which the events occur at different places) the interval is dilated. In order for Newton's second law ($\mathbf{F} = \dot{\mathbf{p}}$) to be invariant under the Lorentz transformation, it is necessary to modify the definition of $\mathbf{p}$ in terms of $\mathbf{v}$ for a fast moving particle; this modification is confirmed by experiments.

The theory which is described here is called *special* relativity, because the relativity principle states only that physical laws have the same form in a special class of coordinate systems—namely, the inertial systems. Dropping this restriction, Einstein later (1916) formulated a theory, called *general* relativity, in which all coordinate systems (not only inertial ones) are equivalent. Special relativity is very useful in more advanced treatments of many areas of physics, especially when the physical quantities are expressed in terms of "four-vectors," which transform like vectors under the Lorentz transformation. We will not try to develop the treatment of four-vectors in this book, but we shall have many occasions to use the new relativistic relation between momentum and velocity.

PROBLEMS

2–1.   Solve Eq. 2–5 for x_1, y_1, z_1, and t_1 in terms of x_2, y_2, z_2, and t_2.

2–2.   A rocketship moves by an observer with a speed of .9c. He measures the rocket to be 10 meters long. How long is the rocket as measured by its pilot?

2–3.   In Problem 2–2 the pilot flashes two lights 5 meters apart (in the direction of motion) simultaneously. The observer (at a relative speed of .9c) does not think the two lights flashed at the same time. What time interval did he measure between them?

2–4.   An electron beam is aimed down through a two-mile long cylinder. How fast does an electron move if it sees the cylinder to be only one foot long? What is the electron's momentum?

2–5.   In Problem 2–4 how much time does the electron spend in the cylinder according to the clock of (a) the cylinder? (b) the electron?

2–6.   An observer sees two rockets approaching him from opposite directions, both at a speed of .8c. What is the relative speed of the two rockets?

2–7.   A fleeing car at a speed of v is being pursued by a police cruiser at a speed of $2\,v$. What is the relative speed of the two cars? Find the correction to the result of Newtonian mechanics in terms of v/c, assuming this ratio to be very small.

2–8.   From Eq. 2–8 show that if $\dot{x}_2^2 + \dot{y}_2^2 + \dot{z}_2^2$ equals c^2, then so does $\dot{x}_1^2 + \dot{y}_1^2 + \dot{z}_1^2$.

2–9.   Verify that Eq. 2–8 results from the derivation outlined at the beginning of Section 2–6.

2–10.   Verify that the expressions for the relativistic momentum before the collision, Eq. 2–11, and after the collision, Eq. 2–12, are identical. (Note the expressions for $\dot{x}_2$ and $\dot{x}_2'$ in Eq. 2–10 and for m_r in Eq. 1–10.)

REFERENCES

A. Einstein, "On the Electrodynamics of Moving Bodies," translated in *The Principle of Relativity* (Dover Publications, 1923).

C. W. Sherwin, *Basic Concepts of Physics* (Holt, Rinehart, & Winston, 1961), Ch. 4.

P. G. Bergmann, *Introduction to the Theory of Relativity* (Prentice-Hall, 1947), Ch. III, IV.

E. P. Ney, *Electromagnetism and Relativity* (Harper & Row, 1962).

3/the conservation laws of mechanics

When a particle moves in a known force field $\mathbf{F}(\mathbf{r})$, *the equation of motion, Eq. 1–7, can in principle always be integrated to yield the particle's trajectory* $\mathbf{r}(t)$ *in terms of its initial position and velocity. In practice, however, the solution of this problem may be exceedingly difficult, if the force field is a complicated one. It is true that with the present-day high speed computers many problems that once seemed insoluble can now be successfully attacked. Nevertheless, when faced with a difficult problem in mechanics, it is always helpful to recognize those physical quantities which remain unchanged or* conserved *throughout the motion. The information one seeks can sometimes be obtained directly from conservation equations alone without explicitly solving for the trajectories. Such conserved quantities therefore play a very special role in the study of physics. In mechanics the most important conserved quantities are linear momentum, angular momentum, and total energy.*

3–1 CONSERVATION OF LINEAR MOMENTUM

For a single particle, the law of conservation of linear momentum follows directly from Newton's second law of motion, Eq. 1–7. If no net force acts on a particle, $\mathbf{F} = 0$, it follows that

$$\frac{d\mathbf{p}}{dt} = 0$$

or

$$\mathbf{p} = \text{const} \tag{3–1}$$

This may now seem like a fairly obvious result, although it took someone like Newton to recognize that force does not "cause" motion, but rather a *change* in motion. It is called Newton's first law. By virtue of Newton's third law, this conservation law can be extended to any system of several particles, provided there is no net *external force* acting on the system. By an external force we mean one which is exerted on the particles by some outside agency. The forces the particles exert on each other are termed *internal forces.*

We shall prove the momentum conservation theorem for a system of two particles. The generalization to an arbitrary number of particles is left as an exercise. With no external forces, the only force acting on particle "one" is the force exerted by particle "two," which we denote by $\mathbf{F}_{12}$. The equation of motion for particle "one" with momentum $\mathbf{p}_1$ must therefore take the form:

$$\mathbf{F}_{12} = d\mathbf{p}_1/dt$$

Similarly for particle "two,"

$$\mathbf{F}_{21} = d\mathbf{p}_2/dt$$

where $\mathbf{F}_{21}$ is the force particle "one" exerts on particle "two." By Newton's third law the two forces are equal in magnitude and opposite in direction (one is the equal and opposite *reaction* to the other). Therefore the sum of $\mathbf{F}_{12}$ and $\mathbf{F}_{21}$ vanishes,

$$\mathbf{F}_{12} + \mathbf{F}_{21} = d(\mathbf{p}_1 + \mathbf{p}_2)/dt = 0$$

or

$$\mathbf{p}_1 + \mathbf{p}_2 = \text{const} \tag{3-2}$$

When two particles interact, Newton's third law tells us that the changes in the momenta of the particles are equal and opposite, leaving the total momentum unchanged. We shall find later (Chapter 6) that this knowledge is crucial in the study of collisions of particles.

The proof of the conservation law of the total linear momentum can be extended to an arbitrary number of particles (Prob. 3–1). We may state the law as follows: *In the absence of a net external force the total linear momentum of a system of N particles remains unchanged,*

$$\sum_{i=1}^{N} \mathbf{p}_i = \text{const} \tag{3-3}$$

Here $\mathbf{p}_i$ is the momentum of the i'th particle.

3-2 WORK AND KINETIC ENERGY

We suppose that a force $\mathbf{F}$ acts on a particle at the point $\mathbf{r}$; $\mathbf{F}$ may vary from point to point, so that $\mathbf{F}$ is a vector function of the position vector $\mathbf{r}$:

$$\mathbf{F} = \mathbf{F}(\mathbf{r})$$

We do not have to assume that we know the position of the particle at any particular time. (In fact, that is the solution which we are trying to find.) But we know that if the particle *were* at $\mathbf{r}$, then the force on it *would be* $\mathbf{F}(\mathbf{r})$.

Now the *work dW* that the force **F** does on the particle in a displacement *d***r** is defined to be the product of the component $F \cos \theta$ of force parallel to *d***r**, times the magnitude $|d\mathbf{r}|$ (Fig. 3–1):

$$dW \equiv F \cos \theta \, |d\mathbf{r}|$$
$$= \mathbf{F} \cdot d\mathbf{r}$$
$$= F_x dx + F_y dy + F_z dz$$

Incidentally, it is important to notice that $|d\mathbf{r}|$ cannot be written *dr*:

$$|d\mathbf{r}| \neq dr$$

For example, if the displacement is along a circle with its center at the origin, $|\mathbf{r}| \equiv r = \text{const}$, and so $dr = 0$; on the other hand, in this same displacement **r** changes, so that *d***r** is different from zero, and therefore $|d\mathbf{r}| \neq 0$. In fact,

$$|d\mathbf{r}| = \sqrt{dx^2 + dy^2 + dz^2} = \sqrt{d\mathbf{r}\cdot d\mathbf{r}}$$

whereas

$$dr = \frac{\partial r}{\partial x}\,dx + \frac{\partial r}{\partial y}\,dy + \frac{\partial r}{\partial z}\,dz$$
$$= \frac{xdx + ydy + zdz}{\sqrt{x^2 + y^2 + z^2}} = \frac{\mathbf{r}\cdot d\mathbf{r}}{r}$$

(For motion along a circular path, **r** and *d***r** are perpendicular to each other, so that $\mathbf{r}\cdot d\mathbf{r} = 0$.) Although this point is very important in understanding the definition of work, it need not cause any practical confusion here, since we shall always use the second and third forms of the above definition in our actual calculations. (We may also note that $v \equiv |\mathbf{v}| \equiv \left|\frac{d\mathbf{r}}{dt}\right| \neq \frac{dr}{dt} \equiv \dot{r}$ is implied.)

The *total* work done by the force in a displacement from $\mathbf{r}_1$ to $\mathbf{r}_2$ is obtained by integration (Fig. 3–2):

$$W_{12} \equiv \int dW = \int_{\mathbf{r}_1}^{\mathbf{r}_2} \mathbf{F} \cdot d\mathbf{r}$$
$$= \int_C (F_x dx + F_y dy + F_z dz) \qquad (3\text{–}4)$$

This integral is a *line integral*, and its value depends on the curve C along which the particle moves, in general. If the curve C is specified, e.g., by

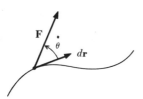

Fig. 3–1

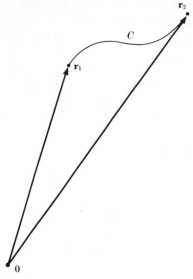

Fig. 3–2

giving $y = y(x)$ and $z = z(x)$, then F_x, F_y, F_z, can be expressed as functions of x. Furthermore, $dy = (dy/dx)dx$, $dz = (dz/dx)dx$, and the integration can be performed in the ordinary way. That the work may depend on the path is physically obvious in the case of friction, for example. If you push a box along the floor, doing work against friction, the work that you do in pushing it from one point to another would depend on how circuitous a path you chose.

From the equation of motion an important theorem can be proved about the work done by the total force. We will first prove it for the nonrelativistic case. Substituting from Eq. 1–7 into Eq. 3–4 defining work,

$$W_{12} = \int_1^2 \mathbf{F} \cdot d\mathbf{r} = \int_1^2 \frac{d\mathbf{p}}{dt} \cdot d\mathbf{r} = \int_1^2 d\mathbf{p} \cdot \frac{d\mathbf{r}}{dt} = \int_1^2 \mathbf{v} \cdot d\mathbf{p}$$

This expression depends only on the general form of Newton's law, and therefore it always holds. Nonrelativistically, the relation between $\mathbf{p}$ and $\mathbf{v}$ is $\mathbf{p} = m\mathbf{v}$, so that $d\mathbf{p} = md\mathbf{v}$ and $\mathbf{v} \cdot d\mathbf{p} = m\mathbf{v} \cdot d\mathbf{v} = \frac{1}{2}md(v^2)$. Thus,

$$W_{12} = \int_1^2 \mathbf{v} \cdot d\mathbf{p} = \int_1^2 \frac{1}{2}md(v^2) = \frac{1}{2}mv_2^2 - \frac{1}{2}mv_1^2 = T_2 - T_1$$

where
$$T \equiv \frac{1}{2}mv^2 = p^2/2m \tag{3–5}$$

The quantity T is the nonrelativistic *kinetic energy*. That is, we have shown, for arbitrary forces, that the work W_{12} done by the total force on the particle as it moves along its actual path between points 1 and 2 equals the difference in the values of the kinetic energy function at the two points:

$$W_{12} = T_2 - T_1 = \Delta T \tag{3–6}$$

This theorem states, in an integral form, how the force changes the momentum of the particle, since W is an integral of the force (with respect to position) and T is a function of momentum. This is what the law of motion $\mathbf{F} = \dot{\mathbf{p}}$ states in differential form. (Another way of stating the law in integral form is the impulse theorem:

$$\int \mathbf{F}dt = \Delta\mathbf{p})$$

The above theorem, Eq. 3–6, does not constitute a complete solution to the equation of motion; it merely tells how the velocity would change *if* we knew the path the particle follows. It is important to notice that the work W_{12} must be the work done by the *total* force acting on the particle, since the total force must appear in Newton's law. Thus, if I push a box along the floor with constant velocity, I do work on it. Nevertheless, its velocity does not change, because friction does an equal work of negative sign, so that the total work is zero and the kinetic energy stays constant.

The utility of the kinetic energy function, $T = \frac{1}{2}mv^2$, in nonrelativistic mechanics stems largely from the fact that Eq. 3–6 is found to hold true. The specific functional form of T is incidental. A theorem similar to Eq. 3–6 would be equally useful in relativistic mechanics, and if we have to modify the functional form of kinetic energy to make Eq. 3–6 hold at relativistic speeds, so be it. To prove the analogous relativistic theorem, we again start with

$$W_{12} = \int_1^2 \mathbf{F}\cdot d\mathbf{r} = \int_1^2 \mathbf{v}\cdot d\mathbf{p}$$

In order to carry out the integration, we must this time make use of the relativistic relation between $\mathbf{p}$ and $\mathbf{v}$, Eq. 1–9, which yields, on calculating the differential,

$$d\mathbf{p} = \frac{md\mathbf{v}}{(1 - v^2/c^2)^{1/2}} + \frac{m\mathbf{v}d(v^2)}{2c^2(1 - v^2/c^2)^{3/2}}$$

Taking the dot product with $\mathbf{v}$ on both sides, after some algebra (Prob. 3–3), we find

$$\mathbf{v}\cdot d\mathbf{p} = \frac{\frac{1}{2}md(v^2)}{(1 - v^2/c^2)^{3/2}}$$

Then

$$W_{12} = \int_1^2 \frac{\frac{1}{2}md(v^2)}{(1 - v^2/c^2)^{3/2}} = \left.\frac{mc^2}{(1 - v^2/c^2)^{1/2}}\right]_1^2 = \Delta(m_r c^2) \qquad (3\text{–}7)$$

It is now clear that we could recover Eq. 3–6 in relativistic mechanics by defining the kinetic energy T to be

$$mc^2/(1 - v^2/c^2)^{1/2} = m_r c^2$$

where m_r is the relativistic mass defined in Eq. 1–10. This definition, however, would not agree with the nonrelativistic expression, Eq. 3–5, in the limit of small velocities. We shall see that in order to make it agree we must subtract the constant term mc^2:

$$T \equiv m_r c^2 - mc^2 = mc^2 \left[\frac{1}{\sqrt{1 - v^2/c^2}} - 1 \right] \qquad (3\text{--}8)$$

The constant term does not alter the difference $T_2 - T_1$, and hence Eq. 3–6 still holds if T is defined by Eq. 3–8. With this definition, Eq. 3–5 is recovered in the nonrelativistic limit. Expanding T in a Taylor series in (v^2/c^2), we obtain,

$$T = mc^2[(1 - v^2/c^2)^{-1/2} - 1]$$

$$= mc^2 \left[1 + \tfrac{1}{2}\left(\frac{v^2}{c^2}\right) + \tfrac{3}{8}\left(\frac{v^2}{c^2}\right)^2 + \cdots - 1 \right]$$

or

$$T = \tfrac{1}{2}mv^2 \left[1 + \tfrac{3}{4}\frac{v^2}{c^2} + \cdots \right] \qquad (3\text{--}9)$$

Eq. 3–9 agrees with Eq. 3–5 for $(v/c)^2$ small compared to unity. The relativistic kinetic energy Eq. 3–8 is compared with the approximations of Eq. 3–5 and 3–9 in Fig. 3–3.

Let us return to the "constant" mc^2 which we subtracted from $m_r c^2$ in defining T. This term mc^2, known as the *rest energy*, has an important physical significance. Experimentally one finds that this rest energy can be converted into other forms of energy, such as radiant energy or kinetic energy, with a corresponding reduction in the rest mass. This conversion can be complete, as in the annihilation of a particle and an antiparticle (Chapter 17), or partial, as in the case of nuclear fusion and fission (Chapter

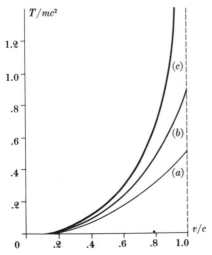

Fig. 3–3. Nonrelativistic kinetic energy (a), *first approximation to relativistic kinetic energy* (b), *and exact relativistic kinetic energy* (c).

30). When the rest mass is not constant, we must of course use the full relation, Eq. 3–7,

$$W_{12} = \Delta(m_r c^2) = \Delta(T + mc^2) \tag{3–7}$$

This result, which is completely general, can be stated in the following way: *The work done by the total force acting on a particle equals the increase in the sum of the kinetic energy and the rest energy of the particle.* When the rest mass of the particle does not change, this statement reduces to the earlier one, Eq. 3–6.

With the relativistic definitions of **p**, Eq. 1–9, and T, Eq. 3–8, you can verify the following identity:

$$p^2 c^2 = T(T + 2mc^2) \tag{3–10}$$

This relation between the momentum and the kinetic energy is very useful in relativistic mechanics. Equation 3–10, when divided by $2\,mc^2$, takes the form

$$\frac{p^2}{2m} = T(1 + T/2mc^2)$$

illustrating that the nonrelativistic approximation, $T = p^2/2m$, is adequate as long as $T/2mc^2$ is small, that is, when the kinetic energy is small compared to the rest energy.

3-3 POTENTIAL ENERGY

The force acting on a particle, unlike the mass, which is a property of the particle itself, describes the effect which its environment has on the particle. The statement of a physical problem consists primarily in the specification of the forces which are acting (and its solution consists in calculating the resulting motions which can occur). Very often, however, it is more convenient to describe the effect of the environment in terms of a potential energy. This description is entirely equivalent to that in terms of force, but the calculational problem may be simplified. Some examples of potential energy—gravitational and elastic—are already familiar. In this section we shall develop the concept of potential energy and see how conservation of total energy can facilitate the analysis of a problem.

When the force acting on a particle can be derived from a potential energy, considerable insight into the motion of the particle can be gained from a qualitative consideration of the potential energy. In addition, the potential energy contributes a step toward the actual quantitative solution of the equations of motion. Not every force can be derived from a potential energy, of course. In particular, a frictional force cannot. But in the microscopic problems of the motion of atoms and electrons, with which we shall principally be concerned, friction forces do not occur, and it is most convenient to describe the problem in terms of the potential energy (and in quantum mechanics it is essential to do so).

If the potential energy $V(\mathbf{r})$ exists, it is by *definition* a function such that the force is its negative gradient (Eq. 1–4):

$$\mathbf{F} = -\boldsymbol{\nabla}V \qquad (3\text{–}11)$$

i.e., such that

$$F_x = -\partial V/\partial x \qquad F_y = -\partial V/\partial y \qquad F_z = -\partial V/\partial z$$

It is obvious that a constant can always be added to any $V(\mathbf{r})$ without affecting Eq. 3–11, since the gradient of a constant equals zero. Potential energy functions that differ only by a constant must therefore describe the same force field. For this reason we can freely add constants to the potential energy function without any change in the physics of the situation.

An example of a force derivable from a potential is the uniform gravitational force, Eq. 1–15,

$$\mathbf{F} = -mg\mathbf{e}_z$$

You can easily verify that this force is derived from the potential energy

$$V = mgz$$

by the rules given in Eq. 3–11.

Now if a potential energy function exists, it follows that

$$W_{12} \equiv \int_1^2 \mathbf{F}\cdot d\mathbf{r} = \int_1^2 -\boldsymbol{\nabla}V\cdot d\mathbf{r} = -\int_1^2 \left(\frac{\partial V}{\partial x}\,dx + \frac{\partial V}{\partial y}\,dy + \frac{\partial V}{\partial z}\,dz\right)$$

$$= -\int_1^2 dV$$

or

$$W_{12} = -(V_2 - V_1) = -\Delta V \qquad (3\text{–}12)$$

where $V_2 \equiv V(\mathbf{r}_2)$ and $V_1 \equiv V(\mathbf{r}_1)$. The work W_{12}, which the force $\mathbf{F} = -\boldsymbol{\nabla}V$ does on the particle as it moves along any path between the points $\mathbf{r}_1$ and $\mathbf{r}_2$, is equal to the decrease in the potential energy. We have made no nonrelativistic approximations in proving Eq. 3–12, so this result holds relativistically as well as nonrelativistically.

We see that the work W_{12} depends only on the values of the potential energy V at the end points $\mathbf{r}_1$ and $\mathbf{r}_2$ of the path; it is independent of the actual path followed between the end points. In this respect such a force differs from forces in general, where the work may very well depend on the path, as was pointed out in connection with Eq. 3–4. In fact, this *independence of path* can be shown to be a necessary and sufficient condition for the existence of a potential V as defined by Eq. 3–11. Indeed, the derivation of Eq. 3–12 shows that this condition is necessary; to show that it is sufficient requires a mathematical theorem which is beyond our present scope.

The independence of path condition is in an integral form. An equivalent necessary and sufficient condition for the existence of $V(\mathbf{r})$ in a *differential* form is that the curl of the force should vanish everywhere: $\nabla \times \mathbf{F} = 0$, or using Eq. 1–5,

$$\frac{\partial F_y}{\partial z} = \frac{\partial F_z}{\partial y} \qquad \frac{\partial F_z}{\partial x} = \frac{\partial F_x}{\partial z} \qquad \frac{\partial F_x}{\partial y} = \frac{\partial F_y}{\partial x}$$

This condition provides an easy test to see whether or not a given force can be derived from a potential. The necessity of the condition is easily shown (Prob. 3–5), while the proof of sufficiency is again above our present level.

3–4 CONSERVATION OF ENERGY

If there exists a potential energy function, then the two theorems, Eq. 3–7 and Eq. 3–12, which state that the work done by the force is equal to the increase in kinetic and rest energies on the one hand, and equal to the decrease in potential energy on the other, can be combined to give the *conservation of total energy* theorem. Since $W_{12} = \Delta(T + mc^2)$ and $W_{12} = -\Delta V$, then $\Delta(T + V + mc^2) = 0$, or

$$T + V + mc^2 = \text{const} \qquad (3–13)$$

This result is completely general, provided of course that the potential energy V exists. The *total energy E*, which is constant throughout the motion of the particle, is defined as

$$E \equiv T + V + mc^2 \qquad (3–14)$$

Whenever the rest mass of the particle (or the system of particles) remains constant, as is the case in most ordinary problems, we may as well incorporate the constant mc^2 into V, which is only defined to within a constant anyway. Then we can write

$$E = T + V \qquad (3–15)$$

which may be a more familiar relation to you. When the rest mass changes, however, there must be a corresponding change in $T + V$, and Eq. 3–14 must be employed.

In the absence of forces, $V = 0$, a particle moves with the constant total energy

$$E = T + mc^2 \qquad (3–16)$$

Substituting for T from Eq. 3–16 into Eq. 3–10, we obtain the following relation between the total energy E and the momentum p of a *free particle* (i.e., with $V = 0$):

$$E^2 = p^2c^2 + m^2c^4 \qquad (3–17)$$

We shall find this result useful in discussing collisions of relativistic particles (Chapter 6), because it involves two quantities—momentum and total energy—which are conserved in such a collision. Another expression for the total energy E of a free particle, in which E is expressed as a function of the particle's speed v instead of its momentum p, is also useful for later purposes. This relation results immediately on substituting the relativistic definition of kinetic energy T, Eq. 3–8, into Eq. 3–16:

$$E = \frac{mc^2}{\sqrt{1 - v^2/c^2}} \qquad (3\text{–}18)$$
$$= m_r c^2$$

Since the existence of the potential energy function implies the conservation of total energy, forces derivable from a potential by Eq. 3–11 are called *conservative forces*. The fundamental velocity independent forces discussed in Chapter 1, such as the gravitational force or the coulomb force, are conservative in this sense. Frictional forces are not conservative.

Let us consider the *nonrelativistic* motion of a particle with a constant rest mass. The conservation of total energy theorem, Eq. 3–15, can now be used to obtain qualitative information about the motion of the particle in the following way: the total energy E is a constant, and the function V is assumed to be known at every point. (It is just the specification of V, i.e., of the force acting on the particle, which describes the physical situation the particle is in.) Then, using the energy conservation theorem, we can find the speed of the particle at every point of its orbit. Nonrelativistically, $T = \frac{1}{2}mv^2$, in which case Eq. 3–15 can easily be solved for v,

$$v = \sqrt{\frac{2}{m}[E - V(\mathbf{r})]} \qquad (3\text{–}19)$$

This does not give complete information about the motion of the particle, since the orbit itself is not known. But it is often very helpful, as we shall see.

This approach is especially fruitful if the problem is a *one-dimensional problem*, for in this case the energy conservation theorem does lead to a complete solution of the motion. It also gives an example of the kind of qualitative information we can obtain from the potential energy. In this case the potential energy is a function of only one spatial variable, say x, so that Eq. 3–19 simplifies to

$$v = \sqrt{\frac{2}{m}[E - V(x)]} \qquad (3\text{–}20)$$

Note that the speed of the particle depends on $\sqrt{E - V}$. Thus, if the total energy, which is constant, equals E_1, and the particle is near the origin (Fig. 3–4), it must remain in the region where $V \leq E_1$, since when $V > E_1$ the velocity would be imaginary. As a matter of fact, the speed is zero where $V = E_1$ (where the curves cross), and the kinetic energy is equal to their difference $E_1 - V$ elsewhere, so the particle must oscillate back and forth in the trough below E_1, turning around ($v = 0$) at the crossing points. Another type of motion could occur with the same total energy E_1, if the particle started far to the right of the origin. Then the particle would come in to the left, losing speed as $E_1 - V$ decreased, stop and turn around where the curves cross, and then be repelled to the right, away from the origin again. It could not get into the trough. You should describe to yourself what would be the possible motions if the total energy were E_2.

This kind of qualitative description of the motion is reminiscent of the motion of a roller-coaster moving on a track which has the profile of the potential energy curve. In fact, this analogy is completely accurate, since the gravitational potential energy of the roller-coaster (mgz) has the same profile as the track. Thus it is quite legitimate to visualize the motion of a ball sliding (without friction) in a trough with the shape of the potential energy curve.

In the one-dimensional case, our approach also leads to a quantitative solution to the equation of motion. Since $v = dx/dt$, we can write, using Eq. 3–20,

$$\int dx / \sqrt{\frac{2}{m}[E - V(x)]} = \int dt = t \qquad (3\text{–}21)$$

We have thus reduced the problem of integrating the equation of motion to a "quadrature." A quadrature means a definite or indefinite integral that you have to evaluate, and this is a much simpler problem than finding the solution to a differential equation. (The term "quadrature" is introduced in place of integral, because the solution of a differential equation is also called an "integral" of the equation, even though it may not be expressible as a quadrature.) Of course, it may not be possible to express the integral in analytical form $t = t(x)$ using known functions, and even if it is possible you may not be able to solve $t(x) = t$ for $x = x(t)$, but in any case the solution is in a form which can easily be handled by numerical techniques. In more than one dimension, the problem cannot always be brought into this tractable state.

It is interesting to note that Newton's equation of motion is a second order differential equation (i.e., an equation involving no derivative higher than the second), which must be integrated twice, in order to have the description of the motion in non-differential form. What the energy conservation theorem amounts to is an integration of the equation *once* with complete generality (i.e., for any force, so long as it can be derived from a

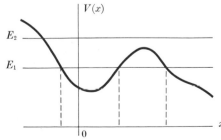

Fig. 3–4

potential energy function). It remains to integrate the equation a second time. What we have just seen is that this is always possible by a quadrature for a one-dimensional nonrelativistic problem.

3-5 CONSERVATION OF ANGULAR MOMENTUM

We have seen that the linear momentum is conserved in the absence of an external force, and that the total energy is conserved in a force field derivable from a potential energy function. Next we shall prove that the *angular momentum* of a particle about a given point is conserved, provided the net *torque* about that point equals zero. First, we must define the angular momentum of a particle, as opposed to that of a rigid body.

The angular momentum $\mathbf{L}$ about a point $\mathbf{r}_0$ of a particle which is located at $\mathbf{r}$ and moving with a momentum $\mathbf{p}$, is defined to be

$$\mathbf{L} \equiv (\mathbf{r} - \mathbf{r}_0) \times \mathbf{p} \qquad (3\text{-}22)$$

The magnitude of $\mathbf{L}$ is then

$$L = |\mathbf{r} - \mathbf{r}_0|\, p \sin \theta = p\rho$$

where θ is the angle between $\mathbf{r} - \mathbf{r}_0$ and $\mathbf{p}$. (See Fig. 3–5.) The angular momentum is therefore the *moment of the momentum*, i.e., the momentum p times its "moment arm" $\rho = |\mathbf{r} - \mathbf{r}_0| \sin \theta$, the perpendicular distance from the point $\mathbf{r}_0$ to the line of the momentum vector. Similarly, the torque $\mathbf{N}$ about the point $\mathbf{r}_0$ is defined to be the *moment of the force* about that point,

$$\mathbf{N} \equiv (\mathbf{r} - \mathbf{r}_0) \times \mathbf{F} \qquad (3\text{-}23)$$

Here, $\mathbf{F}$ is the force acting on the particle at the point $\mathbf{r}$. The definition of torque given by Eq. 3–23 is clearly the same as the elementary definition of the moment of a force acting on a rigid body about a certain pivot. It is expressed concisely by the vector-product notation, and in addition its vector character specifies the direction of the axis about which the torque is tending to produce a rotation. The definition of angular momentum given by Eq. 3–22, however, is not so obviously related to one in terms of the moment of inertia and angular velocity of a rigid body. Nevertheless,

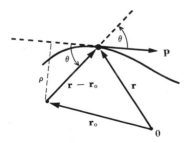

Fig. 3–5

it can be shown that if each particle of a rigid body possesses an angular momentum as defined above, and if these angular momenta are summed over all the particles of the body, then one derives as a consequence the total angular momentum of the body expressed in the usual way in terms of the moment of inertia. The definition for a single particle is therefore the more fundamental definition. Just as in the case of rigid bodies, the rate of change of the angular momentum of a particle is equal to the torque acting on it, and we shall next prove this theorem from the definitions given above.

We are interested in calculating how **L** varies with time:

$$d\mathbf{L}/dt = \frac{d}{dt}[(\mathbf{r} - \mathbf{r}_0) \times \mathbf{p}] = \mathbf{v} \times \mathbf{p} + (\mathbf{r} - \mathbf{r}_0) \times \dot{\mathbf{p}} = (\mathbf{r} - \mathbf{r}_0) \times \mathbf{F} = \mathbf{N}$$

In this derivation, we have used the facts that $\frac{d}{dt}(\mathbf{r} - \mathbf{r}_0) = \mathbf{v}$ because $\mathbf{r}_0$ is constant, and that $\mathbf{v} \times \mathbf{p}$ vanishes since the two vectors **v** and **p** are parallel, even in the relativistic case. We have proved, using only the equation of motion, that for any force the time rate of change of the angular momentum about any point is equal to the torque about that point,

$$\mathbf{N} = \dot{\mathbf{L}} \tag{3-24}$$

This theorem is quite analogous to the relation between the rate of change of linear momentum and force, $\mathbf{F} = \dot{\mathbf{p}}$.

It is clear that if the torque, **N**, equals zero, the angular momentum, **L**, is a constant of the motion. In particular, as we will now prove, a particle moving in any of a general class of force fields called *central force fields* conserves its angular momentum about the center of force. A force field is said to be central, when for all **r** the force vector **F(r)** passes through a common fixed point, the center of force. The gravitational and coulomb forces (owing to a single point mass or charge) are important examples of central force fields. With the force center chosen as the origin, all central forces can be written as follows:

$$\mathbf{F} = F(\mathbf{r})\mathbf{e}_r \tag{3-25}$$

Here $F(\mathbf{r})$ is an arbitrary scalar function of **r**, and $\mathbf{e}_r = \mathbf{r}/r$ is the unit vector in the **r** direction. It is clear that **F** passes through the origin for all **r** (Fig. 1–8), so that the torque about the origin (the force center) must vanish: letting $\mathbf{r}_0 = 0$ in Eq. 3–23,

$$\mathbf{N} = \mathbf{r} \times \mathbf{F} = rF(\mathbf{r})(\mathbf{e}_r \times \mathbf{e}_r) = 0$$

Consequently, the angular momentum about the origin is conserved for all central force fields,

$$\mathbf{L} = \mathbf{r} \times \mathbf{p} = \text{const} \tag{3-26}$$

Since **L** is perpendicular to both **r** and **p** (Fig. 3–6), the vectors **r** and **p** define a plane perpendicular to **L** (unless **r** and **p** are parallel, in which case **L** equals zero). With **L** constant, as is the case for central forces, this plane

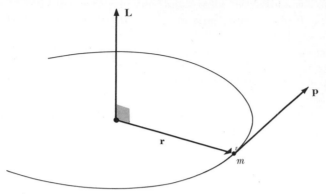

Fig. 3–6

remains fixed for all time. Since the vector **r**, denoting the position of the particle, always lies in this plane, the motion must be two dimensional rather than three dimensional. Motion in a central force field is in other words *confined to a plane* containing the force center and perpendicular to the constant angular momentum vector.

To get a better feeling for what the angular momentum **L** of a particle is, let us decompose the momentum vector **p** in a particular coordinate system. At the particular instant we are considering, let two of the three fixed, mutually perpendicular unit vectors, e_r and $e_\perp$, lie in the (**r**, **p**) plane, with one of these, e_r, pointing along **r**, the vector from the force center to the particle. Then we can write

$$\mathbf{p} = p_r \mathbf{e}_r + p_\perp \mathbf{e}_\perp$$

The radial component does not contribute to the angular momentum: $\mathbf{L} = \mathbf{r} \times \mathbf{p} = r p_\perp (\mathbf{e}_r \times \mathbf{e}_\perp)$. Since $|\mathbf{e}_r \times \mathbf{e}_\perp|$ equals unity, we have $L^2 = r^2 p_\perp^2$, or $p_\perp^2 = L^2/r^2$. Nonrelativistically, the *kinetic energy* function is therefore

$$T = p^2/2m = \frac{1}{2m}(p_r^2 + p_\perp^2) = \frac{1}{2m}(p_r^2 + L^2/r^2) \qquad (3\text{–}27)$$

a result which we shall find useful. We see that $L^2/2mr^2$ is the kinetic energy associated with the motion perpendicular to **r**. Since $p_r = mv_r = m\dot{r}$, Eq. 3–27 can also be written

$$T = \tfrac{1}{2}m\dot{r}^2 + \frac{L^2}{2mr^2} \qquad (3\text{–}28)$$

So far in this section we have limited ourselves to discussing the angular momentum of a single particle. Let us now turn our attention to *systems* of two or more particles. Consider a particle of mass m_1 and momentum $\mathbf{p}_1$ at $\mathbf{r}_1$ and a second article of mass m_2 and momentum $\mathbf{p}_2$ at $\mathbf{r}_2$. We have already established that in the absence of external forces, the total linear momentum is conserved, $\mathbf{p}_1 + \mathbf{p}_2 = \text{const}$ (Eq. 3–2). The total angular momentum of the two-particle system about an arbitrary point, which we are free to choose as the origin, is given by $L = r_1 \times p_1 + r_2 \times p_2$. The time rate of change of L is then

$$\dot{L} = \dot{r}_1 \times p_1 + r_1 \times \dot{p}_1 + \dot{r}_2 \times p_2 + r_2 \times \dot{p}_2$$
$$= r_1 \times \dot{p}_1 + r_2 \times \dot{p}_2$$

where we have used the fact that the cross product of parallel vectors vanishes. With no external forces, $\dot{p}_1$, which is equal to the force F_{12} exerted by particle 2 on particle 1, must be equal and opposite to $\dot{p}_2$, the force F_{21} exerted by particle 1 on particle 2. Hence

$$\dot{L} = (r_1 - r_2) \times F_{12}$$

If we assume that the force F_{12} acts along the vector $r_1 - r_2$ joining the two particles, as is usually the case, it follows that $\dot{L} = 0$, or that the total angular momentum is conserved,

$$L = L_1 + L_2 = \text{const} \tag{3-29}$$

This result can be extended to a system of an arbitrary number of particles, provided the internal forces between pairs of particles act along the straight lines connecting them. The conservation law can then be stated quite generally (including the relativistic case) as follows: *The total angular momentum of a system of* N *particles is conserved in the absence of an external torque,*

$$\sum_{i=1}^{N} L_i = \text{const} \tag{3-30}$$

Returning to the two particle system with no external forces, we may assume that the total linear momentum is not only constant, but equal to zero, i.e., we will work in the so-called *rest frame* of the system,

$$p_1 + p_2 = 0 \tag{3-31}$$

The angular momentum about a point r_0 is then given by

$$L = (r_1 - r_0) \times p_1 + (r_2 - r_0) \times p_2$$
$$= r_1 \times p_1 + r_2 \times p_2 = (r_1 - r_2) \times p_1 \tag{3-32}$$

We thus see a further interesting result, that the angular momentum is independent of the point r_0, i.e., it is the same about every point in the rest frame. In particular, it is equal to the angular momentum of particle 1 about the instantaneous position of particle 2 (and vice versa).

To summarize the results of this section, we have seen in the first place that when a single particle is moving in a given force field, the particle's angular momentum (about a certain point) is constant if the torque (about the same point) is zero. This result is analogous to the constancy of the linear momentum of a particle when the force is zero. In particular, for all central forces the angular momentum about the force center is constant.

Secondly, we have seen that the total angular momentum of a system of particles is constant when no external torques are acting on the system, provided the internal forces between each pair of particles act along the lines joining the particles. This result is analogous to the constancy of the total linear momentum of a system of particles in the absence of external forces.

3–6   THE REDUCED MASS

We shall conclude this chapter by introducing a notion, the reduced mass, which greatly facilitates the application of these ideas to any system of *two* interacting particles—the so-called *two-body problem*. The effect of introducing the reduced mass is to reduce the two-body problem to an equivalent single-particle, or one-body, problem. Thus any two-body problem with a given interaction force can be solved, provided that the corresponding problem, of a single particle moving about a fixed force center under the influence of the same force, can be solved. (On the other hand, it is possible to show that the three-body problem cannot be solved completely.) The result will justify the assertion made in connection with Eq. 1–12, that if one of the two particles is much more massive than the other, the massive one remains almost fixed.

In what remains, we assume that the motion is nonrelativistic, and that we are in the rest frame of the system, where the total momentum is zero. Then Eq. 3–31 becomes

$$m_1\dot{\mathbf{r}}_1 + m_2\dot{\mathbf{r}}_2 = 0$$

Integrating this equation we arrive at $m_1\mathbf{r}_1 + m_2\mathbf{r}_2 = $ constant. The constant (vector) of integration is usually written $(m_1 + m_2)\mathbf{r}_c$, the vector $\mathbf{r}_c$ giving the position of the *center of mass* (Fig. 3–7), so that

$$m_1\mathbf{r}_1 + m_2\mathbf{r}_2 = (m_1 + m_2)\mathbf{r}_c \tag{3–33}$$

Since $\mathbf{r}_c$ is constant, we may as well choose the center of mass as the origin, $\mathbf{r}_c = 0$, in which case $\mathbf{r}_2$ is directly proportional to $\mathbf{r}_1$:

$$\mathbf{r}_2 = -\ (m_1/m_2)\mathbf{r}_1 \tag{3–34}$$

What this result tells us is that if we know $\mathbf{r}_1$ as a function of time, we have also the solution for the motion of particle 2. Alternatively if we know the relative position of the two particles $(\mathbf{r}_1 - \mathbf{r}_2)$, as a function of time, we can solve for $\mathbf{r}_1$ and $\mathbf{r}_2$ separately by making use of Eq. 3–34. In addition,

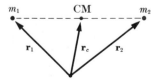

Fig. 3–7

we have the information that the center of mass of the two particles remains at rest (in the rest frame). What we have to do now is show how to calculate the relative separation of the two particles $(\mathbf{r}_1 - \mathbf{r}_2)$.

Solving for the relative motion is in fact equivalent to solving for the motion of a (fictitious) single particle in a central force field. This can be seen by rewriting Eq. 3–34 to give the relative separation

$$\mathbf{r}_1 - \mathbf{r}_2 = \mathbf{r}_1 + (m_1/m_2)\mathbf{r}_1 = \frac{m_1 + m_2}{m_2}\,\mathbf{r}_1$$

or

$$\mathbf{r}_1 = \frac{m_2}{m_1 + m_2}\,(\mathbf{r}_1 - \mathbf{r}_2)$$

Now we may substitute this value of $\mathbf{r}_1$ into the equation of motion for particle 1,

$$\mathbf{F}_{12} = m_1\ddot{\mathbf{r}}_1$$

The result is

$$\mathbf{F}_{12} = \frac{m_1 m_2}{m_1 + m_2}\,(\ddot{\mathbf{r}}_1 - \ddot{\mathbf{r}}_2)$$

If we define the *reduced mass* as

$$m \equiv \frac{m_1 m_2}{m_1 + m_2} \tag{3–35}$$

and write the relative separation as $(\mathbf{r}_1 - \mathbf{r}_2) = \mathbf{r}_{12}$, then the equation of motion becomes

$$\mathbf{F}_{12} = m\ddot{\mathbf{r}}_{12} \tag{3–36}$$

Usually $\mathbf{F}_{12}$ lies along (and is a function of) $\mathbf{r}_{12}$. We have shown, therefore, that a two-particle problem, with the interparticle force along the line connecting the two particles, is equivalent to the problem of a single fictitious particle, moving with the reduced mass in a central force field.

When the mass of one particle m_1 is very much less than the mass of the other m_2, the reduced mass is approximately equal to the smaller of the two masses:

$$m = m_1\,\frac{m_2}{m_1 + m_2} \approx m_1 \qquad m_1 << m_2$$

In these cases (e.g., a small planet around the sun, or an electron around a nucleus) it is approximately correct to assume that the heavy particle is at rest and the light one moves around it, since by Eq. 3–34, $|\dot{\mathbf{r}}_2| = \frac{m_1}{m_2}|\dot{\mathbf{r}}_1| \ll |\dot{\mathbf{r}}_1|$.

However, when the two masses are equal, $m_1 = m_2$, the reduced mass equals half of either mass (e.g., the two-nucleon nucleus, the deuteron), and it is clear that we cannot assume that either particle is at rest. The problem is no harder to solve in this case, but we must be certain to use the reduced mass in our equations.

It is perhaps worth pointing out that the total angular momentum $\mathbf{L}$ of the two-particle system is also expressible in terms of the reduced mass m and interparticle separation $\mathbf{r}_{12}$:

$$\mathbf{L} = \mathbf{r}_{12} \times m\dot{\mathbf{r}}_{12} \qquad (3\text{–}37)$$

The angular momentum is therefore the same as that which the fictitious particle with the reduced mass m would have if it were moving around a fixed origin at the distance $\mathbf{r}_{12}$. This result is easily obtained from Eqs. 3–32 and 3–34, and will be left as an exercise. (See Probs. 3–11 and 3–13.)

PROBLEMS

3–1.   Prove Eq. 3–3 for an arbitrary number of particles.

3–2.   Suppose a particle enters a resisting medium, where the only force acting on it is given by Eq. 1–17. What is the shape of the particle's path? Calculate the length of the path from the kinetic energy theorem, Eq. 3–6: if the particle initially has a speed v_0, find v_0 in terms of the path length R. (An analogous situation is sometimes used to infer the speed of a nuclear particle, from a measurement of its "range" R in a certain medium. In that case, the force law is not given by Eq. 1–17.)

3–3.   Carry through the complete derivation of Eq. 3–7.

3–4.   (a) If an electron has a velocity 1/10 the velocity of light, compare its actual kinetic energy with the nonrelativistic approximation to it.
(b) What is the kinetic energy of an electron moving at 99.99% of the speed of light?

3–5.   Show that $\nabla \times \mathbf{F} = 0$ is a necessary condition for the existence of a potential function V, such that $\mathbf{F} = -\nabla V$.

3–6.   For the following forces, does V exist? If so, find it.
(a) $F_x = y$, $F_y = x$, $F_z = 0$.
(b) $F_x = y$, $F_y = y$, $F_z = 0$.

3–7.   The potential energy of an electron in the hydrogen molecule ion, $H_2{}^+$, is

$$V = -\frac{e^2}{r_1} - \frac{e^2}{r_2}$$

where r_1 and r_2 are the distances of the electron from the two nuclei, at the points $(-d/2, 0, 0)$ and $(+d/2, 0, 0)$ respectively. Calculate the force on the electron.

3–8.   Suppose the potential energy of a particle moving in one dimension on the x-axis is

$$V = -\frac{1}{x} + \frac{1}{x^2}$$

Sketch the potential energy curve, and give a qualitative discussion of the types of motion which could occur.

3–9.   Solve the problem of the constant gravitational force by using the first integral given by the conservation of energy. That is, for the force $\mathbf{F} =$

− $mg\mathbf{e}_z$, use the potential energy, carry out the quadrature, and solve for $z(t)$.

3–10. Suppose a particle of mass m moves in a circle of radius r about the origin. What are the magnitude and direction of its angular momentum about the origin?

3–11. Derive Eq. 3–37.

3–12. Show that, in the rest frame (where the center of mass is at rest), the kinetic energy of a system of two particles is $T = \frac{1}{2} m v_{12}{}^2$, where m is the reduced mass and v_{12} is the relative speed.

3–13. Consider the uniform circular motion of two particles of masses m_1 and $m_2 = 2m_1$ about their center of mass, which we take to be the origin. How big is the reduced mass? If the circle traced by m_1 has a radius r_1, what is the radius of the circle traced by m_2? The period of one revolution of m_1 is P_1. What is the period of m_2? Describe the motion of the "fictitious particle" with the reduced mass. If it is circular, what is its radius? If it is periodic, what is its period? Verify that the angular momentum of the two particles equals the angular momentum of the one fictitious particle with reduced mass.

REFERENCES

R. J. Stephenson, *Mechanics and Properties of Matter* (John Wiley & Sons, 1960, 2nd ed.), Ch. 3.

R. A. Becker, *Introduction to Theoretical Mechanics* (McGraw-Hill, 1954), Ch. 5.

4/the harmonic oscillator

The theory that has been developed on the basis of the potential energy and energy conservation will next be applied to two problems which will prove to be very important in the discussion of the mechanics of atomic motions. The harmonic oscillator problem is the easier, as it turns out to be an inherently one-dimensional problem, and it will be treated first. Then the problem of the motion of a particle in an inverse square law force field will be discussed. Since the earliest analysis of the latter kind of motion was in the study of the planets in their orbits around the sun, the problem is often called planetary motion. Planetary motion, as we shall see, is inherently a two-dimensional problem. (Problems that are inherently three dimensional cannot often be solved exactly.)

A three-dimensional harmonic force, Eq. 1–16, is defined as $\mathbf{F} = -\ K\mathbf{r} = -\ K r\mathbf{e}_r$, $\mathbf{r} = x\mathbf{e}_x + y\mathbf{e}_y + z\mathbf{e}_z$ where $\mathbf{e}_r$ is the unit vector in the direction of $\mathbf{r}$, and $\mathbf{r}$ is the length of $\mathbf{r}$. This force is proportional to the distance of the particle from the origin, and always attracts the particle toward the origin. Clearly it is a generalization of the ordinary one-dimensional harmonic oscillator. It is not so easy to demonstrate the three-dimensional oscillator by means of a model as it is to exemplify a one-dimensional oscillator by a mass on a spring, but this inconvenience is not too unfortunate, because we will see that the three-dimensional oscillator is really just three one-dimensional oscillators. (A pendulum free to move in all directions behaves as a two-dimensional harmonic oscillator for small amplitudes.)

4–1 ONE-DIMENSIONAL OSCILLATOR

If the three components of the vector equation of motion

$$\mathbf{F} = m\ddot{\mathbf{r}} = -\ K\mathbf{r}$$

are equated separately, three scalar equations result:

$$F_x = m\ddot{x} = -Kx$$
$$F_y = m\ddot{y} = -Ky$$
$$F_z = m\ddot{z} = -Kz$$

Each of the coordinates therefore varies individually like the one-dimensional harmonic oscillator (one says the equations are *separable*), and to get the three-dimensional motion, we have only to construct the vector with the components $x(t)$, $y(t)$, $z(t)$. This composition will be examined later, but first we will solve the one-dimensional problem using the potential energy point of view.

The one-dimensional linear force is derivable from a potential energy (as in fact are all one-dimensional forces which depend only on the position). Clearly,

$$F_x = -Kx = -dV/dx \quad \text{with} \quad V = \tfrac{1}{2}Kx^2$$

You should verify (Prob. 4–1) that the three-dimensional force is derivable from

$$V = \tfrac{1}{2}Kx^2 + \tfrac{1}{2}Ky^2 + \tfrac{1}{2}Kz^2$$

by

$$\mathbf{F} = -\nabla V$$

The one-dimensional potential curve (Fig. 4–1) is a parabola, symmetrical about $x = 0$, with the equation

$$V(x) = \tfrac{1}{2}Kx^2 \tag{4-1}$$

The apex of the parabola can be taken at the origin, because an arbitrary constant can be added to any potential energy: since the force is the derivative of the potential energy, any constant can be added to the potential energy without changing the force derived from it. Thus the potential energy (and therefore also the total energy) is determined only to within an *arbitrary additive constant*.

If the total energy of the particle is the constant E, we see qualitatively (Fig. 4–1) that its motion is an oscillation back and forth between $x = +A$ and $x = -A$. The value of A is determined by the fact that the curves E and V intersect at $x = \pm A$, so that $E = V(A)$. Therefore

$$E = \tfrac{1}{2}KA^2 \tag{4-2}$$

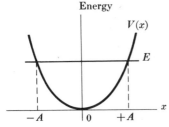

Fig. 4–1. *Harmonic oscillator potential energy.*

The value of A is greater the higher the total energy E. The particle approaches $x = +A$ with a speed which decreases as $\sqrt{E - V}$ decreases; when $V = E$, the speed is zero, the particle turns around, and accelerates toward the origin, where the speed and kinetic energy are maximum. It then decelerates, stops, and turns around at $x = -A$, etc. The maximum velocity at the origin can be found very easily from Eq. 3–20,

$$v = \sqrt{2(E - V)/m}$$

since $V = 0$ at the origin $x = 0$. Therefore, $v(0) \equiv v_{\max} = \sqrt{2E/m}$. Inserting the value of E in terms of A from Eq. 4–2, this expression becomes $v_{\max} = A\sqrt{K/m}$. We may also write

$$v_{\max} = A\omega_0 \tag{4-3}$$

where

$$\omega_0 \equiv \sqrt{K/m} \tag{4-4}$$

(Note that the new constant ω_0 must have the dimension of one over time, since A has the dimension of length and v of length over time; we shall see below that ω_0 is actually related to the frequency of the oscillatory motion of the particle.)

Using the energy approach, we have been able to learn quite a bit about the motion, from Eqs. 4–2 and 4–3, without having to do any specific integrations at all. The motion is a *periodic* motion. The maximum excursion from the origin (in either direction, since the potential energy is symmetrical), is the *amplitude A*. The total energy E is proportional to A^2. It is also proportional to the force constant K, which specifies the *strength* of the linear restoring force. For a given amplitude, the maximum velocity is large for a strong force (large K), but small for a heavy particle (large m). It is obvious that the motion is periodic no matter how large the amplitude, since the parabolic curve goes up to infinity.

It is also interesting to know the time required for one complete oscillation, i.e., the period of the motion. This information cannot be obtained without actually solving for the motion of the particle as a function of time, $x = x(t)$. That is, it is necessary to integrate the equation of motion a second time, to obtain the *complete solution*. We shall do so by the quadrature explained generally in Section 3–4. Thus, using Eq. 3–21,

$$v = dx/dt = \sqrt{(2E - Kx^2)/m}$$

or

$$t = \int dt = \int dx/\sqrt{(2E - Kx^2)/m} \tag{4-5}$$

The quadrature can be carried out by making a change of variables which will remove the constants from under the radical:

$$\frac{\sqrt{\dfrac{2E}{K}}\, d\sqrt{\dfrac{K}{2E}}\, x}{\sqrt{\dfrac{2E}{m}}\,\sqrt{1 - \dfrac{K}{2E}x^2}} = \frac{1}{\omega_0}\frac{d\xi}{\sqrt{1 - \xi^2}}$$

where $\xi \equiv \sqrt{\dfrac{K}{2E}}\, x = x/A$. If we now make the trigonometric substitution $\sin \theta \equiv \xi$,

$$\frac{1}{\omega_0} \frac{d\xi}{\sqrt{1 - \xi^2}} = \frac{1}{\omega_0} d\theta$$

since $\qquad d\xi = \cos \theta\, d\theta \qquad$ and $\qquad 1 - \xi^2 = 1 - \sin^2 \theta = \cos^2 \theta$

Now Eq. 4–5 becomes

$$t = \int \frac{1}{\omega_0}\, d\theta$$

This transformed equation is trivial to integrate.

$$\theta = \omega_0 t + \phi$$

where ϕ is an arbitrary constant of integration. Going back to the original variable by using the two transformation equations,

$$x = A \sin (\omega_0 t + \phi) \qquad\qquad (4\text{--}6)$$

Eq. 4–6 gives $x = x(t)$, the desired complete solution of the one-dimensional harmonic oscillator problem.

From Eq. 4–6, it is possible to see at once that the *period* of the motion is

$$P = 2\pi/\omega_0$$

since x assumes the same value again when t increases by $2\pi/\omega_0$. That is, $x(t') = x(t)$ if $t' = t + 2\pi/\omega_0$, as may be seen by substituting t' in Eq. 4–6. The *frequency* of the oscillation is $\nu = 1/P$, and so

$$\nu = \omega_0/2\pi \qquad\qquad (4\text{--}7)$$

The parameter ω_0 is called the *angular frequency*. The arbitrary constant ϕ determines the *phase* of the motion (Fig. 4–2). It really does nothing more than prescribe when we start counting the time. (When we compound the motions in more than one dimension, it has somewhat more significance.) The other of the two arbitrary constants involved in the integration of a second order equation, however, has a more important physical significance. That arbitrary constant is E, the total energy of the particle. In terms of

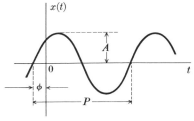

Fig. 4–2. Simple harmonic motion.

these two arbitrary constants, substituting Eqs. 4–2 and 4–4 into Eq. 4–6, the solution is

$$x(t) = \sqrt{2E/K} \sin (\sqrt{K/m}\ t + \phi)$$

To recapitulate, E and ϕ are arbitrary constants of integration (which have physical significance); K describes the environment of the particle, the strength of the force acting on it; and m is a property of the particle itself—its mass.

The solution given by Eq. 4–6 can be expressed in an alternative way which is frequently useful. Expanding the sine by the formula for the sine of a sum of two angles,

$$x = A \sin (\omega_0 t + \phi)$$
$$= A \cos \phi \sin \omega_0 t + A \sin \phi \cos \omega_0 t$$

Thus the same solution can be written

$$x = a \sin \omega_0 t + b \cos \omega_0 t \qquad (4–8)$$

where $\qquad a \equiv A \cos \phi \qquad b \equiv A \sin \phi$

This is another form of the general solution, with the two arbitrary constants a and b, which are related to the constants A and ϕ. Conversely, any solution of the form Eq. 4–8 could be expressed in the form Eq. 4–6, with

$$\phi \equiv \tan^{-1} b/a \qquad A \equiv \sqrt{a^2 + b^2}$$

We therefore see that the sine and cosine functions have the interesting property that the sum of any two of them (with the same frequency) is equal to a sine (or cosine) with a different amplitude and phase. This fact means that sine and cosine solutions can be used in any combination we choose, the amplitudes and phases being related by expressions like the above. These relations afford flexibility in the mathematical form of the solution, so that we can pick a particular form which is most useful for our immediate purpose. This flexibility will be exploited later, in Chapter 16.

4–2 TWO-DIMENSIONAL OSCILLATOR

Now we may consider the problem of compounding the sinusoidal motion of three one-dimensional oscillators to give the solution for the general three-dimensional harmonic oscillator. First, we should notice that the harmonic oscillator force

$$\mathbf{F} = -Kr\mathbf{e}_r$$

is a central force, as defined previously by Eq. 3–25, and that therefore the angular momentum of the particle moving under its influence is a conserved quantity. The fact that the angular momentum is conserved means that, even though the particle is allowed to move in three dimensions, the motion actually restricts itself entirely to a plane (which plane is determined by the initial conditions of the motion). Since this plane can be chosen as the x–y coordinate plane, it is sufficient to compound only two oscillators instead of three. Let the solutions $x = x(t)$ and $y = y(t)$ be

$$x = A \sin (\omega_0 t + \phi)$$
$$y = B \sin (\omega_0 t + \psi)$$

Suppose first that the two motions have the *same phase*. Then $\phi = \psi$, and, dividing in order to eliminate t, we obtain as the *equation of the orbit*,

$$y/x = B/A$$

This orbit is a straight line through the origin, with slope B/A (Fig. 4–3(a)). Suppose next that the motions are 90° out of phase, so that $\psi = \phi + \pi/2$. Then

$$y = B \cos (\omega_0 t + \phi)$$

and squaring and adding the two equations, we get for the orbital equation

$$(x/A)^2 + (y/B)^2 = 1$$

This orbit is an *ellipse*, whose horizontal semi-axis is A and vertical semi-axis B (and if $A = B$ it is a circle) (Fig. 4–3(b)). All the other intermediate cases are inclined ellipses which can be guessed from these two cases (Fig. 4–3(c)), but their actual analysis gets rather messy geometrically. Since we will not need any of these results in our future discussion, we will drop the problem here, although it should be emphasized again that in every case the motion can be decomposed into one-dimensional harmonic motions of the same frequency. A very important practical application of this theory is to the analysis of sinusoidal electrical signals displayed on an oscilloscope. The relative amplitude and phase of two signals can be measured by observing the elliptical pattern. (In the case of the oscilloscope, the two signals could also have different frequencies; in that event, more complicated Lissajous figures result, like figure eights. This kind of "orbit" cannot occur with a central force.)

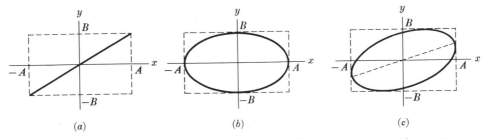

(a)   (b)   (c)

Fig. 4–3. Harmonic oscillator orbits: (a) in phase, (b) 90° out of phase, (c) 65° out of phase.

4–3 DAMPED HARMONIC MOTION

As a digression at this point, it is worthwhile to consider a different mathematical approach to the one-dimensional harmonic oscillator problem, since this approach is also applicable when *damping* is included. Let us include, as a first approximation, a damping force which is linear in the velocity (i.e., proportional to it), just as the harmonic restoring force is linear in the displacement from the origin. That is, we add a force $- R\,\dot{\mathbf{r}}$, which always opposes the motion of the particle. This kind of force law would be applicable, for example, to a simple pendulum whose motion is damped by air resistance, Eq. 1–18. The variables are still separable, so that it is sufficient to consider the equation of motion in only one dimension:

$$F_x = - Kx - R\dot{x} = m\ddot{x}$$

This force clearly cannot be the derivative with respect to x of any function of x, since it depends on $\dot{x}$ as well as x. Therefore we cannot use the potential energy approach. But rewriting the equation of motion as

$$\ddot{x} + 2b\dot{x} + \omega_0{}^2 x = 0 \qquad b \equiv R/2m \qquad \omega_0{}^2 \equiv K/m$$

we see that we still have a linear homogeneous differential equation with constant coefficients. (By "linear" is meant an equation which contains no powers of the dependent variable, x, or its derivatives, higher than the first power; and by "homogeneous" is meant that it contains no power lower than the first, i.e., no constant term.) We may therefore employ a device which yields a solution of any such equation, of any order (or indeed of any system of simultaneous linear homogeneous equations with constant coefficients, of any order). The trick is to substitute a trial solution of the form $x = \exp \lambda t$. Doing so, we obtain an algebraic equation

$$\lambda^2 + 2b\lambda + \omega_0{}^2 = 0$$

It is obvious that this substitution will always yield an algebraic equation which λ must satisfy. This is real progress, since an algebraic equation, no matter how difficult to solve, is always easier than the analogous differential equation. The substitution reduces the problem to finding a λ (a solution of the algebraic equation) which will make the assumed solution $x = \exp \lambda t$ actually satisfy the differential equation.

Since the algebraic equation is quadratic here, the solution is easy:

$$\lambda = - b \pm \sqrt{b^2 - \omega_0{}^2}$$

Let us concentrate on the case when the damping is small, i.e., let us assume $b^2 \leq \omega_0{}^2$. Then we should write, since $\sqrt{b^2 - \omega_0{}^2}$ is imaginary,

$$\lambda = - b \pm i\omega \qquad \text{where} \qquad i \equiv \sqrt{-1} \qquad \omega \equiv \sqrt{\omega_0{}^2 - b^2}$$

The $\pm$ signs indicate that we have two solutions corresponding to the two values of λ. A solution can thus be written

$$x = e^{-bt}(A_1 e^{i\omega t} + A_2 e^{-i\omega t})$$

where A_1 and A_2 are the two arbitrary constants in the general solution of a second order equation. You can verify that for any linear homogeneous equation, a constant times a solution is again a solution, and the sum of any two solutions is a solution (that is, any linear combination of solutions is a solution).

To reduce this to the form of our previous solution, let $A_1 = Ae^{i\phi}$, $A_2 = 0$. (Since we have let complex numbers creep into our formalism, we may as well let the constants A_1 and A_2 be complex too. There are other choices of A_1 and A_2 we could make, but they all give equivalent results.) Then, using De Moivre's theorem,

$$x = Ae^{i\phi}e^{-bt}e^{i\omega t} = Ae^{-bt}[\cos (\omega t + \phi) + i \sin (\omega t + \phi)]$$

Now if a function whose values are complex numbers satisfies a linear homogeneous differential equation, the equation must be satisfied separately by the real and imaginary parts of the complex function (see Prob. 4–9). Thus we can write the *real* solution to the equation (the only solution which has any physical meaning) as either the real or the imaginary part of the complex solution: e.g.,

$$x = Ae^{-bt} \sin (\omega t + \phi) \tag{4–9}$$

This solution has two arbitrary constants (A, ϕ), as it must. If $b = 0$ (no damping), it reduces to our previous solution. When $b \neq 0$, the position of the particle still oscillates sinusoidally with time, but the amplitude of the motion decreases exponentially, with a time constant b (Fig. 4–4). The larger is b, the sooner the amplitude of the motion damps to zero. (In this idealized description, it never actually reaches zero.) In addition, the frequency ω of the motion is somewhat smaller than the natural frequency $(\omega_0 = \sqrt{K/m})$ without damping. As the amplitude decreases, so does the energy, according to Eq. 4–2.

The damped harmonic oscillator is a problem which is immensely important in practical applications. Besides, even though we have said that friction does not figure in atomic motions, there are cases of microscopic problems in which energy losses occur, and these can be represented as a damping of the motion. The above analysis is relevant to these situations.

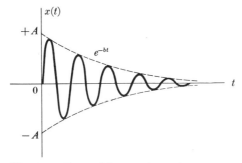

Fig. 4–4. *Damped harmonic motion.*

Although we cannot strictly analyse the problem completely using the potential energy diagram in such circumstances, the potential energy approach is still useful, for a qualitative discussion of the motion. It is still legitimate to visualize an object sliding along the potential energy curve, but now the object should be imagined to slide with friction. For example, an object sliding in the parabolic harmonic oscillator potential energy trough would gradually die down because of frictional losses, until it came to rest at the bottom of the trough (at the origin).

4-4 MOLECULAR VIBRATIONS

As a numerical example of one-dimensional harmonic motion, we may now consider the vibration of a diatomic molecule. We shall see in Chapter 14 that the force between the two atoms of the molecule is approximately a harmonic force, like that exerted by a spring:

$$F_x = - Kx$$

Here x represents the increase over the equilibrium separation of the atoms (i.e., the amount by which the "spring" is stretched), not their total separation, which is greater than zero even in equilibrium. (See Fig. 4–5.) Neither atom is held fixed in space, but the reduced mass concept, Eq. 3–35, can be used:

$$m = m_1 m_2 / (m_1 + m_2)$$

Then the vibrational frequency, from Eqs. 4–7 and 4–4, is

$$\nu = \frac{1}{2\pi} \sqrt{\frac{K}{m}} \tag{4-10}$$

The reduced mass can be computed from the atomic masses of the atoms forming the molecule. Furthermore, the vibrational frequency can be derived from the experimental optical absorption spectrum of a gas composed of the molecules in question. Using these data, we can compute the force constant K. For example, for the NaCl molecule, the atomic mass of Na is 23.0 and that of Cl is 35.5, so that the reduced mass is (in "atomic mass units," or amu).

$$m = 23.0 \times 35.5 / (23.0 + 35.5) = 14.0 \text{ amu}$$
$$= 14.0 \times 1.67 \times 10^{-24} = 2.33 \times 10^{-23} \text{g}$$

The observed vibration frequency for NaCl is

$$\nu = 1.14 \times 10^{13} \text{ sec}^{-1}$$

m_1 m_2

Fig. 4–5. Model of diatomic molecule.

(corresponding to an absorption in the infrared region of the optical spectrum). Then from Eq. 4–10, we find

$$K = 1.2 \times 10^5 \text{ dyne/cm}$$

It is interesting to note that this interatomic force constant—about 100 g-force/cm—is of the same order of magnitude as the force constant of a rather weak steel spring. This fact gives some intuitive feeling for the strength of the interatomic forces, although it has no deep significance.

We can also compute the energy of vibration. The energy depends on the amplitude of vibration, and this must obviously be less than the equilibrium separation of the atoms (the unstretched length of the "spring"). Indeed, the harmonic force approximation holds only so long as the amplitude is small compared to this quantity. The equilibrium separation can be measured (from the spectrum, or by electron diffraction), and for NaCl the experimental value is 2.51 Å. Suppose we let the amplitude of vibration A be about 5% of this value, say $A = 0.14$ Å. Then, from Eq. 4–2,

$$E = \tfrac{1}{2} KA^2 = \frac{1}{2}\, 1.2 \times 10^5 \times 0.14^2 \times 10^{-16} = 1.2 \times 10^{-13} \text{ erg}$$
$$= 1.2 \times 10^{-13}/1.6 \times 10^{-12} = 0.07 \text{ eV}$$

This is not a very large energy on the atomic scale; it is only about 2% of the chemical energy (3.6 eV) which holds the NaCl molecule together. These relations are illustrated in Fig. 4–6.

The NaCl molecule not only can absorb light, but it also emits light when it vibrates. The emission of light energy results in a decrease of the vibrational energy of the molecule, so that the amplitude of vibration decreases according to Eq. 4–9. The damping constant b can be taken as

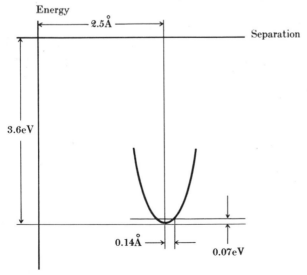

Fig. 4–6. Interatomic energy of NaCl molecule.

about 10^3 sec^{-1} for this case, so that the vibrational excitation only persists for about 10^{-3} sec. This short time interval is nevertheless enormously long on the atomic scale, since in this interval the atom executes about 10^{10} oscillations. Finally, however, the vibration will die away and the molecule will return to its lowest energy state. If in an ordinary gas the molecules are in constant vibration, that is because they are continually being excited by thermal energy, as we shall see in Chapter 9.

PROBLEMS

4-1.   Show that $\mathbf{F} = - K\mathbf{r}$ is derivable from the potential energy

$$V = \tfrac{1}{2} Kx^2 + \tfrac{1}{2} Ky^2 + \tfrac{1}{2} Kz^2$$

4-2.   Show that the potential energy $V = \tfrac{1}{2} Kx^2$ averaged over one period of the motion is

$$\overline{V} = \tfrac{1}{4} KA^2$$

(*Hint:* Show that

$$\overline{x^2} = \frac{1}{P} \int_0^P [x(t)]^2 dt = \tfrac{1}{2}A^2)$$

What is the average kinetic energy?

4-3.   Suppose a particle moves in one dimension under the potential

$$V = \tfrac{1}{2}Kx^2 + D/x^2$$

Sketch the potential energy and discuss the motion qualitatively. Calculate the turn-around points, for a given total energy E.

4-4.   Calculate the frequency of a 1 kg mass suspended on a spring with force constant $K = 10^5$ dyne/cm.

4-5.   Find the equation of the orbit when two perpendicular harmonic oscillations are added together 45° out of phase.

4-6.   For a two-dimensional oscillator with amplitudes A and B in the x- and y-directions, respectively, show that the total energy E is

$$E = \tfrac{1}{2}K (A^2 + B^2)$$

(*Hint:* Substitute the solution $x = A \sin (\omega_0 t + \phi)$, $y = B \sin (\omega_0 t + \psi)$, in the energy expression.)

4-7.   For any linear homogeneous differential equation with constant coefficients, show that if $x(t)$ satisfies the equation, then $Ax(t)$ does too, for any constant A. Also show that if $x_1(t)$ and $x_2(t)$ are two solutions of the equation, then $x_1(t) + x_2(t)$ is a solution too.

4-8.   Show that for a nonlinear equation, e.g.,

$$\ddot{x} + cx^2 = 0$$

the assertions of Prob. 4-7 do not hold.

4-9.   Suppose the complex function $z = x + iy$ satisfies a differential equation $\ddot{z} + a\dot{z} + bz = 0$, where a and b are real constants. Show that x and y satisfy the same differential equation. (*Hint:* A complex number is zero only if its real and imaginary parts are zero.)

4-10. The *logarithmic decrement* δ of a damped harmonic oscillator is defined as the natural logarithm of two successive displacements separated by one period $P = 2\pi/\omega$.

$$\delta \equiv \ln \frac{x(t)}{x(t + P)}$$

From Eq. 4-9 show that δ is a constant and find its value. (In particular, it is the logarithm of the ratio of two successive maxima.)

4-11. Obtain the real solution for the damped harmonic oscillator when the damping is large and discuss the motion.

4-12. It is interesting to compare the force constants for some other alkali halide molecules with that of NaCl computed in Section 4-4. For NaBr, KCl, and KBr, the observed vibrational frequencies are 0.94, 0.84, and 0.69 $\times 10^{13}$ sec^{-1}, respectively. Calculate the reduced masses for these molecules and their force constants. Is there any regularity in the variation of the force constant with the position of the atoms in the periodic table?

4-13. According to classical electromagnetic theory, the rate at which a charged particle radiates energy (i.e., the radiated power) is

$$\frac{2}{3}\frac{e^2}{c^3}\ddot{x}^2$$

where e is the magnitude of the electron charge.
(a) What is the average power radiated, using Eq. 4-6 and $\overline{x^2} = \frac{1}{2}A^2$ (Prob. 4-2)?
(b) If the damping is small, show that the rate at which the energy of an oscillator decreases is approximately KA^2b, from Eq. 4-2. (*Hint:* As suggested by Eq. 4-9, let the amplitude be $A = A_0 e^{-bt}$.)
(c) By equating the results of (a) and (b), show that

$$b \cong \frac{1}{6}\frac{e^2}{c^3}\frac{\omega^2}{m}$$

REFERENCES

R. J. Stephenson, *Mechanics and Properties of Matter* (John Wiley & Sons, 1960, 2nd ed.), Ch. 5.

R. A. Becker, *Introduction to Theoretical Mechanics* (McGraw-Hill, 1954), Ch. 7.

5/the inverse square force law

The inverse square law force, like the harmonic oscillator force, is always directed toward (or away from) the origin. Instead of being proportional in magnitude to the distance from the origin, however, it is proportional to the inverse square of the distance, so that

$$\mathbf{F} = -\,(K/r^2)\mathbf{e}_r \qquad \mathbf{e}_r \equiv \mathbf{r}/r$$

Again, $\mathbf{e}_r$ is the unit vector in the direction of $\mathbf{r}$, and r is the magnitude of $\mathbf{r}$. K is a constant which can be positive or negative but will be positive in our first application. For example, if the force is the gravitational *attraction, Eq. 1–12,*

$$K = GmM$$

where G is the gravitational constant, m is the mass of the particle, and M is the mass of the attracting body. If the force is the coulomb attraction, Eq. 1–13,

$$K = -\,q_1q_2$$

where q_1 and q_2 are the charges on the interacting particles. In the gravitational case K is always positive, but in the electrostatic case it could also be negative (repulsion) if the two charges had the same sign.

In this chapter, we shall take many of our examples from the gravitational case, discussing the motions of planets, satellites, space vehicles, etc. (Section 5–4). Particularly because of the present practical interest in space navigation, new research is currently being done in celestial mechanics. These macroscopic problems seem at first sight to be at variance with our main program, of exploring microscopic physics. Nevertheless, we feel justified in including them because, in addition to their inherent interest, they can serve as analogs to microscopic systems in which the force is electrostatic rather than gravitational.

Since these two forces are identical except for a numerical coefficient, all the results are also applicable to microscopic charged particles—at least to the extent that classical (non-quantum) mechanics is applicable at all, as is often the case. Satellites and planets can therefore provide a useful introduction to the analysis of orbits in the inverse-square-law force field, in a context which is more familiar and easily visualized. In later chapters we shall consider additional microscopic examples.

5-1   THE $1/r$ POTENTIAL

If the equations of motion were written out in Cartesian coordinates (cf. Eq. 1–12′), all the variables x, y, z would be mixed up in each of the three equations, with the result that the variables are *not separable*. (If the equations are written in the polar coordinate system, the variables *are* separable, and the equations can be solved in closed form without great difficulty; but we will not take this approach.) Using the general test ($\nabla \times \mathbf{F} = 0$), however, you can show that there exists a potential energy function V from which the force can be derived. We will find V and deduce as much information as we can from it.

In fact, we will show that $V = -K/r$. The arbitrary constant involved in V has been chosen so that $V = 0$ when $r = \infty$, in accord with a convention universally adopted with the inverse square law force. To find V, notice first that

$$2\mathbf{r}{\cdot}d\mathbf{r} = d(\mathbf{r}{\cdot}\mathbf{r}) = d(r^2) = 2rdr$$

Then

$$- V(r) = W = \int \mathbf{F} \cdot d\mathbf{r} = - \int_{\infty}^{r} \frac{K}{r^2} \frac{\mathbf{r}{\cdot}d\mathbf{r}}{r} = - \int_{\infty}^{r} \frac{Kdr}{r^2} = \frac{K}{r}$$

The work done in going between two points 1 and 2 is independent of path, as always when a potential energy exists. Why this is so here can be seen by considering the two paths A and B (Fig. 5–1(a)). The force always points towards 0, so that on path A a certain work is done in going along the radial part of the path and no work is done on the circular part (since the force is perpendicular to the displacement). Any other path B can be approximated as closely as desired by little radial and circular segments (Fig. 5–1(b)). The work is the total work done on the radial segments, since no work is done on the circular segments. (The circles—really spheres—centered about 0 are the equipotential surfaces.)

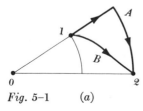

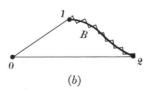

Fig. 5–1   (*a*)   (*b*)

Since the potential energy is $- K/r$, the total energy is

$$E = \tfrac{1}{2}mv^2 - K/r = \text{const} \qquad (5\text{-}1)$$

We may first consider the case when the motion is *one dimensional*. The motion does not have to be one dimensional, but it would be if the particle were started with its initial velocity toward or away from the origin: since the force is toward the origin, so is the acceleration, and therefore the particle would never acquire any velocity perpendicular to its original motion. In this case the speed v of the particle is equal to the rate of change of the length of the vector $\mathbf{r}$, i.e.,

$$v = \dot{r}$$

Then Eq. 5–1 becomes

$$E = \tfrac{1}{2}m\dot{r}^2 - K/r \qquad (5\text{-}2)$$

which can be integrated once (cf. Eq. 3–21), with a result which is expressible in closed form. This integration will be left as a problem, and we will consider the motion qualitatively, using Fig. 5–2.

Notice that if $E < 0$ (say $E = E_1$) the particle can only go out to a certain distance r_1, stop, turn around, and fall back to the origin. If, on the other hand, $E > 0$ ($E = E_2$), it can go off to infinity, i.e., escape from the attracting force altogether. A particularly interesting case occurs when $E = 0$. This case gives the least speed the particle can have, say at $r = R$, and still escape from the attracting center. The corresponding speed is called the *escape velocity*, and it can be found by inserting into Eq. 5–2 the values of $\dot{r}$ and r at the two positions where these are known: $\dot{r} = v_{\text{escape}}$ and $r = R$ at the starting point (by definition); and $\dot{r} = 0$ and $r = \infty$ when the particle is infinitely far from the origin. The speed is zero at infinity because a particle which was still moving "at infinity" would have some kinetic energy, and so would not have the *least* energy needed to escape. Thus

$$E = \tfrac{1}{2}\, mv^2{}_{\text{escape}} - K/R = \tfrac{1}{2}\, m0^2 - K/\infty = 0$$

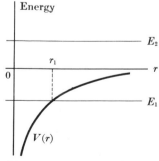

Fig. 5–2. *1/r potential energy.*

and solving for v_{escape},

$$v_{\text{escape}} = \sqrt{\frac{2K}{mR}} \qquad (5\text{-}3)$$

An interesting case is the gravitational one, since the escape velocity is the speed a rocket must acquire in order to escape from the gravitational field of the earth or other body. In this case, we must insert $K = GmM$, where m is the mass of the rocket and M that of the earth, and interpret R, the distance from the force center where the particle starts with v_{escape}, as the radius of the earth. Then

$$v_{\text{escape}} = \sqrt{\frac{2GM}{R}} \qquad (5\text{-}3')$$

The escape velocity is *independent of the mass of the rocket*, and depends only on the mass and radius of the earth (M and R). Since $G = 6.67 \times 10^{-8}$ dyne cm^2/g^2, $M = 6 \times 10^{27}$ g, and $R = 6.4 \times 10^8$ cm, the velocity of escape *from the earth* is

$$v_{\text{escape}} = 11 \text{ km/sec}$$

Although we have discussed the escape velocity in terms of the one-dimensional problem, it is important to note that the escape velocity has the *same* magnitude, no matter in which direction the particle takes off: when $E = 0$, $v = 0$ at $r = \infty$, whether the velocity at $r = R$ is directly away from the force center or in any other direction.

5-2   THE EFFECTIVE POTENTIAL ENERGY

When we come to the general three-dimensional motion, it is no longer true that $v = \dot{r}$. For example, if the particle were going in a circle around the origin, $\dot{r} = 0$ ($r = $ const), but the speed v is different from zero. We can no longer use the equation $E = \frac{1}{2}m\dot{r}^2 - K/r$; but the equation $E = \frac{1}{2}mv^2 - K/r$ is still true. This energy conservation equation again gives a useful approach to the analysis of the motion, particularly when used in conjunction with a second equation which expresses the *conservation of angular momentum*. The inverse square law force is a central force, since it is proportional to $\mathbf{e}_r$, and so the vector angular momentum is constant throughout the motion. Just as in the case of the harmonic force, the constancy of the angular momentum vector means that the motion occurs entirely in a certain plane, determined by the initial conditions, and we may as well choose the x–y coordinate plane to coincide with the plane in which the particle moves. The present case, in contrast to the harmonic oscillator, is still essentially two-dimensional, however, and so the energy conservation equation is not immediately integrable. To obtain another needed integral of the equation of motion, we can now exploit the equation which states that the *magnitude* of the angular momentum is constant: $L = $ constant. This information is most useful in conjunction with Eq. 3–28 for the kinetic energy T,

$$T = \tfrac{1}{2}m\dot{r}^2 + \frac{L^2}{2mr^2}$$

With $L = $ const, the only remaining time derivative is $\dot{r}$. Because of the importance of this result, let us rederive it here.

With the motion occurring in the x–y plane, $\mathbf{L}$ is parallel to the z-axis, and therefore its magnitude is

$$L = L_z$$

We have explained in general (Section 3–5) that the magnitude of the angular momentum L is the moment of momentum about a point (the origin of the central force, if L is to be constant) and is given in Cartesian coordinates by

$$L_z = (\mathbf{r} \times \mathbf{p})_z = xm\dot{y} - ym\dot{x} = L$$

Now let us further specify our coordinate system so that, at a certain instant, the particle lies on the x-axis. Then $L = xm\dot{y}$, since $y = 0$. Also $r = x$, and $\dot{r} = \dot{x}$ (Fig. 5–3), so that $\dot{y} = L/mr$. Therefore, *at this instant*,

$$v^2 = \dot{x}^2 + \dot{y}^2 = \dot{r}^2 + L^2/m^2r^2$$

Since the chosen instant is completely arbitrary, however, this relation between v^2 and L^2 is true throughout the motion. The relation derived from the constancy of the angular momentum can be combined with the independent relation between v^2 and E, which expresses energy conservation, Eq. 5–1, to give

$$E = \tfrac{1}{2}m\dot{r}^2 + L^2/2mr^2 - K/r \qquad (5\text{--}4)$$

We have thereby related r and its time derivative to the two constants E and L.

Equation 5–4 is interesting because it enables us to discuss the variation of r with time. (In fact, it also enables us to find $r(t)$ by a quadrature, which can be carried out in closed form, but we will not do this.) We have expressed E as a function of the single variable r and its derivative. Therefore, as far as r is concerned, we can discuss the problem as if it were a one-dimensional problem, and so obtain qualitative information about how r will vary in the motion. The only thing we have to remember is the fact (not expressed in Eq. 5–4) that at the same time r is varying, the particle is

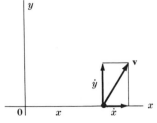

Fig. 5–3

also moving *around* the origin in the direction perpendicular to **r**. (See Fig. 5–4. Actually, we know v^2, and we know $\dot{r}^2$, so we could also compute the other component of velocity.) When we treat the problem as one-dimensional, however, and discuss only r, we notice that effectively the "potential energy" is not just $- K/r$, but is an *effective potential energy*,

$$V' = - K/r + L^2/2mr^2 \tag{5–5}$$

We shall next see how we are able to base a fairly complete analysis of the motion on the equation

$$E = \tfrac{1}{2}m\dot{r}^2 + V'(r) \tag{5–6}$$

obtained from Eqs. 5–4 and 5–5.

5-3   BOUND ORBITS

In this section we shall limit our attention to the case when the force constant K is positive (attractive force). Then $V'(r)$ varies as in Fig. 5–5. At large distances, the effective potential energy V' resembles the $- 1/r$ potential, because $1/r^2$ goes to zero more rapidly than $1/r$ as r goes to infinity. At small distances, on the other hand, V' looks like $1/r^2$, because $1/r^2$ goes to infinity faster than $1/r$ as r goes to zero. The general shape of the curve is as shown, no matter what the value of L: (except $L = 0$), but the scale depends on the magnitude of L: the minimum of the curve occurs when $dV'/dr = 0$, or when (differentiating Eq. 5–5)

$$r = L^2/Km \equiv a_0 \tag{5–7}$$

The corresponding value of V', obtained by substituting this value of r in Eq. 5–5, is

$$V'(a_0) = - K^2m/2L^2 = - K/2a_0 \tag{5–8}$$

When L is small, the minimum occurs at a small radius a_0 and it is very deep. For $L = 0$, V' reduces to $- K/r$ as in Fig. 5–2.

The simplest type of motion which could occur with the effective potential energy V' (Fig. 5–5) is when the particle is "at rest" at the bottom of the trough, i.e., when $r = a_0$ all the time. The particle is not actually at

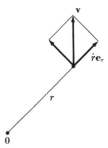

Fig. 5–4

rest: although $\dot{r} = 0$, so that the distance from the origin is constant (a_0), the particle is moving *around* the origin with angular momentum

$$L = \sqrt{Kma_0}$$

obtained by solving Eq. 5–7 for L. Since the distance is constant, the particle is moving in a *circular orbit*. The total energy E is equal to V' for this orbit, because $\dot{r} = 0$, so that from Eqs. 5–6 and 5–8,

$$E = -K/2a_0 = E_0$$

The speed v can be found from $E = \frac{1}{2}mv^2 + V$, since $V = -K/a_0$ when $r = a_0$. Thus

$$v = \sqrt{K/ma_0} \equiv v_0$$

for the circular orbit. (This is of course the result which is obtained in the elementary way by equating the attracting force to the mass times the centripetal acceleration. It also comes from $L = mva_0 = \sqrt{Kma_0}$.) Note that the escape velocity $(E = 0)$ at the same distance is, according to Eq. 5–3, just $\sqrt{2}$ times the speed in the circular orbit $(E = E_0)$:

$$v_{escape} = \sqrt{2}\,v_0$$

If the energy E is somewhat greater than E_0, but the angular momentum L is the same, the particle moves in an orbit in which r varies between a minimum value a_1 and a maximum value a_2 (Fig. 5–6). Since r assumes these extreme values when $\dot{r} = 0$, we can calculate a_1 and a_2 by writing

$$E = -K/r + L^2/2mr^2$$

and solving for r: a quadratic equation in r results, with the two solutions

$$r = -\frac{K}{2E}\left[1 \pm \sqrt{1 + 2EL^2/mK^2}\right]$$

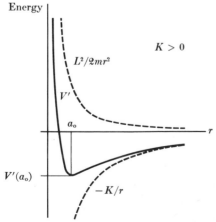

Fig. 5–5. *Effective potential energy (attractive force).*

Recalling that E is negative, the two solutions for r are

$$a_1 = -\frac{K}{2E}(1 - e) \qquad a_2 = -\frac{K}{2E}(1 + e) \qquad (5\text{–}9)$$

where we have used the abbreviation

$$e = \sqrt{1 + 2EL^2/mK^2} \qquad (5\text{–}10)$$

First, let us note that for the circular orbit just considered, $E = -K/2a_0$ and $L^2 = Kma_0$, so that $e = 0$ and $a_1 = a_2 = -K/2E = a_0$, in agreement with our previous result. For a higher energy orbit, $e > 0$, and we can obtain an interesting result by adding a_1 and a_2 from Eq. 5–9:

$$a_1 + a_2 = -K/E \qquad (5\text{–}11)$$

All of the orbits with $E < 0$ are called *bound orbits*, because the value of r is bounded—the distance of the particle from the origin varies between a_1 and a_2, never becoming larger than a_2.

In order to visualize these orbits in two dimensions, it is essential to remember that the particle is moving *around* the origin, at the same time its distance from the origin is varying between a_1 and a_2. A complete solution of the problem would show that the orbit is an *ellipse*, with one focus at the origin (Fig. 5–7). The quantity $a_1 + a_2$ is the major axis of the ellipse, which we may call $2a$. From Eq. 5-11,

$$E = -K/2a \qquad (5\text{–}12)$$

for all the elliptical orbits, where a is the *semimajor axis* of the ellipse. This result is a generalization of the relation for the circular orbit, since a circle is a limiting case of an ellipse with the semimajor and semiminor axes equal (to the radius of the circle). The quantity e defined by Eq. 5–10 is called the *eccentricity* of the ellipse. The circular orbit has zero eccentricity. For all the possible elliptical orbits

$$0 \le e < 1$$

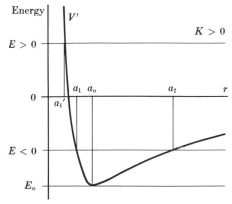

Fig. 5–6

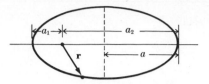

Fig. 5–7. Inverse-square-law orbit.

When $E \geq 0$, $e \geq 1$, and these orbits are not bound orbits. They will be discussed further in Section 5–5.

Instead of cataloguing the orbits with given angular momentum L as a function of the total energy E, it is instructive to think of the orbits with given E and various values of L. All such orbits have the same semimajor axis a, according to Eq. 5–12, because the total energy depends *only* on the semimajor axis of the ellipse. The eccentricity of the ellipses corresponding to different L varies between 0 for the circular orbit and 1 for $L = 0$ (Eq. 5–10). The circular orbit of a given energy has the highest angular momentum of all orbits with that energy, and the more eccentric the ellipse, the smaller the angular momentum. The extreme case, $L = 0$ ($e = 1$), gives an orbit which is a line of length $2a$ (Fig. 5–8). If a particle had $v = 0$ at $r = 2a$, it would follow this orbit. (Note that $E = \frac{1}{2}m0 - K/2a$.) The *line orbit* is something of an idealization as the particle approaches the origin, because the speed becomes infinite, but the other portions of such an orbit are often of interest.

Incidentally, we may recall that the harmonic force also resulted in an elliptical orbit for the particle. The difference is that in that case the *center* of the ellipse was at the origin of the force, whereas in the inverse square case, the *focus* of the ellipse is at the origin. One should not conclude that *all* central forces lead to elliptical orbits. It happens that the two we have considered are the *only* ones which do.

Just as in the case of the harmonic oscillator, in order to find the *period* of the motion, it is necessary to solve the problem completely by integrating the equations of motion once more. This integration can be carried out in closed form in the inverse square law case, but we will not do it, and will merely quote the result. In the particular case of the circular orbit, the period can be found by elementary means. It is just the circumference of the circle divided by the speed, or

$$P = 2\pi \, a_0/v_0$$

Fig. 5–8. Orbits of equal energy and different angular momentum.

Substituting the value of v_0 for the circular orbit, one gets

$$P = 2\pi\sqrt{a_0{}^3m/K}$$

As it turns out, exactly the same result holds for the elliptical orbits, with a_0 replaced by a.

$$P = 2\pi\sqrt{a^3m/K} \tag{5-13}$$

To summarize the most useful results of the above rather lengthy discussion, let us point out again that they are straightforward generalizations of the equations which apply to a circular orbit. The latter can be derived by equating the inverse square law force $F = - K/a_0{}^2$ to the centripetal force $- mv^2/a_0$. The value $v = K/ma_0$ is then substituted into the equation for E, Eq. 5-1, or for P to give our main results, Eqs. 5-12 and 5-13. These equations are so easy to derive for the circular orbit that it is unnecessary to memorize them; one has only to remember that the radius a_0 of the circle should be replaced by the semimajor axis a of the ellipse. Then the speed v can be calculated at any point on the orbit, by substituting for E and V in Eq. 3-19, $v = \sqrt{2(E - V)/m}$. (See Eq. 5-15 below). Finally, the maximum and minimum distances from the origin are given by combining Eqs. 5-9 and 5-12. Only the expression for the eccentricity e, Eq. 5-10, is difficult to remember, but it can be calculated from the other equations with a moderate amount of algebra (Prob. 5-11). We may collect the important equations here:

$$a = - K/2E \qquad a = \tfrac{1}{2}(a_1 + a_2) \tag{5-12}$$

$$e = \sqrt{1 + 2EL^2/mK^2} \tag{5-10}$$

$$a_1 = a(1 - e) \qquad a_2 = a(1 + e) \tag{5-14}$$

$$v = \sqrt{\frac{K}{m}}\sqrt{\frac{2}{r} - \frac{1}{a}} \tag{5-15}$$

$$P = 2\pi\sqrt{a^3m/K} \tag{5-13}$$

These are the relations we shall need in discussing the applications in the following sections. The first three specify the geometry of the orbit in terms of the energy E, and the angular momentum L, or vice versa. The last two specify the speed at any point and the period; note that both these quantities depend only on a (or E), not on e (or L).

5-4   PLANETARY MOTION

In this section we shall consider some practical applications to problems about natural and artificial satellites of the sun. Since the sun is about 1000 times more massive than the largest planet (Jupiter), the reduced mass, Eq. 3-35, is essentially equal to the mass of the satellite, and the sun remains approximately fixed, very close to the center of mass of the solar system.

The determination of the orbits of artificial satellites, or space vehicles, is currently stimulating a great deal of research on planetary motion, for the first time since the 19th century. The natural satellites of the earth and sun provided the initial stimulus to the understanding of planetary motion, and indeed of mechanics. In this case, the force is the gravitational force, so that $K = GmM$, m being the mass of the particle (satellite) and M that of the attracting body. Then Eqs. 5–15 and 5–13 become

$$v = \sqrt{GM} \sqrt{\frac{2}{r} - \frac{1}{a}}$$

$$P = 2\pi \sqrt{a^3/GM}$$

Note that both these relations are *independent of m*, the mass of the orbiting body, for the same reason that all objects fall to the ground with the same acceleration g. The second relation is *Kepler's third law*. If M is the mass of the sun, it is very convenient to use a particular set of units (neither mks nor cgs), in which the earth–sun distance (the Astronomical Unit, abbreviated au) is the unit of length, and the period of the earth (the year) is the unit of time. The conversion factors are:
1 au $= 93 \times 10^6$ mi $= 1.49 \times 10^8$ km $= 500$ light-sec $= 1.6 \times 10^{-5}$

light-yr

1 yr $= 3.15 \times 10^7$ sec
1 au/yr $= 4.75$ km/sec
In this set of units, $P = 1$ yr when $a = 1$ au; then Kepler's law shows that it must be true that $\sqrt{GM} = 2\pi$ when expressed in these units. The equations now become simplified,

$$v = 2\pi \sqrt{\frac{2}{r} - \frac{1}{a}} \tag{5–15'}$$

$$P = a^{3/2} \tag{5–13'}$$

and this is of course the justification for using them.

As a first example, we shall consider the problem of *comets*. For one thing, they have very eccentric orbits, and so we will exercise more than just the elementary theory of circular orbits. Secondly, not much is known about them and they are currently interesting objectives of a space probe. A few of them, the "short period" comets, have orbits which lie entirely inside Pluto's orbit of semimajor axis about 40 au. Since they come close to the sun, the major axis ($2a$) of the comet's orbit is less than about 40 au. The period, from Eq. 5–13', is

$$P < 20^{3/2} \cong 90 \text{ yr}$$

Many of these short period comets have been observed regularly. Most comets, however, have orbits with very large a and eccentricity e very close to 1. Let us suppose, for example, that

$$a = 10^4 \text{ au}$$

Then from Eq. 5–13′

$$P = 10^6 \text{ yr}$$

In the history of the solar system (about 10^{10} yr), such a comet could have made several thousand visits to our vicinity, although we shall see below that it probably has not actually done so.

Let us assume furthermore that the comet's closest approach to the sun is 1 au. The closest and farthest points, called *perihelion* and *aphelion*, respectively, are given by Eq. 5–14. The eccentricity of the orbit e can be computed from the perihelion equation,

$$a_1 = a(1 - e) = 1 \text{ au}$$
$$e = 1 - a_1/a = 1 - 10^{-4} = 0.9999$$

The eccentricity is therefore very close to 1 indeed; if it were exactly 1, the orbit would not be a bound orbit, and the comet would not belong to the solar system but would be a visitor from interstellar space. The other relation of Eq. 5–14 gives for the aphelion distance

$$a_2 = a(1 + e) = 1.9999 \, a \cong 2 \times 10^4 \text{ au}$$

It is also interesting to compute the speeds at perihelion and aphelion from Eq. 5–15′. At perihelion ($r = a_1$)

$$v_1 = 2\pi\sqrt{2/1 - 1/10^4} \cong 2\sqrt{2} \, \pi \text{ au/yr} = 42 \text{ km/sec}$$

The earth's speed in its own orbit is

$$v_0 = 2\pi \text{ au/yr} = 30 \text{ km/sec}$$

The comet has a somewhat higher speed at the same distance from the sun because it has larger total energy per unit mass. (The total energy itself is much smaller, since comets have rather small masses.) At aphelion ($r = a_2$)

$$v_2 = 2\pi\sqrt{\frac{2}{a(1 + e)} - \frac{1}{a}} \cong 2\pi \sqrt{\frac{1 - e}{2a}} = \frac{2\pi}{a} \sqrt{\frac{a_1}{2}}$$
$$= \sqrt{2} \, \pi \times 10^{-4} \text{au/yr} = 2.1 \text{ m/sec}$$

The comet is therefore barely moving at aphelion—perhaps at a fairly brisk walking pace.

It is instructive to calculate the speed the comet would have at its aphelion distance if it were in a circular orbit (shown by the dashed line in Fig. 5–9), rather than in its actual eccentric orbit. This circular orbit has a radius $a' = 2a$. Inserting into Eq. 5–15′,

$$v = 2\pi\sqrt{\frac{2}{a'} - \frac{1}{a'}} = \frac{2\pi}{\sqrt{2a}}$$
$$= \sqrt{2}\pi \times 10^{-2} \text{au/yr} = 210 \text{ m/sec}$$

This speed is still rather small—about 470 mph, less than the speed of a jet airliner. Now the current idea of the origin of comets is that there is a large reservoir of small objects drifting around in nearly circular orbits at a dis-

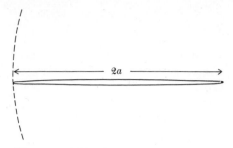

Fig. 5–9. Orbit of a comet.

tance of the order of 10^5 au from the sun. They are far enough from the sun (about 1 light-yr) that their motion may be perturbed by another star. If one is nearly brought to rest by this interaction, it will come in close to the sun in an elliptical orbit. The comets must belong originally to the solar system, because none are observed in orbits with e significantly greater than 1 (unbound orbits). On the other hand, while they are near the sun they may be sent into slightly unbound orbits by perturbations by planets (especially Jupiter, whose mass is more than 1/1000 that of the sun). This perturbation is possible because e is already so close to 1, and it suggests that most such comets probably do not make periodic visits to the sun's neighborhood.

As a second example, we will analyze a problem of *interplanetary travel*, involving an artificial solar satellite. Consider the problem of sending a space vehicle from the earth to Mars. The earth moves in a (nearly) circular orbit of radius a_1, and Mars in a (nearly) circular orbit of radius a_2. We wish to launch a "particle" from Earth, so that it will orbit about the sun, and intersect the orbit of Mars. (We will choose the launching time so that Mars is *there* when the vehicle intersects its orbit.) That is, we wish to send the vehicle on a ballistic (unpowered) flight from Earth to Mars, and, furthermore, to do so as economically as possible. Now of all the orbits which intersect both Earth's and Mars' orbits, the one of lowest total energy is the one with the smallest semimajor axis, i.e., the "line" orbit of major axis a_2. This would be the most direct flight, over the shortest possible distance. Although in this orbit the vehicle has the smallest possible energy, it is not the most economical, when we remember that the vehicle before launching is already travelling with the earth's orbital velocity without any expenditure at all. If we also wish to have the vehicle impact on Mars with (nearly) zero velocity, we shall see that the elliptical orbit which is tangent to the two circular orbits requires that we impart to the vehicle less initial and terminal impulse. In fact, it is possible to show that this elliptical orbit is the *"minimum energy"* orbit, in the sense that it requires the least initial and terminal impulse. In this calculation we will neglect the gravitational attraction of the earth (and of Mars), since escape velocity from Earth can be taken into account separately, to a good approximation.

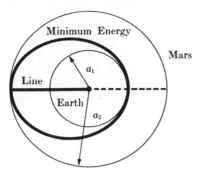

Fig. 5–10. Orbits between Earth and Mars.

First, we notice (Fig. 5–10) that for the line orbit $2a = a_2$, and for the elliptical orbit $2a = a_1 + a_2$. Then from Eq. 5–15′ we calculate the vehicle speed at the point of departure ($r = a_1 = 1$):

$$v_1 = v_0 \sqrt{2(1 - a_1/a_2)} \quad \text{for the line}$$

and

$$v_1' = v_0 \sqrt{2/(1 + a_1/a_2)} \quad \text{for the ellipse}$$

where

$$v_0 = 2\pi/\sqrt{a_1} = 2\pi$$

is the speed of the earth in its (circular) orbit. Notice that $v_1' > v_1$ (unless $a_2 = \infty$, when both become equal to the escape velocity from the sun's field, $\sqrt{2}\, v_0$). When we compute the *velocity relative to Earth*, however, we see the advantage of the elliptical vehicle orbit. For the line orbit (Fig. 5–11(a)),

$$|\mathbf{v}_1 - \mathbf{v}_0| = \sqrt{v_1^2 + v_0^2}$$

$$= v_0 \sqrt{3 - 2a_1/a_2} > v_0$$

but for the elliptical orbit (Fig. 5–11(b))

$$v_1' - v_0 = v_0 \left[\sqrt{2/(1 + a_1/a_2)} - 1 \right] < v_0$$

In fact, since the radius of Mars' orbit is about 1.5 times the radius of Earth's orbit, the required relative speeds are $1.3v_0$ and $0.1v_0$, respectively,

Fig. 5–11(a)   *Fig. 5–11(b)*

for the direct and for the minimum energy orbit. Since $v_0 = 30$ km/sec, these speeds are 39 and 3 km/sec. The saving in fuel required in the minimum energy orbit is appreciable. It is important to take into account the escape from the earth's gravitational field (escape velocity 11 km/sec), but this can be done separately to a good approximation. (It is also worthwhile to take advantage of the earth's rotation in launching, but this is much less important: the speed of the earth's surface is only 0.5 km/sec.) A similar economy in fuel is afforded by the minimum energy orbit in the terminal deceleration required, as can be calculated in a similar way. The time required for the journey in the minimum energy orbit is $\frac{1}{2}P'$, where, according to Kepler's law, Eq. 5–13', with $a = \frac{1}{2}(a_1 + a_2)$,

$$P' = [\tfrac{1}{2}(a_1 + a_2)]^{3/2} = 1.4 \text{ yr}$$

so that the trip requires 0.7 yr or about $8\frac{1}{2}$ months.

Many other such problems can be at least partially solved using only the techniques we have developed. A few of these will be given as problems. In analyzing satellite orbits near the surface of the earth, cognizance should be taken of a theorem which states that a spherically symmetric distribution of mass (e.g., the earth) produces the same force as if all the mass were concentrated at the center, so long as you are outside it. (This theorem is an immediate consequence of Gauss's law.) Thus the earth can be treated as the source of an inverse square force (unless the satellite orbit intersects its surface, in which case contact forces must be taken into account). In spite of the current practical interest in such problems, it should be admitted that our true motive for treating the inverse square force in such detail derives from its application (coulomb force) to the interactions of the microscopic particles—electrons, protons, etc.—which are our main concern. (See Chapter 18.)

5–5   UNBOUND ORBITS

If the force is attractive ($K > 0$) and $E > 0$, the particle can go off to infinity and the orbit is an *unbound orbit* (Fig. 5–6). The distance of closest approach to the origin (force center) is a_1', which can be computed by exactly the argument leading to Eq. 5–9. Now, since E is positive,

$$a_1' = \frac{K}{2E}(e - 1) \tag{5–9'}$$

with e given by Eq. 5–10. For the unbound orbit, $e > 1$. The other solution to the quadratic equation is negative and so has no meaning; there is only one position where $\dot{r} = 0$ in an unbound orbit. Again recalling that the particle is moving around the origin with angular momentum L at the same time that r decreases from infinity to a_1' and then increases to infinity again, the orbit will have the shape illustrated in Fig. 5–12.

The second of the solutions, Eq. 5–9, does nevertheless have significance.

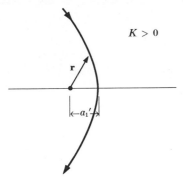

Fig. 5–12. Hyperbolic orbit with inverse-square-law attraction.

It is the distance of closest approach to the force center for the case of a *repulsive force*, for which $K < 0$. Then the only *possible* orbits are those for which $E > 0$ (Fig. 5–13). Substituting $\dot{r} = 0$ in the energy equation as before leads to the Eq. 5–9. Now the second solution is positive,

$$a_2' = \frac{-K}{2E}\,(e + 1) \qquad\qquad (5\text{–}9')$$

For $K < 0$, the first solution represents a negative value of r and must be ignored. Again, we may sketch the orbit in which the particle comes in from infinity to a_2' and then recedes to infinity again (Fig. 5–14). Note that for the same values of E and L, $a_1' < a_2'$, since the particle is pulled toward the origin in one case and pushed away in the other.

A complete solution to the problem would show that these two orbits are actually the two branches of a *hyperbola*. It is interesting geometrically to combine them into a single graph (Fig. 5–15), although it must be remembered that the two branches result from completely different forces, one attractive and one repulsive. A given particle could follow only one branch or the other. If this time we define (dropping the $'$)

$$2a = a_2 - a_1$$

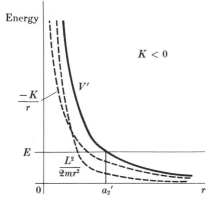

Fig. 5–13. Effective potential energy (repulsive force).

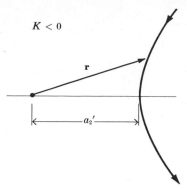

$K < 0$

r

a_2'

Fig. 5–14. Hyperbolic orbit with inverse-square-law repulsion.

the total energy again depends only on a. Summarizing the equations which apply to the unbound orbits, $E > 0$,

$$a = |K|/2E \quad a = \tfrac{1}{2}(a_2 - a_1) \tag{5–16}$$

$$e = \sqrt{1 + 2EL^2/mK^2} \tag{5–10}$$

$$a_1 = a(e - 1) \quad a_2 = a(e + 1) \tag{5–17}$$

$$v = \sqrt{\frac{|K|}{m}} \sqrt{\frac{1}{a} \pm \frac{2}{r}} \tag{5–18}$$

For unbound orbits the period P is infinite, since the particle never returns. (The upper sign in Eq. 5–18 applies to the attractive force, the lower sign to the repulsive force.)

It is worthwhile to analyze the geometry of the hyperbolic orbits in more detail. If no force were acting, the particle would move along one of the dashed lines (the asymptotes of the hyperbolas), and its closest approach to the origin would be at the distance b (Fig. 5–15). The distance b is called the

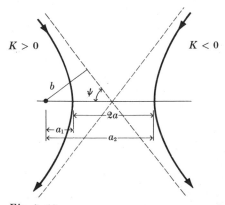

$K > 0$ $K < 0$

b ψ

$2a$

a_1

a_2

Fig. 5–15

impact parameter, and the shape of the orbit depends on its value. For example, the angle ψ is given by

$$\sin \psi = \frac{b}{a_1 + a} = \frac{b}{ea} \tag{5-19}$$

The values of e and a depend on the energy E and the angular momentum L, Eqs. 5–16 and 5–10, and we shall now show that b is also related to E and L. Suppose the particle is infinitely far away, moving along one of the dashed lines with speed v_∞. Since the potential energy is zero at infinity, from Eq. 3–19,

$$v_\infty = \sqrt{2E/m}$$

(as also follows from Eq. 5–18 and 5–16). Furthermore, b is the *moment arm of the velocity* at this point, so that the angular momentum is

$$L = mv_\infty b,$$

or

$$L^2 = m^2 v_\infty^2 b^2 = 2mEb^2$$

This equation shows the relation between b and the mechanical parameters E and L: for a given energy, b is proportional to L. Let us substitute the above value of L^2 into Eq. 5–10 and solve for b, to give a relation which will prove to be useful later:

$$b = \frac{|K|}{2E} \sqrt{e^2 - 1} = a\sqrt{e^2 - 1} \tag{5-20}$$

(using Eq. 5–16).

This relation also enables us to complete our discussion of the geometry, by substituting into Eq. 5–19:

$$\sin \psi = \frac{\sqrt{e^2 - 1}}{e}$$

From Fig. 5–16, this is more simply expressed by

$$\cos \psi = 1/e \tag{5-21}$$

When ψ is large, the particle is very little deviated by the force; Eq. 5–21 shows that this is the case when e is large, i.e., when E or L are large, or when K is small (Eq. 5–10). These results correspond with intuition, since large L (large b) means a wide miss of the force center, and small K means a weak force. It is important to note that b is the same, for given E and L, for either the attractive or the repulsive force; this fact justifies our having drawn the same asymptotes for the two branches of the hyperbola in Fig. 5–15.

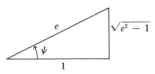

Fig. 5–16

5-6   RUTHERFORD SCATTERING

As an example of motion in a hyperbolic orbit, we shall consider the deflection of an alpha particle by an atomic nucleus. This problem is of great historical importance, because the experiment was used by Rutherford (1911) to show that the positive charge in an atom is concentrated in a very small *nucleus*, whose diameter is only about 10^{-12} cm, or about 10^{-4} times the diameter of the whole atom. Both the alpha particle and the atomic nucleus are positively charged, so that the coulomb force between them is repulsive. The force constant K is negative:

$$K = - q_1 q_2 = - Z_1 Z_2 e^2 \qquad (5\text{-}22)$$

where $Z_1 = 2$ is the atomic number of the alpha particle (He nucleus), Z_2 is the atomic number of the target nucleus, and e is the magnitude of the electron charge. The analysis is simplified if the target consists of a heavy element, since then the reduced mass is practically equal to the alpha particle mass (4 amu). For example with a gold target, one of those used by Rutherford, the atomic mass is 197. The reduced mass is only 2% less than the alpha particle mass, and the Au nucleus remains nearly at rest.

It is useful to consider first the simple case in which the impact parameter b (and angular momentum L) is zero, i.e., the alpha particle travels head-on toward the Au nucleus ($Z = 79$), since this case already shows clearly how the experiment clarified the structure of the Au atom. If $L = 0$, then $e = 1$ (Eq. 5-10), and

$$a_2 = 2a \text{ (Eq. 5-17)} = |K|/E \text{ (Eq. 5-16)} = Z_1 Z_2 e^2 / E$$

(This equation also follows in an elementary way by inserting $\dot{r} = 0$, $r = a_2$, into the one-dimensional energy conservation expression Eq. 5-2.) If $E = 5$ MeV, the approximate energy of the natural alpha particles used by Rutherford, then the distance of closest approach would be

$$a_2 = 2 \times 79 \times (4.8 \times 10^{-10} \text{ esu})^2 / 5 \times 10^6 \text{ eV} \times 1.6 \times 10^{-12} \frac{\text{erg}}{\text{eV}}$$

$$= 5 \times 10^{-12} \text{ cm}$$

(Remember that if the formula is evaluated using mks units, a factor $1/4\pi\epsilon_0$ must be inserted into Eq. 5-22.)

The observation of alpha particles which were returned directly backward from the gold atoms would indicate that the $1/r^2$ force law must be obeyed down to very small distances, and so the positive charge must be confined to a correspondingly small volume. If, by contrast, the positive charge were spread more or less uniformly over the whole volume of the atom, the interaction force would never rise high enough to deflect the alpha particles backwards, and they would all pass through the gold in the forward direction. (Such a model of the atom had been previously proposed by Thomson. See Prob. 5-22.)

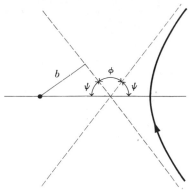

Fig. 5–17. Alpha-particle orbit.

A more detailed confirmation of the force law, Eq. 5–22, actually was provided by observing the *angle* through which alpha particles were deflected
when the impact parameter was greater than zero. The angle between the
incoming and outgoing directions of the alpha particle's trajectory is ϕ
(Fig. 5–17). We wish to obtain a relation between ϕ and b. A relation between b and the angle ψ is already contained in Eq. 5–20:

$$b = \frac{|K|}{2E} \sqrt{e^2 - 1} = \frac{|K|}{2E} \tan \psi$$

(cf. Fig. 5–16). It remains only to relate ψ to ϕ. Clearly, since

$$\phi + 2\psi = \pi \qquad \psi = \frac{\pi}{2} - \frac{\phi}{2}$$
$$\tan \psi = \cot \phi/2$$

Thus,

$$b = \frac{|K|}{2E} \cot \frac{\phi}{2} = \frac{Z_1 Z_2 e^2}{2E} \cot \frac{\phi}{2} \qquad (5\text{–}23)$$

For a given energy of the alpha particle E, Eq. 5–23 gives the required relation between ϕ and b. (See Fig. 5–18.)

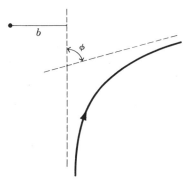

Fig. 5–18. Rutherford scattering angle.

The experiment consists in directing a beam of alpha particles against a gold foil and measuring the angle at which they are deflected. It is of course impossible to control macroscopically the impact parameter, the distance by which the initial direction of a certain particle misses a certain nucleus. One therefore obtains a range of angles ϕ, related to the range of random impact parameters b by Eq. 5–23. What one actually observes is the fraction of the particles which are deflected through various angles ϕ. The analysis of this kind of *scattering* experiment will be completed in Chapter 6.

PROBLEMS

5–1. Write the inverse square law force in Cartesian coordinates and show that the components satisfy the general condition for the existence of a potential energy function.

5–2. Integrate the equation

$$E = \tfrac{1}{2}m\dot{r}^2 - K/r$$

to find r as a function of t. Assume $E < 0$, $K > 0$.

5–3. Tabulate the escape velocities from the various planets and the moon. (Data on the planets is found in the *Handbook of Chemistry and Physics*.)

5–4. Suppose a rocket is shot straight up from the earth's surface (radius R) to a height H, neglecting the earth's rotation. Show that the launch speed is

$$v_H = \sqrt{\frac{H}{R+H}}\; v_{\text{escape}}$$

How large is v_H for $H = 500$ km?

5–5. Consider a spherical galaxy, 10^{21} cm in radius, containing 10^{10} stars, each of mass 10^{33} g. Find the escape velocity of a star from the galaxy, if the star is at the edge of the galaxy. Assume the distribution of stars is spherically symmetric. (The velocity of our sun, a typical star, is nearly this much, but it is not at the edge of our galaxy.)

5–6. Suppose a rocket is launched straight up from the surface of the earth (neglect the earth's rotation) with a speed v_L, such that when the rocket has "escaped" from the earth's gravity it still has a speed v_F. Find the expression for v_L, in terms of v_F and the "escape velocity" v_{escape}.

5–7. Consider the potential energy of a rocket on the line joining the earth (mass M) and the moon (mass M'), including the attraction of the moon

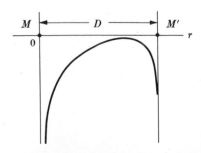

(Prob. Fig. 5–7). (The force acting on the rocket is not a central force, but only one-dimensional motion is under consideration.) Show that the maximum potential energy is at a distance from the earth given by

$$r/D = 1/(1 + \sqrt{M'/M})$$

where D is the earth–moon distance. Show that the velocity required at $r = R$ in order just to reach this point is 99% of the escape velocity. Here, $M/M' = 80$ and $D/R = 60$.

5–8.   Writing the potential energy for the harmonic oscillator as $V = \tfrac{1}{2}Kr^2$, sketch the effective potential V', and discuss the possible motions.

5–9.   Find the speed and the period for a circular satellite orbit just above the earth's surface. How would the speed, the angular momentum, and the period differ for an elliptical orbit with perigee just above the earth's surface.

5–10.   The distance of the Moon from the earth is 240,000 mi. Calculate the mass of the earth.

5–11.   Note in Prob. Fig. 5–11 that at the distance of closest approach to the origin a_1, the angular momentum is $L = mva_1$. Use this relation, together with Eqs. 5–12, 5–14, and 5–15, in order to derive Eq. 5–10.

5–12.   Find the speed at any point and the distance of closest approach to the origin for an orbit with $E = 0$, $L \neq 0$. (This orbit is a *parabola*.)

5–13.   Show that for the harmonic oscillator orbit in Prob. Fig. 5–13, the angular momentum L is

$$L = \sqrt{Km}\,AB$$

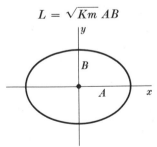

5–14.   Find the minimum velocity (relative to earth) with which a solar probe would have to be launched in order to come close to the sun (neglecting earth's gravity). Find the time required for the journey to the sun. Compare the technical difficulty with that of sending a probe outside the solar system.

5–15.   For Halley's comet, the period is about 75 yr and the eccentricity of the orbit is $e = 0.967$. Calculate the perihelion and aphelion distances in au.

5–16.   Suppose a comet, in an orbit with E nearly zero, makes a perfectly inelastic head-on collision with the earth. Assuming the comet's diameter is about 1 km and its density is about 0.1 g/cm³, calculate the energy dissipated. Express the result in megatons of TNT. (1 megaton = 4 × 10¹⁵ joule.)

5-17.   Compare the (relative) impact speeds on Mars for a space vehicle in direct and minimum energy orbits.

5-18.   Calculate the launch speed in the minimum energy orbit to (a) Jupiter; (b) Venus. Neglect the pull of the earth.

5-19.   The planet Pluto has an orbit with semimajor axis $a = 40$ au and eccentricity $e = 0.25$. Find its period, perihelion distance, and aphelion distance.

5-20.   Suppose a Rutherford scattering experiment were performed with protons instead of 5 MeV alphas. What energy would the protons have to have in order to follow just the same trajectories as the 5 MeV alphas? (First prove that the trajectory depends only on E/K, for a given impact parameter.)

5-21.   In the Thomson model of the atom, the positive charge is smeared uniformly through a sphere the size of the atom (about 10^{-8} cm in diameter), instead of being concentrated at the center (in a sphere about 10^4 times smaller). Calculate the potential energy of a charged particle (e.g., an alpha) in the Thomson model. *Hint:* Recall from electrostatics that when you are outside a sphere of charge, the force is the same as if the charge were concentrated at the center; but when you are inside, the force contribution due to charge at a greater radius is zero. By integrating the force, show that the potential energy *inside* the atomic sphere of radius r_0 is

$$V = -\frac{3}{2}\frac{K}{r_0} + \frac{1}{2}\frac{K}{r_0^3}r^2 \qquad r \leq r_0$$

5-22.   Sketch the potential energy of an alpha particle for the Thomson model of the atom, both inside and outside the atom. (See Prob. 5-21.) On the same graph, sketch the potential energy for the nuclear model. Indicate the energy and distance scales on the graph, and indicate the total energy of a 5 MeV alpha particle.

5-23.   Write down the potential energy of an electron inside the Thomson atom and draw a sketch of it. (See Prob. 5-21.) Assume the other electrons of the atom neutralize all the positive charge except for $+e$, so that effectively $Z_2 = 1$. Calculate the frequency of oscillation for the electron in this potential.

REFERENCES

R. J. Stephenson, *Mechanics and Properties of Matter* (John Wiley & Sons, 1960, 2nd ed.), Ch. 4.

G. R. Fowles, *Analytical Mechanics* (Holt, Rinehart & Winston, 1962), Ch. 6.

R. A. Becker, *Introduction to Theoretical Mechanics* (McGraw-Hill, 1954), Ch. 10.

6/collisions and scattering

In this chapter we will consider the interaction of two particles having positive total energy, $E > 0$, *with the understanding that the potential energy is equal to zero when the particles are infinitely far apart. Such an interaction will be referred to as a* collision. *Since the total energy is positive, the system is unbound in the sense defined in Section 5–5, where we discussed the interaction of two particles through a force field varying as* $1/r^2$. *This is an example of a* long range *interaction. Other forces, such as those which come into play when two neutral atoms or two billiard balls bump into each other, have a very* short *range, i.e., they drop off with distance much faster than* r^{-2}. *Short range interactions last for a very short time, but are typically strong enough to alter the momenta of the particles significantly during this brief period. Because of the strength of such interactions, it is permissible to ignore external forces, even when present during a short range collision, at least during the brief duration of the collision.*

For the sake of economy, and because we often do not know the exact nature of a force field, we will discuss the collision process for an arbitrary conservative interparticle force. Since the external force is assumed to be negligible compared to the inter-particle force, the linear and angular momenta must be conserved during the collision, along with the total energy. (See Chapter 3.) Up to now we have considered problems in mechanics in which the energy conservation law alone yielded useful results. In collision problems, however, it is essential to make full use of the linear momentum conservation law. We shall see first that a great deal of information about the motion can be obtained even if nothing is known about the nature of the interaction force. Later we shall see (Section 6–3) that if the exact force law is known, a more detailed (in fact complete) description can be obtained, or conversely, if the motion is observed in detail, an unknown force law can be inferred.

Let us consider one particle of rest mass m_1 and momentum $\mathbf{p}_1$ incident on a particle of rest mass m_2 which is at rest. (The target in a collision experiment is usually stationary.) After the collision the first particle will have a momentum $\mathbf{p}_1'$, the second particle a momentum $\mathbf{p}_2'$. The angle θ_1 between the directions of $\mathbf{p}_1$ and $\mathbf{p}_1'$ is called the scattering angle. *The angle θ_2 is called the angle of* recoil. *One also says that m_1 is "scattered into" the angle θ_1. (See Fig. 6–1.)*

Many of the particles one wishes to study are known to have an internal structure, so that it is possible to change their rest energies, or even break them in two, during the collision process. In order to maintain generality, therefore, let us assume that after the collision the two particles may have different masses, m_1' and m_2'. (In this case it may not make any sense to draw a distinction between the scattering and the recoil angle.) These relations are illustrated in Fig. 6–1. Since it has been assumed that the conditions of energy and momentum conservation are satisfied, we can write down at once that

$$E_1 + E_2 = E_1' + E_2' \tag{6–1}$$

$$\mathbf{p}_1 + \mathbf{p}_2 = \mathbf{p}_1' + \mathbf{p}_2' \tag{6–2}$$

equating the total energy before the collision to the total energy afterward, and likewise for the momentum. (In this chapter, $\mathbf{p}_2 = 0$.) Since the potential energy V is zero before and after the collision, the energies E_i are given in the most general case by Eq. 3–17,

$$E_i = \sqrt{p_i^2 c^2 + m_i^2 c^4} \tag{6–3}$$

The initial discussion will be based on Eqs. 6–1 and 6–2 alone, and so we shall neglect any information which can be obtained from the conservation of angular momentum. Later (Sections 6–4, 6–5) the incoming angular momentum will also be considered in terms of the impact parameter (or the distance by which the initial path of particle 1 would miss particle 2). We have already seen something of the role played by the impact parameter in Section 5–6, for the case of one particular force law.

6–1   ELASTIC COLLISIONS

Our intention is now to try to deduce as much information as we can merely from Eqs. 6–1 and 6–2. Equation 6–2 is a vector equation, which results in three scalar equations satisfied by the components of the particle momenta.

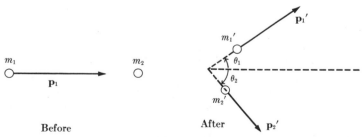

Before   After

Fig. 6–1

If the total energy in the form Eq. 6–3 is substituted into Eq. 6–1, one more equation satisfied by the momentum components is obtained. These four equations do not of course determine the final momenta completely when the initial momenta are known, because neither the force law nor the impact parameter has been specified. They will, however, yield a surprising amount of information in particular cases.

Let us consider first cases in which the masses of the particles remain unchanged,

$$m_1' = m_1 \qquad m_2' = m_2$$

Such cases are called *elastic collisions*. In this case, Eqs. 6–1 and 6–3 become

$$\sqrt{p_1^2c^2 + m_1^2c^4} + m_2c^2 = \sqrt{p_1'^2c^2 + m_1^2c^4} + \sqrt{p_2'^2c^2 + m_2^2c^4} \quad (6\text{–}4)$$

since $p_2 = 0$. Alternatively, using Eq. 3–16, we could write that *kinetic energy* is conserved in the collision, since the rest energies are unchanged:

$$T_1 = T_1' + T_2'$$

In the nonrelativistic limit we then have the simpler relation

$$\frac{p_1^2}{2m_1} = \frac{p_1'^2}{2m_1} + \frac{p_2'^2}{2m_2} \qquad (6\text{–}5)$$

For particles moving at relativistic speeds comparable with the speed of light c, however, we must take care to use Eq. 6–4 instead of Eq. 6–5.

A familiar nonrelativistic example of such a collision is the elastic collision of two billiard balls. Our definition of elastic collisions clearly coincides with the elementary one in which the kinetic energy is stipulated to be constant (Eq. 6–5). It is less obvious that the opposite case, of inelastic collisions, is consistent with our definition. For example, a familiar inelastic collision is that of two lead balls, where some of the kinetic energy is converted into heat, even though the masses of the balls are apparently unchanged. This discrepancy is only apparent, however. In fact, the extra heat energy is equivalent to an actual increase in mass, according to $E = mc^2$, so that the masses *are* changed, in accordance with our definition. The change in mass is unmeasurably small of course in this case, since the loss of kinetic energy is negligible in comparison to the rest energies of the balls, but it is just sufficient to preserve the energy and mass balances. Inelastic collisions are treated in more detail in the next section.

Having considered the proper form of the energy conservation relation, Eq. 6–1, to use in the elastic case, let us turn to the momentum conservation relation Eq. 6–2. Setting $\mathbf{p}_2 = 0$, it becomes

$$\mathbf{p}_1 = \mathbf{p}_1' + \mathbf{p}_2' \qquad (6\text{–}2')$$

First, note that the vectors $\mathbf{p}_1'$ and $\mathbf{p}_2'$ define a plane, and $\mathbf{p}_1$ must also lie in the same plane—i.e., the three momentum vectors are *coplanar*. Since the right-hand side of Eq. 6–2' has no component perpendicular to this plane, neither can the left-hand side, so that $\mathbf{p}_1$ lies in the plane. This conclusion follows from momentum conservation alone and has nothing to do with whether the collison is elastic, so every collison in which one particle is initially at rest is confined to a plane.

In many experiments it is possible to control the momentum of the incoming particle before the collision. Let us assume, therefore, that $\mathbf{p}_1$ is known along with the masses m_1 and m_2. We would like to know what information this gives us about the final momenta $\mathbf{p}_1'$ and $\mathbf{p}_2'$. The two vectors have a total of six unknown components for which we have only four equations, the three components of Eq. 6–2', and the energy relation, Eq. 6–4 or Eq. 6–5. The final momenta $\mathbf{p}_1'$ and $\mathbf{p}_2'$ are in other words not determined completely by the knowledge of $\mathbf{p}_1$, a result that should not surprise us since we do not know the nature of the force. If two of the six components of $\mathbf{p}_1'$ and $\mathbf{p}_2'$ were specified, however, we could solve for the remaining four unknowns, since we have four equations relating them. We have already remarked that the vectors $\mathbf{p}_1$, $\mathbf{p}_1'$, and $\mathbf{p}_2'$ lie in the same plane. The orientation of this plane about $\mathbf{p}_1$ as an axis is usually not of much interest, since it has no effect on the motion of the particles in the plane. If we take the plane as given, $\mathbf{p}_1'$ and $\mathbf{p}_2'$ have only two components each for a total of four unknowns. Relating these we now have three equations, two from Eq. 6–2' for the components of momentum in the plane, plus the energy equation. The motion after the collision is then determined if we specify one of the four unknowns, or a parameter relating them, such as the angle θ_1, through which particle 1 is scattered. The remaining three parameters, e.g., p_1', p_2', and θ_2, can then be solved for. The arithmetic involved in calculating p_1', p_2', and θ_2 in terms of θ_1 is left as an exercise (Prob. 6–1).

In the special case of equal masses, $m_1 = m_2 = m$, we can prove an amusing result for the case of nonrelativistic motion. Squaring Eq. 6–2', we find

$$p_1{}^2 = (p_1')^2 + (p_2')^2 + 2\mathbf{p}_1' \cdot \mathbf{p}_2'$$

while Eq. 6–5 reduces to

$$p_1{}^2 = (p_1')^2 + (p_2')^2$$

when the masses are equal. Consequently $\mathbf{p}_1' \cdot \mathbf{p}_2' = 0$, i.e., $\mathbf{p}_1'$ and $\mathbf{p}_2'$ are perpendicular. If you have ever played pool or billiards you may have observed that the balls move at right angles after the collision. The situation is illustrated in Fig. 6–2, where the angles have the same meaning as in

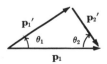

Fig. 6–2

Fig. 6–1. The construction is clearly consistent with Eq. 6–2′, and we see that $p_1' = p_1 \cos \theta_1$ and $p_2' = p_1 \sin \theta_1$.

Another special case of interest is the case of one mass much less than the other, say $m_1 \ll m_2$. Again assuming the motion to be nonrelativistic, it follows that the last term in Eq. 6–5, the kinetic energy of the heavy particle initially at rest, must be much smaller than the kinetic energy of the incoming particle. More specifically, multiplying Eq. 6–5 by $2m_1$, the equation takes the form

$$p_1^2 = p_1'^2 + \left(\frac{m_1}{m_2}\right)p_2'^2$$

If, as a lowest approximation, we set m_1/m_2 equal to zero, we get

$$p_1' \approx p_1 \tag{6–6}$$

(Such a procedure would be fraught with danger if $p_2'^2$ could be much larger than p_1^2 and $p_1'^2$, but such is not the case, since $\mathbf{p}_2'$ equals $\mathbf{p}_1 - \mathbf{p}_1'$ according to Eq. 6–2′.) Making use of Eqs. 6–6 and 6–2′ we then find p_2' to be

$$(p_2')^2 = (\mathbf{p}_1 - \mathbf{p}_1')^2 = p_1^2 + p_1'^2 - 2\,p_1 p_1' \cos \theta_1$$
$$\approx 2\,p_1^2\,(1 - \cos \theta_1)$$

or

$$p_2' \approx p_1\sqrt{2(1 - \cos \theta_1)} \tag{6–7}$$

Finally θ_2 is obtained from the component of Eq. 6–2′ perpendicular to $\mathbf{p}_1$:

$$p_1' \sin \theta_1 = p_2' \sin \theta_2$$

or

$$\sin \theta_2 = \frac{p_1'}{p_2'}\sin \theta_1 \approx \frac{\sin \theta_1}{\sqrt{2(1 - \cos \theta_1)}} \tag{6–8}$$

where we have used the expressions for p_1' and p_2' from Eqs. 6–6 and 6–7.

The relations of Eqs. 6–6 to 6–8 are plotted in Fig. 6–3 as a function of the scattering angle θ_1. We see that for $\theta_1 \approx 0$ (a glancing collision),

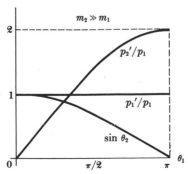

Fig. 6–3. *Momenta and recoil angle as functions of scattering angle, for elastic scattering of a light by a heavy particle.*

$p_2' \approx 0$; on the other hand, for $\theta_1 = \pi$ (a head-on collision), $p_2' = 2p_1$ and $\theta_2 = 0$. These results are intuitively obvious; but it is not so obvious that for the glancing collision $\theta_2 \approx \pi/2$, or that when $\theta_1 = \pi/2$ then $\theta_2 = \pi/4$. The equations also give the results for all the intermediate values of the scattering angle θ_1.

The above results are of course only approximately correct. The approximation can be improved if desired as follows. We may substitute the approximate result for p_2' given by Eq. 6–7 back into Eq. 6–5, in order to obtain a more accurate result for p_1':

$$(p_1')^2 = p_1{}^2 - \frac{m_1}{m_2}(p_2')^2 \cong p_1{}^2\Big[1 - \frac{m_1}{m_2}\,2(1 - \cos\theta_1)\Big]$$

or taking the square root and expanding in a power series,

$$p_1' \cong p_1\Big[1 - (1 - \cos\theta_1)\frac{m_1}{m_2}\Big]$$

If we utilize this expression for p_1' instead of Eq. 6–6 in our derivation of p_2', a similar improvement on Eq. 6–7 results. Likewise a more accurate value of $\sin\theta_2$ could be obtained. In all these expressions, the correction is small, of the order of $m_1/m_2 \ll 1$. The procedure could indeed be repeated as often as desired, in order to obtain better and better approximations.

This kind of calculation exemplifies an approach which is often used in theoretical physics—the method of *successive approximations*. We first make a crude approximation to p_1', and obtain a corresponding value of p_2'. In this "0th order approximation" the small quantity m_1/m_2 does not appear (i.e., it is set equal to zero). Then we use the 0th order value of p_2' to compute a first order value of p_1', and from it a first order value of p_2'. In the first order approximation, (m_1/m_2) occurs to the first power. The process could be repeated again, using the first order p_2' to compute a second order p_1', and then a second order p_2'. In the second order approximation, $(m_1/m_2)^2$ would appear, and so on. This important technique is akin to an expansion in power series, and has very wide applicability. (Here of course the problem can be solved exactly, so the approximation method would not be worth carrying very far.)

6-2   INELASTIC COLLISIONS

If the masses of the particles change during the collision, it is termed an *inelastic* collision. Equations 6–1 and 6–2 still apply, but we can no longer assume that $m_1 = m_1'$, $m_2 = m_2'$. Let us first consider the proper form of the energy conservation equation for a nonrelativistic collision, in which all the kinetic energies are small compared to the rest energies of the particles. An example of such a collision would be that between two lead balls. Perhaps more interesting examples are provided by reactions in nuclear physics where two colliding nuclei interact with each other to produce two totally different nuclei. The mechanism of such a process will be treated in detail later (Chapter 30); here we need only suppose that such reactions can occur.

In the nonrelativistic case, it is again convenient to consider the kinetic energies, since they are simply related to the momenta. In this case, from

$$E_1 = E_1' + E_2'$$

and

$$E_i = T_i + m_i c^2$$

we obtain

$$T_1 = T_1' + T_2' + Q \qquad (6\text{–}9)$$

where

$$Q \equiv (m_1' + m_2' - m_1 - m_2)c^2$$

If Q is positive, the kinetic energies after the collision are less than the kinetic energy before the collision. A macroscopic example of such a case occurs when some kinetic energy is converted into heat (with a corresponding increase in rest mass of the colliding objects, even though it may be unmeasurably small). Such cases also occur in nuclear collisions, where some of the kinetic energy is converted into internal energy of the product nuclei. In nuclear collisions, these internal energies are often very large, so that the change in rest mass may be appreciable. When Q is positive, the collision is called *endoergic*. In nuclear reactions, Q is as often negative as positive, meaning that internal energy is released in the reaction, appearing as kinetic energy. (Such is the case in fission and fusion reactions.) When Q is negative, the reaction is termed *exoergic*. Macroscopic collisions could also be exoergic, but they are less common; they would have to be especially contrived, so as to involve a release of stored chemical or mechanical energy. When $Q = 0$, the collision is elastic (cf. Eq. 6–5).

Having determined the proper form of the energy conservation relation to use in the present case, we may now proceed to combine it with the momentum conservation expression, Eq. 6–2′, which still holds without any modification. If Q is known, we can again solve for p_1', p_2' and θ_2 in terms of θ_1 and p_1. Instead of rederiving all the expressions of the preceding section with $Q \neq 0$, we will consider a typical example of a nonrelativistic nuclear reaction.

One of the most important nuclear fusion reactions is that of two heavy hydrogen isotopes, called deuterons, into a neutron and a helium isotope,

$$_1\text{H}^2 + _1\text{H}^2 \rightarrow _0\text{n}^1 + _2\text{He}^3$$

The importance and the nature of this reaction are discussed further in Chapter 30. All we need to know for the present is that the increase in rest energy is

$$Q = (m_1' + m_2' - m_1 - m_2)\, c^2 \cong -3.3 \text{ MeV}$$

Here MeV stands for "million electron volts." One electron volt is the energy acquired by a particle with one electronic charge, 4.8×10^{-10} esu, when falling through a potential of one volt ($= 1/300$ statvolts); 1 eV $=$ $4.8 \times 10^{-10} \times 1/300$ ergs $= 1.6 \times 10^{-12}$ ergs. The reaction goes most readily (Chapter 30) when the incoming deuteron has a kinetic energy T_1 of about 0.1 MeV.

Since the rest energies of the particles are of the order of 10^3 MeV, it is legitimate to use the nonrelativistic expression for the kinetic energies. Furthermore let us assume for simplicity that $\mathbf{p}_1$, $\mathbf{p}_1'$ and $\mathbf{p}_2'$ are collinear, with $\mathbf{p}_1'$ and $\mathbf{p}_2'$ in opposite directions. Squaring Eq. 6–2' we then obtain,

$$p_1{}^2 = (p_1')^2 + (p_2')^2 - 2\,p_1'p_2'$$

If $m_1' = m_n$ is the mass of the neutron, the mass of the deuteron m_1 is nearly equal to $2m_n$ and the mass of $_2\mathrm{He}^3$, m_2', is very close to $3m_n$. Dividing by $2m_n$, the above equation may therefore be written,

$$2T_1 = T_1' + 3T_2' - 2\sqrt{3T_1'T_2'}$$

or substituting for T_2' from Eq. 6–9:

$$2T_1 = T_1' + 3(T_1 - T_1' - Q) - 2\sqrt{3T_1'(T_1 - T_1' - Q)}$$

After squaring once we have a quadratic equation in T_1', which, when solved, yields

$$T_1' = -\tfrac{3}{4}Q + \tfrac{1}{2}T_1 \pm \sqrt{\tfrac{1}{2}T_1(-\tfrac{3}{4}Q + \tfrac{3}{8}T_1)}$$

With $Q = -3.3$ MeV and $T_1 = 0.1$ MeV, the two results for the neutron energy are $T_1' \cong 2.85$ MeV, and $T_1' \cong 2.15$ MeV. Since we considered $\mathbf{p}_1$ and $\mathbf{p}_1'$ collinear, θ_1 is equal to $0°$ or $180°$. (See Fig. 6–4.) The higher energy corresponds to $\theta_1 = 0$, i.e., neutrons in the "forward" direction, or the direction of the incoming deuteron. For an angle θ between $0°$ and $180°$ the neutron is found to have an energy between our two solutions of 2.85 and 2.15 MeV. This reaction provides a common laboratory source of neutrons. (More frequently the target nucleus is tritium, $_1\mathrm{H}^3$, another isotope of hydrogen. That reaction is also exoergic, with an even greater energy release, producing neutrons of approximately 14 MeV.) This kind of neutron source gives a monoenergetic beam at any given angle—i.e., all the neutrons in the beam have the same energy—a convenient property for some kinds of laboratory experiments. Indeed, the energy of the beam can be varied (within rather narrow limits) by picking off the beam at different angles.

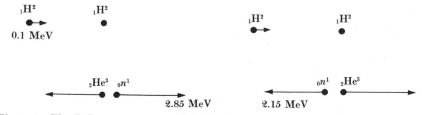

Fig. 6–4. *The D-D reaction between two deuterons.*

6–3   DECAY OF UNSTABLE PARTICLES

A more exotic example of an "inelastic collision" is the decay of a single unstable particle into two other particles. This sort of event is frequently encountered in high energy physics. It may seem at first to be stretching our terminology to call such an event "inelastic," or even a "collision," since there is no target particle (m_2) at all. A single particle merely breaks up spontaneously into two other particles. Nevertheless, even in this kind of event energy and momentum must be conserved, and so it is a collision in the sense that it can be analyzed by means of Eq. 6–1 and 6–2. Furthermore, it is inelastic according to our definition, because the rest masses of the particles are different after the collision. This kind of decay is generally relativistic as well as inelastic, and so we must revert to the most general energy-momentum relation, Eq. 6–3.

We shall consider a typical example of an unstable particle decaying, the so-called *lambda-zero decay*. An event of this nature can be observed by one of the many detection devices designed by nuclear physicists, such as a "cloud chamber," a "nuclear emulsion," or a "bubble chamber," all of which make the tracks of individual charged particles visible. The momenta of the particles can often be measured, e.g., by measuring their deflection in a magnetic field. Suppose that a photograph of a bubble chamber looks like Fig. 6–5, in which the heavy lines represent visible tracks of charged particles, and the dashed line is merely drawn for reference. It is assumed that an uncharged particle, call it Λ^0, is created at point A and travels to point B, where it decays into 2 particles. These are subsequently identified as a positively charged proton with a known rest mass equal to 1836 m_e (m_e = electron mass), and a negatively charged π-meson with a rest mass of 273 m_e.

Suppose now that our measurements yield $\theta_1 = 12°$, $\theta_2 = 44°$, p_1' (proton) = 448 MeV/c and p_2' (π-meson) = 136 MeV/c. Momenta are often measured in units of MeV/c, where c is the speed of light. Since pc has the dimensions of energy, this is perfectly legitimate; but it is important to realize that a particle with momentum equal to X MeV/c does *not* have an energy equal to X MeV unless the rest mass is equal to zero. This may be seen from Eq. 6–3. What can we now deduce regarding the properties of the neutral particle, Λ^0? It would be especially useful to know its rest mass, in order to see whether this is a known particle or a new discovery.

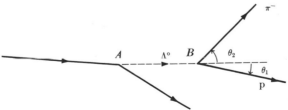

Fig. 6–5. Decay of a Λ^0 particle.

Conservation of momentum in the Λ^0 decay along the direction of motion of Λ^0 is expressed by (multiplying by c)

$$cp_1 = cp_1' \cos \theta_1 + cp_2' \cos \theta_2$$
$$= 448 \text{ MeV} \cos 12° + 136 \text{ MeV} \cos 44° = 536 \text{ MeV}$$

Next we take note of energy conservation. Since

$$m_e c^2 = 9.11 \times 10^{-28} \text{ g} \times \left(3.00 \times 10^{10} \frac{\text{cm}}{\text{sec}} \right)^2 = 8.20 \times 10^{-7} \text{ ergs}$$
$$= (8.20 \times 10^{-7} \text{ erg}/1.602 \times 10^{-12} \text{ erg/eV}) = 0.511 \text{ MeV}$$

it follows that $m_1' c^2 = 1836 \times 0.511 \text{ MeV} = 938 \text{ MeV}$ and $m_2' c^2 = 273 \times 0.511 \text{ MeV} = 140 \text{ MeV}$. Substituting these values into the energy equation, we arrive at an expression which determines m_1, the mass of Λ^0:

$$E_1 = \sqrt{(p_1 c)^2 + (m_1 c^2)^2} = \sqrt{(p_1' c)^2 + (m_1' c^2)^2} + \sqrt{(p_2' c)^2 + (m_2' c^2)^2}$$
$$= \sqrt{(536)^2 + (m_1 c^2)^2} = \sqrt{448^2 + 938^2} + \sqrt{136^2 + 140^2}$$
$$= 1040 + 195 = 1235 \text{ MeV}$$

Then

$$m_1 c^2 = \sqrt{1235^2 - 536^2} = 1114 \text{ MeV}$$

so that

$$m_1 = \frac{1114}{.511} m_e = 2180 \, m_e$$

This is indeed equal to the accepted value of the mass of the Λ^0 particle within one-tenth of one per cent (Chapter 31). In fact, it was in just such an experiment that the Λ^0 particle was discovered.

We will not pursue the subject of decay-type collisions further at this point, but several other examples will be discussed later, in Chapters 17 and 31.

6–4 SCATTERING CROSS SECTION

When a beam of particles is directed at a material target, some of the particles will be deflected out of their original trajectories as a result of collisions with particles in the target. The study of this *scattering* process is of great importance in physics. From careful measurements and a detailed analysis of how the particles scatter much can be learned about the nature of the inter-particle force. Most of our knowledge of nuclear forces has been gained just this way, and it was an early scattering experiment of Rutherford (Chapter 5) which demonstrated the existence of a small but massive positively charged nucleus.

Many of the parameters useful in a discussion of scattering can best be understood in terms of a specific model of the inter-particle force. Particularly simple is the *hard sphere* model in which the particles are assumed to be spherical in shape and perfectly elastic and incompressible. The potential energy as a function of the distance r between one hard sphere of radius a_1 and another of radius a_2 is illustrated in Fig. 6–6. No force acts when the interparticle distance is greater than $a_1 + a_2$. When r equals $a_1 + a_2$ the spheres touch and an infinite repulsive force results. In practice no spheres are perfectly hard, but steel balls for example and, on the microscopic scale, inert gas atoms have interparticle potentials approaching that of Fig. 6–6.

If a hard sphere of radius a_1 and velocity $\mathbf{v}$ is incident on a target consisting of hard spheres at rest with radii a_2, a collision will result whenever the center of the incoming particle gets within a distance $a_1 + a_2$ of the center of one of the target particles. Each particle in the target therefore presents to the incoming particle an effective target area

$$\sigma = \pi(a_1 + a_2)^2 \qquad (6\text{--}10)$$

called the *scattering cross section*, or more precisely the *total* or *integrated* scattering cross section to distinguish it from the differential scattering cross section to be defined later. Consider now a cylinder with a base area equal to the cross section, $\sigma = \pi(a_1 + a_2)^2$, and a length equal to the distance $dx = v\,dt$ traveled by the incoming particle in the time dt, and with the axis of the cylinder along the direction of motion (Fig. 6–7). If the center of one of the target particles lies in this cylinder, a collision will take place within the time dt. The probability $d\Pi$ of a collision is therefore just equal to the probability that the center of a target particle lies in the cylinder, which in turn is equal to the target particle density, n particles/cm³, multiplied by the volume of the cylinder σdx:

$$d\Pi = n\sigma\,dx = n\sigma\,v\,dt \qquad (6\text{--}11)$$

This equation gives the relation between the scattering cross section and the probability of collision per unit distance, $d\Pi/dx$, or per unit time $d\Pi/dt$:

$$d\Pi/dx = n\sigma$$
$$d\Pi/dt = n\sigma v$$

So far we have not considered through what angle the incoming particle is scattered. To study this problem, let us make the simplifying assumption

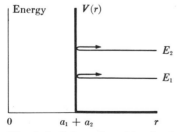

Fig. 6–6. Interaction of hard spheres.

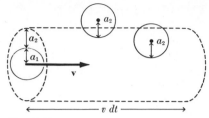

Fig. 6–7

that the scattered particle is much lighter than the scattering particle so that the latter may be assumed to remain at rest throughout the collision process. As we have already seen (Eq. 6–6), the momentum of the incoming particle may then change in direction, but its magnitude will remain unaltered by the collision. The angular deflection of the scattered particle will in general depend on the *impact parameter b*, the perpendicular distance from the center of the scattering particle to the line of approach of the incoming particle (Fig. 6–8(a)). We have already seen what this dependence is in the case of an inverse square force law between the particles in Eq. 5–23.

To obtain the corresponding relation for hard spheres, consider Fig. 6–8. At the moment of collision the force on the incoming particle acts along the line connecting the centers of the two spheres, or in the y-direction in the coordinate system drawn in Fig. 6–8. Since there is no force in the x-direction, the momentum of the incoming particle in the x-direction is unchanged. We also know that the magnitude of the total momentum vector of the incoming particle is unchanged (Eq. 6–6), so the magnitude of the y-component is unchanged as well. The y-component of the momentum will therefore precisely be reversed into its negative during the collision. The incoming particle will in other words be "reflected" by the x-axis, i.e., the angle of incidence is equal to the angle of reflection or $\alpha_1 = \alpha_2$ in Fig. 6–8. The geometry of the situation should quickly persuade you that the

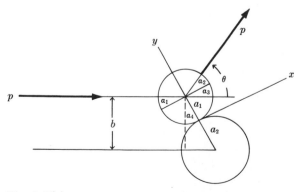

Fig. 6–8(a)

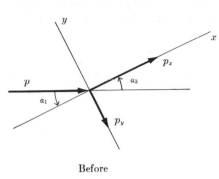
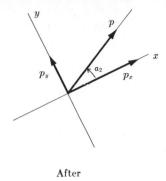

Before   After

Fig. 6–8(b)

angles α_1, α_2, α_3 and α_4 in Fig. 6–8 are all equal. Since the scattering angle θ is equal to $\alpha_2 + \alpha_3$ or equal to $2\alpha_4$, it follows that

$$\theta = 2\alpha_4 = 2 \cos^{-1}[b/(a_1 + a_2)] \qquad (6\text{–}12)$$
$$b \leq a_1 + a_2$$

If a particle with impact parameter b is scattered into the angle θ as given by Eq. 6–12 (for hard spheres), all the particles in the cylindrical shell in Fig. 6–9 with impact parameters between b and $b + db$ will be scattered into angles between θ and $\theta + d\theta$, the relation between $d\theta$ and db being obtained by taking the derivative of Eq. 6–12. The cross section of the cylindrical shell $2\pi b\, db$ is therefore the *cross section for scattering into angles between θ and $\theta + d\theta$*, denoted by $(d\sigma/d\theta)\, d\theta$, or in general

$$\left|\frac{d\sigma}{d\theta}\right| = 2\pi b \left|\frac{db}{d\theta}\right| \qquad (6\text{–}13)$$

By Eq. 6–12, for hard spheres

$$b = (a_1 + a_2) \cos (\theta/2)$$

and

$$\frac{db}{d\theta} = -\tfrac{1}{2}(a_1 + a_2) \sin (\theta/2)$$

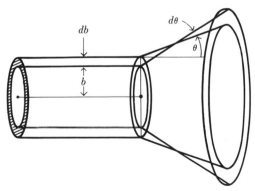

Fig. 6–9

so that the scattering cross section for angles between θ and $\theta + d\theta$ is given by, in the case of hard spheres,

$$\left|\frac{d\sigma}{d\theta}\right| = 2\pi(a_1 + a_2) \cos\left(\frac{\theta}{2}\right) \tfrac{1}{2} (a_1 + a_2) \sin\left(\frac{\theta}{2}\right)$$

$$= \frac{\pi}{2}(a_1 + a_2)^2 \sin\theta \qquad\qquad (6\text{--}14)$$

A more widely used *differential cross section* is the cross section for scattering into a small solid angle $d\Omega$, denoted by $\dfrac{d\sigma}{d\Omega} d\Omega$. An element of solid angle in spherical coordinates (Fig. 6–10) is equal to $d\Omega = \sin\theta\, d\theta\, d\phi$, and $\left|\dfrac{d\sigma}{d\theta}\right|$ $d\theta$ may be obtained by integrating $\left|\dfrac{d\sigma}{d\Omega}\right| d\Omega$ over all angles ϕ:

$$\left|\frac{d\sigma}{d\theta}\right| d\theta = \sin\theta\, d\theta \int_0^{2\pi} d\phi \left|\frac{d\sigma}{d\Omega}\right|$$

$$= 2\pi \sin\theta\, d\theta \left|\frac{d\sigma}{d\Omega}\right|$$

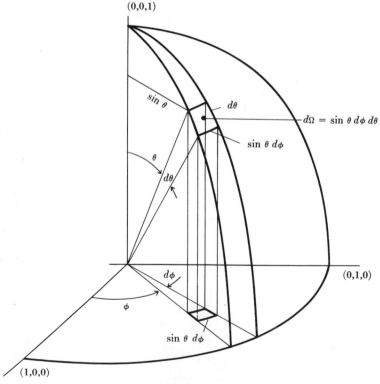

Fig. 6–10. Element of solid angle, an area on the unit sphere equal to $\sin\theta\, d\theta\, d\phi$ in spherical coordinates.

where we have used the fact that for a central potential $|d\sigma/d\Omega|$ is independent of ϕ. Our result is therefore in general

$$\left|\frac{d\sigma}{d\Omega}\right| = \frac{1}{2\pi \sin \theta}\left|\frac{d\sigma}{d\theta}\right| \qquad (6\text{--}15)$$

From Eqs. 6–14 and 6–15 it follows that the scattering cross section per unit solid angle for hard spheres is equal to

$$\left|\frac{d\sigma}{d\Omega}\right| = \tfrac{1}{4}(a_1 + a_2)^2 \qquad (6\text{--}16)$$

We see that $|d\sigma/d\Omega|$ is independent of the scattering angle, i.e., there is a uniform probability of scattering into any element of solid angle (Fig. 6–11). This is a result peculiar to the hard sphere interaction. Thus for the coulomb interaction we will find that $|d\sigma/d\Omega|$ does depend on θ. Finally we make the observation that if we integrate the differential cross sections given in Eq. 6–14,

$$\int_0^\pi \left|\frac{d\sigma}{d\theta}\right| d\theta$$

or in Eq. 6–16,

$$\int_0^{4\pi} \left|\frac{d\sigma}{d\Omega}\right| d\Omega$$

we recover the integrated cross section given in Eq. 6–10.

6–5 COULOMB SCATTERING

The differential cross sections for coulomb scattering may be obtained from Eq. 5–23 and its derivative:

$$b = \frac{Z_1 Z_2 e^2}{2E} \cot \frac{\theta}{2}$$

$$db = -\frac{Z_1 Z_2 e^2}{4E \sin^2 \theta/2} d\theta$$

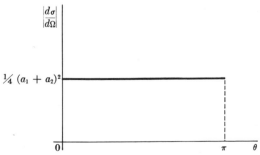

Fig. 6–11. *Differential cross section for scattering of hard spheres.*

The differential cross section for scattering into angles between θ and $\theta + d\theta$ is then, according to Eq. 6–13,

$$\left|\frac{d\sigma}{d\theta}\right| = \pi \left(\frac{Z_1 Z_2 e^2}{2E}\right)^2 \frac{\cos \theta/2}{\sin^3 \theta/2} \tag{6–17}$$

Similarly the differential cross section per unit solid angle becomes (Eq. 6–15),

$$\left|\frac{d\sigma}{d\Omega}\right| = \left(\frac{Z_1 Z_2 e^2}{4E \sin^2 \theta/2}\right)^2 \tag{6–18}$$

This is the well-known *Rutherford cross section.* In contrast to the result for hard spheres, Eq. 6–16, the coulomb field cross section depends strongly on the angle θ (Fig. 6–12), and also on the energy E of the incoming particle. This angle dependence can be understood qualitatively from the long range nature of the coulomb force. Even particles with very large impact parameters will be deviated a little. The cross section $2\pi\, b\, db$ for scattering through a small angle θ will therefore be very large, and it tends to infinity as θ approaches zero. For a large angle scattering, however, the particles must get close to each other for the force to be strong enough to effect this large change in momentum. This means that the impact parameter and consequently the cross section will be small.

The agreement between the Rutherford scattering experiments and the theoretical relationship of Eq. 6–18, in particular the angle dependence shown in Fig. 6–12, provided most convincing evidence that the $1/r^2$ force law holds down to very small distances in the interior of an atom. Exactly how small a distance, at a given scattering angle, is specified by Eq. 5–23. Deviations from the theoretical law must of course be expected for very small angle scattering, since the theoretical curve has a singularity at $\theta = 0$. (See below.) Deviations should also be expected for sufficiently large θ and E (or small Z_1, Z_2), when the impact parameter becomes as small as the actual extent of the nucleus. Then the particles interact by the characteristic nuclear forces rather than simply the coulomb force, and Eq. 5–23 can no longer hold. These deviations can tell us something about the range of the nuclear forces.

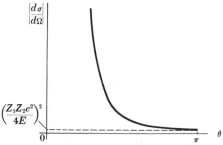

Fig. 6–12. *Differential cross section for coulomb scattering.*

The total or integrated cross section,

$$\sigma = \int_0^\pi \left| \frac{d\sigma}{d\theta} \right| d\theta \quad \propto \int_0^\pi \frac{\cos \frac{\theta}{2}}{\sin^3 \frac{\theta}{2}} d\theta$$

is clearly infinite, since in the neighborhood of $\theta = 0$ the integrand varies as $1/\theta^3$. A charged particle, therefore, presents an infinitely large target to another charged particle, which just expresses the fact that if the particles are separated by a distance r no matter how large, they still interact with a force $Z_1 Z_2 e^2 / r^2$. In practice, however, a charge is effectively shielded by other charges. Thus in the Rutherford experiment the charge of the positive nucleus is shielded by the negative electrons. Also in a gas of positive and negative charged particles, called a plasma (Chapter 11), one finds that the potential of a charged particle is well described by a potential of the form

$$Ze[\exp (-r/\lambda_D)] \frac{1}{r}$$

where λ_D is a characteristic plasma distance. The total cross section with this interaction potential is perfectly finite.

So far we have assumed that the force law is known and from it we have calculated the various cross sections. Usually in physics one is faced with the much harder problem of using experimental cross section data to investigate an unknown law of force. The most common way of tackling this problem is to assume some simple shape for the potential, say

$$V = \alpha r^{-\beta} e^{-\gamma r}$$

and to see whether the parameters α, β, and γ can be chosen so as to agree with the data. We will attempt such an analysis for the neutron-proton potential in Chapter 28 and will not pursue it any further here. It is important to emphasize, however, that a given scattering experiment can probe a potential only so far. For example, if the force is the coulomb force, a particle with energy E can only get within a distance r such that $E = Z_1 Z_2 e^2 / r$, or $r = Z_1 Z_2 e^2 / E$, and it can only get this close when the impact parameter is equal to zero. This energy dependence may be seen clearly by referring to

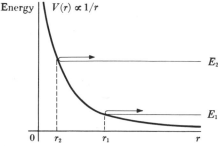

Fig. 6–13. *Interaction of charged particles.*

Fig. 6–13. Consider two incoming particles with energy E_1 and E_2 respectively. The particle with the lower energy E_1 will have converted all its kinetic energy into potential energy by the time it reaches r_1, at which time its radial motion must reverse. The higher energy particle, on the other hand, will get down to a smaller separation r_2. As the energy increases we penetrate closer and closer to the center of the potential. In this sense the coulomb potential is a "soft sphere" in contrast to the hard sphere potential depicted in Fig. 6–6, where no matter what the energy the particles cannot approach closer than the sum of their radii, $a_1 + a_2$. Since all physical potentials are "soft" to a certain degree, physicists are anxious to accelerate particles to higher and higher energies in order to probe the nature of the forces at very small distances. An even more compelling need for high energies will become evident when we study quantum mechanics, Part III. We will find that all particles have wave properties with a wavelength inversely proportional to the momentum of the particle. Since an incoming particle cannot "see" structures much smaller than its wavelength, it is clear that we have to go to high momenta in order to probe the detailed shape of a potential. Scattering experiments are now carried out with particles having energies as high as 3×10^{10} eV or 30 GeV (1 GeV = 1 giga electron volt = 10^9 eV), and plans are being laid for accelerators capable of energies even much higher than this.

PROBLEMS

6–1.   From Eqs. 6–2′ and 6–5, solve for p_1', p_2', and θ_2, in terms of p_1 and θ_1. Show that the result agrees with Eqs. 6–6 to 6–8 for $m_1/m_2 \ll 1$.

6–2.   Find the largest angle at which a particle of mass m_1 can be scattered elastically by a particle of mass m_2, if $m_1 > m_2$: solve the equations for $\cos \theta_1$ in terms of p_1'/p_1 (with m_2/m_1 as a parameter) and differentiate with respect to (p_1'/p_1).

6–3.   An incoming marble collides with a target marble of half the mass of the incoming marble. The scattering angle and recoil angle are both observed to be 30°. Calculate the momenta and velocities of the outgoing marbles, relative to the incoming marble. Was the collision elastic?

6–4.   Two balls of different and unknown masses collide elastically. Before the collision ball 2 is at rest and ball 1 moves with velocity v_1. After the collision ball 1 is found to be moving in a direction at right angles to its original motion with velocity $v_1/2$. (a) In what direction is ball 2 moving after the collision? (b) Can the speed of ball 2 be found from the data given? If your answer is yes, find the speed. If it is no, explain why not.

6–5.   A neutron of mass m moving with velocity v_0 penetrates into a crystal composed of atoms of mass M. The neutron bumps into one of the crystal atoms. The encounter can be treated just like a collision of elastic spheres (the neutron having no electric charge).
    For the case of a head on collision with an atom at rest, find what multiple of the neutron's original momentum is given to the atom, and what

fraction of its energy as a function of mass ratio, M/m. Show that for $M/m = 100$ the atom gets about 4% of the neutron's energy.

6–6. A lead ball of mass 1 kg, moving at 1 m/sec, collides head-on with an identical ball which is at rest. After the collision, the two balls stick together. Calculate Q for the collision, expressing it as a fraction of the incoming kinetic energy. What is the increase in rest mass of the two balls?

6–7. In the "D–D reaction," where a deuteron bombards deuterium (at rest) to produce neutrons, assume the incoming deuterons have been accelerated to 0.1 MeV. Find the energy of the neutrons which come off at 90° to the incoming deuteron beam.

6–8. A proton with kinetic energy T_p and mass M_p collides with a Li^7 nucleus at rest (Prob. Fig. 6–8). A reaction liberating energy Q takes place; as a result two α particles emerge symmetrically with respect to the line of collision with identical speeds v_α. Assuming that all speeds are very small compared to the speed of light, derive expressions for (a) v_α in terms of Q, T_p and M_α and (b) $\cos \theta$ in terms of Q, T_p, M_α and M_p. If Q is much larger than T_p, what can you say about θ?

6–9. A mass of 1 g collides head on with a mass of 3 g which is initially at rest. The 1 g mass scatters back the way it came with the same speed as it had initially. Find the Q of the scattering in terms of the original kinetic energy of the 1 g mass.

6–10. A meson of mass m_π comes to *rest* and disintegrates into a muon of mass m_μ and a neutrino of *zero mass*. Show that the kinetic energy of the muon is

$$T_\mu = \frac{(m_\pi - m_\mu)^2}{2m_\pi} c^2$$

6–11. A hypothetical particle of rest mass M_0 decays at rest into two neutrinos of zero rest mass. (a) What is the angle between the two neutrinos? (b) What are their speeds? (c) What are their energies (in terms of M_0)?

6–12. Suppose a neutral pi meson decays into two photons (rest mass = 0) and the photons make equal angles θ with the incident direction. Show that

$$\sin \theta = \frac{m_\pi c^2}{T_\pi + m_\pi c^2}$$

6–13.   The differential cross section for Rutherford scattering of α particles (with energy E) at an angle θ is

$$d\sigma = A \; \frac{\cos\left(\dfrac{\theta}{2}\right) d\left(\dfrac{\theta}{2}\right)}{\sin^3\left(\dfrac{\theta}{2}\right)}$$

where $A = 2\pi \, (Ze^2/E)^2$. What is the total cross section for scattering in the backward direction ($\theta \geq \pi/2$)?

6–14.   In an α-particle scattering experiment, what is the minimum kinetic energy (in MeV) the α particle would have to have in order to probe the size of the nucleus itself (about 5×10^{-13} cm)—i.e., to give a deviation from the Rutherford scattering law? Answer for boron ($Z = 5$) and for mercury ($Z = 80$) nuclei.

6–15.   Suppose that in an α-particle scattering experiment, the alpha collides with an electron in the material (as is inevitable, because of the coulomb attraction). In order to estimate the maximum energy lost by the alpha through this mechanism, analyze the kinetic energy which an electron would acquire if a 5 MeV alpha made a head-on collision with it.

REFERENCES

K. R. Symon, *Mechanics* (Addison-Wesley, 1960, 2nd ed.), Ch. 3, 4.

D. Bohm, *Quantum Theory* (Prentice-Hall, 1951), Ch. 21.

II
KINETIC THEORY
OF MATTER

Up to this point we have studied the physics of particles, whose only property was their mass, and whose only possible mode of behavior was to move with a certain velocity along a certain trajectory. Clearly only a very small part of our experience of the physical world can be directly described in these terms. The flow of liquids, the strength of solids, the action of machines, the generation of heat and light, not to mention the more subtly contrived behavior of vacuum tubes and transistors, all demand more complicated terms of reference for their description. Yet the triumph of physical science, and the focus of its continuing aim, is in the attempt to reduce these complex phenomena to the mechanics of particles—atoms and electrons—moving in accordance with simple laws. This is what we mean by "explain" and "understand." In the next chapters we shall see that a wide variety of problems can be explained by the application of the mechanical principles we have considered. Eventually, however, we shall be surprised to find (or at least the physicists of fifty years ago were surprised to find) that some cannot, and that the mechanical principles themselves have to be reformulated in a new quantum mechanics. Finally, perhaps we shall not be so surprised to learn that some problems of high energy nuclear physics even resist explanation in terms of quantum mechanics. Sometime in the next fifty years you will probably learn the reformulation of quantum mechanics itself, or perhaps even contribute to it. In Part II, however, we shall try to understand some of the properties of materials in bulk, by applying the classical mechanical principles studied in Part I to the atoms or molecules which make up the material.

Materials are commonly divided into solids, liquids, and gases. The distinctions between these states of matter can be made fairly precise, but the usage in science generally agrees with that of common parlance, and so it does not have to be belabored here. Highly ionized gases, i.e., gases consisting of charged particles (usually electrons and heavy positive ions), are called plasmas. *A plasma is sometimes considered a fourth state of matter, because the presence of coulomb forces between the particles has profound and characteristic effects. Of these states, the gaseous state is the simplest to analyze in terms of an atomic model, and it is essentially completely understood today. The plasma state and the solid state are comparatively more complicated, in different ways, but great progress has been made toward their understanding. As a consequence—and also as a cause—of this, they are of immense technological interest currently, most dramatically directed toward fusion reactors in the former case and electronic devices in the latter. The structure of the liquid state is the most complicated, and rather meagre results have been obtained up to the present in attempts to analyze it. Therefore we shall refer to liquids only peripherally, but outline a theory of gases, plasmas, and solids, in that order.*

7/equation of state for gases

*As a first example of this approach toward matter in extension, we shall consider gases, since they will prove to be the easiest point of departure. Our aim will be to construct an atomic model which will be capable of correctly accounting for observed properties of gases. We begin with the simplest mechanical properties of gases, which we shall first review before attempting to explain them. A given amount of gas has a certain mass, but it is not located at a point—in fact it will fill up whatever volume is made available to it. We therefore adopt the vol*ume V *as one of the variables which describe the* state of the gas. *In fact, let us assume* V *is the volume of one* mole *of the gas. A mole, or a gram-molecular weight, contains* N_0 *molecules, where* N_0 *is* Avogadro's number,

$$N_0 = 6.02 \times 10^{23} \; molecules/mole$$

The corresponding mks quantity is sometimes taken to be the kilogram-mole, *so that*

$$N_0 = 6.02 \times 10^{26} \; molecules/kg\text{-}mole$$

(Unless otherwise stated, V *in the following sections will refer to one mole or one kg-mole. The results are easily adapted to other quantities of gas, however, since* n *moles occupy a volume* nV; *i.e., volume is an* additive *quantity, also called an "extensive" quantity.) Since the gas is inclined to escape from its container, the container must exert a* pressure P *(force per unit area) on the gas, and the gas exerts the same pressure* P *on the container, by Newton's third law. Finally, the gas will be at a certain temperature* T. *The gas could also have other properties such as color, odor, electrical conductivity, etc., but we shall not worry about these at present.*

7–1   THE IDEAL GAS LAW

It is a fact of experience that the three variables P, V, T, which describe the state of the gas cannot all be chosen independently. That is, they are related by an equation

$$P = P(V,T)$$

This equation is called the *equation of state* for the gas. For many gases under ordinary conditions the equation of state can be represented approximately by

$$P = RT/V$$

or

$$PV = RT \tag{7–1}$$

where R is a constant. This equation is called the *ideal gas law*.

It seems almost incredible that for all these gases, R has the same value: if V is in cm^3/mole, P in dyne/cm^2, and T in deg K, then $R = 8.31 \times 10^7$ erg/mole-deg. In mks units, V is in m^3/kg-mole, P in newton/m^2, and $R = 8.31 \times 10^3$ joule/kg-mole-deg. A more common unit for high pressures is the *atmosphere*, where 1 atm $= 1.013 \times 10^6$ dyne/cm^2; a common unit for low pressures is the *millimeter of mercury* (or Torr), where 1 atm $=$ 760 mm Hg, or 1 mm Hg $= 1.333 \times 10^3$ dyne/cm^2. It is easiest to remember R in other units: since 1 cal $= 4.19 \times 10^7$ erg,

$$R \cong 2 \text{ cal/mole-deg}$$

(The accurate value is about 1% smaller, 1.986 cal/mole-deg, but 2 is usually sufficiently close.) The ideal gas law gives a *macroscopic* description of the various states of a gas. For any actual gas, it is only an approximate description; the hypothetical gas to which it would apply exactly is called an *ideal gas*. Our aim is to understand the gas law in *microscopic* terms. We shall see that the ideal gas law results when certain very simple assumptions are made about the atoms or molecules which make up the gas.

The explanation, first given by Daniel Bernoulli in the 18th century, is probably already familiar, but we shall recapitulate it because of its fundamental importance. The idea is that the gas, which is composed of molecules flying about in the container, exerts a pressure on the walls of the container because of the continual pounding of the molecules as they collide with the walls. A molecule moving with momentum mv_x toward a wall perpendicular to the x-direction will have its x-component of velocity reversed by an elastic collision with the wall. After the collision the x-component of momentum is $- mv_x$, so that the change in momentum per collision is

$$2mv_x$$

According to Newton's second law, the force exerted by the wall on the molecules is the change of momentum per unit time, and this quantity is the change of momentum per collision $(2mv_x)$ times the number of collisions per second. Referring to unit area of the wall, the pressure P (force per unit area) is

$$P = 2mv_xF \qquad (7\text{--}2)$$

where F is the number of collisions per unit time and per unit area.

We must therefore compute the number of collisions with the wall. Let us, more generally, compute the number of molecules which would cross an imaginary plane in the gas perpendicular to the x-axis. If the imaginary plane coincides with a wall, this number is the required number of collisions. Suppose for simplicity that all the molecules have the same velocity $\mathbf{v}$, or rather that half have the velocity $\mathbf{v}$ and half have the velocity $-\mathbf{v}$ (since the total velocity adds to zero, unless the gas is flowing). Now consider a certain volume of the gas consisting (Fig. 7–1) of a parallelopiped whose base is a unit area of the given plane perpendicular to the x-axis and whose edge is the vector $\mathbf{v}$. Every molecule with velocity $\mathbf{v}$ which lies in this volume at a certain instant will go a distance v and pass through the base of the prism in the next unit of time. Therefore, the *flux* of molecules per unit area (number passing through unit area per unit time) is the number of molecules per unit volume with velocity $\mathbf{v}$, or one-half the total number of molecules per unit volume n, times the volume of the prism, which is v_x. Thus

$$F = \tfrac{1}{2}nv_x \qquad (7\text{--}3)$$

This formula will often prove useful in the future; now it enables us to find the pressure P from Eq. 7–2

Combining Eqs. 7–2 and 7–3, we have

$$P = nmv_x^2$$

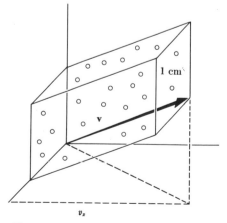

v_x

Fig. 7–1

We may suspect that all the molecules do not actually have the same velocity **v**, as assumed above. In Chapter 9 we shall study in detail how the molecular velocities vary, but for the present it will be sufficient to take account of the variation merely by replacing v_x^2 by its average value $\overline{v_x^2}$. Furthermore, since

$$v^2 = v_x^2 + v_y^2 + v_z^2$$

then

$$\overline{v^2} = \overline{v_x^2 + v_y^2 + v_z^2} = \overline{v_x^2} + \overline{v_y^2} + \overline{v_z^2}$$

(i.e., the operations of averaging and adding commute). Now the direction which we choose for the x-axis is wholly arbitrary and so it must be that

$$\overline{v_x^2} = \overline{v_y^2} = \overline{v_z^2}$$

Thus,

$$\overline{v^2} = 3\overline{v_x^2}$$

and

$$P = \tfrac{1}{3}nm\overline{v^2}$$

Finally we may note that if N_0 is the number of molecules per mole and V is the volume per mole, then the number of molecules per unit volume n is

$$n = N_0/V$$

Therefore

$$PV = \tfrac{1}{3}N_0 m\overline{v^2} \tag{7-4}$$

This relation shows that the inverse proportionality between P and V expressed by the ideal gas law is a result of purely mechanical considerations about the motion of the molecules constituting the gas.

The complete gas law, Eq. 7-1, contains in addition the absolute temperature T, a concept which has no role in the mechanics of particles. We shall see in Chapter 9 how temperature is related to the average speed of the molecules in a gas containing a large number of molecules; but here it is enough to observe that in order to obtain agreement between Eqs. 7-1 and 7-4, we must assume that

$$\tfrac{1}{3}N_0 m\overline{v^2} = RT$$

This relation can also be written as

$$\tfrac{1}{2}m\overline{v^2} = \tfrac{3}{2}kT \tag{7-5}$$

where

$$k \equiv R/N_0 = 1.38 \times 10^{-16} \text{ erg/deg} = 1.38 \times 10^{-23} \text{ joule/deg}$$

is called *Boltzmann's constant*. In this form our assumption states that the average kinetic energy of the molecules is proportional to T. The proportionality constant involves the universal constant k, which might be called "the gas constant for one molecule" (gas constant per mole/number of molecules per mole). Later we shall see that the proportionality between kinetic energy and absolute temperature has a profound significance, and shall be able to attach a meaning to the factor $\frac{3}{2}$. This connection between average kinetic energy and temperature will be derived from general considerations in Chapter 9.

Here we should point out some useful relations involving the *density* of the gas ρ and the *molecular weight M*: the molecular "weight" means the mass of one mole of molecules, so that

$$M = N_0 m$$

(If, in mks units, N_0 is referred to a kg-mole, then the molecular weight M has its normal numerical value.) The density means the mass of one unit volume of molecules, so that

$$\rho = nm$$

Therefore,

$$\rho = M/V$$

In these terms, the ideal gas law can be rewritten

$$\rho = (M/RT)P \qquad (7\text{–}6)$$

At constant temperature, the density of a gas is proportional to the pressure.

A most important point of this section has been introduced as a tacit assumption but now it must be explicitly emphasized. In our mechanical derivation, it was assumed that the molecules of the gas collided with the walls of the containing vessel (thus exerting pressure on it), but that they *never* collided with each other. In other words, we have assumed that the molecules were *point masses*, between which there were *no forces acting*. It is just this assumption that leads to the particular equation of state known as the ideal gas law. If there *were* forces acting between the molecules, a different expression for the equation of state would be derived. In fact, there *are* forces acting, and the ideal gas law does not apply exactly to any real gas. Observed deviations from the ideal gas law can therefore be extremely interesting, because they give a clue to the forces acting between the molecules.

7–2   INTERMOLECULAR FORCES

The macroscopic ideal gas law has just been derived on the basis of some very simple microscopic assumptions about the molecules which make up the gas. Every one knows, however, that the ideal gas law is an approximation which under certain circumstances is inadequate—for example, when oxygen condenses into a liquid. All gases, even helium, condense into liquids

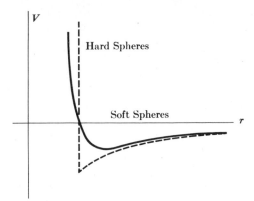

Fig. 7–2. Interatomic potential energy.

at sufficiently low temperatures. Furthermore, the theoretical assumptions which have been made—namely that the molecules are point masses which do not interact with each other—are in themselves highly suspect. A much more realistic equation of state for the gas can be derived if we recognize that the molecules do have an extension (since the gas cannot be squeezed down into nothing) and do attract each other (since the gas can condense into a cohering aggregate). We shall in Section 7–3 derive a refinement of the ideal gas law by taking these interactions approximately into account.

The form of the interaction can be guessed at least qualitatively by noting that the force must be repulsive at very small interatomic distances when the atoms actually come into contact, or more realistically stated when they begin to overlap or interpenetrate each other. On the other hand, at larger separations the atoms must attract each other, or else the gas would never condense because there would be no force holding it together. We may therefore draw a smooth potential energy curve (Fig. 7–2) which gives an attractive force at large distances and a repulsive one at small, with some assurance that it will have the right general form for any kind of atom (although it could differ in detail for atoms or molecules of different kinds). If the atoms were *hard spheres*, the force would become infinite when

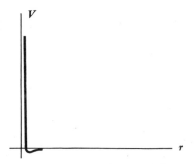

Fig. 7–3. Interatomic potential energy.

they came into contact, as shown by the dashed line. This curve will be recognized as less realistic than the full curve for *"soft spheres,"* although sometimes it is a useful approximation.

Since we are discussing a gas, in which the forces are not very important (as we know from the fact that the ideal gas law is nearly correct), it is useful to redraw the same potential energy curve on a demagnified scale (Fig. 7–3). From this picture one sees how it happens that the forces are not very important: if, on the average, the atoms stay far apart, then most of the time they are at large separations where the forces are negligible. Only occasionally, during "collisions," do they come close enough to each other for the forces to act strongly. Thus the farther apart the atoms are on the average, or the larger the molar volume, the more nearly the ideal gas law may be expected to hold. In the opposite extreme, when the atoms are very close and the forces are strong, the material may cease being a gas altogether and condense into a liquid or solid.

7–3   VAN DER WAALS' EQUATION OF STATE

Next, the kind of effect which these forces will have on the equation of state must be examined. We may start with the ideal gas law and try to predict what modifications will be introduced. First, the *repulsive force* can be taken into account most simply in the hard sphere approximation. In this approximation, each molecule has a definite volume, so that if V is the volume of the vessel which contains one mole (N_0 molecules) of the gas, then the volume which is not occupied by the molecules themselves and is actually available for them to move around in is $V - b$, where b is approximately N_0 times the volume of one molecule. The pressure is thereby increased, so that instead of $P = RT/V$, we should write

$$P = RT/(V - b) \tag{7–7}$$

This equation is called the *Clausius equation of state*. According to this equation of state the pressure P goes to infinity as V approaches b, as it should since the hard spheres themselves are incompressible.

To relate b more carefully to the molecular diameter, let us note that any given molecule excludes the centers of other molecules from a sphere circumscribed about the center of the given molecule (Fig. 7–4). The radius of this sphere is equal to the diameter d of the molecule, so that its "volume of exclusion" is 8 times the molecular volume. Each pair of molecules excludes each other from a volume of this size. In order to avoid counting each pair

Fig. 7–4. Sphere of exclusion about an atom.

twice, we therefore multiply by $\frac{1}{2}N_0$ to find the total excluded volume in one mole:

$$b = \frac{1}{2}N_0 \frac{4\pi}{3} d^3 \qquad (7\text{-}8)$$

This result should hold for a *rarefied gas*, where on the average the particles are far apart. As we approach the dense liquid phase, however (i.e., as V approaches b), it gets more and more likely that a given molecule should have the center of another molecule within a distance $2d$ of its own. In this case the "volumes of exclusion" of the two molecules overlap (Fig. 7–5). The volume surrounding these two molecules from which a third molecule is excluded is clearly less than in the case of no overlap. Consequently, the total excluded volume, b, in the gas is reduced as we approach the liquid phase.

The repulsive forces have now been approximately incorporated into the equation of state, but we have still to discuss the *attractive force*. Its effect will be to give the molecules a tendency to cohere together, thereby reducing the pressure which they exert on the walls of the containing vessel. A molecule which is about to collide with the wall of the vessel is attracted inward toward the body of the gas, and so it does not hit the wall so hard as it would in the absence of the attractive forces, and the pressure is smaller than for an ideal gas. The number of molecules which are approaching the wall and are attracted away from the wall is proportional to n (the number of molecules per unit volume), and also the number which is attracting them from the interior is proportional to n. Then P will be decreased proportionally to n^2, or proportionally to $1/V^2$ (recalling that $n = N_0/V$). Thus instead of $P = RT/(V - b)$ we should write

$$P = RT/(V - b) - a/V^2 \qquad (7\text{-}9)$$

where a is a constant. This equation is *van der Waals' equation of state*, named after the physicist who proposed it (1873) on the basis of similar reasoning. The reasoning is admittedly somewhat hazy and various attempts have been made to improve on it. They have generally led to mathematical complications out of proportion to the improvement in the agreement with experiment, however, so that we shall discuss only the van der Waals equation.

The van der Waals equation describes a departure to be expected from the ideal gas law. Amazingly, it also describes something like the liquefaction of the gas, even though it was designed only to be a small modification of the ideal gas law. If we plot the *isotherms* (constant temperature lines)

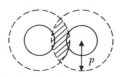

Fig. 7–5. Overlap of spheres of exclusion about two nearby atoms.

on a P versus V diagram, at high temperatures they are slightly distorted versions of the ideal gas hyperbolas (Fig. 7–6). At lower temperatures, however, they have a dip, which represents an unstable region. As the volume is decreased, the state of the gas follows the dotted line through the unstable region. This decrease of volume while the pressure remains constant corresponds to the progressive liquefaction of larger fractions of the gas. When the entire mole of gas is liquefied, the pressure increases much more steeply with a further decrease of volume, corresponding to the relatively incompressible liquid phase. At temperatures higher than those for which the isotherms have a dip, there is no phenomenon like liquefaction or condensation. The temperature at which the dip just vanishes is called the *critical temperature*. It will be seen that this isotherm has a horizontal inflection point. The pressure and volume at the inflection point of the critical isotherm are called the *critical pressure* and *critical volume*. It is easily shown that the critical volume V_c is

$$V_c = 3b$$

for the van der Waals equation. (See Prob. 7–4.) This means that a measurement of the critical volume can give an estimate of the volume occupied by N_0 molecules, or, dividing by N_0, of the volume of a single molecule.

The van der Waals equation

$$(P + a/V^2)(V - b) = RT$$

is not very useful as a quantitative description of the liquifaction of a gas, even though it gives a correct qualitative picture in this high density, low temperature region. No more should be expected, because it was derived by making only some slight modifications in the assumptions which led to the ideal gas law. It is useful, however, in describing departures from the ideal gas law, even near the critical point. The critical point is given by Prob. 7–4

$$V_c = 3b \qquad P_c = a/27b^2 \qquad T_c = 8a/27bR \qquad (7\text{–}10)$$

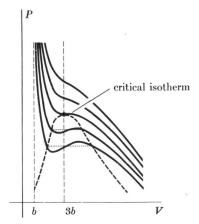

Fig. 7–6

Fig. 7–6. Isotherms for a van der Waals gas.

The *critical ratio* RT_c/P_cV_c, which would equal one for an ideal gas, has the value

$$RT_c/P_cV_c = 8/3 = 2.67 \qquad (7\text{--}11)$$

for a van der Waals gas, regardless of the particular values of a and b. If the van der Waals equation were a fully adequate description of non-ideal gases, every gas should show the value 2.67 for the critical ratio.

The critical pressure, volume, and temperature have been measured for many gases. (The critical point has been defined above theoretically in terms of the isotherms predicted by the van der Waals equation, but the actual isotherms have a similar shape, and the experimental critical point can be defined as the horizontal inflection point.) For example, for nitrogen gas N_2, the experimental values are

$$V_c = 90 \text{ cm}^3/\text{mole} = 0.09 \text{ liter/mole}$$
$$P_c = 3.4 \times 10^7 \text{ dyne/cm}^2 = 33.5 \text{ atm}$$
$$T_c = 126°\text{K} = -147°\text{C}$$

Recalling that one mole of an ideal gas at standard conditions occupies 22.4 liters, we see that the gas is quite dense at the critical point; in fact, the density is 0.31 g/cm^3, approaching that of the normal liquid at a pressure of 1 atm. These experimental values give a critical ratio of

$$RT_c/P_cV_c = 3.43$$

for nitrogen. Thus the critical ratio predicted by van der Waals equation, Eq. 7–11, is of the right order of magnitude, but somewhat too small. All other gases show similar results for the critical ratio, with values ranging between 3 and 5; all are of the same order of magnitude but somewhat higher than the van der Waals value.

As a description of the equation of state for a real gas above the critical point, the van der Waals equation is moderately successful. If the "constants" a and b are allowed to be functions of temperature, although the original spirit of the equation is compromised to some extent, the agreement with experiment is more satisfactory. (We have already seen that b should be expected to decrease, as we approach the liquid phase.) Other equations have been proposed, but none is wholly adequate. Perhaps the best approach is simply to use a power series expansion. One in inverse powers of V of the form

$$PV/RT = 1 + B/V + C/V^2 + D/V^3 + \cdots$$

is called the *virial equation of state*, and can give a good practical representation of experimental results if the coefficients B, C, D, etc., are functions of temperature. The deviations from the ideal gas law are not extreme at moderate pressures. Some data are shown in Fig. 7–7.

The main point for our present purposes is that, with the help of a me-

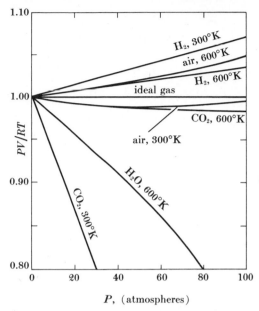

Fig. 7-7. Deviations from the ideal gas law for some actual gases.

chanical theory, we can deduce, from the measurable behavior of a macroscopic gas, something about the microscopic properties of the atoms which
make up the gas. From Eq. 7–8, the observed critical volume V_c implies
that the molecular diameter d is of the order of a few Ångstrom ($1\text{Å} =$
10^{-8}cm). (See Prob. 7–5.) In the next chapter, we shall see that by considering some more complex phenomena, we can obtain more detailed and
precise information about the size of molecules.

PROBLEMS

7–1.   Suppose He gas at standard conditions is contained in a vessel. (*a*) Calculate the root-mean-square speed of an atom. (*b*) Find the mean distance between He atoms. (*c*) How many atoms hit one square centimeter of the wall
in one second? (*d*) Compute the density of the gas.

7–2.   A vacuum system has a volume of 30 liter and is at a pressure of 10^{-8} mm
Hg, at room temperature. (*a*) How many molecules are in the system?
(*b*) Assuming the residual gas is air, how many molecules bombard the surface, per cm² per sec?

7–3.   Compute the mean kinetic energy of molecules at the following temperatures: 78°K (boiling point of N_2), 300°K, 3000°K, 10^6°K. Express the results in ergs and also in electron volts. (1 eV $= 1.6 \times 10^{-12}$ erg.)

7–4.   Prove that for the van der Waals equation, a horizontal inflection point occurs at $V_c = 3b$, $T_c = 8a/27\,bR$, $P_c = a/27\,b^2$. (*Hint:* Differentiate Eq. 7–9
twice.)

7–5.   Look up V_c for He gas. From it, calculate b, and the approximate volume
and diameter of one He atom.

7–6.   A useful form of the equation of state is

$$PV/RT = 1 + B/V + C/V^2 + D/V^3 + \cdots$$

This relation is called the *virial equation of state*. Show that the van der Waals equation of state can be written in virial form with

$$B = b - a/RT, \; C = b^2, \; D = b^3, \text{ etc.}$$

(*Hint:* $V/(V - b) = 1 + b/V + b^2/V^2 + \cdots$).

7–7.   Some experimental data for argon gas are the following:

T	B	C
$300°K$	-15.2 cm³/mole	990 (cm³/mole)²
500	8.4	710

Calculate the van der Waals constants a and b at each temperature. (Cf. Prob. 7–6.)

7–8.   The *Dieterici equation of state* is

$$P(V - b) = RT \exp(-a/RTV)$$

where a and b are constants. (The values of a and b which fit this equation to the data are not the same as the values which fit the van der Waals equation.) Show that for the Dieterici equation, at the critical point

$$V_c = 2b$$

and

$$RT_c/P_cV_c = e^2/2 = 3.69$$

7–9.   Calculate the temperature at which the root-mean-square speed (Eq. 7–5) of a nitrogen molecule equals the escape velocity from the earth. Repeat for the moon. The mass of the moon is about 1/80 that of the earth, and its volume is 1/50.

7–10. Look up data for the critical temperature, pressure, and volume in the *Handbook of Chemistry and Physics*, and construct a table of P_cV_c/RT_c for some common gases.

REFERENCES

F. W. Sears, *Thermodynamics* (Addison-Wesley, 1953, 2nd ed.), Ch. 11.

J. Jeans, *An Introduction to the Kinetic Theory of Gases* (Cambridge, 1940), Ch. III.

W. P. Allis and M. A. Herlin, *Thermodynamics and Statistical Mechanics* (McGraw-Hill, 1952), Ch. 3.

E. H. Kennard, *Kinetic Theory of Gases* (McGraw-Hill, 1938), Ch. I, V.

8/transport phenomena in gases

We have so far been successful in deducing a modification of the equation of state for a gas from the assumed properties of the molecules which constitute the gas. If our aim, however, is to turn around and infer something about the invisible molecules from the observed properties of the gas, we have been somewhat less successful. The forces between the molecules have a rather small effect on the equation of state, simply because most of the time the molecules are not interacting with each other (when they are far apart). To get more definite information about the interaction, we can seek phenomena which are more sensitive to our assumed model for the interaction forces. These should depend on the moment when the atoms are close together, i.e., on collisions. A number of such processes are known, e.g., thermal conductivity, viscosity, and diffusion. They are lumped together under the designation "transport processes," because in each case something is transported through the gas—energy, momentum, and mass, respectively, in the three processes mentioned. We shall see that the rate of transport (which can be measured) depends sensitively on the collisions between atoms, because the collisions deflect and retard the transport of the quantity through the medium. Though the molecular diameter introduces only a small correction into the equation of state, the transport processes will be found to be proportional to it (in fact, to its square), because the frequency of the collisions depends on the cross-sectional area of the molecules which are colliding with each other.

8-1 MEAN FREE PATH

Before considering how the frequency of collisions of the molecules in the gas determines the measurable transport properties, we shall first investigate how the frequency of collisions itself depends on the size of the molecules. More precisely stated, we want to know how it depends on the forces which act between pairs of molecules. As we have seen, these forces may be expected to be attractive at large distances and repulsive when the molecules are close together. The "hard sphere" case, in which each molecule has a definite size, is merely a specialized force law in which the attractive component is zero and the repulsive component suddenly goes to infinity when the molecules come into contact. Some similar problems have already been treated in Section 6–4. There we saw how a *scattering experiment* gives information about the force law. In the Rutherford scattering experiment, for example, a measurement of the differential scattering cross section for alpha particles on gold atoms confirmed the law of coulomb repulsion between the nuclei down to very small distances. In principle, similar scattering experiments could be used to infer the force law between *neutral* atoms and molecules, just as for charged particles. Very severe practical obstacles stand in the way of this approach, however, due to the great experimental difficulty in producing and detecting beams of neutral particles. We shall therefore be concerned here with the *integrated scattering cross section*, rather than the differential one. If the molecules are hard spheres, the cross section is simply related to their diameter (Eq. 6–10); but even for more complicated force laws, the integrated cross section will be assumed to be finite, so that it can be specified by a certain number σ.

We shall now review how the frequency of collisions is related to the cross section of the molecules. If a given molecule with speed v sweeps through a cloud of similar molecules at rest, in one second it will sweep through v cubic centimeters each containing n molecules. (See Fig. 8–1.) In passing through a square centimeter, it encounters nv molecules per second, and if the collision cross section for the molecule is σ, then the total area comprising obstacles to its unimpeded motion is $nv\sigma$. The ratio of this area to one square centimeter is the probability that it will collide with, or be scattered by, another molecule, per second. We define τ as the *mean free time* between collisions, so that $1/\tau$ is the collision probability per second. Then

$$1/\tau = nv\sigma \qquad (8\text{–}1)$$

This important formula relates the mean time between collisions to the size, the speed, and the density of the molecules. Another useful concept is the mean distance between collisions, or the *mean free path L*. Since

$$L = v\tau \qquad (8\text{–}2)$$

then

$$L = 1/n\sigma \qquad (8\text{–}3)$$

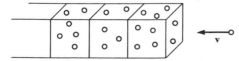

Fig. 8–1

We should clarify our reference to $1/\tau$ as a collision *probability* per unit time, since the total probability of having a collision in time t would appear to be t/τ, and t/τ may very well be a number greater than 1, unlike a genuine probability. What is really meant is the following. Suppose a large number N of molecules were incident on the gas of Fig. 8–1 instead of a single molecule. Then in a short time interval dt, a certain fraction dN/N of the incident molecules would collide with the molecules of the gas, and the fraction would be proportional to the length of time dt considered:

$$dN/N = -\,(1/\tau)\,dt \qquad\qquad (8\text{–}4)$$

The proportionality constant $(1/\tau)$ specifies the fraction which collides per second, and the minus sign is used because N means the number which has *not* yet suffered a collision. If we identify the probability of a collision $d\Pi$ with the fraction which collides $-\,dN/N$ and use Eq. 8–1 for $(1/\tau)$, we obtain exactly Eq. 6–11 again,

$$d\Pi = n\sigma v\,dt$$

Now to find the total fraction which has not collided up to the time t, Eq. 8–4 must be integrated to obtain $N = N(t)$:

$$N/N_i = e^{-t/\tau}$$

the integration constant N_i representing the initially incident number. Therefore the fraction which *has* collided is

$$1 - N/N_i = 1 - e^{-t/\tau}$$

It is this function (Fig. 8–2) which actually represents the collision probability, and it approaches 1 asymptotically for long times. For short time intervals, however, the exponential can be expanded in a power series,

$$1 - e^{-t/\tau} = t/\tau + \cdots$$

showing that $1/\tau$ is the initial probability per unit time of a collision, in agreement with Eq. 8–4. A similar consideration shows that $1/L$ is the initial probability of a collision per unit length.

It has been assumed so far that the incident molecule has the speed v and all the target molecules are at rest. This is the assumption which would be appropriate to describe the scattering of a monoenergetic beam of molecules with speed v on a solid target, but that is not really the case in which we are interested here. To find the collision frequency for a molecule in a

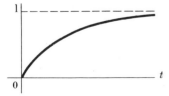

Fig. 8–2. Probability of collision after time t.

gas, all the target molecules must themselves be assumed to be moving around, since they are actually indistinguishable from the particular molecule which has been singled out for consideration. Furthermore, the molecules do not all have the same speed, as will be discussed in Chapter 9. The result of making these refinements, however, is merely to introduce a numerical factor $\sqrt{2}$, and to replace v with the average speed $\bar{v}$. Thus the correct formulas are

$$1/\tau = \sqrt{2}\, n\bar{v}\sigma \tag{8-5}$$

$$L = 1/\sqrt{2}\, n\sigma \tag{8-6}$$

Equation 8–2 is of course still correct,

$$L = \bar{v}\tau \tag{8-2}$$

It is worth emphasizing that according to Eq. 8–6 the mean free path L is inversely proportional to the density of the molecules, but it does not depend on their speed. The mean *time* between collisions, on the other hand, does depend on the speed. One can visualize this difference by imagining a moving picture of the flight of a molecule, as it moves along its path experiencing collisions with other molecules (Fig. 8–3). Now if the moving picture were speeded up, the collisions would occur more frequently in time, but the distance between any two successive collisions would be unchanged. This fact is important because according to Eq. 7–5 the average speed of the molecule is related to the temperature T. Consequently, the mean free path is *independent of temperature*, provided the density of the gas remains constant, as would be so if a fixed amount of gas is inside a rigid container. If the volume of the gas is not fixed, however, the formula

$$n = N_0/V$$

shows the dependence on molar volume. For an ideal gas, one may write $V = RT/P$, so that

$$n = (N_0/RT)P \tag{8-7}$$

For an ideal gas at a given temperature, L is *inversely proportional to pressure*.

Finally, let us relate the collision cross section to the size of the molecules, for the case of the hard sphere interaction. Reference to Figs. 6–7 and 7–4 shows that a molecule will collide with another identical molecule if the

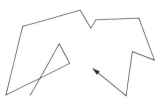

Fig. 8–3. Path of a molecule.

impact parameter is less than d, the diameter of the molecule. Therefore (cf. Eq. 6–10)

$$\sigma = \pi d^2 \qquad (8\text{–}8)$$

By relating the mean free path to the measured transport properties and the scattering cross section to the mean free path (Eq. 8–6), we shall obtain values for molecular diameters from Eq. 8–8. Even if the force law is more complicated than the hard sphere interaction, the measured cross section determines an *effective diameter* defined by Eq. 8–8.

8–2   THERMAL CONDUCTIVITY

As an example of a phenomenon which depends on the scattering cross section or the mean free path of the molecules, let us consider the thermal conductivity of the gas. The theory of diffusion or of viscosity is essentially the same, but thermal conductivity is perhaps a more familiar effect. It means that when two portions of a body of gas are at different temperatures, energy in the form of heat will flow from the hotter to the colder region. Why this should happen is immediately clear from the fact, pointed out in the preceding chapter, that the (average) kinetic energy of a molecule is proportional to the temperature T. Consider an imaginary plane in the gas. If it is hotter on one side of the plane and colder on the other, the molecules which cross from the hot to the cold side carry more kinetic energy with them than those which cross in the opposite direction. There is thus a net transport of energy from the hot to the cold side. If the "hot" molecules never collided with other molecules, they would fly infinitely far (or to the end of the container) carrying their load of high kinetic energy, so that the thermal conductivity would be infinite. It is only because they are impeded by collisions that the thermal conductivity is finite. In fact, in gases thermal conductivity is comparatively small, as we know from the fact that air is a good heat insulator.

In order to calculate the thermal conductivity, consider the energy flowing across an imaginary plane in the gas. The number of molecules crossing the plane, per unit area and per unit time, is the flux per unit area given by Eq. 7–3: $F = \frac{1}{2} n v_x$. Since the molecules in the gas actually have a range of velocities, we may replace v_x by its average value $\overline{v_x}$. Furthermore, as we shall see in Chapter 9, $\overline{v_x}$ is not very different from the average speed $\overline{v}$. (What we actually mean is $|\overline{v_x}|$; the value of $\overline{v_x}$ itself is zero, because equally many molecules travel from left to right as from right to left.) Let us therefore be satisfied with a very rough calculation, and drop all the numerical factors which are not too different from 1. Then the flux of molecules crossing the plane in one second from left to right is approximately

$$F \cong \tfrac{1}{2} n \overline{v} \qquad (8\text{–}9)$$

with the same number crossing from right to left.

Suppose the average energy of a molecule at the position of the plane is $\overline{E}$. (See Fig. 8–4.) If the gas is cooler on the left, and each molecule crossing the plane from left to right carries with it a kinetic energy $\overline{E} - \Delta\overline{E}$ (on the average), then the molecules crossing in the opposite direction from right to left will carry a slightly higher average kinetic energy $\overline{E} + \Delta\overline{E}$. Therefore the *net* heat energy flowing across the plane per square cm per second is

$$H \cong \tfrac{1}{2}n\bar{v}(\overline{E} - \Delta\overline{E}) - \tfrac{1}{2}n\bar{v}(\overline{E} + \Delta\overline{E})$$
$$= - n\bar{v}\,\Delta\overline{E} \tag{8-10}$$

Now we may assume that when the molecules traveling from left to right made their last collision just before crossing the plane, they acquired the energy characteristic of that point in the gas, and likewise for the molecules travelling from right to left. Since, on the average, a molecule made its last collision a distance L behind the plane (according to the meaning of the mean free path L), we have

$$\Delta\overline{E} = L(d\overline{E}/dx) \tag{8-11}$$

The actual reason the average energy varies with position is that we have assumed that the temperature does, and so we may write

$$\frac{d\overline{E}}{dx} = \frac{d\overline{E}}{dT}\frac{dT}{dx}$$

Substituting into Eq. 8–10,

$$H = - n\bar{v}L(d\overline{E}/dT)(dT/dx)$$

The quantity (dT/dx) is the measured temperature gradient; it remains only to consider the meaning of the factor $(d\overline{E}/dT)$.

The average energy of a monatomic ideal gas of point particles is given as a function of temperature by Eq. 7–5, since the total energy of a particle is in this case just the translational kinetic energy $\tfrac{1}{2}m\overline{v^2}$. Then

$$\overline{E} = \tfrac{1}{2}m\overline{v^2} = \tfrac{3}{2}kT \tag{7-5}$$

and

$$d\overline{E}/dT = \tfrac{3}{2}k \tag{8-12}$$

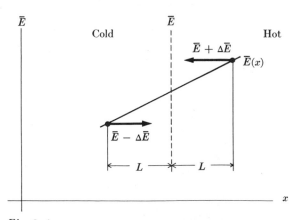

Fig. 8–4

So that our result need not be limited only to this ideal monatomic case, however, we may instead take a less fundamental theoretical approach, and relate $(d\overline{E}/dT)$ in a completely general way to quantities which can be measured experimentally. First we notice that $n\overline{E}$ is the total energy in a unit volume of the gas. Then $n(d\overline{E}/dT)$ is the increase in energy when a unit volume is heated up one degree, or the *heat capacity* per unit volume. It is more convenient to refer to the specific heat *per unit mass c*. Since

$$\frac{\text{heat capacity}}{\text{volume}} = \frac{\text{specific heat}}{\text{mass}} \cdot \frac{\text{mass}}{\text{volume}} = c\rho$$

where ρ is the density of the gas, then

$$n(d\overline{E}/dT) = \rho c \qquad (8\text{--}13)$$

Finally, making this substitution, we find for the heat flow

$$H \cong -\rho c \overline{v} L (dT/dx)$$

That is, H is found to be proportional to the temperature gradient (dT/dx). The proportionality constant is by definition the *thermal conductivity* κ:

$$H = -\kappa(dT/dx) \qquad (8\text{--}14)$$

so that the result for the thermal conductivity is

$$\kappa \cong \rho c \overline{v} L \qquad (8\text{--}15)$$

where c is the specific heat per unit mass (measured at constant volume).

The reasoning we have used to derive this expression for κ is admittedly crude, but a careful, and quite lengthy, calculation gives the same answer, except for a factor of $25\pi/64 = 1.23$. The formula relates the measurable macroscopic quantities κ, ρ, and c, to the microscopic molecular properties $\overline{v}$ and L. In the last chapter we saw how $\overline{v}$ and L could be estimated from measurable quantities with the help of theory. Using all these values, one gets quite reasonable agreement with the formula. It has already been pointed out, however, that the mean free path is insensitively determined by the equation of state, so that the principal use of the thermal conductivity formula is for a more accurate determination of the mean free path L, and thereby of the molecular diameter.

The *pressure dependence* of the thermal conductivity of a gas can be inferred from the pressure dependence of each of the factors in Eq. 8–15. According to Eq. 7–6, at constant temperature,

$$\rho \propto P$$

and Eq. 8–6 shows that

$$L \propto 1/P$$

Since c and $\overline{v}$ are approximately independent of P, the theory predicts that the thermal conductivity of a gas is *independent of pressure*. This intuitively surprising result is actually confirmed over a wide range of pressures. It must break down at very low pressures, however, when the mean free path L becomes so large that it is comparable with the size of the container holding the gas. Then there are few collisions between molecules in the volume of the gas, L is constant, and the thermal conductivity decreases with P as the density ρ decreases with P. This effect is also observed experimentally, and in fact it is utilized in a practical pressure measuring device (the "thermocouple gauge"). (See Prob. 8–4.)

In order to see the *temperature dependence* which is expected, let us substitute values appropriate for a gas of hard spheres. As already noted in Eqs. 8–12 and 8–13, $\rho c = n \, d\bar{E}/dT = \tfrac{3}{2}nk$. From Eq. 8–6, $L = 1/\sqrt{2} \, n\sigma$. The scattering cross section σ is πd^2, since two identical molecules will collide if they approach to within the sum of their radii or their diameter d. The mean velocity $\bar{v}$ can be calculated approximately from $\tfrac{1}{2}m\overline{v^2} = \tfrac{3}{2}kT$ to be $\sqrt{3kT/m}$. As will be seen in the next chapter, the correct value for the average speed $\bar{v}$ is really 8 per cent less than this root-mean-square speed: $\bar{v} = \sqrt{8kT/\pi m}$. Using all these substitutions, we get

$$\kappa = \frac{75}{64\sqrt{\pi}} \sqrt{\frac{k^3}{m}} \frac{1}{d^2} T^{1/2} \qquad (8\text{–}16)$$

The temperature dependence predicted is proportional to the square root of T (from $\bar{v}$), so that if measured thermal conductivity values are plotted versus absolute temperature on log–log paper, a straight line with slope 0.5 should be obtained. Experimental results for all gases give approximately straight lines, with a slope of about 0.5, so that our theory is further confirmed. The results are not exact, however, and in the next section we shall see that the discrepancy can provide further insight into the nature of the intermolecular forces.

8–3   REPULSIVE FORCE

The slopes actually obtained in a log κ versus log T plot are significantly greater than 0.5. Instead of being a disappointment, however, this fact should invite us to re-examine the assumptions of our theory, to see if different assumptions will give a different temperature dependence, thereby affording an empirical decision about which are the correct assumptions concerning the microscopic behavior of the molecules. The most vulnerable assumption is that the gas is made of *hard* spheres. If the spheres are slightly soft, in a high energy collision (occurring more often at high temperature), the molecules will be less sharply deviated, so that they travel farther in their original direction. This "persistence of velocity" effect will give a larger thermal conductivity at high temperature, so that the slopes should be somewhat greater than 0.5. The experimental deviation is in fact in this direction, so that we may profitably investigate this lead.

We shall do so using a technique known as *dimensional analysis*. This technique may seem like dirty pool to some, and like the royal road to the inner secrets of nature to others, but actually it is a perfectly valid argument which does not always give useful results. With some prior knowledge and informed insight into the problem, as we have in the present case, the method sometimes yields an essentially complete solution to the problem. It rests on the convention that the dimensions on two sides of an equation should be the same, in order for the equation to hold no matter what units we use (say inches or centimeters). You should already be acquiring the habit to "check the dimensions" of your calculations, as an aid in spotting mistakes. Dimensional analysis is a sophisticated version of this activity.

From our hard sphere calculation, Eq. 8–16, we have seen that κ depends on Boltzmann's constant k, the mass of the molecules m, the temperature T, and the diameter of the molecules d. What we now wish to do (Fig. 8–5) is to replace the "hard" diameter d by a more realistic force law, $V(r) = B/r^n$. Our previous calculation gave a result which can be expressed as

$$\kappa = m^{\alpha} k^{\beta} d^{\gamma} T^{\delta} \qquad (8\text{–}17)$$

with the values for the exponents

$$\alpha = -\tfrac{1}{2} \qquad \beta = \tfrac{3}{2} \qquad \gamma = -2 \qquad \delta = \tfrac{1}{2} \qquad (8\text{–}18)$$

There was in addition a dimensionless constant, $75/64\sqrt{\pi}$.

Let us first check that this formula is "dimensionally homogeneous," i.e., that the units are the same on the two sides of the equation. For dimensions, we will use mass M, length L, and time T, and in addition temperature Θ. Using square brackets to mean "the dimensions of," obviously,

$$\begin{aligned} [m] &= M \\ [d] &= L \qquad\qquad (8\text{–}19) \\ [T] &= \Theta \end{aligned}$$

The dimensions of k we have to figure out: the units of k are erg/deg (since kT is an energy). Ergs are units of work, which is force times distance (L), and force is mass (M) times acceleration (L/T^2). Therefore ergs have the dimensions ML^2T^{-2}, and

$$[k] = ML^2T^{-2}\Theta^{-1} \qquad (8\text{–}20)$$

The thermal conductivity κ has dimensions which will make the defining formula Eq. 8–14

$$H = -\kappa \, dT/dx$$

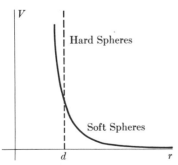

Fig. 8–5. *Repulsive interaction of atoms.*

dimensionally homogeneous. The heat flux per unit area H has units erg/cm²-sec and the temperature gradient dT/dx has units deg/cm, so that

$$[\kappa] = (ML^2T^{-2})(L^{-2}T^{-1})(L\Theta^{-1})$$
$$= MLT^{-3}\Theta^{-1} \tag{8-21}$$

We now can see that the dimensions check: inserting Eqs. 8–18 to 8–21 into Eq. 8–17,

$$(M)^{-1/2} \ (ML^2T^{-2} \ \Theta^{-1})^{3/2} \ (L)^{-2} \ (\Theta)^{1/2} = MLT^{-3} \ \Theta^{-1}$$

an identity.

If we next wish to assume that the repulsive potential is B/r^n instead of suddenly going to ∞ at $r = d$, then we have only to assume that κ depends on the parameter B instead of the parameter d; by analogy with Eq. 8–17,

$$\kappa = m^\alpha k^\beta B^\gamma T^\delta \tag{8-22}$$

The problem is now to determine α, β, γ, δ so that the formula will be dimensionally homogeneous. Since B/r^n has the units erg,

$$[B] = (ML^2T^{-2})L^n$$
$$= ML^{2+n}T^{-2} \tag{8-23}$$

Then we must have, substituting Eqs. 8–19, 8–20, 8–21, and 8–23 into Eq. 8–22,

$$MLT^{-3} \ \Theta^{-1} = M^\alpha \ (ML^2T^{-2} \ \Theta^{-1})^\beta \ (ML^{2+n}T^{-2})^\gamma \ \Theta^\delta$$

or, equating the powers of M, L, T, and Θ on each side of the equation,

$$1 = \alpha + \beta + \gamma$$
$$1 = 2\beta + (2 + n)\gamma$$
$$- 3 = - 2\beta - 2\gamma$$
$$- 1 = - \beta + \delta$$

The remaining mathematical problem, to solve this set of simultaneous linear equations, is easy: the solution is

$$\alpha = - 1/2$$
$$\beta = 3/2 + 2/n$$
$$\gamma = - 2/n$$
$$\delta = 1/2 + 2/n$$

Substituting these exponents into the assumed formula for κ, we have the desired result,

$$\kappa = \text{const} \ \sqrt{k^3/m} \ (k/B)^{2/n} \ T^{1/2+2/n} \tag{8-24}$$

We have now obtained the formula for κ by dimensional analysis, solely by requiring that our answer should be dimensionally homogeneous. To do so, we had to know what quantities κ depended on and then merely write down the equations for their dimensions. It is true that we do not obtain a possible dimensionless constant multiplier, like $75/64\sqrt{\pi}$, but usually this can be found by making the formula reduce to a simpler case, Eq. 8–16. What is much more interesting, we obtain a new temperature dependence of κ. We see that the exponent of T is $\frac{1}{2} + 2/n$. For the hard sphere case $(n = \infty)$, the exponent is 0.5, as we already knew. For somewhat soft spheres, however, the exponent will be greater than 0.5. For example, for He the measured exponent is 0.64. From this value, we can determine that $n = 14$ for He. Similarly, for Ne we find that $n = 12$.

The analysis of the temperature dependence of thermal conductivity for gases thus really gives some new insight into the interactions between the molecules. We learn not only the rough "size" of the molecules, but also something about how the forces between them vary with distance. They depend on a relatively high power of the separation r $(n > 10)$, so that the molecules are quite "hard" (compared to the coulomb repulsion, for example, for which $n = 1$). We shall find later that this conclusion is confirmed and strengthened by the analysis of the solid state of matter. An actual comparison between a $1/r^{10}$ and a $1/r$ (coulomb) potential is illustrated in Fig. 8–6, where we have plotted the $1/r^n$ potential for $n = 1$ and $n = 10$. The potential could be written $V(r) = B/r^n = B'/(r/d)^n$, for purposes of plotting. Then d is an "effective diameter" of the molecule, since the curve takes off toward infinity at about $(r/d) = 1$ or $r = d$. The case of $n = 10$ is seen to be not too different from the hard sphere case $(n = \infty)$, shown by the dashed line.

8–4   VISCOSITY

The viscosity of a fluid (gas or liquid) is responsible for the frictional drag, or viscous force, which one part of the fluid exerts on an adjacent part, if the two parts are in relative motion. It is not in evidence at all in a fluid at rest, but produces important effects when it is flowing. Suppose a gas is flowing

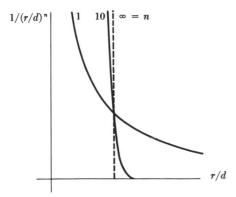

Fig. 8–6. Repulsive potential power law.

in the y-direction, with a flow velocity $\mathbf{u}$ which increases in the x-direction (Fig. 8–7). Consider two layers, separated by a distance Δx. The layer on the right, which is flowing slightly faster, exerts a force on the left-hand layer which tends to drag it along. We shall see that the force which acts on a unit area of the plane separating the two layers, called the *shear stress S*, is proportional to $\Delta u/\Delta x$, or in the limit, to du/dx. The proportionality constant is called the *viscosity* η:

$$S = -\eta \, (du/dx) \qquad\qquad (8\text{–}25)$$

The stress S has the same dimensions as pressure P; the difference is that the pressure P is a force per unit area acting perpendicular to the area in question, whereas S acts parallel to the area. (It might be thought that S and P should be treated as vectors. We shall return to this point in Chapter 12, and here simply regard them as the magnitude of a vector.) Our aim is to explain the coefficient η in molecular terms, just as we explained the thermal conductivity coefficient κ in the analogous Eq. 8–14.

The molecules of the gas are moving around with an average speed $\bar{v}$ which is much greater than the flow speed u. As we saw in Chapter 7, at room temperature the molecular speeds are of the order of 10^5 cm/sec, or rather greater than the speed of sound. Thus $\mathbf{u}$ can be considered small for most subsonic flow velocities, and it is simply added to the random velocity $\mathbf{v}$. As a molecule flies across the plane (dashed line in Fig. 8–7), it carries with it its flow velocity $\mathbf{u}$, or equivalently a *flow momentum* $m\mathbf{u}$. The molecules which cross from the fast side to the slow side carry more momentum than those which cross in the opposite direction. Thus there is a net transfer of momentum across the plane. According to Newton's second law, the time

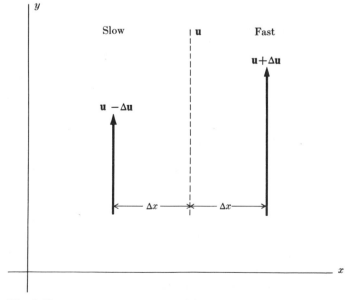

Fig. 8–7

rate of this momentum transfer is equal to the force acting across the plane.

To make this argument quantitative, consider the flux of molecules crossing the plane in one second in each direction, equal to $\frac{1}{2}n\bar{v}$ according to Eq. 8–9. Those going from left to right carry a flow momentum $m(u - \Delta u)$, and those going from right to left carry $m(u + \Delta u)$. In analogy to Eq. 8–10, the net flow momentum transferred across unit area of the plane per second is equal to the shear force per unit area S:

$$S \cong - n\bar{v}m \, \Delta u$$

Now, just as in Eq. 8–11, the molecules crossing the plane can be assumed to have picked up their flow momentum the last time they made a collision, and so

$$\Delta u \cong L(du/dx)$$

Inserting this expression, and recalling that $nm = \rho$, we have

$$S = - \rho\bar{v}L(du/dx)$$

so that

$$\eta \cong \rho\bar{v}L \qquad (8\text{--}26)$$

Comparison of Eq. 8–26 with Eq. 8–15 shows that our theory predicts that

$$\kappa \cong c\eta$$

Our rough results can be improved, and the most careful calculations which have been carried out indicate that

$$\kappa \cong \tfrac{5}{2}c\eta \qquad (8\text{--}27)$$

The coefficient is exactly $\frac{5}{2}$ for an inverse fifth power repulsion, and is 1% higher for hard spheres. This relation is particularly interesting, because it involves only measurable quantities. It is substantiated experimentally for the noble gases He, Ne, and A, and so the value of L which is calculated from the theory of viscosity is in agreement with the value calculated from the theory of thermal conductivity. For more complicated molecules, the agreement with Eq. 8–27 is not so close. For most gases the ratio $\kappa/c\eta$ is less than 2, instead of the value 2.5 predicted by Eq. 8–27. It appears that the refinements which lead to the factor 2.5 instead of 1 are not justified for the internal motions of the molecule, like vibration and rotation. Nevertheless, the theory has produced a remarkable result in Eq. 8–27, by correlating a thermal property (κ) and a mechanical property (η), which at first sight would not be thought to have any relation to each other.

The pressure and temperature dependence of viscosity are approximately the same as for the thermal conductivity, since the specific heat is nearly constant, as we shall see in Chapter 9. Some experimental results are shown in Fig. 8–9. Surprisingly, the viscosity is independent of pressure (or density), at least over the range where the mean free path is short compared to the size of the container. The *increase* of the viscosity of a gas with temperature is also somewhat surprising, in contrast to the more familiar behavior of liquids, which become less viscous as their temperature is raised.

8–5   DIFFUSION

The diffusion of one kind of gas into another is also a phenomenon which depends on the transport of something—in this case not the transport of energy or momentum, but of the molecules themselves. It leads to the slow mixing of two kinds of gas which are originally separate but in contact. For example, if a bottle of ammonia were uncapped some distance away, it would be quite a while before you could smell it. The ammonia molecules themselves we know to be moving extremely rapidly (0.6 km/sec, at room temperature), but their net progress is very slow because of their innumerable collisions with other molecules. We shall see that the flow of molecules across a certain plane is proportional to the gradient of the concentration (density) of that kind of molecule (Fig. 8–8):

$$J^* = - D(dn^*/dx) \qquad (8\text{--}28)$$

This equation may be compared with Eqs. 8–14 and 8–25. The coefficient D is called the *diffusion coefficient*, and the equation itself is called *Fick's Law*.

In Eq. 8–28, we have written J^* for the net flux of molecules per unit area and n^* for their number per unit volume, because the kind of molecules whose diffusion we are considering must be distinguished from the molecules through which they are diffusing. (Actually, each kind is diffusing through the other kind.) The quantities J^* and n^* refer only to the kind we are considering, not the total. Now introducing two different species of molecules raises complications which can be handled in a straightforward way (by introducing a mean free path for each species), but which we have hitherto avoided. In order to avoid this complication in discussing diffusion, let us consider only *self-diffusion*, where all the molecules are of the same kind but we imagine that we have tagged some of them so that we can fol-

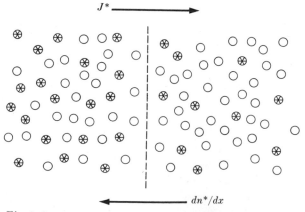

Fig. 8–8

low the progress of those particular ones. Unfortunately, while this assumption simplifies the problem, it is strictly nonsense: it says that all the molecules are identical, but some are different. The only way that a molecule
can be marked is to make it different.

What actually makes the assumption meaningful and worth considering
is that it is possible to make them only slightly different, so that they can
be distinguished from the unmarked molecules in some way, but their
interaction with the other molecules, in particular their mean free path, is
just the same as for an unmarked molecule. The way certain atoms can be
distinguished is by using different *isotopes* of the same element. Different
isotopes of an element have different masses but exactly the same chemical
properties—i.e., exactly the same interaction with other atoms. Particularly in the case of a heavy element, the percentage difference even in the
masses is small, so that the tagged atoms or molecules are almost identical.
Practically, it is especially convenient to use an isotope which is *radioactive*,
since then the concentration of tagged molecules can be measured by counting the radioactive decays, employing standard techniques of nuclear
physics. Therefore we intend to consider self-diffusion, recognizing that the
coefficient of self-diffusion can be measured by allowing a sample of gas
containing radioactive atoms to diffuse into an ordinary gas of the same
kind.

After this explanation, the actual kinetic calculation of the self-diffusion
coefficient is even easier than the two preceding cases. Here it is the flux itself of tagged molecules which differs in the two directions. Let the concentration of tagged molecules be $n^* - \Delta n^*$ to the left of the plane and
$n^* + \Delta n^*$ to the right. Then the net flux across the plane in one second is,
from Eq. 8–9,

$$J^* = \Delta F^* = \tfrac{1}{2}(n^* - \Delta n^*)\bar{v} - \tfrac{1}{2}(n^* + \Delta n^*)\bar{v}$$
$$= - \bar{v}\Delta n^*$$

Again,

$$\Delta n^* \cong L(dn^*/dx)$$

so that

$$J^* = - \bar{v}L(dn^*/dx)$$

and

$$D \cong \bar{v}L \tag{8–29}$$

Comparison of Eq. 8–29 with Eq. 8–26 shows that

$$\eta \cong \rho D \tag{8–30}$$

Again, a more careful calculation (for hard spheres) shows that

$$\eta = \tfrac{5}{6}\rho D$$

The cross sections or molecular diameters computed from measured diffusion coefficients agree reasonably well (within about 20%) with those obtained from viscosity measurements, so that our theory gives a consistent
picture of all these transport phenomena. From Eq. 8–29 it is obvious that

D increases as $T^{1/2}$ (with $\bar{v}$), and decreases as $1/P$ (with L).

8-6   TRANSPORT PROPERTIES OF GASES

In order to have some idea of what our calculated transport coefficients mean, let us consider some numerical examples for a typical gas. We have seen that the diffusion coefficient is

$$D \cong \bar{v}L \tag{8-29}$$

where $\bar{v}$ is the mean speed of the molecules and L is their mean free path. The viscosity is

$$\eta \cong \rho D \tag{8-30}$$

where ρ is the mass density of the gas. The thermal conductivity is

$$\kappa \cong c\eta \tag{8-31}$$

where c is the specific heat per unit mass (measured at constant volume, and thus often designated c_V). We must therefore estimate the magnitudes of $\bar{v}$, L, ρ, and c. As an example, let us choose argon, a gas of medium molecular weight which approximates an ideal gas at room temperature.

For argon, the molecular weight is $M = 40$ and the diameter d is approximately $4\ \text{Å} = 4 \times 10^{-8}$ cm. The specific heat, according to Eq. 8–12, is $d\bar{E}/dT = \frac{3}{2}k$ for one molecule of an ideal gas. Multiplying by N_0/M, the number of molecules in a gram, and recalling that $N_0 k = R$, the gas constant per mole, we have

$$c = \frac{3}{2}\frac{R}{M} = \frac{3}{2}\frac{2\ \text{cal/mole-deg}}{40\ \text{g/mole}} = \frac{3}{40}\ \text{cal/g-deg} \cong 0.3 \times 10^7\ \text{erg/g-deg}$$

The density ρ is the molecular weight divided by the volume of one mole, V. At standard conditions for an ideal gas $V = 22.4$ liter, so that

$$\rho = \frac{M}{V} = \frac{40\ \text{g/mole}}{22.4\ \text{liter/mole}} \cong 2 \times 10^{-3}\ \text{g/cm}^3$$

The mean free path L depends on n, the number of molecules per unit volume (Eq. 8–6). At standard conditions for an ideal gas,

$$n = \frac{N_0}{V} = \frac{6.02 \times 10^{23}\ \text{molecules/mole}}{22.4 \times 10^3\ \text{cm}^3/\text{mole}} \cong 3 \times 10^{19}\ \text{cm}^{-3}$$

Then, using Eq. 8–8 for the cross section,

$$L = \frac{1}{\sqrt{2}\,n\pi d^2} = \frac{1}{\sqrt{2} \times 3 \times 10^{19}\text{cm}^{-3}\pi \times 4^2 \times 10^{-16}\text{cm}^2}$$
$$\cong 6 \times 10^{-6}\text{cm}$$

Finally, we may approximate $\bar{v}$ by the rms speed,

$$\bar{v} \cong v_{\text{rms}} = \sqrt{\frac{3kT}{m}} = \sqrt{\frac{3RT}{M}} = \sqrt{2\,\frac{3}{2}\frac{R}{M}\,T}$$
$$= \sqrt{2 \times 0.3 \times 10^7\ \text{erg/g-deg} \times 300\ \text{deg}} \cong 4 \times 10^4\ \text{cm/sec}$$

These values are all fairly representative for a gas at room temperature and atmospheric pressure.

The diffusion coefficient is then given by

$$D \cong \bar{v}L = 0.25 \text{ cm}^2/\text{sec}$$

In order to appreciate what this figure means, we must quote a mathematical result which would take too long to derive here. If some argon is initially concentrated in a localized region of an atmosphere of air, for example, Eq. 8–28 shows that the argon diffuses away from the region of high concentration, thereby altering the argon concentration at all points. (The molecular diameter for air is about the same as for argon, so that we may use the self-diffusion formula as an approximation to this case.) If this problem is formulated mathematically and solved, one finds that the time t required for an appreciable concentration of argon to diffuse to a distance x from the original region is given by

$$t \cong x^2/D \qquad (8\text{–}32)$$

(Note that this formula is suggested by the dimensions of D.) If $x = 1\text{m}$, then $t = 4 \times 10^4$ sec. The fact that the gas requires more than 10 hr to diffuse 1m shows that diffusion is a slow process. In normal circumstances mixing is accomplished much more quickly in fluids by convection or stirring. Slow as it is, diffusion in gases proceeds about a hundred thousand times faster than diffusion in liquids, where the atoms are very close together. Diffusion in solids is even slower than in liquids. Nevertheless, diffusion in solids is sometimes very important, since mixing cannot occur by any other process. (See Chapter 15.)

The viscosity, from Eq. 8–30, is

$$\eta \cong \rho D \cong 0.5 \times 10^{-3} \text{ g/cm-sec}$$

The cgs unit of viscosity, g/cm-sec, or equivalently dyne-sec/cm^2 (cf. Eq. 8–25), is called a *poise*, after Poiseuille, who investigated viscous flow (1843). The viscosity of gases is usually expressed in *micropoise* $= 10^{-6}$ poise; the result of our estimate, 500 micropoise, is a fairly large value, as gases go. To have some feeling for its magnitude, it may be compared with a typical liquid viscosity. The viscosity of *liquids* is expressed in *centipoise* (cp) $= 10^{-2}$ poise. The viscosity of water at 20°C happens to be 1.00 cp, a fact which makes it very easy to remember this value. Thus a typical gas is perhaps a hundred times less viscous than a typical liquid. (Of course, some liquids composed of complex molecules, like tar or molasses, may be very much more viscous.) For this reason, an air film is a far better lubricant than an oil film, and an "air bearing" has very small friction.

Some experimental viscosity data for argon and some other gases are illustrated in Fig. 8–9, on a log–log plot. According to Eqs. 8–27 and 8–16, viscosity, like thermal conductivity, should be approximately proportional to $T^{1/2}$. The curves in Fig. 8–9 *are* approximately straight lines with slope one-half, but there are deviations which are not insignificant. The higher slope is partially explained if the molecules are not hard spheres (Section 8–3).

The thermal conductivity, from Eq. 8–31, is

$$\kappa \cong c\eta \cong 1.5 \times 10^3 \text{ erg/cm-sec-deg}$$
$$= 4 \times 10^{-5} \text{ cal/cm-sec-deg}$$

The thermal conductivity of a gas is comparatively small. A typical *liquid* has a value about ten times larger; water has the relatively high value 1.4×10^{-3} cal/cm-sec-deg. Typical *solids* which are compact (i.e., non-porous) also have higher thermal conductivities than gases, say ten to a hundred times greater. Solids which are *metals* have very much higher values yet: copper and silver, of all materials at room temperature, have the highest thermal conductivity value, which happens to be 1.0 cal/cm-sec-deg. The extraordinarily large values in metals depend on the motion of *electrons* in the metals, and this effect will not be discussed until Part IV. Gases, in spite of their small thermal conductivity, do not make good practical thermal insulators unless convection is prevented. Otherwise, convection carries heat through a fluid much faster than conduction.

Let us summarize the results of this chapter. From the properties of the molecules, the values of the transport coefficients can be calculated using Eqs. 8–29 to 8–31. Then the flow of heat, momentum, or molecules can be calculated from the corresponding gradient of temperature, flow velocity, or concentration, by means of Eqs. 8–14, 8–25, or 8–28, respectively. The latter calculation involves a mathematical problem which is undoubtedly familiar to you for simple planar or cylindrical geometry, but which can become quite challenging for more complicated geometries. We must forego a discussion of it, however, because in the present context our true interest lies in the inverse procedure: from the measured values of the coefficients (inferred from the actual observations by a mathematical analysis of the experimental geometry), we have deduced some of the properties of the microscopic particles which make up the gas.

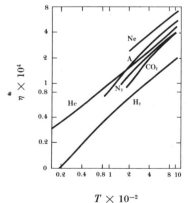

$$T \times 10^{-2}$$

Fig. 8–9. Viscosity of some actual gases.

PROBLEMS

8-1.   For helium gas, the experimental thermal conductivity measured at standard conditions is 3.4×10^{-4} cal/cm-sec-deg. Compute the diameter of an He atom. The value for argon is 3.9×10^{-5} cal/cm-sec-deg. Why is the value for argon an order of magnitude smaller than the value for helium?

8-2.   Calculate the mean free path and the mean time between collisions for He gas at standard conditions, using the diameter of Prob. 8-1.

8-3.   Assume that the thermal conductivity of a gas κ is proportional to a product of powers of the following quantities: mean free path L, mean speed $\bar{v}$, heat capacity *per unit volume* C. Use a dimensional analysis to find how κ depends on them.

8-4.   The thermocouple gauge is one type of pressure measuring device used in vacuum work. It consists of an electrically heated wire at the center of a tube which contains the gas whose pressure is to be measured. A thermocouple is attached to the hot wire, and it measures the wire's temperature, which depends on the thermal conductivity of the surrounding gas. Make an estimate of the pressure range in which the gauge would work, if the dimension of the tube is about 1 cm. Assume the diameter of an air molecule (mainly N_2) is effectively 4.2 Å.

8-5.   Ammonia gas NH_3 is rather far from an ideal gas at standard conditions. Look up the thermal conductivity, density, etc., and calculate the mean free path and effective diameter at standard conditions. You will probably not be able to find a value tabulated for the specific heat measured at constant volume c_V, since it is easier experimentally to measure the specific heat at constant pressure c_P. For all gases, however, the relation

$$c_P - c_V = R$$

holds fairly closely. (Also, you might compare the tabulated density with that expected if NH_3 were ideal.)

8-6.   Some measured thermal conductivities κ (from W. G. Kannuluik and E. H. Carman, Proc. Phys. Soc. (London) **65B**, 701 (1952)) are

T (°K)	90.2	194.7	273.2	373.2	491.2	579.1
He	1655	2706	3406	4165	4947	5504
Ne	489	876	1110	1357	1595	1789
A	141	293	394	506	614	685
Kr		152	208	272	340	388
Xe		91	123	168	208	237

The units of κ are 10^{-7} cal/cm-sec-deg. For each gas, plot κ versus T on log–log graph paper. From the slopes, calculate the exponent m in the empirical law

$$\kappa = \text{const } T^m$$

Assuming an nth-power-law repulsive potential energy of interaction between the atoms, what is the appropriate exponent n for each gas?

8–7.   Consider an "air track," a perforated surface on which an object (the "rider") floats on an air cushion due to compressed air forced through the perforations. The rider can move along the track with very small friction because of the low viscosity of the air acting as lubricant. (*a*) Supposing that the diameter of an air molecule is 4.2 Å, compute the viscosity of air. (*b*) As the rider moves along the track, the layer of air in contact with the rider may be assumed to move at the speed of the rider, u, while the layer of air in contact with the track is at rest. Compute the frictional drag force, if the contact area is A and the thickness of the air film is Δx. (*c*) Write the equation of motion for the rider. Solve it for the position of the rider as a function of time. How far will the rider travel before coming to rest if its mass is 200 g, its initial speed is 1 m/sec, A = 50 cm², and Δx = 0.25 mm?

8–8.   Viscosity, like thermal conductivity, becomes pressure dependent when the mean free path L becomes comparable with the size of the container H. Since you know that the viscosity η depends in this case on ρ, $\bar{v}$, L, H, and pressure P, try to find the dependence by the method of dimensional analysis. (It is frustrating that the method will not give the desired answer in this case, but nevertheless it is instructive to see that it can fail and why.)

8–9.   Look up experimental values of viscosity η, specific heat c_V, and thermal conductivity κ in the *Handbook of Chemistry and Physics*. (The specific heat at constant volume c_V can be computed from c_P as in Prob. 8–5.) Tabulate the ratio $\kappa/c\eta$ for as many gases as possible.

8–10.   Calculate the diffusion coefficient for H_2O molecules through air, assuming the effective diameter of the water molecule is 3.4 Å. ("Effective" diameter means that the formula for self-diffusion coefficient may be used.)

8–11.   Calculate the rate of evaporation of a beaker of water, at room temperature, using the diffusion coefficient of Prob. 8–10. (Prob. Fig. 8–11.) Assume that the partial pressure of water vapor at the liquid surface is the equilibrium vapor pressure, 20 mm Hg, and that at the top of the beaker it is zero. Treat the water vapor as an ideal gas (not true, but close enough).

REFERENCES

F. W. Sears, *Thermodynamics* (Addison-Wesley, 1953, 2nd ed.), Ch. 13.

J. Jeans, *An Introduction to the Kinetic Theory of Gases* (Cambridge, 1940), Ch. VI–VIII.

E. H. Kennard, *Kinetic Theory of Gases* (McGraw-Hill, 1938), Ch. IV.

P. W. Bridgman, *Dimensional Analysis* (Yale University Press, 1931).

9/the maxwell-boltzmann distribution

In calculating the properties of gases which depend on the speed of the molecules and on collisions between them, we have so far assumed that every molecule had the same speed v. *It may be suspected that this assumption is inaccurate, and indeed we have already anticipated its revision by replacing* v *with an average speed* v̄ *in our formulas. In fact, on reflection, it is obvious that the molecules* cannot *all have the same speed: even if originally all the speeds were the same, as a result of collisions between molecules some would acquire greater and some smaller speeds, according to the momentum conservation law applied to (non-collinear) elastic collisions. The molecules will eventually attain a certain* distribution *of velocities. It is our present purpose to investigate this distribution and to learn how to calculate from it the various averages of speed and velocity which are required in the kinetic theory of gases.*

Our procedure will be simply to guess what the distribution ought plausibly to be and then to generalize this into the fundamental law of statistical physics. It is actually possible to derive the distribution, in the sense of showing that it is the most probable *or the* equilibrium *distribution; but even these derivations rest on some very subtle fundamental questions which are unsettled and which are the subject of current theoretical research interest in physics. The point of view adopted here will be that the distribution law is one of the basic laws of physics, whose validity, like that of Newton's law of gravitation for example, rests on its ability to predict results which correctly agree with experiment.*

9–1 DISTRIBUTION FUNCTION

In order to describe the distribution of velocities, it would be hopeless to try to specify the velocity of each molecule—there are too many molecules, and besides the velocity of any given molecule is changed every time it

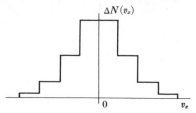

Fig. 9–1. Histogram of molecular velocities.

collides with another one. We therefore content ourselves with considering a number of velocity intervals and specifying the *number* of molecules with velocity in each interval. The assumption that the gas is in equilibrium means that these numbers do not change with time: although the velocity of any given molecule may change, on the average the number of molecules whose velocities lie within a certain range is constant. To be specific, let us consider the x-component of velocity (having chosen a Cartesian coordinate system), and the velocity intervals.

$$0 - 1, 1 - 2, 2 - 3, \ldots \text{ km/sec}$$

as well as the negative intervals corresponding to velocities in the opposite direction. The *distribution function* could now be given by tabulating the numbers of molecules whose x-component of velocity lay in each of these intervals. Alternatively, we could plot a special type of bar graph, called a *histogram*, showing the same information (Fig. 9–1). Incidentally, we already know that the distribution function must be centered at $v_x = 0$, since otherwise the average velocity would be non-zero and the gas would be flowing. Furthermore, the function must be an even function (symmetric about $v_x = 0$), since it is intuitively obvious that equally many molecules have v_x and $- v_x$ (the positive coordinate axis direction being arbitrary). In order for the total kinetic energy of the gas to be finite, the function must approach 0 as v_x goes to ∞.

Since there are ordinarily altogether of the order of 10^{23} molecules in the gas, the number of molecules in each velocity interval will be very large. It would still be very large if we chose intervals of 0.1 km/sec, or even of 0.01 km/sec, etc. (Fig. 9–2). As we decrease the size of the interval, the histogram will approach a *continuous* curve (Fig. 9–3), provided the interval is always large enough to contain very many molecules (and thus not truly

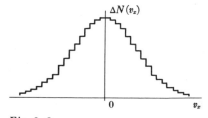

Fig. 9–2

"infinitesimal"). The distribution can therefore be approximated by this limiting continuous curve, with considerable advantage for mathematical calculations.

If the velocity interval dv_x is chosen sufficiently small, the number of molecules $dN(v_x)$ in the interval is proportional to dv_x. It is convenient to define a function $f(v_x)$ by

$$dN(v_x) \equiv Nf(v_x)\,dv_x \qquad (9\text{--}1)$$

where N is the total number of molecules. The quantity $f\,dv_x$ equals the *fraction* of the molecules whose x-component of velocity lies in the interval between v_x and $v_x + dv_x$. Therefore, the *"distribution function"* f itself represents the fraction of molecules with x-velocity between v_x and $v_x + dv_x$, per unit velocity interval. We can also interpret $f\,dv_x$ as the *probability* that a given molecule will have its x-velocity in the interval between v_x and $v_x + dv_x$. Note that

$$\int dN(v_x) = \int_{-\infty}^{+\infty} N\,f(v_x)\,dv_x = N$$

since the integrated number of molecules in all velocity intervals is just the total number of molecules N. Therefore,

$$\int_{-\infty}^{+\infty} f(v_x)dv_x = 1 \qquad (9\text{--}2)$$

The function f is said to be *normalized* to unity.

This property of being normalized to unity is one which a genuine probability ought to have, since the integral represents the probability that the molecule will have any value whatever for its x-velocity. To see this, let us recall that the integral of Eq. 9–2 is the limit of a sum

$$\sum_{i=-\infty}^{+\infty} f(v_{x_i})\Delta v_{x_i}$$

as the size of the intervals Δv_{x_i} is allowed to approach zero. Each term of the sum represents the probability that the molecule's x-velocity lies within that particular interval. A sum of such terms represents the probability that the velocity lies in the first interval, *or* in the second interval, *or* in the third interval, etc., because the probability of having any one of a number of

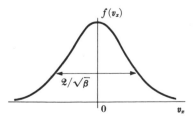

Fig. 9–3. *Distribution function for molecular velocities. The constant β is defined in Sec. 9–4.*

outcomes of an event is the sum of their individual probabilities. The sum over all possible velocity intervals (outcomes) is the probability of lying in any interval whatever. This probability is of course 1: the molecule must have *some* velocity (including 0).

The integral of f over a *finite* interval likewise gives the total probability that the x-velocity will lie within that interval. For example, the probability of having $v_x \geq 0$ is

$$\int_0^\infty f(v_x)dv_x$$

(We have already noted that the value of this integral would be $\frac{1}{2}$, since f is an even function.)

9–2   MAXWELL VELOCITY DISTRIBUTION

Now, having specified the precise meaning of the distribution of velocities, we are ready to guess the mathematical form of the distribution function $f(v_x)$. If the exchanges of velocities among the molecules are random, we may expect the *normal distribution*, more often called the Gaussian distribution in physics:

$$f(v_x) = A_x e^{-\beta v_x^2} \tag{9–3}$$

This function meets the requirements which were noted above: it is an even function of v_x (centered about $v_x = 0$), and it vanishes as v_x goes to ∞. The constant A_x is merely a "normalization constant," whose value must be chosen so that f is normalized to 1, according to Eq. 9–2:

$$\int_{-\infty}^{+\infty} f(v_x)dv_x = 1 = \int_{-\infty}^{+\infty} A_x e^{-\beta v_x^2}dv_x$$

$$= A_x \frac{1}{\sqrt{\beta}} \int_{-\infty}^\infty e^{-\xi^2}d\xi = A_x \frac{1}{\sqrt{\beta}} \sqrt{\pi}$$

(The indefinite integral $\int e^{-\xi^2}d\xi$ cannot be expressed in closed form, but the definite integral $\int_{-\infty}^\infty e^{-\xi^2}d\xi$ can be found in tables.)

Thus

$$A_x = \frac{1}{\int e^{-\beta v_x^2}dv_x} = \sqrt{\beta/\pi} \tag{9–4}$$

The constant β is more interesting because its value determines the *width* of the distribution. For example, the velocity at which f has fallen to $e^{-1} = 1/e = 1/2.718 \ldots$ times its value at $v_x = 0$ is $v_x = 1/\sqrt{\beta}$. The larger β, the narrower the distribution function. We shall see below that β is related to the *temperature* of the gas.

Before considering the physical meaning of β, however, let us generalize the distribution function to three dimensions. It is easy to make this generalization, because the distribution in v_y and v_z must be just the same as the distribution in v_x (the coordinate axis directions being completely arbitrary). In other words, the gas is *isotropic*. Since the probability of having simultaneously a given outcome for a number of independent events is the product of their individual probabilities, we can write, from Eqs. 9–3 and 9–4,

$$f(v_x,v_y,v_z) = f(v_x)f(v_y)f(v_z) = A_x A_y A_z e^{-\beta v_x{}^2} e^{-\beta v_y{}^2} e^{-\beta v_z{}^2}$$
$$= A e^{-\beta(v_x{}^2 + v_y{}^2 + v_z{}^2)} \tag{9–5}$$

with

$$A = \frac{1}{\int\int\int e^{-\beta(v_x{}^2 + v_y{}^2 + v_z{}^2)} dv_x dv_y dv_z} = (\beta/\pi)^{3/2} \tag{9–6}$$

The meaning of $f(v_x,v_y,v_z)$ is that $f(v_x,v_y,v_z)dv_x dv_y dv_z$ is the probability that a molecule will have x-component of velocity in the interval between v_x and $v_x + dv_x$, and at the same time will have y-velocity between v_y and $v_y + dv_y$, and at the same time will have z-velocity between v_z and $v_z + dv_z$.

9–3 CALCULATION OF AVERAGES AND CONCEPT OF TEMPERATURE

The distribution function tells how many molecules have various velocities, but a more useful application of it is in the calculation of the *average* value of some quantity which depends on the velocity. If $g(\mathbf{v}) = g(v_x,v_y,v_z)$ is a function of velocity $\mathbf{v}$, then the average value of g is

$$\bar{g} \equiv \int_{-\infty}^{\infty} \int_{-\infty}^{\infty} \int_{-\infty}^{\infty} g(v_x,v_y,v_z)\, f(v_x,v_y,v_z) dv_x dv_y dv_z \tag{9–7}$$

That is, for each velocity $\mathbf{v} = (v_x,v_y,v_z)$ we multiply the appropriate value of g by the probability that this value of $\mathbf{v}$ will occur, and sum (integrate) over all values of $\mathbf{v}$. For example, the kinetic energy is a quantity which depends on $\mathbf{v}$, and indeed so is the total energy, which is equal to the kinetic energy when no forces act on the molecules (in the ideal gas):

$$E = \tfrac{1}{2}mv^2 = \tfrac{1}{2}m(v_x{}^2 + v_y{}^2 + v_z{}^2) \tag{9–8}$$

Let us calculate $\bar{E}$:

$$\bar{E} = \frac{\int\int\int E e^{-\beta(v_x{}^2 + v_y{}^2 + v_z{}^2)} dv_x dv_y dv_z}{\int\int\int e^{-\beta(v_x{}^2 + v_y{}^2 + v_z{}^2)} dv_x dv_y dv_z} \tag{9–9}$$

The denominator is merely the normalization constant, Eq. 9–6. Substituting E from Eq. 9–8, we get the sum of three integrals of the form

$$\frac{\displaystyle\int_{-\infty}^{\infty} \tfrac{1}{2}mv_x{}^2 e^{-\beta v_x{}^2} dv_x \int_{-\infty}^{\infty}\int_{-\infty}^{\infty} e^{-\beta(v_y{}^2 + v_z{}^2)} dv_y dv_z}{\displaystyle\int_{-\infty}^{\infty} e^{-\beta v_x{}^2} dv_x \int_{-\infty}^{\infty}\int_{-\infty}^{\infty} e^{-\beta(v_y{}^2 + v_z{}^2)} dv_y dv_z}$$

Splitting up the first of the three integrals in this way, we see that the integrals over v_y and v_z cancel in the numerator and denominator, since they are identical. The remaining integral over v_x becomes

$$\frac{\frac{1}{2}m \int_{-\infty}^{\infty} v_x^2 e^{-\beta v_x^2} dv_x}{\int_{-\infty}^{\infty} e^{-\beta v_x^2} dv_x} = \frac{\frac{m}{2\beta} \int_{-\infty}^{\infty} \xi^2 e^{-\xi^2} d\xi}{\int_{-\infty}^{\infty} e^{-\xi^2} d\xi}$$

after introducing the dimensionless variable of integration $\xi^2 \equiv \beta v_x^2$.

We have already noted in Eq. 9–4 that the definite integral in the denominator has the value

$$\int_{-\infty}^{\infty} e^{-\xi^2} d\xi = \sqrt{\pi}$$

The definite integral in the numerator can also be evaluated. Actually, it is easy to obtain it from the other one, using a slightly sneaky mathematical trick: consider the integral

$$\int_{-\infty}^{\infty} e^{-\lambda \xi^2} d\xi = \sqrt{\frac{\pi}{\lambda}}$$

where λ is simply a parameter. Now differentiate both sides of this equation with respect to λ, differentiating the left-hand side under the integral sign. The result is

$$- \int_{-\infty}^{\infty} \xi^2 e^{-\lambda \xi^2} d\xi = - \frac{\sqrt{\pi}}{2\lambda^{3/2}}$$

If we now set $\lambda = 1$, we have the desired result:

$$\int_{-\infty}^{\infty} \xi^2 e^{-\xi^2} d\xi = \frac{1}{2}\sqrt{\pi}$$

Using the values for the definite integrals in numerator and denominator, we find that

$$\frac{\frac{m}{2\beta} \int_{-\infty}^{\infty} \xi^2 e^{-\xi^2} d\xi}{\int_{-\infty}^{\infty} e^{-\xi^2} d\xi} = \frac{1}{2} \frac{m}{2\beta} \tag{9–10}$$

Now in $\bar{E}$ there are three terms all of this same form: one from $\frac{1}{2}mv_x^2$ which we have just evaluated, and two more from $\frac{1}{2}mv_y^2$ and $\frac{1}{2}mv_z^2$ which have identical values. Therefore $\bar{E}$ is just three times Eq. 9–10, or

$$\bar{E} = \frac{3}{2} \frac{m}{2\beta} \tag{9–11}$$

This relation between the average energy of the molecules and the constant β allows us to read some physical significance into β. The larger β, the smaller the average energy $\bar{E}$ of a molecule.

The calculation of the average energy of a molecule in terms of β can be turned around and used to interpret β physically, since we have already seen in Eq. 7–5 that, when the potential energy is zero,

$$\bar{E} = \tfrac{3}{2}kT \tag{9–12}$$

In order for Eq. 9–11 to agree with this elementary formula, we must conclude that

$$\beta = m/2kT \tag{9–13}$$

This relation introduces the concept of *temperature* into the statistical theory. With the substitution of Eq. 9–13, the complete velocity distribution function given by Eqs. 9–5 and 9–6 becomes

$$f(\mathbf{v}) = (m/2\pi \, kT)^{3/2} \, e^{-m(v_x{}^2+v_y{}^2+v_z{}^2)/2kT} \tag{9–14}$$

This function is called the *Maxwell distribution of velocities*. The higher the temperature, the wider the distribution, and the more molecules with high velocities.

9–4 MAXWELL SPEED DISTRIBUTION

The distribution function can also be expressed in another form which is often convenient. We may consider the vector $\mathbf{v}$ to represent a *point*—not a point in ordinary space, but a point in *"velocity space."* So far, in considering the components v_x, v_y, v_z, we have been using a Cartesian coordinate system in velocity space. It is not necessary to use this particular coordinate system, however, and in fact it is interesting to use spherical coordinates instead, in which we specify the vector $\mathbf{v}$ by its length v and direction angles θ and ϕ. (See Fig. 9–4(a).)

Now instead of

$$f(v_x,v_y,v_z)dv_xdv_ydv_z$$

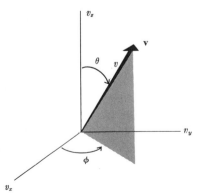

Fig. 9–4(a). *Velocity vector* $\mathbf{v}$.

which represents the fraction of molecules in the volume element $dv_x dv_y dv_z$ of velocity space (i.e., whose velocity components are between v_x and $v_x + dv_x$, v_y and $v_y + dv_y$, v_z and $v_z + dv_z$), we may consider

$$f_1(v, \theta, \phi)v^2 dv \sin\theta \, d\theta \, d\phi$$

which represents the fraction in the volume element $v^2 dv \sin\theta \, d\theta \, d\phi$ of spherical coordinates. (See Fig. 9–4(b).) The new function $f_1(v, \theta, \phi)$ is obtained from $f(v_x, v_y, v_z)$ merely by substituting the coordinate transformation

$$v^2 = v_x{}^2 + v_y{}^2 + v_z{}^2$$

into Eq. 9–14:

$$f_1(v, \theta, \phi) = (m/2\pi \, kT)^{3/2} \, e^{-mv^2/2kT} \qquad (9\text{–}15)$$

In these coordinates, the distribution function depends on only one of the coordinates v, and is independent of the other two θ, ϕ. That is, the distribution is *isotropic*—the probability of moving in any direction in space is the same—as it must be from symmetry, because there is nothing to single out any particular direction physically.

Since the distribution is isotropic, there is little reason for interest in the angles θ and ϕ. Let us define a new function $f_1(v)$ by

$$f_1(v) \, dv \equiv \int_0^\pi \sin\theta \, d\theta \int_0^{2\pi} d\phi f_1(v, \theta, \phi)v^2 dv$$

Then $f_1(v) \, dv$ is the fraction of molecules whose speed v lies in the interval between v and $v + dv$, *regardless* of the direction of motion, since the probability has been summed over all angles by the integration over θ and ϕ. The integration of the element of solid angle $\sin\theta \, d\theta \, d\phi$ is easily carried out to give the total solid angle 4π, because $f_1(v, \theta, \phi)$ can be taken outside the integral. Therefore

$$f_1(v) = 4\pi(m/2\pi \, kT)^{3/2} \, v^2 e^{-mv^2/2kT} \qquad (9\text{–}16)$$

This function is the *Maxwell distribution of speeds*, shown in Fig. 9–5.

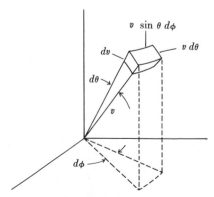

Fig. 9–4(b). *Volume element using spherical coordinates in velocity space.*

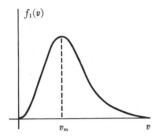

Fig. 9–5. *Maxwell distribution of molecular speeds.*

Although the most probable velocity is 0, the *most probable speed* v_m (Fig. 9–5) is not 0, but is (Prob. 9–4)

$$v_m = \sqrt{2kT/m} \qquad (9\text{–}17)$$

This seemingly paradoxical result really just depends on the different choices of volume element in the two cases—the little cube $dv_x dv_y dv_z$—or the spherical shell $4\pi v^2 dv$. In Fig. 9–6(a) is shown the volume element $dv_x dv_y dv_z$ which goes with the velocity distribution function Eq. 9–14, and in Fig. 9–6(b) is shown one octant of the spherical shell volume element which goes with the speed distribution Eq. 9–16. As we see in Fig. 9–3, the most probable values of the velocity components are zero, so that the "density" of molecules in velocity space is greatest at the origin and tails off as the distance v from the origin increases. On the other hand, the volume of the spherical shell in Fig. 9–6(b) increases as the surface area v^2, and the number of molecules in the volume element, which is equal to the density times the volume, has a maximum value at $v = v_m$.

The reason for introducing a new form of the Maxwell distribution is that it is more convenient for calculating averages of quantities which are func-

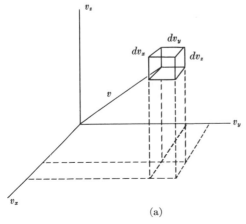

(a)

Fig. 9–6(a)

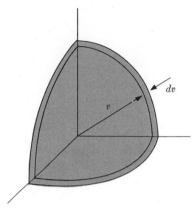

Fig. 9–6(b)

tions of the molecular speed. For example, we could calculate the average value of the speed itself (Prob. 9–2):

$$\bar{v} = \int_0^\infty v f_1(v) \, dv = \sqrt{8kT/\pi m} \qquad (9\text{--}18)$$

This result may be compared with the rms speed,

$$(\overline{v^2})^{1/2} = \sqrt{3kT/m} \qquad (9\text{--}19)$$

Although the latter quantity is only 7% more than $\bar{v}$, the difference points up the fact that the operation of averaging does not generally commute with other operations, such as squaring. (See also Prob. 9–3.)

9–5   EFFUSION

As an example of the use of the velocity distribution function, let us calculate the rate at which molecules would emerge into a vacuum from a small hole in a container of gas. This effect is called effusion and is distinct from the ordinary flow of a gas out of a large hole. By a "small" hole, we mean one which is small enough that the few molecules which leave through it have an imperceptible effect on the velocity distribution in the main body of the gas. Thus the rate at which molecules are removed from the gas by escaping through the hole must be small compared to the rate at which the remaining molecules can regain their equilibrium velocity distribution. (Note that the escaping molecules tend to subtract from the fraction of molecules whose velocity vector points in the general direction of the hole, and so they would modify the Maxwellian distribution.) If, on the other hand, the hole is large the Maxwellian distribution is severely modified: instead of a distribution in which the average velocity is zero, there will be a net flow velocity toward the hole. This problem can be handled using the concept of viscosity discussed in Chapter 8.

In order to calculate the effusion, let us go back to Eq. 7–3 and take the average on both sides of the equation. On the right-hand side, we actually mean the average of the absolute value of v_x: half the molecules are traveling away from the hole with negative values of v_x, and this fact was already taken into account explicitly by the factor $\frac{1}{2}$ introduced into Eq. 7–3. Thus

$$\bar{F} = \tfrac{1}{2}n \, \overline{|v_x|}$$

gives the average number of molecules which cross unit area of the hole in one second.

The calculation of $\overline{|v_x|}$, using Eqs. 9–7 and 9–3, proceeds as follows.

$$\overline{|v_x|} = \int_{-\infty}^{+\infty} |v_x| f(v_x) dv_x = 2A_x \int_0^\infty v_x e^{-\beta v_x^2} dv_x = \frac{2A_x}{2\beta} \int_0^\infty e^{-\xi^2} d(\xi^2)$$

where $\xi^2 \equiv \beta v_x^2$. Thus, using Eqs. 9–4 and 9–13,

$$\overline{|v_x|} = \frac{A_x}{\beta} = \sqrt{\frac{2kT}{\pi m}}$$

Comparison with Eq. 9–18 shows that

$$\overline{|v_x|} = \tfrac{1}{2}\bar{v}$$

so that we have finally

$$F = \tfrac{1}{4}n\bar{v} \tag{9 20}$$

This important equation gives the flux from the hole per unit area, or indeed the flux of molecules per unit area in one direction across any plane in a Maxwellian gas.

9–6 THE BOLTZMANN DISTRIBUTION

Having seen some of the usefulness of the distribution function, we may now guess how to generalize it. We have posited that when no forces were acting on the molecules, i.e., when

$$E = \tfrac{1}{2}m(v_x^2 + v_y^2 + v_z^2)$$

then according to Eq. 9–14

$$f(v_x, v_y, v_z) = Ae^{-E/kT}$$

Thus the higher the energy the smaller the probability that a molecule will occupy that state. The required generalization is just that this statement is universally true. Suppose for example that there is an external (conservative) force acting on the molecules. In this case the total energy of a molecule becomes

$$E = \tfrac{1}{2}m(v_x^2 + v_y^2 + v_z^2) + V(x,y,z)$$

Then the probability of finding a molecule depends on *position* as well as velocity:

$$f(v_x,v_y,v_z,x,y,z)dv_xdv_ydv_zdxdydz$$
$$= A'e^{-E/kT}dv_xdv_ydv_zdxdydz \qquad (9\text{-}21)$$

is the probability that a molecule will have velocity in the volume element of velocity space $dv_xdv_ydv_z$ (at the point (v_x,v_y,v_z)), and at the same time will have its position in the volume element $dxdydz$ (at the point (x,y,z)) of ordinary "*configuration space.*" (The six-dimensional space which is the product of velocity space and configuration space is called "phase space.") This generalized distribution function is called the *Boltzmann distribution*.

Let us first consider the Boltzmann distribution for the case we have already analyzed, in order to see how we go back to the previous result. If no force acts on the molecules, $V = 0$, and

$$f(v_x,v_y,v_z,x,y,z) = A'e^{-m(v_x{}^2+v_y{}^2+v_z{}^2)/2kT}$$

In this case the distribution is *uniform* (in configuration space) because f is actually independent of x, y, z. That is, the probability of being at any point in the volume Ω of the container is the same. Since x, y, z do not appear in f, we might introduce another function by integrating over the entire volume of the container.

$$f(v_x,v_y,v_z,) \equiv \int\int\int dxdydz\, f(v_x,v_y,v_z,x,y,z)$$
$$= A'\Omega\, e^{-m(v_x{}^2+v_y{}^2+v_z{}^2)/2kT}$$

This function is the same as the Maxwell distribution Eq. 9-14 (if the new normalization constant A' contains the factor $1/\Omega$). It is sufficient to work with this distribution function if we tacitly recall that the spatial distribution is uniform, even though that fact is not expressed explicitly. (An analogous procedure was used in the Maxwell speed distribution, which does not explicitly state that the distribution is isotropic.)

9-7   LAW OF ATMOSPHERES

A non-trivial application of the Boltzmann distribution is to a gas which is in a *uniform gravitational field*, so that

$$V(x,y,z) = mgz$$

The complete distribution function is then, from Eq. 9-21,

$$f(v_x,v_y,v_z,x,y,z) = A'\, e^{-m(v_x{}^2+v_y{}^2+v_z{}^2)/2kT}\, e^{-mgz/kT}$$

First note that the distribution function is independent of x and y so that the distribution is uniform in each horizontal plane; it is not surprising that a vertical force does not redistribute the molecules horizontally. We might therefore just bear this fact in mind but integrate over x and y in order to eliminate them from explicit consideration. More importantly, notice that the distribution function is the product of a function only of position and a function only of velocity. The latter function of velocity is just the Maxwellian distribution. This means that for any given value of z, the velocity distribution at that point is exactly Maxwellian, just as if no force were acting at all. Therefore we might also integrate over the velocity components and just keep in mind that at every point there is a Maxwellian distribution of velocity. The result,

$$f_2(z) = \int \int \int \int \int dv_x dv_y dv_z dx dy \, f(v_x, v_y, v_z, x, y, z)$$
$$= A'' \, e^{-mgz/kT} \qquad (9\text{-}22)$$

is called the *law of atmospheres*. It states that the probability of finding a molecule (which is proportional to the density, or the pressure, of the gas) decreases exponentially with altitude. If the earth's atmosphere had a uniform temperature (a rather poor approximation to the fact), the law would be closely obeyed, since the "thickness" of the atmosphere is only a few hundred miles, in which distance the gravitational force is roughly constant.

9-8 HEAT CAPACITY OF POLYATOMIC GASES

As a second example of the Boltzmann distribution, let us return to the ideal gas with no forces acting, but let us suppose that the molecules are not monatomic. In this case of an extended molecule, a rotational term must be added to the kinetic energy:

$$E = \tfrac{1}{2}mv^2 + \tfrac{1}{2}I\omega^2$$

Here I is the moment of inertia and ω the angular velocity. In fact, since the molecules can rotate freely in space, they could rotate about any of three coordinate axes, and in general the moment of inertia I will be different about each axis. Then

$$E = \tfrac{1}{2}m(v_x^2 + v_y^2 + v_z^2) + \tfrac{1}{2}I_x\omega_x^2 + \tfrac{1}{2}I_y\omega_y^2 + \tfrac{1}{2}I_z\omega_z^2$$

The distribution function is

$$f_3(v_x, v_y, v_z, \omega_x, \omega_y, \omega_z)$$
$$= A''' \, e^{-m(v_x^2 + v_y^2 + v_z^2)/2kT} \, e^{-(I_x\omega_x^2 + I_y\omega_y^2 + I_z\omega_z^2)/2kT} \qquad (9\text{-}23)$$

The average energy of a molecule can again be calculated from

$$\bar{E} = \int E \, f_3 \, dv_x dv_y dv_z d\omega_x d\omega_y d\omega_z$$

As before in Eq. 9–9, we obtain three terms of the form of Eq. 9–10,

$$\frac{kT \displaystyle\int_{-\infty}^{\infty} \xi^2 e^{-\xi^2} d\xi}{\displaystyle\int_{-\infty}^{\infty} e^{-\xi^2} d\xi} = \tfrac{1}{2}kT \qquad (9\text{-}24)$$

for the 3 velocity components; but now there are three more identical terms for the components of angular velocity. The average energy per molecule for an extended (polyatomic) molecule is therefore

$$\bar{E} = 3kT$$

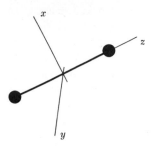

Fig. 9–7. Diatomic molecule.

If the molecule is diatomic (Fig. 9–7), the moment of inertia is 0 about one axis (through the two nuclei), so there are only 5 terms, and

$$\bar{E} = \tfrac{5}{2}kT$$

(If the molecule is monatomic, the moment of inertia is 0 about all three axes, so $\bar{E} = \tfrac{3}{2}kT$.) These cases illustrate the *law of equipartition of energy*: every *degree of freedom* contributes $\tfrac{1}{2}kT$ to the average energy. (In this sense a degree of freedom means any variable which appears quadratically in the energy function.)

The equipartition law makes contact with experiment through the *heat capacity*. We have just shown that the average energy of a single molecule is

$$\bar{E} = (n/2)kT \tag{9-25}$$

where n is the number of degrees of freedom. Since in one mole there are N_0 molecules, the thermal energy contained in a mole is

$$U_T = N_0\bar{E} = (n/2)RT \tag{9-26}$$

The heat capacity per mole of the gas is the rate of change of this internal energy with temperature (assuming that the volume of the gas remains constant):

$$C_V \equiv dU_T/dT = (n/2)R \tag{9-27}$$

The molar heat capacities for *all ideal gases* should be as given in Table 9–1.

These values agree quite well with experiment for many gases, at least near room temperature. At much lower and at much higher temperatures deviations occur, always in the direction of an increase of heat capacity with

Table 9–1

gas	n	C_V
monatomic	3	$(3/2)R$
diatomic	5	$(5/2)R$
polyatomic	6	$3R$

an increase of temperature. The reason for these deviations will be examined in greater detail in Chapters 14 and 18. Suffice it to say here that they are our first evidence of a quantum mechanical effect, the breakdown of the classical equipartition-of-energy law. At low temperatures the average energy associated with molecular rotation is less than we have calculated, and at high temperatures appreciable energy begins to be associated with the vibration of the molecule, which we have ignored.

It is worth emphasizing that we have returned to the assumption of an ideal gas in discussing the detailed distribution function for the gas. Even though we have been able to consider an external force field acting on all molecules alike, we have not admitted forces *between* molecules (except for instantaneous elastic collisions). The reason does not lie in any limitation of the Boltzmann distribution. The reason is merely that we would encounter an extremely formidable mathematical problem if we included interactions between the molecules. In that case, the (potential) energy of any given molecule would depend not only on the position of that molecule itself but also of every other molecule in the gas. In other words there is a *correlation* between the molecules. Instead of 6 variables, a very large number would enter (the distances from all the other molecules). The distribution function would then no longer be a "single particle distribution function" giving the probability of finding a single molecule at a given point in (the six-dimensional) phase space. Rather it would be a "many-particle distribution function" for all the particles in the system, giving the probability of finding particle 1 at point 1 in phase space and simultaneously particle 2 at point 2, particle 3 at point 3, and so forth. Thus, even though it would be possible to write down the distribution function in an exact way, the mathematical problem of rigorously calculating anything from it is exceedingly difficult. Up to now, attempts to treat non-ideal gases, or especially liquids, in a rigorous way have had only modest success. Nevertheless, the Boltzmann distribution remains in principle as the basic law of physics for large assemblies of particles in equilibrium.

Although the many-particle distribution function of a large number of particles is always of the Boltzmann kind, there exist important single particle equilibrium distributions that are quite different. We will discuss these further after first having studied the laws of quantum mechanics. Suffice it to say here that the Pauli exclusion principle (Chapter 22) and the indistinguishability of particles (Chapter 26) lead to a correlation of the particles, even though there may be no ordinary forces acting between them. Again the many-particle distribution function for the whole system is a Boltzmann distribution. If no ordinary forces are acting, it is possible to deduce a single particle equilibrium distribution function as well. This will, however, not be a distribution of the Maxwell-Boltzmann kind. For a system of particles that obeys the exclusion principle, such as a gas of free electrons, the distribution will be of the so-called Fermi-Dirac kind (Chapter 26). For other quantum mechanical systems, such as a photon gas, not subject to the exclusion principle, yet another single-particle distribution results, called the Bose-Einstein distribution (Chapter 26).

PROBLEMS

9-1.   Calculate $\overline{v^2}$ from the *speed* distribution $f_1(v)$.

9-2.   Calculate $\bar{v}$.

9-3.   Compare $\overline{(1/v)}$ with $1/\bar{v}$.

9-4.   From the Maxwell speed distribution, show that $v_m = \sqrt{2kT/m}$.

9-5.   Calculate the pressure at any height z in the atmosphere, by considering the total weight of gas, per square cm, above the point in question. Assume the ideal gas law. Show that the same result follows from the Boltzmann distribution (law of atmospheres).

9-6.   Find the temperature of the atmosphere (on the average), assuming

$$\rho = 10^{-13} \text{ g/cm}^3 \text{ at a height of 230 km}$$

9-7.   Calculate the specific heat of He and N_2 at 0°C in cal/g-deg, using the classical equipartition law. Compare with tabulated values. What is the number of degrees of freedom for each gas?

9-8.   What is the average kinetic energy of a deuterium atom at 10^7 °K? (This is the magnitude of the temperature which must be attained in a fusion reactor.) Give the result in eV.

9-9.   Certain chemical reactions cannot take place unless the colliding molecules have more than a certain minimum kinetic energy E_0. (a) From the distribution function, obtain an expression for the fraction of molecules whose kinetic energy exceeds E_0. (b) Assuming $E_0 \gg kT$, evaluate the integral of (a) approximately. *Hint:* By integrating by parts, show that

$$\int_{\xi_0}^{\infty} e^{-\xi^2}d\xi \cong e^{-\xi_0^2}/2\xi_0$$

since

$$\int_{\xi_0}^{\infty} \frac{e^{-\xi^2}}{\xi^2} d\xi < \frac{1}{\xi_0^2} \int_{\xi_0}^{\infty} e^{-\xi^2}d\xi$$

(c) If $E_0 = 30$ kcal/mole, what fraction of molecules have greater energy at 300°K? at 500°K? By what factor would the rate of the reaction increase when T increases from 300 to 500°K?

9-10.   The molecules which leave a small hole by effusion have a higher average energy than that of the gas inside the container, $\tfrac{3}{2}kT$. The reason is that, according to Eq. 7-3, molecules with high v_z are more likely to leave. For the molecules which get out, $\tfrac{1}{2}mv_y^2$ and $\tfrac{1}{2}mv_z^2$ are each $\tfrac{1}{2}kT$ as usual, but the average of v_x^2 can be calculated from $v_x^2 F/\bar{F}$. Show that this calculation leads to a total average energy of $2\,kT$. *Hint:* Show first that

$$\int_0^\infty \xi^3 e^{-\xi^2} d\xi = \frac{1}{2}$$

by using the same mathematical trick which was used in Section 9–3, and the value of $\int_0^\infty \xi e^{-\xi^2} d\xi$ which can be obtained by elementary means.

9–11.   Suppose two containers of gas communicate with each other by a small hole, and the two containers are maintained at different temperatures T_1 and T_2. When a steady state exists, there will be no net flow of gas from one container to the other. In the steady state, find (a) the ratio of densities n_1/n_2; (b) the ratio of pressures P_1/P_2; (c) the rate of transport of energy from the container at T_1 to that at T_2, assuming $T_1 > T_2$.

9–12.   For molecules in an isothermal atmosphere, calculate the average potential energy of the molecules. How does it compare with the average kinetic energy?

REFERENCES

F. W. Sears, *Thermodynamics* (Addison-Wesley, 1953, 2nd ed.), Ch. 12.

J. Jeans, *An Introduction to the Kinetic Theory of Gases* (Cambridge, 1940), Ch. IV.

E. H. Kennard, *Kinetic Theory of Gases* (McGraw-Hill, 1938), Ch. II, III.

10/weakly ionized gases

Up to now the discussion has been limited to electrically neutral gases. If some or all of the molecules in the gas are electrically charged, or ionized, *the properties of the gas are in some ways radically different. A neutral gas can be ionized by having a negatively charged* electron *stripped off some of the neutral molecules, leaving these as positively charged* ions. *The ionized gas is therefore usually a mixture of at least three kinds of particles; electrons, singly ionized positive ions, and neutral molecules. Sometimes multiply ionized ions (molecules with more than one electron stripped off) are also present and, if the gas is not monatomic, both atomic and molecular ions may play a role. It is even possible for some neutral molecules to capture electrons to form negatively charged molecular ions. We will ignore these complications, however, since ordinarily the three first-mentioned species are the important ones.*

Let n_+, n_-, *and* n_0 *denote the particle densities of positive ions, electrons, and neutral molecules respectively. Normally* $|n_+ - n_-| \ll n_+$, *or*

$$n_+ \approx n_- \qquad \qquad (10\text{--}1)$$

so that the gas is approximately neutral on a macroscopic scale. If a large excess of one charge existed in one region of the gas with an excess of opposite charge elsewhere, electrostatic fields would necessarily be present to drive the gas towards macroscopic neutrality. Only where the density of charged particles is very low, or in very non-uniform regions at the boundaries of the gas, can the neutrality condition, Eq. 10–1, be violated.

Since the properties of an ionized gas depend critically on the degree of ionization, it is important to examine the factors which determine the ionization ratio, n_+/n_0. *This ratio is known to vary from about* 10^{-10} *in a weak electric discharge to about* 10^{12} *in the solar corona.*

When the electrons are affected more by collisions with neutral molecules than with positive ions, we say the gas is weakly ionized. *On the other hand when electron-ion interactions dominate, the gas is considered to be highly ionized and is called a* plasma *(Chapter 11). The degree of ionization dividing these domains depends on the temperature and to a lesser extent on the density of the gas. For a given degree of ionization, electron-ion collisions are relatively more important at low temperatures than at high temperatures. Typically, however, we can refer to a gas for which the ionization ratio is greater than about 10^{-3} as highly ionized, provided* T *is roughly 10^3–10^4°K. It may seem surprising that when an electron is surrounded by 1000 times as many neutrals as ions, electron-ion collisions can still be more important than electron-neutral collisions. The reason lies in the long range nature of the coulomb interaction, which can lead to an electron's being deviated more by a few distant ions than by numerous neutrals close by. In this chapter we will mainly concern ourselves with weakly ionized gases, $n_+/n_0 < 10^{-3}$, although the next section actually applies for any ionization ratio.*

10-1   IONIZATION OF A GAS IN THERMAL EQUILIBRIUM

One finds experimentally that it takes a certain amount of energy, called the *ionization energy,*

$$E_i = e\Phi_i \tag{10-2}$$

to tear an electron off a neutral atom or molecule. The quantity Φ_i, known as the *ionization potential*, is typically of the order of 10 volts. Thus the hydrogen atom has an ionization potential of 13.6 volts, while cesium has a low value of 3.9 volts and helium a high value of 24.5 volts. The reason for these differences will become clear in Chapters 22 and 23. The ionization voltages are quite modest, but when the ionization energies are compared to the mean kinetic energy, $\frac{3}{2}kT$, of a gas in thermal equilibrium, we see that a mean energy of 1 eV($= 1.60 \times 10^{-12}$ ergs) corresponds to a temperature of 7730°K:

$$T = \frac{1\text{eV}}{3k/2} = \frac{2 \times 1.60 \times 10^{-12}\text{erg}}{3 \times 1.38 \times 10^{-16} \dfrac{\text{erg}}{\text{deg}}} = 7730°\text{K}$$

It is clear that only at extremely high temperatures does the mean kinetic energy, or *thermal energy*, of the gas particles exceed the ionization energy. Nevertheless, even for thermal energies far below the ionization energy, there will be some particles at the high energy end of the Maxwell-Boltzmann distribution that have enough kinetic energy to produce ionization during a collision. This ionization mechanism is referred to as *thermal ionization*. As the temperature is raised there will be more of these high energy particles, so the rate of thermal ionization increases with temperature.

Ions and electrons are formed through ionizing collisions, but can also disappear through the opposite process of *recombination*. As the name suggests, this is a process in which an electron and an ion combine to form a neutral molecule. The equilibrium degree of ionization is that at which the rates of ionization and recombination are equal. Using statistical methods similar to those introduced in Chapter 9, it is possible to arrive at the *equilibrium* ionization ratio, without considering the complicated details of the ionization and recombination processes.

In Chapter 9 we discussed the fact that the probability per unit volume of phase space of finding a system with an energy E is proportional to the Boltzmann factor $e^{-E/kT}$. At the moment we are only interested in the relative densities of particles at a given temperature; we don't care what their speeds are. To compute the probability Π of finding a particle, of any speed, per unit volume, we integrate over velocity space in the same way we did to arrive at the law of atmospheres:

$$\Pi \propto \int_{-\infty}^{\infty} dv_x \int_{-\infty}^{\infty} dv_y \int_{-\infty}^{\infty} dv_z e^{-E/kT} \propto \int_{0}^{\infty} dv \, v^2 e^{-E/kT}$$

In equilibrium the density is proportional to Π:

$$n \propto \int_{0}^{\infty} dv \, v^2 e^{-E/kT}$$

The probability of finding a free electron-ion pair in a unit volume must equal the product of the (independent) probabilities of finding either particle:

$$\Pi_{+-} = \Pi_+ \Pi_- \propto \int_{0}^{\infty} dv_- v_-^2 e^{-m_- v_-^2/2kT} \int_{0}^{\infty} dv_+ v_+^2 e^{-m_+ v_+^2/2kT}$$

$$\propto (kT)^3$$

The probability Π_0 of finding a neutral molecule, i.e., a bound electron-ion pair, of any kinetic energy $\frac{1}{2}m_0 v_0^2$, but the fixed potential energy $V = -E_i$, is proportional to:

$$\Pi_0 \propto \int_{0}^{\infty} dv_0 v_0^2 \, e^{-(m_0 v_0^2/2 - E_i)/kT} \propto (kT)^{3/2} e^{E_i/kT}$$

Since in equilibrium the probabilities are proportional to the densities we have

$$\frac{n_+ n_-}{n_0} \propto \frac{\Pi_{+-}}{\Pi_0} \propto (kT)^{3/2} e^{-E_i/kT}$$

The actual constant of proportionality can only be calculated using quantum mechanics. When it is inserted, we have the so-called *Saha equation*

$$\frac{n_+ n_-}{n_0} = \left(\frac{2\pi m_- kT}{h^2}\right)^{3/2} e^{-E_i/kT} \tag{10-3}$$

where h is called Planck's constant, and we have assumed $m_+ = m_0$. The ionization ratio n_+/n_0 is seen to vary as

$$\frac{n_+}{n_0} \propto \frac{T^{3/2}}{n_-} e^{-E_i/kT}$$

or if $n_+ = n_-$:

$$\frac{n_+}{n_0} \propto \frac{T^{3/4}}{n_0^{1/2}} e^{-E_i/2kT} \tag{10-4}$$

The reason why the degree of ionization goes up with temperature is easy to understand. When T goes up there are more particles with kinetic energy greater than E_i and thus capable of ionizing collisions. Consequently the ionization rate increases rapidly with T. The recombination process on the other hand does not require any energy; on the contrary the ionization energy E_i is released in the process. There is then no reason to expect the recombination rate to rise exponentially with T as does the ionization rate. The net result is a rapid increase in the level of ionization with increasing temperature, as indicated in Eq. 10–4.

The fact that the ionization ratio increases with decreasing gas density n_0 is perhaps less obvious. The reason is that the recombination process involves encounters between more particles than the ionization process. Thus ionization by electron impact is the result of a two-body collision and goes at a rate proportional to $n_- n_0$, the product of electron and neutral molecule densities. The inverse recombination process goes via a three-body collision (Fig. 10–1) in which one ion and two electrons interact simultaneously. (A third particle is in fact necessary to conserve energy and momentum during the recombination, as seen in Prob. 10–1.) The rate is therefore proportional to $n_-^2 n_+$. For a given ionization ratio the rate of ionization is thus proportional to n_0^2, while the rate of recombination is proportional to n_0^3. In other words, as n_0 decreases, the recombination rate goes down more rapidly than the ionization rate, leading to an increased level of ionization. As an example consider hot gaseous nebulae at a temperature of 6000°K and a very low total particle density of about 10^3 particles/cm³. By Saha's equation these gases are essentially completely ionized with an ionization ratio $\frac{n_+}{n_0}$ of the order of 10^7, while the solar surface at the same temperature but at a total particle density of 10^{16} cm⁻³, has an ionization ratio of only 10^{-3}. Let us illustrate the Saha equation for a hydrogen gas. In Fig. 10–2 the curves of n_+/n_0 equal to 1 and equal to 100 are plotted as functions of ion density and temperature, using Eqs. 10–3 and 10–1.

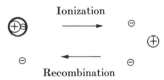

Fig. 10–1. *Ionization involves a two-body collision, recombination a three-body collision.*

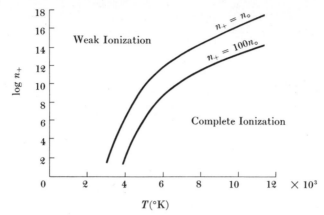

Fig. 10–2. *Hydrogen ion density* vs *temperature for ionization ratios of 1 and 100.*

We have discussed the degree of ionization under the assumption that the gas is in thermal equilibrium. However, it takes very high temperatures and low densities to achieve appreciable ionization. Merely heating a gas in a furnace is usually not sufficient. With a good vacuum ($n_0 \approx 10^{10}$ cm^{-3}) and the hottest furnace ($T \approx 3 \times 10^3$ °K) the ionization ratio is only $\sim 10^{-13}$ for hydrogen (although $\sim$20 for cesium). Since it is difficult to produce a high degree of ionization by simple heating, most ionized gases in the laboratory are produced by passing a current through the gas, as in the case of a fluorescent lamp. Such a gas is not in thermal equilibrium, because there must be a net flow of charged particles in the gas. The equilibrium Maxwell distribution is isotropic in velocity space, and therefore permits no flows. Nevertheless, if the departure from equilibrium is slight, as in the main body of a high pressure arc, the Saha equation may be considered approximately valid.

When the current is imposed by an external electric field (Section 10–3), the ionization mechanism may still be the thermal ionization process described in this section. This will be the case for a weak electric field and/or a short mean free path (high density), in which case the kinetic energy picked up by a charged particle during the "free fall" in the field between collisions is small compared to the ionization energy. The kinetic energy picked up by the charged particles from the field will then be shared with all the particles of the gas through elastic collisions. The net result will be a heating of the gas, called *ohmic heating,* similar to the one you are familiar with in solid conductors. This in turn, as we have already seen, leads to increased thermal ionization.

When the electric potential energy drop over one mean free path is comparable to the ionization energy, a charged particle can gain enough kinetic energy between successive collisions to cause ionization. This so-called *field ionization* plays an important role in low pressure discharges, where the mean free path is long. In some devices thermal ionization may actually dominate in one region and field ionization in another. In regions where field ionization prevails, we are far from thermal equilibrium and should not expect the Saha equation to have any validity.

10-2   DIFFUSION CURRENT

The most important difference between an ionized gas and a neutral gas lies in the ability of the former to sustain an electric current. An electric current, of course, is no more than a net transport of electrically charged particles. Since an ionized gas contains electrons and positive ions free to move, it must necessarily be a conductor. We have already seen (Chapter 8) that diffusion represents one way in which particles may be preferentially transported in one direction. If we have a concentration of charged particles in a given region of the gas, they will quickly diffuse into regions of lower concentration.

According to Eq. 8-28, the particle diffusion current density J in the x-direction is given by

$$J = -D\,dn/dx$$

Here D is the coefficient for diffusion of charged particles of density n through the largely neutral gas of density n_0. We shall let this equation stand for either of the two equations

$$J_+ = -D_+dn_+/dx \qquad J_- = -D_-dn_-/dx$$

omitting the subscripts when they are not explicitly needed. In most of our applications, $n_+ = n_- = n$. Even so, in general $D_+ \neq D_-$. (For a weakly ionized gas we can assume that the ions and electrons diffuse independently.) The diffusion coefficient D, Eq. 8-29, is approximately $\bar{v}L$, L here being the mean free path of a charged particle between collisions with neutral molecules. (In general, $L_+ \neq L_-$.) If the particles carry a charge q, the electric current density j associated with the particle diffusion current density J is

$$j = qJ = -qD\,dn/dx \qquad (10\text{-}5)$$

Equation 10-5 holds for both electrons ($q = -e$) and positive ions ($q = +e$), but the ion contribution to the electric current is usually negligible in a gas. This conclusion follows from Eq. 8-29 for the diffusion coefficient D. The mean free paths for the electrons and heavy ions are roughly the same, $L_+ \approx L_-$. The electrons have essentially zero diameter themselves, but it is then the diameter of the neutral molecules with which they collide that determines the collision cross section. On the other hand, when the gas is in thermal equilibrium the mean speed of the electrons is much higher than that of the heavy ions. For both, we may use the approximation $\bar{v} \cong \sqrt{3kT/m}$, so that from Eq. 8-29

$$\frac{D_-}{D_+} \approx \left(\frac{m_+}{m_-}\right)^{1/2} \tag{10-6}$$

Since the electron mass is about $1/2000$ the proton mass, then even for the lightest gas, H_2, the electron speed is $\sqrt{4000} \approx 60$ times greater than the positive-ion speed; for argon, the electron speed is nearly 300 times greater than the speed of the ion. The free electrons will therefore carry most of the current. If the gas as a whole is electrically neutral, the numbers of negative and positive ions are equal, but the electrons carry the current while the positive ions remain essentially at rest.

10-3 CONDUCTIVITY

In addition to the electric current caused by diffusion, it is clear that we must also get a current when an electric field is applied across the gas. The electric field will cause the positive charges to move in the direction of the field and the negative charges to move in the opposite direction, both components contributing to a current directed along the field. We define the *electrical conductivity* of the gas, σ, to be the electric current density $\mathbf{j}$ flowing in response to an applied field $\mathbf{E}$, per unit field:

$$\mathbf{j} \equiv \sigma \mathbf{E} \tag{10-7}$$

Again, if two kinds of charge carriers contribute significantly, we have $\mathbf{j}_+ = \sigma_+ \mathbf{E}$, $\mathbf{j}_- = \sigma_- \mathbf{E}$, with the observed conductivity equal to $\sigma_+ + \sigma_-$. (In a gas, σ_+ is usually negligible.) Let us take $\mathbf{E}$ to be in the x-direction. Since the electric field $\mathbf{E}$ is then related to the electrical potential Φ by

$$\mathbf{E} = -\frac{d\Phi}{dx}\,\mathbf{e}_x$$

the equation defining σ can be written as

$$j = -\sigma\frac{d\Phi}{dx} \tag{10-8}$$

in closer analogy with the other transport coefficients defined in Eqs. 8–14, 8–25, and 8–28.

In a gas, the electron current is usually dominant when compared to the positive ions. The forces acting on electrons and (singly ionized) ions are equal, but because of their smaller mass the electrons will accelerate faster in the field and traverse a mean free path in a much shorter time than the ion. The mean directed velocity of the electrons will therefore be much higher. It is always true, therefore, that in an ionized gas where the macroscopic neutrality condition holds ($n_+ \approx n_-$) the current is predominantly carried by the electrons.

In the presence of both an electric field and a density gradient, the total electric current density is obtained by adding Eqs. 10–5 and 10–8

$$j = -\sigma\frac{d\Phi}{dx} - qD\frac{dn}{dx} \tag{10-9}$$

Since the currents induced by the density gradient, Eq. 10–5, and the electrical potential gradient, Eq. 10–8, are both limited by the same mechanism, namely collisions with neutral molecules, the coefficients σ and D may be expected to be proportional to each other. We will see that this is in fact so. Let us suppose that the gas is placed in the electric field in such a way that no current is flowing. This situation could be realized, at least in principle, by putting the gas between the plates of a condenser and preventing the ions from being neutralized at the electrodes. If no current flows, according to Eq. 10–9

$$0 = -\,\sigma(d\Phi/dx) - qD(dn/dx)$$

What this means is that in equilibrium a concentration gradient is set up such that the electric current due to the applied potential gradient is just balanced by a diffusion current in the opposite direction, so that the net current is zero. (See Fig. 10–3.) The required concentration gradient is

$$dn/dx = -(\sigma/qD)(d\Phi/dx) \tag{10–10}$$

The equilibrium distribution function for the charged particles in the imposed electric field would be expected to be a Boltzmann distribution, Eq. 9–21, with the potential energy of the particle equal to $q\Phi$. After integrating over velocity space, the distribution in configuration space, in analogy to Eq. 9–22, is

$$f_2(x) = A'' e^{-q\Phi/kT}$$

The density of the charged particles, when in equilibrium, should be proportional to $f_2(x)$, so that

$$n(x) = n' e^{-q\Phi/kT} \tag{10–11}$$

Here n' is a constant which represents the density of charged particles where $\Phi = 0$. The variation in density is analogous to the law of atmospheres, Eq. 9–22, but here the particles distribute themselves non-uniformly

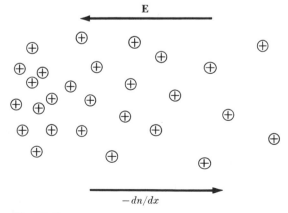

Fig. 10–3

in space under the influence of an electric field rather than a gravitational field.

Differentiating Eq. 10–11,

$$dn/dx = n'(-q/kT)e^{-q\Phi/kT} \ (d\Phi/dx) = -(nq/kT)(d\Phi/dx)$$

Now if the coefficient of $d\Phi/dx$ in this equation is equated with that in Eq. 10–10, we obtain the *Einstein relation*,

$$\sigma = (nq^2/kT)D \tag{10–12}$$

It is clear that this relation holds for any charge carrier in Boltzmann equilibrium with the field, provided we insert the particle density and charge appropriate to that carrier. Besides the proportionality to D, σ is seen to be proportional to the density of charged particles n. If there are no charged particles, $n = 0$, the conductivity vanishes, as is intuitively obvious. It is also worth noting that in a gas, since $D \propto L \propto 1/n_0$, the conductivity is proportional to the ionization ratio, $n_+/n_0 \approx n_-/n_0$, but is otherwise *independent of the pressure*.

10–4   GAS DISCHARGE

As a numerical example of electrical conduction in a gas, let us again use argon, and assume that the degree of ionization n/n_0 is small. In discussing the electrical quantity σ, it is convenient to use mks units, since the usual unit of resistance is the ohm. Then our previous result (Section 8–6) at standard conditions for the diffusion coefficient of atoms or ions is

$$D_+ = 0.25 \text{ cm}^2/\text{sec} = 2.5 \times 10^{-5}\text{m}^2/\text{sec}$$

In practice, most interesting cases of conduction occur at lower pressures, but as noted the conductivity σ proves to be independent of pressure for a given degree of ionization (n/n_0). As already remarked in Eq. 10–6, the electron speed and therefore the electron diffusion coefficient will be about 300 times larger, or

$$D_- \cong 7 \times 10^{-3}\text{m}^2/\text{sec}$$

Now inserting $q = 1.6 \times 10^{-19}$ coulomb, $k = 1.38 \times 10^{-23}$ joule/deg, and $T = 300°$K into Eq. 10–12, gives

$$\sigma \cong \sigma_- \cong 10^6(n/n_0)(\text{ohm–m})^{-1}$$

where we have used

$$n_0 = 3 \times 10^{19}\text{cm}^{-3} = 3 \times 10^{25}\text{m}^{-3}$$

Electrical conductivity is usually tabulated in the "mixed" units, (ohm–cm)$^{-1}$, and in these units

$$\sigma \cong 10^4(n/n_0)(\text{ohm–cm})^{-1}$$

For $(n/n_0) = 0.01\%$, about the largest value for which our theory strictly applies, $\sigma \cong 1$ (ohm-cm)$^{-1}$. This value represents an appreciable conductivity, although it is about a million times smaller than the values typical of metals—about 10^6 (ohm-cm)$^{-1}$.

Our result for the electrical conductivity can be applied in a rough way to a real *gas discharge*, like the one in a fluorescent lamp or a neon sign. If the discharge is 1 m long and 1 cm^2 in cross section, with $\sigma = 1$ (ohm cm)$^{-1}$, one finds for the *resistance R*,

$$R = \frac{100}{\sigma \times 1} = 100 \text{ ohm}$$

Actual discharges do have resistances of roughly this order of magnitude, but the real situation is much more complicated than we have described. The reason for the complication does not lie in a failure of the Einstein relation, Eq. 10–12; but rather in a variation of the degree of ionization, n/n_0. Indeed, as we saw in Section 10–2, the degree of ionization may depend on the current, through ohmic heating, or on the electric field, because of field ionization. Since σ depends on the degree of ionization, which in turn depends on the current or voltage, the current-voltage relation given by Eq. 10–7 is not really a linear one for a gas discharge. That is, in this case σ is not a constant but rather a function of voltage (or current).

For a known degree of ionization, our calculation is approximately valid. In order to calculate the actual current-voltage relation for a gas discharge, however, one would have to be able to calculate the degree of ionization, as a function of current. This kind of calculation is quite difficult. In the first place, the collisions are in part *inelastic*, whereas we have assumed them to be elastic. The inelastic nature of the collisions can be inferred from the light that is emitted by the atoms which are struck by electrons. As we shall see in Chapter 18, some of the electron's kinetic energy is absorbed by the struck atom, which later emits the absorbed energy as light. In the second place, the *maintenance* of the ionization itself depends on the collisions (Section 10–1), since an electron can knock an additional electron off a neutral atom which it strikes, or it can recombine with a positive ion to form a neutral atom. The conditions are especially complex near the electrodes, where the neutrality condition Eq. 10–1 usually breaks down, and much of the voltage drop in the discharge tube actually occurs there. As we have discussed, the degree of ionization depends on the current which is flowing, so that the conductivity is current-dependent. The current-voltage relation of a gas discharge is therefore not linear. It is in fact observed to be nonlinear, in a complicated way.

10–5 MOBILITY

Since the conductivity is proportional to the density of charge carriers according to Eq. 10–12, for some purposes it is more convenient to discuss a quantity which is independent of the density, namely the *mobility*. If the charge carriers have a non-zero average velocity (*not* speed), often called the flow velocity or the *drift velocity*, **u**, the particle current density **J** (Section 10–2) is given by $\mathbf{J} = n\mathbf{u}$. The electric current density is then

$$\mathbf{j} = q\,\mathbf{J} = q\,n\,\mathbf{u} \tag{10-13}$$

If the drift of the charge carriers is caused by an electric field $\mathbf{E}$, it follows from Eq. 10–7 that

$$\sigma\mathbf{E} = q\,n\,\mathbf{u} \tag{10-14}$$

The *mobility* μ is now defined as the drift velocity per unit electric field:

$$\mathbf{u} \equiv \mu\mathbf{E} \tag{10-15}$$

and upon comparing with Eq. 10–14 we find

$$\sigma = qn\mu \tag{10-16}$$

The mobility of a charge carrier is therefore also the "conductivity per unit-charge density" of that carrier. In terms of the mobility, the *Einstein relation*, Eq. 10–12, becomes

$$\mu = qD/kT \tag{10-17}$$

which shows that the mobility is indeed independent of n. Unlike the conductivity, the mobility depends on the total pressure through the mean free path, since $D \approx \bar{v}\,L$, $L \propto 1/n_0$ (Chapter 8), but not on the ionization ratio.

From Eq. 10–17 we find, with the values of D_- and T at standard conditions (Section 10–4), for the electron mobility

$$\mu_- \cong 0.3 \text{ m}^2/\text{V-sec} = 3000 \text{ cm}^2/\text{V-sec}$$

The mobility of the positive argon ions would be 300 times smaller or

$$\mu_+ \cong 0.001 \text{ m}^2/\text{V-sec} = 10 \text{ cm}^2/\text{V-sec}$$

(The mks units of mobility are inferred from Eq. (10–15) to be (m/sec)/(V/m) = m²/V-sec. The mixed units (cm/sec)/(V/cm) = cm²/V-sec are more common in the literature.) These rough estimates are a bit high, but of the right order of magnitude. At a lower pressure of say 1/100 atmosphere, D and μ would of course be 100 times greater, both for the electrons and the positive ions (Chapter 8).

Our value for the electron mobility in argon gas is higher than the electron mobility in metals, where the current is also due to electron motion (Part IV). The reason that the metal has a larger conductivity is that the *density* of electrons is much higher in the metal. (Cf. Eq. 10–16.)

PROBLEMS

10–1.   Show that a free electron and a free ion cannot recombine in the absence of a third particle. *Hint:* Write down the energy and momentum conservation equations.

10–2.   Calculate the ionization ratio n_+/n_0 for cesium, hydrogen, and helium at $T = 10^4$ °K. Assume $n_+ + n_0$ equal to 10^{15} cm^{-3} and $n_- = n_+$.

10-3.   Assuming reasonable values for the diffusion coefficient D, estimate the conductivity of cesium vapor at 10^{-6} mm Hg pressure and a temperature of $T = 300°K$. Repeat for the same pressure and $T = 1500°K$. *Hint:* Use the Einstein relation and Saha's equation.

REFERENCES

J. L. Delcroix, *Introduction to the Theory of Ionized Gases* (Interscience Publishers, 1960), Ch. 7–9.

S. C. Brown *et al.*, "Outline of a Course in Plasma Physics," (*Am. J. Phys.* **31**, 637 (1963)).

S. C. Brown, *Basic Data of Plasma Physics* (M.I.T. Press and John Wiley & Sons, 1959).

D. J. Rose and M. Clark, Jr., *Plasmas and Controlled Fusion* (M.I.T. Press and John Wiley & Sons, 1961).

11/properties of plasmas

When the degree of ionization in a gas is high enough for its dynamical behavior to be governed by electromagnetic forces, the properties of the medium are sufficiently different from those of a neutral gas to warrant a new name. Such a highly ionized gas is called a plasma, *a name due to I. Langmuir (1929).*

In contrast to a weakly ionized gas, the interactions which play the greatest role in a plasma are those between charged particles, i.e., electron–electron, electron–ion, and ion–ion collisions. For the study of most plasma properties the neutral molecules play a completely negligible role. This is obviously the case if the gas is completely ionized, but because of the long-range nature of the coulomb forces it is often a valid approximation at ionization ratios as low as 10^{-3}. In this chapter we will therefore ignore the neutral molecules and treat the plasma as if it were completely ionized.

11–1 THE PLASMA STATE

In a sense the plasma is the normal state of matter. Only in very atypical parts of the universe, such as on Earth, do solids, liquids, and neutral gases predominate. Most matter in the universe is either sufficiently hot (e.g., the stars) or sufficiently diffuse (e.g., interstellar matter) to be highly ionized, according to Eq. 10–3.

Closer to home, the outer layer of the earth's atmosphere, called the *ionosphere*, is an ionized gas of great significance in the propagation of radio waves. Beyond the ionosphere, in what is now referred to as the *magnetosphere*, recent satellite experiments have revealed the presence of the *Van*

Allen radiation belts (Section 11–6), a high energy plasma apparently trapped in the magnetic field of the earth. The magnetosphere may be thought of as that region surrounding the earth and its atmosphere where the magnetic field of the earth predominates over the general interplanetary magnetic field. This region is thought to reach out about 10 earth radii. Both the magnetosphere and the ionosphere are strongly affected by *solar flares*, short lived "hot spots," which suddenly appear on the solar surface accompanied by the ejection of large numbers of high energy particles. Such a disturbance on the sun usually propagates through the interplanetary plasma to the earth in one or two days, where it may produce such striking effects as *auroral displays* and *magnetic storms*.

Even on the surface of the earth plasmas are now readily produced, most notably in nuclear fusion research devices. The possible use of plasmas in thermonuclear reactors and in the rockets of long-range space vehicles has suddenly made them a medium of great technological as well as scientific interest.

A plasma will obey the macroscopic neutrality condition, Eq. 10–1,

$$n_+ \approx n_- \approx n$$

and in equilibrium the distribution functions of both species are Maxwellian at some temperature T. Such a plasma can therefore be completely characterized by the two parameters n and T. We will see in Section 11–3 that any particle in a plasma interacts simultaneously with a large number of others. In a plasma we are therefore dealing with a true "many-body problem" in the sense that the many-body distribution function discussed at the end of Chapter 9 should really be used in a statistical description of the medium. However, the interactions between the plasma particles are weak and partly cancel each other, because $n_+ \approx n_-$. As a result the average potential energy of a particle with respect to the rest of the plasma is very much smaller than the average kinetic energy, $\tfrac{3}{2}kT$. The particles are in this sense nearly free, and it is approximately correct to ignore the potential energy in the many-body Boltzmann distribution function. It is for this reason that we can describe the particles in a plasma in terms of single-particle Maxwellian distribution functions. This is not to say that the plasma particles are uncorrelated. They are in fact correlated through the macroscopic neutrality condition. It is only when this condition holds that the average potential energy of a particle is small compared to the average kinetic energy. Those regions of an ionized gas where the neutrality condition is violated are not considered a part of the plasma proper. Thus the transition region between a plasma and a solid, where $n_- \neq n_+$, is referred to as a *sheath*, Section 11–5. Here the kinetic and potential energies become comparable.

The macroscopic neutrality, $n_+ \approx n_-$, is certainly one of the most important properties of a plasma. By asking over what distance and for what length of time the neutrality condition can be violated, we will arrive at a fundamental frequency and a fundamental length, which set the natural scales for time and distance in a plasma.

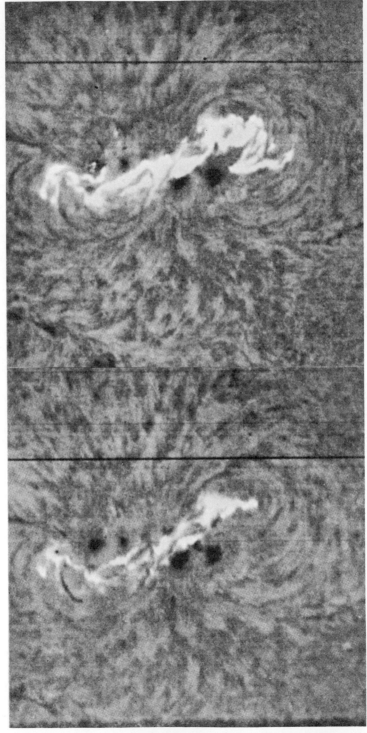

Fig. 11–1(a). *A solar flare.* [*Observatoire de Paris–Meudon photographs.*]

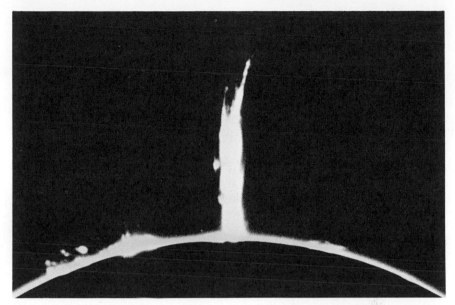

Fig. 11–1(b). *Matter ejected from the sun during a flare. [Courtesy of W. O. Roberts, High Altitude Observatory, NCAR.]*

11-2   PLASMA OSCILLATIONS

If the electrons in a plasma are displaced with respect to the ions, an electric field is set up which tends to pull the electrons back to their equilibrium positions. Consider a uniform plasma slab of thickness l and displace all the electrons a distance x, Fig. 11–2. The resulting situation is similar to that of a parallel plate condenser, where, as you may recall, the electric field is equal to the surface charge density times 4π (or times $1/\epsilon_0$ in mks units). The surface charge density here is clearly en_x, so that the field in the x-direction is

$$E = 4\pi e n\_ x$$

This field acts both on the ions and the electrons, but because of their much larger mass, the ions will essentially remain at rest. The electrons, however, will move.

The force per unit area on the electrons in the slab of thickness l is equal

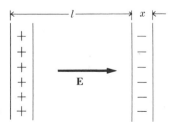

Fig. 11–2

to the number of electrons per unit area, $n_-\, l$, times the charge, $- e$, of an electron, times the electric field:

$$F = (- en_-\, l)E = - 4\pi e^2 n_-{}^2\, lx = - Kx$$

where $K \equiv 4\pi e^2 n_-{}^2 l$. This force acts on the total electron mass per unit area of $M = n_-\, m_-\, l$. By Newton's second law of motion we have

$$M \frac{d^2x}{dt^2} = - Kx$$

which we recognize as the simple harmonic oscillator equation. We found in Chapter 4 that the angular frequency of oscillation is given by $\omega = \sqrt{K/M}$. Substituting the present values for K and M, we see that the plasma oscillates with the angular frequency

$$\omega_p = (4\pi n_-\, e^2/m_-)^{1/2} \tag{11-1}$$

called the *plasma frequency*. This is the natural frequency of the plasma. Wherever the electron gas is displaced slightly with respect to the ion gas, the electron gas will oscillate back and forth in response to the restoring coulomb force of the ions with this characteristic frequency. In time electron-ion collisions, which we have ignored here, will of course damp out the oscillations.

The period of oscillation (Chapter 4) is given by $P = 2\pi/\omega_p$, and since the time from a maximum displacement back to neutrality takes a quarter of a period, we see that the plasma corrects a violation of charge neutrality in a time of the order of $\omega_p{}^{-1}$. This must be considered the natural unit of time in a plasma. For most plasmas it is a very short time indeed. In laboratory plasmas $\omega_p{}^{-1}$ may vary roughly from 10^{-9} sec to 10^{-13} sec (Fig. 11–6).

A plasma oscillation differs from a wave (Chapter 16) in that it does not propagate through the medium, i.e., a local disturbance remains local. You should not infer from this that no waves can propagate in a plasma. On the contrary a large and varied group of wave motions do in fact occur. Even a plasma oscillation does not remain entirely local when the random (or thermal) motion of the electrons is taken into account.

The plasma frequency in the ionosphere is of particular importance to radio communications. An electromagnetic wave can propagate through a plasma only if its frequency is higher than the plasma frequency. A wave impinging on a plasma will be totally reflected if its angular frequency is below ω_p. Very simply this is the principle behind AM radio propagation "beyond the horizon": the radio wave is "bounced off" the ionosphere (Fig. 11–3). The higher frequency TV and FM radio signals, however, go right through the ionosphere, so for good reception it is important to be within "line of sight" of the transmitting antenna. Since ω_p is proportional to $\sqrt{n_-}$, it is clear that anything which affects n_- in the ionosphere, such as a change in n_- from day to night and changes due to solar outbursts or high altitude H bombs, will significantly affect radio communications.

It is interesting that while the theory of plasma oscillations for an ionized

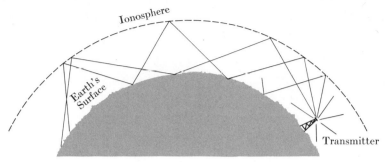

Fig. 11–3. Propagation of low frequency radio waves.

gas was first given by I. Langmuir and L. Tonks in 1929, the same idea was presented much earlier by Lord Rayleigh (1906) in quite a different context. Rayleigh thought of the atom as a "plum pudding" where the electrons were the "plums" distributed more or less uniformly through a pudding of positive charge. He realized that the electrons, when displaced, would oscillate and tried unsuccessfully to relate the frequency of oscillation to atomic spectra. In a sense he had the right theory but applied it to the wrong medium. The plum pudding model, first proposed by J. J. Thomson, was of course disproved by Rutherford's scattering experiments in 1911 (Chapter 5).

11–3   THE DEBYE LENGTH AND SHIELDING

We have discussed the period of time over which a plasma can deviate from charge neutrality. Let us next investigate the distance over which the neutrality condition can be violated. Suppose that all the electrons in a plasma slab of thickness l were displaced a distance l. This could be either in the interior of the plasma or at the edge of it. The situation would then be as depicted in Fig. 11–4, with a local electric field equal to (Section 11–2),

$$E = 4\pi en_l$$

The increase of potential energy ΔV of an electron moving a distance l in the direction of this field is $\Delta V = eEl = 4\pi n_e e^2 l^2$. In the absence of other forces an electron can only increase its potential energy by expending its

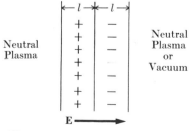

Fig. 11–4

kinetic energy, which for an average electron is of the order of kT. Setting $\Delta V \approx kT$, and defining the *Debye length* λ_D by

$$\lambda_D \equiv (kT/4\pi n_- e^2)^{1/2} \tag{11-2}$$

we find that

$$l \approx \lambda_D$$

The Debye length is therefore the maximum distance over which charge separation can take place through the thermal motion of the particles. This can be understood more directly by noting that (Eqs. 11–1 and 11–2),

$$\lambda_D = \bar{v}\omega_p^{-1} \tag{11-3}$$

where $\bar{v} = \sqrt{kT/m_-}$ is approximately the thermal speed of the electrons (Eq. 9–18). The Debye length is in other words the distance an average electron can travel in the time ω_p^{-1}, the natural response time of a plasma to a violation of charge neutrality. If ω_p^{-1} is the natural unit of time for a plasma, λ_D must be regarded as the natural unit of length.

We shall also find that the Debye length is the distance over which the plasma shields itself from a local excess of charge. Suppose a positive point charge q is inserted into a neutral plasma. The neighboring electrons are attracted to this charge while the positive ions are repelled, so that a negative charge cloud forms around it. Beyond a certain distance the plasma will therefore be shielded from the charge q by this negative charge. Up to a distance where the shielding is incomplete, say 50% or less, the electrostatic potential around the charge q is given by

$$\Phi \approx q/r$$

to a fair approximation. We will assume that the neighboring electrons and ions arrange themselves in a Boltzmann distribution in this potential:

$$n_+ = ne^{-e\Phi/kT} \qquad n_- = ne^{+e\Phi/kT}$$

where n is the constant particle density in the plasma in the absence of the charge q.

We will further assume that the charge q is small enough so that the potential energy $e\Phi$ of an electron or an ion is small compared to the kinetic energy, $\sim kT$. Then we may expand the exponential functions: $n_+ \approx n(1 - e\Phi/kT)$, $n_- \approx n(1 + e\Phi/kT)$; and the net negative charge density, $-e(n_- - n_+)$, can be approximated by

$$-e(n_- - n_+) \approx -en2e\Phi/kT \approx -2e^2nq/rkT$$

With this charge density the total negative charge in a spherical shell centered about q with radius r and thickness dr is equal to the volume $4\pi r^2 dr$ times the charge density: $4\pi r^2 dr(-2e^2nq/rkT)$. Let R be the distance at which the total negative charge surrounding q equals $-q$, i.e., the distance at which the shielding is complete. We find R from the condition:

$$-q = \int_0^R 4\pi r^2 dr \, (-2e^2nq/rkT) = -qR^2 \frac{4\pi ne^2}{kT}$$
$$= -q\frac{R^2}{\lambda_D^2}$$

In other words the Debye length is the distance required for shielding,

$$R = \lambda_D$$

Similarly the total potential energy, V, of the charge q with respect to its shielding cloud will be

$$V \approx \int_0^R \frac{q}{r} 4\pi r^2 dr (2e^2nq/rkT) = 2q^2R/\lambda_D^2$$
$$= 2q^2/\lambda_D \qquad (11\text{-}4)$$

The derivation given here is not rigorous, since Φ is not quite equal to q/r when r approaches λ_D. A more careful analysis shows that the potential is given by

$$\Phi = \frac{q}{r} e^{-r/\lambda_D}$$

This shows that the potential is down from q/r by a factor $1/e$ in a distance λ_D, or by $(1/e)^2$ in $2\lambda_D$. (See Fig. 11-5.) The shielding is therefore virtually complete within a few Debye lengths.

The plasma frequency and the Debye length are probably the two most important plasma parameters. If we substitute for the constants in Eqs. 11-1 and 11-2, we find

$$\nu_p \equiv \omega_p/2\pi = 9.0 \times 10^3 n^{1/2} \text{sec}^{-1} \qquad (11\text{-}5)$$

and

$$\lambda_D = 6.9(T/n)^{1/2} \text{ cm} \qquad (11\text{-}6)$$

where n is expressed in cm^{-3} and T in °K. In Fig. 11-6 we show the values of n, T, ν_p, and λ_D for some of the more important plasmas. Note that for

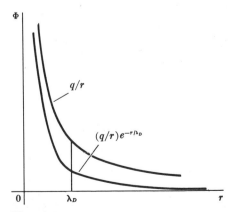

Fig. 11-5

laboratory plasmas λ_D can vary from about 10^{-1} cm for a low pressure discharge to about 10^{-6} cm for a high pressure arc.

In comparing these values for λ_D, Fig. 11–6, with the corresponding interparticle distance, $n^{-1/3}$, we find that λ_D is larger:

$$\lambda_D \gg n^{-1/3}$$

The number of particles Λ in a volume $\sim \lambda_D{}^3$ within the Debye distance of a given particle,

$$\Lambda \equiv n\lambda_D{}^3 \tag{11–7}$$

is therefore very large:

$$\Lambda \gg 1 \tag{11–8}$$

Since there is no significant shielding over distances smaller than λ_D, all of these particles, $n\lambda_D{}^3$, will interact with each other simultaneously. This points up one of the most important differences between a plasma and a neutral gas: in a neutral gas it is very rare for more than two particles to be involved in a given collision, and even two-body collisions are relatively in-

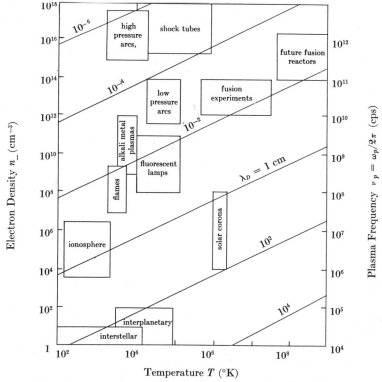

Fig. 11–6. *The electron density, temperature, plasma frequency, and Debye length for some important plasmas.* [*Adapted from* S. C. Brown *et al.,* Am. J. Phys. **31,** *638* (1963).]

frequent, while in a plasma a particle is continuously "colliding" with large numbers of other particles through the long-range coulomb field. The kinetic theory of plasmas is therefore mathematically very complicated. It is tractable at all only because the interactions, though numerous, are weak in the sense that the average potential energy of two interacting particles ($\sim e^2/\lambda_D$) is small compared to the average kinetic energy ($\sim kT$).

Not only is an average interaction weak, but because of the approximate charge neutrality, the potential energy of a given particle with respect to the entire plasma is small compared to kT. We have already calculated the potential energy of a charged particle with respect to the total charge within a Debye length of it (Eq. 11–4). For a particle with charge e it is

$$V \approx 2e^2/\lambda_D$$

It is easy to show that this is small compared to the kinetic energy, $\sim kT$,

$$\frac{kT\lambda_D}{e^2} \gg 1$$

since by Eqs. 11–2 and 11–7,

$$\frac{kT\lambda_D}{e^2} = 4\pi n\lambda_D{}^3 = 4\pi\Lambda \tag{11–9}$$

and Λ is known to be large (Eq. 11–8).

Even the average potential energy between nearest neighbors, $e^2 n^{1/3}$, is small compared to kT:

$$\frac{kT}{e^2 n^{1/3}} \gg 1$$

since $kT/e^2 n^{1/3} = 4\pi(n^{1/3}\lambda_D)^2$ by Eq. 11–2, and as already discussed the Debye length λ_D is large compared to the interparticle distance $n^{-1/3}$. On more immediate physical grounds we can argue that the potential energy, $-e^2 n^{1/3}$, of an average electron and a neighboring ion cannot be large compared to kT, since they would then form a bound system (total energy negative) and would readily recombine. Recombination of the "average" electron-ion pairs is of course incompatible with a highly ionized state of the gas.

11–4   ELECTRICAL CONDUCTIVITY

We have seen that the average interaction potential energy of two particles in a plasma is small compared to their average kinetic energy. Each of the many simultaneous coulomb "collisions" will therefore change the momentum of a particle only slightly, and the direction of the change is random. The net result of this "random walk" does not average to zero, however. In Figs. 11–7(a) and (b) we have indicated how many small random deflections can change the velocity of a particle from its initial to its final value. It is possible to estimate how many of the distant weak collisions are neces-

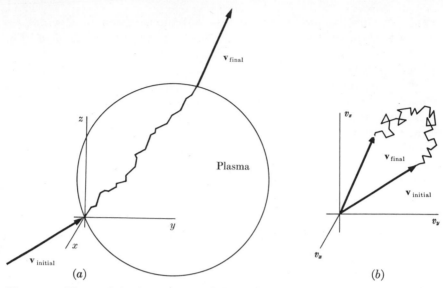

Fig. 11-7. *The net deflection of a particle in a plasma after many weak coulomb collisions depicted in* (a) *coordinate space and* (b) *velocity space.*

sary to deflect a particle significantly, say by 90°. When this is done one finds that an average particle travels a distance, call it λ_{90}, large compared to the Debye length before such a major deflection results. The derivation is too involved for the present discussion, but the result is approximately

$$\lambda_{90} \approx (4\pi)^2 \lambda_D \Lambda / \ln\Lambda$$

In a neutral gas a single collision results in a large deflection on the average, so that λ_{90} in a neutral gas would simply be the mean free path L. By the same token λ_{90} can be regarded as the "effective mean free path" for a charged particle in a plasma:

$$L = \lambda_{90} \approx (4\pi)^2 \lambda_D \Lambda / \ln\Lambda \qquad (11\text{-}10)$$

In the previous chapter we obtained the following expression for the electrical conductivity, Eq. 10-12,

$$\sigma = (nq^2/kT)D \qquad (10\text{-}12)$$

Since D, the coefficient for free diffusion, is approximately equal to (Eq. 8-29)

$$D \cong \bar{v}L \approx L\sqrt{kT/m}$$

the result is

$$\sigma \approx nq^2 \, L/\sqrt{mkT} \qquad (11\text{-}11)$$

In a plasma the diffusion is generally not free (Section 11-5). Nevertheless the above expression for σ, Eq. 11-11, is valid, with L given by Eq. 11-10:

$$\sigma \approx \frac{(4\pi)^2 nq^2 \lambda_D}{\sqrt{mkT}} \frac{\Lambda}{\ln\Lambda} \qquad (11\text{-}12)$$

To satisfy ourselves on this score we will now give a direct derivation of Eq. 11–11 without using the Einstein relation, Eq. 10–12.

When a steady current flows, the drift velocity **u** of the charge carrier is constant. The average gain in momentum of a particle due to the electric field must then equal the average loss of momentum through collisions. We can assume a complete loss of directed (or drift) velocity **u** in each large angle ($\sim 90°$) deflection, that is, after one mean free path, $L = \lambda_{90}$, or in a time $\tau = L/\bar{v}$, assuming $\bar{v} \gg u$. The loss of momentum per unit time (the average frictional force) is then

$$\frac{mu}{\tau} = \frac{mu\bar{v}}{L}$$

while the gain of momentum per unit time (the force due to the field) is clearly qE. Therefore

$$qE = \frac{mu\bar{v}}{L}$$

and the mobility, $\mu \equiv u/E$, is equal to

$$\mu = qL/m\bar{v} \qquad (11\text{–}13)$$

Since the conductivity is related to the mobility by $\sigma = qn\mu$, Eq. 10–16, we have shown that

$$\sigma = nq^2L/m\bar{v} \approx nq^2L/\sqrt{mkT}$$

in agreement with Eq. 11–11.

By making use of Eqs. 11–2 and 11–7, we can rewrite Eq. 11–12 as follows:

$$\sigma \approx (kT)^{3/2}/m_-^{1/2}e^2\ln\Lambda \qquad (11\text{–}14)$$

where we have ignored numerical factors of order unity and as usual assumed that the current carriers are the electrons. A careful calculation (Landshoff, 1949), shows that the numerical factor 0.59 should multiply our rough result, Eq. 11–14. When this factor and the numerical values of m_-, e, and k are inserted, one finds

$$\sigma = 1.5 \times 10^{-4} \; T^{3/2}/\ln\Lambda \; (\text{ohm-cm})^{-1} \qquad (11\text{–}15)$$

where T is expressed in degrees Kelvin. The log function is of course a very slowly varying function of its argument. For most plasmas of interest $\ln\Lambda$ is of the order of 10. The order of magnitude of the conductivity in a plasma is therefore given by the very simple formula

$$\sigma \approx 10^{-5} \; T^{3/2} \; (\text{ohm-cm})^{-1} \qquad (11\text{–}16)$$

At high temperatures the plasma becomes a very good conductor. Thus at the temperatures, $T \approx 10^8 \; °K$, aimed for in thermonuclear fusion reactors

$$\sigma \approx 10^7 \; (\text{ohm-cm})^{-1}$$

as compared to 10^6 (ohm-cm)$^{-1}$ in the best metallic conductors.

Notice in Eq. 11–14 that σ is independent of the plasma density n, except through the slowly varying factor, $\ln\Lambda$. This independence of density is in striking contrast to the situation in a weakly ionized gas, where σ was found to be proportional to n_-. In a weakly ionized gas, where L is largely independent of T, we also see that σ is proportional to $T^{-1/2}$ (within the limit $\bar{v} \approx (kT/m)^{1/2} \gg u$), while in a plasma $\sigma \propto T^{3/2}$ (ignoring $\ln\Lambda$) because L is proportional to T^2. These drastic differences exist because in a weakly ionized gas the electrical resistance is due to collisions of the electrons with the neutral molecules, while in a plasma it is due to collisions of the electrons with the ions.

11–5   AMBIPOLAR DIFFUSION AND SHEATHS

We found in Chapter 10 that in a weakly ionized gas, where the electrons and ions are free to diffuse independently through the mainly neutral gas, the electrons diffuse much more rapidly than the ions. For a gas in thermal equilibrium we arrived at the result in Eq. 10–6,

$$D_-/D_+ = (m_+/m_-)^{1/2}$$

for the ratio of the diffusion coefficients.

The more rapid diffusion of electrons, however, is not consistent with the macroscopic neutrality condition. Suppose $n_+(x) \approx n_-(x)$ initially, so that if there is a gradient in the electron density, the same gradient obtains among the ions. If now the electrons diffuse more rapidly out of a region where n is large than the ions do, the densities n_+ and n_- can no longer be equal.

What in fact happens in a non-uniform plasma is that the electrons start off diffusing more rapidly, thus leaving an excess of ions behind. The resulting charge separation sets up an electric field, which in turn restrains the diffusion of the electrons. The charge separation continues to build up until the electric field completely cancels out the *relative* ion-electron diffusion. The electrons are then tied to the ions and can only diffuse as fast as they do, i.e., slower than the free electron diffusion by roughly $(m_+/m_-)^{1/2}$. This "diffusion together" is called *ambipolar diffusion*. Let us prove that the coefficient of ambipolar diffusion, D_a, actually is much smaller than D_-.

Since an electric field as well as a density gradient is present, we must calculate the currents from Eq. 10–9,

$$j = \sigma E - qD\, dn/dx$$
$$= qD\Big(\frac{nqE}{kT} - \frac{dn}{dx}\Big) \tag{11–17}$$

where we have also made use of Eq. 10–12. We will assume that macroscopic neutrality is maintained, $n_+ \approx n_- \approx n$. With the electrons and ions moving together, the total electric current must vanish: $j = j_+ + j_- = 0$, or $j_+ = -j_-$. Since $D_- \gg D_+$, the electron current j_- will be much larger than j_+ unless the term in parentheses in Eq. 11–17 is very nearly zero for electrons,

$$\frac{n(-e)E}{kT} \approx \frac{dn}{dx}$$

or

$$E \approx \left(-\frac{kT}{e}\right)\frac{1}{n}\frac{dn}{dx}$$

With this electric field, the ion current becomes, according to Eq. 11–17,

$$j_+ = -2eD_+\frac{dn}{dx}$$

We see that under the combined influence of free diffusion and motion in the electric field resulting from charge separation, the ions move twice as fast as in free diffusion alone. In other words the ions and the electrons in a plasma diffuse together with an effective coefficient of diffusion, D_a, equal to

$$D_a = 2D_+ = 2D_-\,(m_-/m_+)^{1/2} \qquad (11\text{–}18)$$

Where the particle density gradients become very large, e.g., at a plasma-solid interface, called a *sheath*, the macroscopic neutrality condition breaks down. Eq. 11–17 still holds for the electrons and the ions, but we are no longer permitted to set $n_+ \approx n_-$. If the plasma is in contact with an insulator, or an electrically insulated (floating) conductor, there can be no net electrical current flowing from the plasma to the solid. We have once more

$$j_+ + j_- = 0$$

If such a wall is suddenly inserted into a uniform plasma, the electrons will initially diffuse more rapidly to the wall than the ions, since $D_- \gg D_+$. This builds up a negative charge on the wall, which discourages further electron diffusion, but encourages ion diffusion, until the two rates are equal. When things settle down, electrons and ions reach the wall in equal numbers and there recombine into neutral molecules. They are therefore lost to the plasma, and unless continuously replenished, the plasma will quickly die. The wall plays a role similar to the hole in the discussion of effusion (Section 9–5). We found there, in Eq. 9–20, that the flow of particles per unit area per unit time equals

$$\bar{F} = \tfrac{1}{4}n\bar{v} = n\sqrt{kT/2\pi m} \qquad (11\text{–}19)$$

using also Eq. 9–18. In the interior of a gas the flow across a plane in one direction is balanced by an equal flow in the opposite direction. At the wall, however, there is no back flow of ions or electrons.

The electron density close to the wall is lowered because the electrons are repelled by the negative charge that has built up on the wall. This negative charge gives rise to a sharp change in the electrostatic potential, the so-called *sheath potential*, Φ_S, close to the wall. The electrons will arrange themselves in a Boltzmann distribution in this potential, so that the density at the wall is down to

$$n_-(\text{wall}) = ne^{-e\Phi_s/kT} \qquad (11\text{–}20)$$

The analogy with the law of atmospheres, Eq. 9–22, should be obvious. While the flow of electrons/cm²-sec across the plasma-sheath interface (Fig. 11–8) is equal to

$$\bar{F}_- = n(kT/2\pi m_-)^{1/2}$$

many of these are repelled by the sheath potential. Only a flow of

$$\begin{aligned} \bar{F}_-' &= n_-(\text{wall})(kT/2\pi m_-)^{1/2} \\ &= (ne^{-e\Phi_s/kT})(kT/2\pi m_-)^{1/2} \end{aligned} \qquad (11\text{–}21)$$

gets through to the wall (Fig. 11–8). On the other hand all the ions that enter the sheath get through to the wall, since the sheath field helps them along. Therefore

$$\bar{F}_+ = \bar{F}_+' = n(kT/2\pi m_+)^{1/2} \qquad (11\text{–}22)$$

represents the ion flow across the plasma-sheath interface as well as the ion flow to the wall. The steady state sheath potential is determined by the condition that the ion and electron flows to the wall must be equal, $\bar{F}_-' = \bar{F}_+'$, or by Eqs. 11–21 and 11–22,

$$e^{-e\Phi_s/kT} m_-^{-1/2} = m_+^{-1/2}$$

The sheath potential is therefore equal to

$$\Phi_s = \frac{kT}{2e} \ln\left(\frac{m_+}{m_-}\right) \qquad (11\text{–}23)$$

The factor $\frac{1}{2}\ln(m_+/m_-)$ is not a large number($\sim$3.8 for atomic hydrogen). Typically the potential energy drop $e\Phi_s$ across the sheath is then 2 or 3 times the average kinetic energy $\frac{3}{2}kT$ of a particle in the plasma.

In Section 11–3 we found that the potential energy associated with charge separation became comparable to the thermal energy $\backsim kT$, when the separation extended over a distance of the order of a Debye length. This is precisely the situation in a sheath, $e\Phi_s \approx kT$, so the sheath thickness must be of the order of λ_D, typical values of which are given in Fig. 11–6.

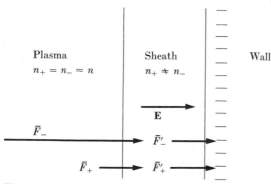

Plasma
$n_+ \approx n_- \approx n$

Sheath
$n_+ \neq n_-$

Wall

E

$\bar{F}_-$

$\bar{F}_-'$

$\bar{F}_+$

$\bar{F}_+'$

Fig. 11–8

11-6   PLASMA IN A MAGNETIC FIELD

Some of the most interesting phenomena of plasma dynamics take place only when the plasma interacts strongly with a magnetic field. A discussion of this fascinating subject can most conveniently (though only approximately) be carried out within a description of the plasma as a continuous fluid (magnetohydrodynamics). To do so here, however, would take us too far afield. Instead we will try to understand the behavior of a plasma by studying the motion of a single charged particle in a magnetic field. In a high temperature or low density plasma, the mean free path of a particle becomes very long, according to Eqs. 11-6, 11-9, and 11-10. The interparticle interactions are then relatively unimportant and may be quite negligible compared to the interactions of the particles with an external magnetic field. Consequently the plasma may be viewed as a collection of charged particles moving almost independently in the external field, subject only to the macroscopic neutrality condition.

The force on a particle with charge q and velocity v moving in a magnetic field $\mathbf{B}$ is (Eq. 1-14)

$$\mathbf{F} = q\mathbf{v} \times \mathbf{B}/c \qquad (11\text{-}24)$$

If $\mathbf{v}$ is parallel to $\mathbf{B}$,

$$\mathbf{F} = d\mathbf{p}/dt = 0$$

or

$$\mathbf{p} = \text{const}$$

We see that motion along the magnetic field is entirely unaffected by the field, Fig. 11-9(a).

If $\mathbf{v}$ is perpendicular to $\mathbf{B}$ on the other hand, the force is equal to $qv\,B/c$ in magnitude and has the direction indicated in Fig. 11-9(b). Since $\mathbf{F}$ is perpendicular to $\mathbf{v}$, no work is done (Chapter 3), so that the kinetic energy

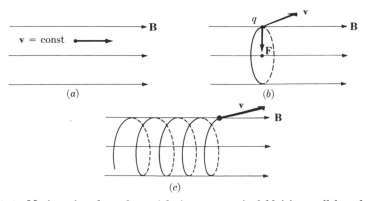

Fig. 11-9. *Motion of a charged particle in a magnetic field* (a) *parallel to the field,* (b) *perpendicular to the field, and* (c) *at an intermediate angle.*

and the speed v remain constant, by Eq. 3–6. The nonrelativistic acceleration, $\mathbf{a} = \mathbf{F}/m$, is perpendicular to $\mathbf{v}$ and its magnitude is

$$a = F/m = qv\,B/mc \qquad (11\text{–}25)$$

Let us assume the magnetic field to be uniform, $\mathbf{B} = $ const. Since the speed
v is constant, it follows from Eq. 11–25 that a is constant as well. The
particle will therefore be in uniform circular motion with a radius R_L, which
as always is related to a and v by $R_L = v^2/a$. Using Eq. 11–25, we obtain

$$R_L = \frac{mvc}{qB} \qquad (11\text{–}26)$$

This length is usually called the *Larmor radius*, and for an average particle
with speed $v \approx \sqrt{kT/m}$ it is equal to

$$R_L \approx c\sqrt{mkT}/qB \qquad (11\text{–}27)$$

The angular frequency of the circular motion, ω_c, called the *cyclotron
frequency*, is given by

$$\omega_c = \frac{v}{R_L} = \frac{qB}{mc} \qquad (11\text{–}28)$$

Unlike the Larmor radius the cyclotron frequency is independent of the
particle speed and is therefore identical for all particles of a given species.
Note that the electron cyclotron frequency is m_+/m_- times greater than the
ion cyclotron frequency, that is, thousands of times greater, while Eq. 11–27
shows that on the average an ion Larmor radius is larger than an electron
Larmor radius by $(m_+/m_-)^{1/2}$. Note also that since by Eq. 11–28 the electron cyclotron frequency is

$$\omega_{c_-} = v_-/R_{L_-} \approx \sqrt{kT/m_-}/R_{L_-}$$

and by Eq. 11–3 the plasma frequency is

$$\omega_p \approx \sqrt{kT/m_-}/\lambda_D$$

the following simple relation,

$$\omega_{c_-}/\omega_p \approx \lambda_D/R_{L_-} \qquad (11\text{–}29)$$

obtains among these four important plasma parameters.

Combining the constant motion along $\mathbf{B}$ with the gyration about $\mathbf{B}$, one
finds that a particle with a velocity component along $\mathbf{B}$ as well as perpendicular to $\mathbf{B}$ must spiral about a field line as shown in Fig. 11–9(c). We see
that the particles have to stick to the field lines, unless they collide
with other particles or objects, such as walls. When the mean free path is
long, as it is in plasmas of high temperature and/or low density (Eq. 11–10),
diffusion *across* the field lines through interparticle collisions will be slow.
If, furthermore, the Larmor radius is small compared to the size of the
plasma, collisions with walls or other extraneous objects will not play a
significant role, and *the plasma is constrained to move along the magnetic
field.*

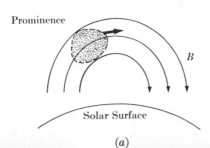

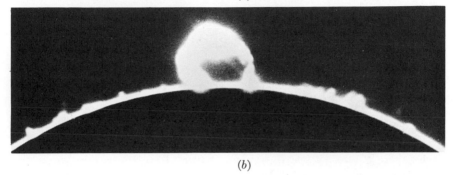

Fig. 11–10(a) and (b). *A solar prominence.* [*Courtesy of W. O. Roberts, High Altitude Observatory, NCAR.*]

In the enormous plasmas of astronomical interest R_L is always small compared to the plasma dimensions. This is also the case in many laboratory plasmas. As an example consider the C-Stellarator at Princeton under the following operating conditions: $B \approx 5 \times 10^4$ gauss, $T \approx 10^6$ °K. According to Eq. 11–27, the Larmor radii of protons and electrons are $R_{L+} \approx 3 \times 10^{-2}$ cm and $R_{L-} \approx 7 \times 10^{-4}$ cm, respectively. The smallest dimension of the Stellarator plasma is of the order of 10 cm or several orders of magnitude larger than R_{L+} as well as R_{L-}.

There are many striking illustrations of the ability of a magnetic field to constrain the motion of a plasma. One example is a *solar prominence*, a plasma emitted from the surface of the sun, which is seen to follow magnetic field lines in long arcs above the solar surface (Fig. 11–10). The ability of a magnetic field to confine a plasma is also of great interest in thermonuclear fusion research. For reasons that will become clear later (Chapter 30), fusion reactors must confine a hydrogen plasma at a temperature of the order of 10^8 °K. To keep the plasma confined without having it touch any material walls (which would quickly cool the plasma), one attempts to make use of the plasma's tendency to cling to magnetic field lines. We have seen, however, that a plasma is perfectly free to move along the magnetic field. Since the fusion reactor cannot be infinitely long, the question is what to do with the two ends. One solution is to join the two ends together in a toroidal configuration, Fig. 11–11(a). Another solution is to strengthen the magnetic field at the ends, Fig. 11–11(b), which tends to reflect most (but not all) of the particles. The Stellarator has a toroidal geometry, while devices with the configuration depicted in Fig. 11–11(b) are called "Magnetic Mirror Machines."

In order to understand how a "magnetic mirror" works, consider a particle gyrating in a region where the field lines converge. If we consider the field **B** at the circle of gyration, we see that it has a component per-

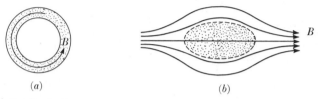

Fig. 11–11. *Confined plasmas.*

pendicular, $B_\perp$, as well as parallel, $B_\parallel$, to the field $\mathbf{B}_0$ at the center of the circle (Fig. 11–12). In addition to the force $qvB_\parallel/c$ towards the center of the circle, there is also a force $F' = qvB_\perp/c$ away from the region where the field lines converge (Fig. 11–12). If the mirror, i.e., the increase in **B** at one end, is strong enough, most particles approaching the mirror will be turned around by this force F'. Some particles travelling along $\mathbf{B}_0$ at the axis of the mirror, however, will always escape.

Though a great deal of progress has been made in fusion research devices with the magnetic field configurations shown in Fig. 11–11 as well as others, the confinement time is still much too short and the temperature achieved too low to promise controlled fusion power in the very near future. One can perhaps take some encouragement from the fact that plasmas are known to be confined over long periods of time by naturally occurring magnetic fields. Thus the Van Allen radiation belts, discovered in recent satellite experiments, are plasmas trapped in the mirror configuration of the earth's magnetic field, Fig. 11–13.

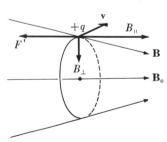

Fig. 11–12. *A magnetic mirror.*

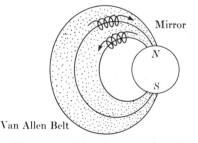

Fig. 11–13. *Plasma trapped in the earth's magnetic field.*

PROBLEMS

11-1.   The frequency of visible light is approximately 6×10^{14} sec^{-1}. What electron density would yield a plasma frequency $\nu_p = 6 \times 10^{14}$ sec^{-1}? Compare this density to the density in a typical atom of radius about 10^{-8} cm.

11-2.   In finding the frequency of plasma oscillations, the ions were assumed to remain at rest. Discuss the effect of the ion motion on the plasma frequency.

11-3.   Calculate the Debye distance and the plasma frequency for the ionized gases described in Prob. 10–2.

11-4.   How many particles are there in a "Debye sphere" $\tfrac{4}{3}\pi\lambda_D^3$, for the ionized gases in Prob. 11–3?

11-5.   Consider a hydrogen plasma at $T = 10^8$ °K and with $n_+ = n_- = 10^{15}$ cm^{-3}. Calculate the ionization ratio, the plasma frequency, the Debye distance, and the number of particles in a "Debye sphere." What is the pressure in this plasma?

11-6.   Calculate the conductivities of the plasmas in Prob. 11–5.

11-7.   The plasma in Prob. 11–5 is embedded in a magnetic field of 10^5 gauss. Calculate the electron and ion cyclotron frequencies and Larmor radii.

11-8.   A cesium plasma at 3000°K is in contact with an insulated metal wall. Calculate the sheath potential.

11-9.   Calculate the coefficient of ambipolar diffusion in terms of D_+ for the hypothetical case of $m_+/m_- = 5$.

11-10. In the plasma of Prob. 11–5, what is the average kinetic energy? What is the average potential energy with respect to the particles in its Debye sphere? What is the average potential energy between nearest neighbors?

11-11. Calculate the conductivity of the cesium vapors of Prob. 10–3, using Eq. 11–12. Compare with the results of Prob. 10–3.

11-12. When the resistivities due to electron-atom collisions and electron-ion collisions are comparable, how would you estimate the actual resistivity or conductivity?

REFERENCES

J. L. Delcroix, *Introduction to the Theory of Ionized Gases* (Interscience Publishers, 1960), Ch. 10, 11.

L. Spitzer, Jr., *Physics of Fully Ionized Gases* (Interscience Publishers, 1962, 2nd ed.).

A. S. Bishop, *Project Sherwood* (Addison-Wesley, 1958).

D. J. Rose and M. Clark, Jr., *Plasmas and Controlled Fusion* (M.I.T. Press and John Wiley & Sons, 1961).

12/equation of state for solids

We have seen that the van der Waals equation of state for a gas gave considerable insight into the atomic structure of the gas, when we tried to explain the equation by means of a microscopic mechanical model. Later we saw that further information was obtained by analyzing transport processes, such as diffusion and thermal conductivity. The specific heat also depended on the structure of the molecules, although in a less detailed way: according to the law of equipartition of energy, the specific heat was independent of the particular kind of atoms, and depended only on whether the molecule was monatomic, diatomic, etc. In the next chapters, we shall make an analogous study of solids, beginning with a macroscopic discussion of the equation of state in this chapter.

As a first approximation, we could treat an extended solid piece of matter as a rigid body. A rigid body is defined as one in which the relative distance between any two points in the body remains fixed, so that whatever happens it preserves its shape. This is obviously a good qualitative description, since most solid objects have a characteristic shape which does not change very much, so long as they are not handled too roughly. Because its shape does not change, a rigid body can be completely described by giving its position and orientation. This could be done by specifying the location of any three of its points at every instant. A more convenient way is to specify the location of one point (usually taken as the center of mass) and the orientation about that point (by three angles). In either method, six variables are required. From the laws of motion governing these variables (force equals mass times acceleration of the center of mass, torque equals rate of change of angular momentum about the center of mass), an important and fascinating theory results. We are not going into this theory, however, because it affords very little insight into the atomic structure of

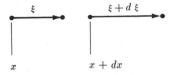

Fig. 12–1. *Tensile strain.*

the body: the only property which a rigid body has (aside from its shape, which need not depend on its atoms) is density, and the density *is determined only by how closely the atoms are packed together and by their mass.*

12–1 STRAIN AND STRESS

We shall therefore go immediately to the next approximation, in which we allow small *relative displacements* of the points of the body. Later (Chapter 15) we will also see what happens when the displacements are not "small." In fact, we will concentrate exclusively on the relative displacements of the points in the body, since the displacement and rotation of the body as a whole are already described by the mechanics of rigid bodies, which we have decided to bypass. Thus we assume that a point of the body which was originally at x is displaced by an amount ξ when the body is *deformed*. If the displacement were the same at all other points, the motion would be a translation as a rigid body; so we assume that at a neighboring point, $x + dx$, the displacement is slightly different, $\xi + d\xi$ (Fig. 12–1). Now the *strain* at the point x is defined as

$$\epsilon \equiv d\xi/dx \qquad (12\text{–}1)$$

i.e., the strain is the relative displacement of two points divided by their distance apart. This strain illustrated is a *tensile* strain, because the points are pulled further apart. If they were pushed closer together, it would be a *compressive* strain.

Actually, $d\xi$ would not have to be in the same direction as dx. For example, we could have a strain in which $d\xi$ was perpendicular to dx. Such a strain is still defined by $\epsilon \equiv d\xi/dx$, but it is called a *shear* strain (Fig. 12–2). In fact, intermediate directions are also possible, and we should really treat $d\xi$ and dx as vectors. In this case, ϵ is a relation between two vectors, called a "second rank tensor" (and expressible as a 3 × 3 matrix), but we will not need to go into this complete description.

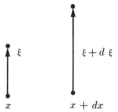

Fig. 12–2. *Shear strain.*

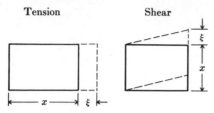

Fig. 12–3. *Total strain.*

If the strain is constant throughout the body, the *total strain* is

$$\epsilon = \xi/x$$

where ξ is the relative displacement of the two ends of the body and x is the total length of the body (Fig. 12–3). If ϵ varies from point to point, a corresponding relation can still be obtained by integration of Eq. 12–1:

$$\xi = \int \epsilon(x) dx$$

The *forces* which produce these deformations (Fig. 12–4) are called tensile (or compressive) forces and shear forces. The *stresses* corresponding to these kinds of forces are defined as the force per unit area:

$$S = F/A$$

The stress has the advantage over the force that it can be defined locally at each point in the body. The stress, like the strain, need not be constant from point to point. It is defined locally as the force vector per unit area, acting across some imaginary unit plane in the interior of the body (Fig. 12–5). In general, it depends on the orientation of the plane, and again all intermediate cases are possible between pure tension (or compression) and pure shear. Therefore the stress is also really a second rank tensor, with 9 components, expressing a relation between 3 force components and 3 direction cosines of the plane on which the force is acting.

A further remark ought to be made about the shear stress. You may have noticed that the body shown under tension in Fig. 12–4 is in static equilibrium, but the one under shear is not: it would be set into counterclockwise rotation. In order for rotational equilibrium to exist, another couple has to act in the opposite direction. This could be provided by a second pair of shear forces acting on the top and bottom faces of the body. Thus in the interior of a material in equilibrium, the shear stresses on the corresponding

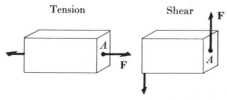

Fig. 12–4. *Tensile force and shear force.*

Fig. 12–5. Tensile stress and shear stress.

perpendicular planes are equal. As a result of this restriction, only 6 of the 9 stress components are independent; for the same reason, the strain also has only 6 independent components instead of 9.

In the case of a solid, we therefore see in general that the number of variables necessary to specify the equilibrium *state* of the system is greater than in the case of a gas. We must give the tensile and shear stresses and strains in each of three directions, or the values of 18 variables (of which 12 are independent), instead of only 2, like P and V in the case of a gas. Actually, we will consider only cases where 2 variables are sufficient for the solid too, such as a simple tension in one direction, or a simple shear in one direction.

12–2   ELASTIC MODULI

Now the equation of state involves the specification of a relation between S and ϵ, just as in the case of a gas it gives a relation between P and V. This relation is written:

$$S = E\epsilon \text{ for tension and compression} \tag{12–2}$$

$$S = G\epsilon \text{ for shear} \tag{12–3}$$

It is interesting that the values of E for tension and compression are always identical to each other, in all materials, but the value of G is generally different from E. The particular values of E and G depend on the material. The quantity E is called *Young's modulus*, and G is called the *shear modulus*. It is a fact that in solids E and G are very nearly constant (independent of stress) over a broad range of stress.

In order to see the meaning of the elastic modulus, let us substitute $S = F/A$ and $\epsilon = \xi/x$ back into Eq. 12–2. Then the equation becomes

$$F = K\xi$$

with $K = EA/x$. That is, the constancy of E is the same as the assertion that *Hooke's Law* applies to the material in question, or that the extension is proportional to the applied force (Fig. 12–6). Young's modulus E is a more interesting quantity than the force constant K though, because K depends on the *shape* of the object. It is intuitively evident that the force required to produce a given extension of a bar is larger the greater the cross sectional

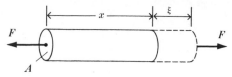

Fig. 12–6

area of the bar, and that the extension produced by a given force is larger the greater the length of the bar. Young's modulus (and also the shear modulus), however, is a property of the *material*, and as such will be of more interest for us.

Incidentally, if Eq. 12–1 is substituted into Eq. 12–3, we obtain

$$S = G \, d\xi/dx$$

a relation which bears a superficial similarity to Eq. 8–25 for the shear stress in a viscous fluid. The difference is that in the fluid the stress is proportional to the variation of *velocity*, whereas here it is proportional to the variation of displacement. A fluid in static equilibrium ($u = 0$) cannot support any shear stress if the fluid is in motion. In other words, the shear modulus for a fluid is always zero.

We may note that a complete specification of the relation between stress and strain would be a "third rank tensor," with 81 components relating the 9 components of stress to the 9 components of strain, in analogy to Eq. 12–2. Because only 6 components are really independent, there are actually only 36 elastic moduli, and the number of these which are independent is further reduced by crystal symmetry (Chapter 13). Nevertheless, complete elasticity theory is rather complicated. It reduces, however, to Eq. 12–2 or Eq. 12–3 for the simple cases in which we are interested.

12–3   THERMAL EXPANSION AND THE EQUATION OF STATE

Just as in the case of a gas, the state of a solid depends on the *temperature* T, as well as the mechanical variables S and ϵ. This dependence is expressed by the linear *thermal expansion coefficient* α. The increase in length ξ is proportional to the increase in temperature ΔT and to the original length x,

$$\xi = \alpha x \Delta T$$

or
$$\epsilon = \alpha \Delta T \qquad (12\text{–}4)$$

Like E, α is nearly constant for a solid near room temperature. (As T goes to $0°\text{K}$, α vanishes, so we cannot take x as the length at $T = 0$ and assume α constant.)

We can combine the above thermal and mechanical causes of strain into a single *equation of state* for a solid, assuming only tensile stresses are applied:

$$\epsilon = (1/E)S + \alpha \Delta T$$

with E and α (approximately) constant. For $\Delta T = 0$, we recover Eq. 12–2; and for $S = 0$, we get Eq. 12–4.

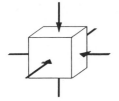

Fig. 12–7. Hydrostatic pressure.

A connection with the familiar equation of state for gases (Chapter 7) can be made if a particular type of stress, called a *hydrostatic pressure*, is considered. Hydrostatic pressure is a tensile or compressive stress which is equal across the planes in all three perpendicular directions (Fig. 12–7). This is the "pressure" P which has been discussed for gases. A change in pressure ΔP causes a change in volume ΔV. The hydrostatic pressure change is related to the *volume strain* $\Delta V/V$ by the *bulk modulus* β by analogy with Eq. 12–2:

$$\Delta P = -\beta \frac{\Delta V}{V} \qquad \text{or} \qquad \beta \equiv -V \frac{\Delta P}{\Delta V} \qquad (12\text{–}5)$$

Since V decreases ($\Delta V < 0$) when P increases ($\Delta P > 0$), β is always positive. The bulk modulus can be measured for a solid, as well as for a gas.

For a solid, the bulk modulus is the same order of magnitude as Young's modulus and the shear modulus. (All the moduli have the dimensions of pressure or stress—dyne/cm²—since the strain is dimensionless.) The bulk modulus of a solid is about a million times bigger than that of a gas under ordinary conditions, however. The reciprocal of the bulk modulus is called the *compressibility*. That is, gases are ordinarily about a million times more compressible than solids. The thermal expansion coefficient of a gas, on the other hand, is only 10 to 100 times bigger than for a solid. The volume expansion coefficient, which can be shown to be three times the linear expansion coefficient α (Prob. 12–1) is defined by

$$\frac{\Delta V}{V} = 3\alpha \, \Delta T \qquad \text{or} \qquad 3\alpha \equiv \frac{1}{V} \frac{\Delta V}{\Delta T} \qquad (12\text{–}6)$$

Let us derive the bulk modulus and thermal expansion coefficient for an *ideal gas*, whose equation of state is given by Eq. 7–1,

$$PV = RT$$

Since P and V are not proportional to each other, we assume ΔP and ΔV are small and write dP and dV. The bulk modulus is then

$$\beta = -V \frac{dP}{dV} = -V(-RT/V^2) = P \qquad \text{with } T \text{ const}$$

(Actually one should write $(\partial P/\partial V)_T$ instead of dP/dV.) The volume coefficient of thermal expansion is

$$3\alpha = \frac{1}{V} \frac{dV}{dT} = \frac{1}{V} \frac{R}{P} = \frac{1}{T} \qquad \text{with } P \text{ const}$$

(Again, $(\partial V/\partial T)_P$ should strictly be written for dV/dT.) Thus for a gas, neither β nor α can be taken as constant. Under standard conditions,

$$\beta = 1 \text{ atm} \approx 10^6 \text{ dyne/cm}^2$$
$$3\alpha = 1/273 \approx 10^{-3} \text{ deg}^{-1}$$

For a gas, both E and G are zero. If you tried to squeeze a gas in a single direction, it would just flow out to the sides. Likewise, if you tried to shear it, it would just give. Furthermore, a gas cannot support a negative pressure (equal tension in all directions), because it will just fill up whatever volume is made available to it, but a solid can.

A liquid is like a gas in that E and G are zero, because its shape can be changed at will, without having to apply any stress. It is more like a solid, however, in that the thermal expansion coefficient and the compressibility are usually much smaller than for gases. Also it can support negative pressures, though not very large ones because its fluidity causes it to break apart (cavitation).

Two distinct problems arise in the elasticity of solids. One problem is, given the values of the elastic moduli for a particular material, to calculate the stresses and strains which arise in an object of a certain shape, under certain conditions. This problem is of enormous engineering importance in the design of structures but has not been of central interest in physics since the nineteenth century. The other problem, which is still of interest in physics and has become of great interest in engineering, is to understand the values of the elastic moduli themselves—why they should be different in Cu and NaCl for instance. This understanding yields to the physicist a more profound insight into the fundamental nature of the interactions between atoms, and to the engineer it promises the hope of designing *materials* for desired properties rather than simply choosing the optimum geometry. We will be concerned only with the second problem, and in the following sections we will try to understand the elastic modulus, the thermal expansion, etc., in terms of a model for the atomic structure of a solid.

PROBLEMS

12–1.   Show that the volume expansion coefficient is 3 times the linear coefficient. (*Hint:* Assume the volume is a cube of side L, so $V = L^3$.)

12–2.   Suppose an aluminum bar is warmed up 1°C. Calculate the stress which would have to be applied to restore it to its original length. (Alternatively, this is the stress the bar would exert if its length were held constant while it was heated.) The (linear) thermal expansion coefficient of Al is $2.4 \times 10^{-5}/°C$, and Young's modulus is 6.9×10^{11} dyne/cm². Express your result in atm.

12–3.   For an ideal gas, show that

$$\frac{\partial P}{\partial T}\Big)_V = \frac{P}{T}$$

What would be the increase in pressure (in atm) if the gas at standard conditions were heated 1°C, keeping the volume constant?

12-4.   When a bar is compressed (or stretched), the work done by the applied force on the bar is stored as elastic energy. (*a*) Prove that the work (energy) per unit volume is

$$W/V = \tfrac{1}{2}E\epsilon^2$$

where ϵ is the strain. (*b*) Compute W/V for aluminum which is compressed 0.1%. For Al, $E = 6.9 \times 10^{11}$ dyne/cm^2. (*c*) One cubic centimeter of Al contains 6×10^{22} atoms. What is the stored energy per atom, in eV?

12-5.   For a number of metallic elements, look up Young's modulus E and the shear modulus G in the *Handbook of Chemistry and Physics*. Tabulate these in the order of increasing Young's modulus. Is there a correlation between E and G?

12-6.   For the metals in the table made in Prob. 12-5, look up and enter the thermal expansion coefficient. Is there any correlation between the expansion coefficient and Young's modulus?

REFERENCE

R. J. Stephenson, *Mechanics and Properties of Matter* (John Wiley & Sons, 1960, 2nd ed.), Ch. 7.

13/crystal structure

In our first approach to the microscopic constitution of solid materials, we will adopt the approximation which we previously said was not very interesting— i.e., we will treat the solid as a rigid body. Instead of studying its motion, how- ever, we will study the only macroscopic mechanical property *that the rigid material has, namely, its density. The density depends on the mass of the atoms, and on their distance apart. We shall see that it is expressible in terms of the molecular weight of the material, the separation of the atoms, and Avogadro's number, and will consider x-ray diffraction methods for measuring the separa- tion. In addition to the* distance *between the atoms, however, a possibly sur- prising result of considering the way the atoms are packed together is that the* angles *between neighboring atoms are also very important. Indeed, it is mainly the angles which distinguish crystals from glasses, or even from liquids, since in all these states of aggregation, the distances are nearly the same. In this initial consideration, we will assume that the atoms are located at fixed posi- tions, from which they never depart. Later, we will allow them to depart, at first only a little way (Chapter 14), and then a long way (Chapter 15).*

13–1 CRYSTALS

All solids can be exhaustively classified into those which are *crystalline* and those which are *amorphous*, depending on whether the (approximately) fixed positions of the atoms or molecules do or do not form a *regular* array (Fig. 13–1). The regular array, if it exists, is called a *crystal structure*, and it is a repeating arrangement of points in three dimensional space. (The periodicity of the structure is described by an abstract array of points called a "lattice." The lattice is important for an advanced analysis of

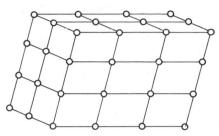

Fig. 13–1

crystal properties. In this introduction, however, we shall not mention the lattice further, in order to skirt confusions between it and the structure, which is a set of points marking the positions of atoms.) For example, the points at the corners of neatly packed identical cubes would be such an array. This particular structure could be specified mathematically as the set of points whose three Cartesian coordinates are integers. As examples in real materials, all metals and salts and most minerals are normally crystalline. Glass, plastics, rubber, etc., are normally amorphous. (Under exceptional circumstances, any of these materials could assume the opposite character, however.)

At first it seems astonishing that so many common substances should happen to be crystalline, rather than having their atoms arranged, much more probably, in some irregular arrangement. Of all the possible ways of arranging them, why should those neighbors around any given atom be arranged just the same as those around any other given atom? Suppose you threw a lot of marbles into a box—wouldn't they have a more or less random arrangement? Yes. But if you jiggled the box for a long time, they would settle down until they were much more closely packed. They would lower their (gravitational) energy by doing so, and the atoms do likewise. A random arrangement is the most probable, but there is some arrangement of neighbors which gives the least energy. Then all the atoms adopt this arrangement of their neighbors, and the structure is regular. In this way the total energy of the assembly is minimized. (Not quite all the atoms adopt the specified arrangement, as we shall see in Chapter 15; but for the present we neglect the deviants.)

Most crystalline materials are actually *polycrystalline*. The arrangement is not strictly periodic, but there are subregions within which the atomic arrangement is periodic (Fig. 13–2). These regions are called *grains*, so that a single grain is actually a crystal as defined above; but at the *grain boundaries*, the orientation of the crystal structure changes. An ordinary sample of metal is polycrystalline, with a grain size which is normally a fraction of a millimeter, but can be larger. This grain structure can be made visible by etching with a suitable dilute acid.

On the other hand, single crystals of many materials can be obtained in large sizes, either naturally or artificially. Diamonds are single crystals, for example, as are other gems, quartz crystals, etc. Sodium chloride crystals

Fig. 13–2. Grain structure of a nickel casting. The individual grains are about 3 mm in diameter. They are rendered visible by etching with an acid, which reacts differently on the different crystal planes exposed on the surface of each grain. [Courtesy of G. A. Colligan and V. A. Surprenant.]

weighing many pounds are manufactured for infrared prisms and lenses, and large germanium and other semiconductor crystals are manufactured for transistors. Each grain of table salt is a small cubic single crystal of sodium chloride. Large metal single crystals are made for research purposes. The grain structure is actually extremely important in determining many properties of a material, in ways which often are not yet understood, but henceforth we shall restrict our attention to the simpler problem of single crystals.

13–2   COMMON CRYSTAL STRUCTURES

First, some of the most commonly occurring crystal structures will be described. (See Fig. 13–4.) The simplest of all is the *simple cubic* (sc) structure described above. Two modifications of the simple cubic structure occur very frequently. The *body centered cubic* (bcc) structure is the same except that there is an atom at the center of each cube; and the *face centered cubic* (fcc) structure has an atom in the center of each face of each cube. Another commonly occurring structure is *hexagonal close packed* (hcp). This structure consists of successive layers of atoms laid in hexagons. (Put a lot of pennies together on a table as closely as you can, and you will see that they

Fig. 13–3. *Large natural crystals of quartz.* [*Courtesy of A. Holden and P. Singer,*
Crystals and Crystal Growing (*Doubleday, New York, 1960*).]

form a hexagonal array.) The "*diamond structure*" can be derived from the
fcc, by looking at a corner atom and 3 of its nearest neighbors (in the center
of adjacent faces). In the interstice formed by these four atoms, called a
tetragonal interstice, put another atom, and do this in every other such
interstice.

It is very interesting to look at the number of *nearest neighbors* of an atom
in each of these structures (also called the *coordination number*). This number is given in Table 13–1 for the structures illustrated in Fig. 13–4. The
fcc and hcp structures both have the coordination number 12. This fact
is not accidental, and in fact the two structures are closely related. They
are both types of *closest packing* of spheres in three dimensions. As has already been noted, a plane of spheres in closest packing forms an hexagonal
array (Fig. 13–5). Another close packed layer of spheres can be piled on the

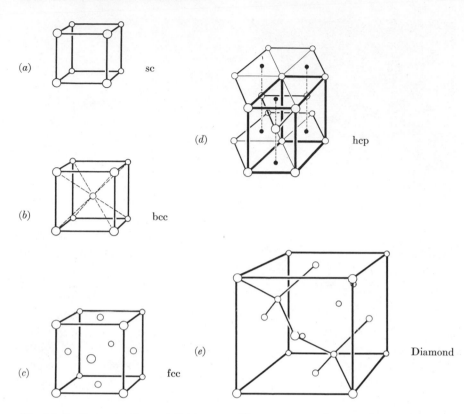

Fig. 13–4. Some simple crystal structures. These structures (except sc) are assumed by many of the elements.

first one, with the spheres fitting snuggly down into the little three-sided hollows indicated by the dots in Fig. 13–5. Only every other hollow can be occupied, however, as they are too close together. It is inconsequential which set of hollows you choose to occupy: the structure is essentially the same in either case. But when a third layer is added, it does make a real difference which set of hollows is chosen this time. If the spheres in the third layer are directly above those in the original plane two layers below, the structure is hcp, as can be seen by comparison with Fig. 13–4(d). If the other alternative is adopted, the structure is fcc. (In both cases, the entire structure is assumed to be built up by repeating the same sequence of three

Table 13–1

Structure	Coordination No.
diamond	4
sc	6
bcc	8
fcc	12
hcp	12

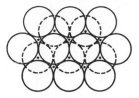

Fig. 13–5. *Close packing of spheres.*

planes.) It is not obvious that the second arrangement is the same as the fcc arrangement of Fig. 13–4(c), but we have tried to suggest the relation in Fig. 13–6. The black atoms all lie on one close-packed plane. The cross-hatched atoms lie on the neighboring close-packed plane. Each of the white atoms lies on a third and a fourth plane, and the line joining the white atoms is perpendicular to the planes. In any case, Fig. 13–5 shows why there are 12 nearest neighbors in both the hcp and fcc structures: 6 in the plane and 3 in the planes above and below.

Now the hcp or the fcc arrangement would seem to be optimum, in that each atom attracts the most atoms that can be geometrically squeezed around it. One of these arrangements always occurs when the interatomic forces are essentially *spherically symmetric*, as in many metals or in rare gas atoms. (Which arrangement occurs depends on rather subtle considerations. If the forces are strictly spherically symmetric, as for the rare gases, then fcc always occurs.) A coordination number which is lower than 12 results when non-spherically symmetric *valence forces* act between the atoms. These valence forces are similar to those which form the chemical bonds in molecules, and they will be studied in greater detail in Chapter 24. To take the extreme example from Fig. 13–4(e), the diamond structure is the structure of carbon (in its diamond modification). The group IV element C has a valence of 4, and therefore this structure with 4 nearest neighbors is favored. In fact, the arrangement of the 4 neighbors of a given C atom is just the same as the arrangement of the 4 H atoms at the corners of a regular tetrahedron surrounding the C atom in a methane molecule, CH_4.

The lower the coordination number, the more volume there is per atom, assuming a given nearest neighbor distance. The nearest neighbor distance may be taken as the diameter of the atom, if we treat the atoms as hard spheres in contact (cf. Chapter 8). An interesting illustration occurs in the case of iron. At room temperature, Fe is bcc (α-iron), but above 900°C it

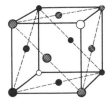

Fig. 13–6. *Close packed planes in fcc structure.*

transforms to the fcc structure (γ-iron). As Fe is heated up, it expands due to thermal expansion, but on reaching the transformation temperature it suddenly contracts, as the atoms fall into the more closely packed fcc arrangement.

13-3   STRUCTURES OF THE ELEMENTS

A majority of the elements crystallizes in one of the structures described in Section 13-2. These are listed in the periodic table of the elements in Table 13-2. Like Fe, some of the elements assume more than one structure; we have usually listed the one which is stable at low temperature. As already noted, the *rare gases* are fcc and most of the *metals* are either fcc or hcp, i.e., one of the close packed structures. A significant number of metals—including all of the alkali metals and many of the transition metals—has the bcc structure. Only a few have less symmetric structures not shown in Fig. 13-4 (denoted by dashes in Table 13-2).

Like C in diamond itself, all the group IVA elements except Pb exhibit the diamond structure, because of their tetravalence. (Tin (Sn) most commonly occurs in another, metallic, form with a less symmetrical structure.) All the other *non-metals* have complicated structures. The reason for the latter fact is that the atoms are capable of forming molecules, like N_2 or Cl_2, which are held together with strong valence forces, and which interact with each other with very much weaker forces. Thus at room temperature N_2 is a gas, and when it does crystallize (at 63°K) the non-spherical diatomic molecules fit into an unsymmetrical structure. It will be possible to understand the reason for some of these differences, at least in a qualitative way, after we have studied the electronic structure of atoms in Chapter 22. The detailed quantitative prediction of an unsymmetrical structure from first principles is a problem which is beyond the reach of present capabilities.

13-4   STRUCTURES OF COMPOUNDS

We may begin a discussion of non-elemental crystals with *alloys*, a type of system which is not strictly a compound. An alloy is a *solid solution* of two or more metals. By solid solution is meant that the constituents are atomically dispersed, i.e., some of the sites are occupied by one kind of atom and some by another. It is not a compound in the strict chemical sense, because solid solutions can usually exist over a rather wide range of compositions, in contrast to the stoichiometric composition of a chemical compound. ("Stoichiometric" means in the proportions specified by the chemical formula of a compound—a ratio of small integers.) A typical example is *brass*, which is a solution of Cu and Zn. Since, according to Table 13-2, pure Cu has the fcc structure and pure Zn is hcp, we might expect that brass which is rich in Cu should be fcc, and brass rich in Zn should have the hcp Zn structure. This expectation is correct. At intermediate compositions, how-

Table 13–2 Periodic Table of the Elements

I	II	III	IV	V	VI	VII	VIII	0
H –								He
Li bcc	Be hcp	B	C dia	N –	O –	F		Ne fcc
Na bcc	Mg hcp	Al fcc	Si dia	P –	S –	Cl –		A fcc
K bcc	Ca fcc	Sc	Ti hcp	V bcc	Cr bcc	Mn bcc	Fe bcc / Co hcp / Ni hcp	Kr fcc
Cu fcc	Zn hcp	Ga –	Ge dia	As –	Se –	Br –		
Rb bcc	Sr fcc	Y	Zr hcp	Nb bcc	Mo bcc	Tc	Ru hcp / Rh fcc / Pd fcc	Xe fcc
Ag fcc	Cd hcp	In –	Sn (dia)	Sb –	Te –	I –		
Cs bcc	Ba bcc	Rare earths	Hf hcp	Ta bcc	W bcc	Re hcp	Os hcp / Ir fcc / Pt fcc	Rn
Au fcc	Hg –	Tl hcp	Pb fcc	Bi –	Po –	At		
Fr	Ra	Ac	Th fcc	Pa	U bcc			

209

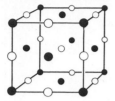

Fig. 13–7. *Sodium chloride structure.*

ever, other more complicated structures take over, and these are rather difficult to predict. Ordinary brass is 2/3 Cu, and fcc.

Among genuine compounds, *ionic crystals* have simple structures similar to those already described. As we shall see, the constituents of an ionic compound, e.g., NaCl, can be taken to be ions, like Na⁺ and Cl⁻. These ions have symmetrical structures, like the rare gas atoms, and so the symmetrical inter-ionic forces lead to simple structures. One of the simplest is called the *sodium chloride* structure. As shown in Fig. 13–7, this structure looks just like sc if the distinction between the two kinds of ions is ignored. Actually, it is like fcc if you look at only one kind of ion—say the black ones, though the white ones are equivalent. (The "lattice" is fcc. With each point of the fcc lattice is associated an NaCl *molecule*. Of course, the Na⁺ and Cl⁻ ions cannot *both* be *at* the lattice point, but that is all right.) All the alkali halide crystals except the Cs halides have the NaCl structure. In addition, many alkali earth oxides and sulfides have this structure.

The Cs halides have a structure which looks like bcc if you ignore the distinction between ions (Fig. 13–8). (Actually, it is sc, with a CsCl molecule associated with each "lattice" point. Note that there is no monatomic example of an sc crystal.) This structure is called the *cesium chloride* structure.

Another simple structure is the cubic *zincblende* structure, typified by ZnS (or zincblende). It is like the diamond structure (Fig. 3–4(e)) if the distinction between Zn and S ions is ignored. Actually, like the NaCl structure, it is related to fcc. The difference is that, starting with the fcc structure, in NaCl the interstitial sites along the cube edges are occupied by the other ion (the so-called octahedral sites). In the ZnS structure, a different set of interstitial sites (called the tetrahedral sites) is occupied. The latter scheme leads to a much more open structure and is evidence for some contribution by valence forces. The zincblende structure would be identical to diamond if the atoms were all the same.

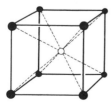

Fig. 13–8. *Cesium chloride structure.*

Molecular compounds, as in the monatomic case (e.g., N_2), have much more complicated structures, of course—particularly organic compounds with large unsymmetrical molecules—but we shall not mention these. We may, however, digress briefly from our concentration on crystals to mention glasses. How the structure of glass differs from a crystal can be seen by considering SiO_2. This substance can have either a crystalline form (*quartz*) or an amorphous form (*silica*). The crystalline form can be schematized as a network of regular hexagons, as in Fig. 13–9(a). The amorphous form is a similar network, but it is irregular—mostly hexagons, but some pentagons and heptagons, etc., as in Fig. 13–9(b). *Glasses* are like silica Si_6O_{12}, except that some of the Si^{++++} ions are substituted by Na^+, Ca^{++}, Pb^{++}, etc. For example, window glass is $Na_2CaSi_5O_{12}$. Note that the valence of the substituents adds up to that of Si. It should not be concluded from this example that all amorphous materials are compounds, however. The elements P and S often occur in amorphous form, for example.

13–5 DENSITY OF CRYSTALS AND INTERATOMIC DISTANCE

The macroscopic density of the crystal is evidently related to the mass of the atoms and to their diameter. It depends in addition on the crystal structure, since this determines how closely the atoms are packed. Consider first the hypothetical example of a simple cubic crystal structure. The smallest cube, shown in Fig. 13–4(a), is called the *unit cell*. If the side of this cube is denoted by a (usually called the "lattice constant"), then for the sc structure,

$$d = a$$

where d is the diameter of the atom, since the cube edge is also the nearest neighbor distance. Here we have assumed that the atoms are hard spheres in contact, with the distance between centers equal to the diameter. The volume associated with one atom is a^3. (Note that only one of the atoms in Fig. 13–4(a) "belongs" to the cube; the others belong to neighboring cubes.) Since the mass of the atom is $m = M/N_0$, where M is the molecular weight and N_0 is Avogadro's number, the density is

$$\rho = M/N_0a^3 \quad \text{(sc)} \tag{13–1}$$

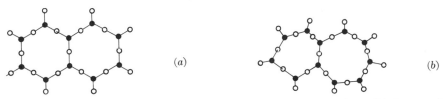

Fig. 13–9. *Schematic representation of crystalline* (a) *and amorphous* (b) *forms of* SiO_2.

To consider a more practical example, for the bcc structure the side of the unit cell is again the cube edge a. Now, however, the nearest neighbor distance (atom diameter) is from a corner to the cube center (Fig. 13–4(b)), or

$$d = a\sqrt{3}/2$$

The volume of the cube is a^3, but two atoms "belong" to the cube this time (a corner atom and the center atom), so that the volume associated with *one* atom is $a^3/2$. Then the density is

$$\rho = 2M/N_0 a^3 \qquad \text{(bcc)} \qquad\qquad (13\text{–}2)$$

For example, the density of Na is 0.97 g/cm³, and the molecular weight is $M = 23.0$. Then

$$\begin{aligned} a &= (2M/N_0\rho)^{1/3} = (2 \times 23/6.02 \times 10^{23} \times 0.97)^{1/3} \text{ cm} \\ &= 4.28 \text{ Å} \end{aligned}$$

The diameter of a sodium atom is therefore

$$d = a\sqrt{3}/2 = 3.71 \text{ Å}$$

In order to decide how many of the atoms shown in each unit cell of Fig. 13–4 *belong* to that unit cell itself, we must assign some to that cell, and then notice that the others occupy corresponding positions in neighboring cells, and therefore belong to those cells. For example, in the fcc unit cell of Fig. 13–4(c), four atoms belong to the cubic cell. We may take these as the lower left-hand front atom, plus the three atoms in the centers of the cube faces adjacent to this corner. Then all of the other atoms will be seen to belong to a cube which is adjacent to this one. For example, the lower right-hand front atom belongs to the cube just to the right of this one, since it is the lower left-hand front atom of that cube; and likewise the lower left-hand rear atom belongs to the cube in back of this one. The atom in the center of the back face is adjacent to the lower left-hand rear atom and so also belongs to the cube in back. An alternative method of counting the atoms in the unit cell is as follows: consider how the planes which form the cube faces divide the spherical atoms and add up the fractions of spheres which lie inside the cube. One octant of each of the eight corner atoms lies inside— adding up to one atom—and one hemisphere of each of the six atoms in the cube faces is inside—adding up to three atoms. The sum is again four atoms in the cell. The numbers of atoms in the unit cell of each of the structures in Fig. 13–4 are summarized in Table 13–3.

Table 13–3

Structure	Atoms in Unit Cell
sc	1
bcc	2
hcp	2
fcc	4
diamond	8

For an example involving an ionic crystal, let us consider NaCl. The sum of the Na^+ and Cl^- radii is one-half the cube edge (Fig. 13–7), or

$$\tfrac{1}{2}(d_1 + d_2) = a/2$$

where d_1 and d_2 are the diameters of the two types of ion. The cubic unit cell contains 4 Na^+ ions and 4 Cl^- ions (i.e., 4 NaCl molecules). Thus

$$\rho = 4M/N_0a^3 \qquad \text{(NaCl)} \qquad (13\text{–}3)$$

where $M = 58.4$ is the molecular weight of NaCl. Then

$$a = (4M/N_0\rho)^{1/3} = (4 \times 58.4/6.02 \times 10^{23} \times 2.16)^{1/3} \text{ cm}$$
$$= 5.63 \text{ Å}$$

This value is also the sum of the Na^+ and Cl^- diameters. One must not conclude, however, that Na^+ accounts for 3.71 Å of the total, because the Na^+ ion, with one electron missing, is much smaller than the neutral Na atom. In fact, the Cl^- ion is nearly twice as large as the Na^+ ion, although the reasoning which leads to this conclusion is too devious for us to consider now.

Finally, we may return to Eq. 13–1 in order to consider the general range of densities which can be expected for all materials. It suggests that crystals of the heavier elements should have higher densities, and this is generally true. From hydrogen to uranium the atomic weight increases by a factor of 238. The heavier atom diameters are also somewhat larger, but not by a factor of more than about 2, as we shall see in Chapter 22. Therefore, the densities can be expected to range over a factor of 20 or 30, and this is also true. The variation with atomic number is by no means monotonic, however: the atomic size increases in any one group (column of the periodic table), but it also decreases sharply from left to right in a given row (Table 13–2) so that there are significant fluctuations throughout the table.

13–6   X-RAY DIFFRACTION

Besides the density, another effect which depends primarily on the arrangement of the atoms in the crystal is the diffraction of an incident x-ray beam in certain well-defined directions. Since crystals are regular arrangements of objects (atoms) which can scatter light, they act like (3-dimensional) diffraction gratings. If light of appropriate wave length is incident on the crystal, it will be diffracted. The appropriate wave length is one of the order of magnitude of the grating spacing (the separation between the atoms), which in this case is about 1 Å. Thus the "light" must be *x-rays*. Indeed, most of the information about the structure of crystals has been obtained in the first place by studying the pattern of x-ray diffraction by the crystal. (More recently, additional information has been obtained by neutron diffraction, but we will not consider this effect here.)

The effect results from the constructive interference of the radiation which is scattered from the various atoms and is a consequence of the

Fig. 13–10. *Scattering from a plane of atoms.*

regularity of their arrangement in space. When radiation, either light or x-rays, is incident on an atom, some of the radiation is *scattered*, in all directions. (The details of the interaction between the radiation and the atom depend on the internal electronic structure of the atom, but this need not be considered in the present calculation.) Since the interaction of x-rays with the atoms is very weak—that is why x-rays penetrate through matter —the only directions in which any appreciable scattered energy will be found are those in which billions of atoms cooperate, the directions of constructive interference. The determination of these "diffraction directions" is merely a geometrical calculation, which we now consider.

First, consider a *plane of atoms* in the crystal. This means a plane on which many atoms lie; the existence of such planes is a consequence of the regular crystal structure. From Fig. 13–10, it is obvious that two incident parallel beams, which are in phase, will be scattered *in phase* (constructive interference), if the scattering angle θ equals the incident angle θ_i, because then the optical path along the two beams is just the same. Because the emergent radiation makes the same angle with the plane as the incident radiation, just as in reflection of light from a mirror, one often speaks of the diffracted beam as a beam which is "reflected" from the plane of atoms.

Because the beam penetrates through millions of planes of the crystal, the phase difference between beams "reflected" from successive planes must also be considered. In Fig. 13–11, the path difference of the two beams shown is the sum of the two distances labeled h. Since $h = d \sin \theta$, where d is the separation of the two neighboring planes, the path difference is $2d \sin \theta$. For constructive interference (reflected beams in phase) the path difference must be an integer n times the wavelength λ of the radiation, or

$$2d \sin \theta = n\lambda \qquad (13\text{–}4)$$

This relation, called the "Bragg condition," specifies the directions (for $n = 1, 2, 3, \ldots$) in which the x-rays will be diffracted from a given set of crystal planes.

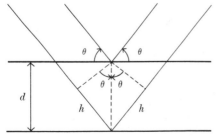

Fig. 13–11

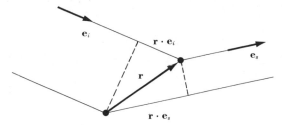

Fig. 13–12

13-7 THE BRAGG CONDITION

Before going to the application of the Bragg condition, it is worthwhile to derive it again in a more rigorous way. Consider two atoms separated by the vector $\mathbf{r}$. Radiation is incident in the direction (Fig. 13–12) $\mathbf{e}_i$ (unit vector), and scattered in the direction $\mathbf{e}_s$. For constructive interference, the path difference must be an integral number of wave lengths, so that

$$\mathbf{r}{\cdot}\mathbf{e}_s - \mathbf{r}{\cdot}\mathbf{e}_i = n\lambda$$

or

$$\mathbf{r}{\cdot}\mathbf{s} = n\lambda \qquad \mathbf{s} \equiv \mathbf{e}_s - \mathbf{e}_i$$

Now the equation $\mathbf{r}{\cdot}\mathbf{s} = $ const, with $\mathbf{s}$ a constant vector, is the vector form of the *equation of a plane* perpendicular to the direction of $\mathbf{s}$. That is clear from Fig. 13–13, since all the vectors $\mathbf{r}$ whose tips lie on the plane have the same component along $\mathbf{s}$ (the projection of $\mathbf{r}$ on $\mathbf{s}$). Thus $\mathbf{r}{\cdot}\mathbf{s}$ is the same for all those vectors. Analytically, the equation is $s_x x + s_y y + s_z z = $ const, which is the equation of a plane in Cartesian coordinates. Then all the atoms (if any) which lie on the plane whose normal is $\mathbf{s}$ interfere constructively with the atom at the origin (at distance d from the plane), provided that

$$\mathbf{r}{\cdot}\mathbf{s} = n\lambda \qquad\qquad (13\text{--}5)$$

This relation is just the *Bragg condition* Eq. 13–4, since, from Fig. 13–14, $|\mathbf{s}| = 2 \sin \theta$, so that $\mathbf{r}{\cdot}\mathbf{s} = d\, 2 \sin \theta$.

In a given crystal structure, many (in fact, infinitely many) different sets of planes containing atoms occur, all with different spacing d between

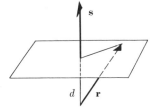

Fig. 13–13. *Vectors* $\mathbf{r}$ *lying on a plane perpendicular to* $\mathbf{s}$.

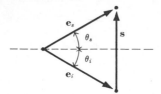

Fig. 13–14

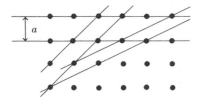

Fig. 13–15

neighboring planes of the set. For all the sets of planes, however, $d \leq a$, where a is the edge of the unit cell (Fig. 13–15). Therefore, no diffraction at all can occur for wave lengths longer than $2a$: since the Bragg condition requires that $\lambda = (2d/n) \sin \theta$, and $d \leq a$, $1/n \leq 1$, $\sin \theta \leq 1$, then

$$\lambda \leq 2a$$

This restriction is what requires the use of x-rays to observe the diffraction. In a solid, the atoms, whose diameters, we have seen, are a few Ångstroms, are "touching," so that a is of the order of a few Ångstroms. The wave length of the radiation must also lie in this region of the spectrum.

The angle θ is determined by the direction of the incident x-ray beam with respect to the crystal for each set of reflecting planes and λ is determined by the means of producing the x-rays (in a way to be considered in

Fig. 13–16(a). *Laue diffraction picture of cubic AgBr crystal, with x-ray beam incident approximately along cube edge. Note four-fold symmetry of the pattern.*

Fig. 13–16(b).   *Laue picture of AgBr with beam along cube body diagonal. Note three-fold symmetry.* [*Photographs by R. W. Christy.*]

Part IV). Thus, for given arbitrary wave length and direction of incidence, it would be mere chance if there were a set of crystal planes for which the Bragg condition were satisfied. Actually to observe diffraction, one must provide either for a continuous range of λ or a continuous range of θ. There are three principal methods for doing so, although there are many more elaborations of these methods used in practice.

(1)   *Laue method:* Single crystal sample, fixed incident angle, continuous wave length range ("white" radiation). Diffracted beams are observed (usually with photographic film) in directions where the Bragg condition is satisfied for some λ and n, for some set of planes.

(2)   *Rotating crystal method:* Single crystal sample, rotation through all incident angles, fixed wave length ("monochromatic" radiation). The diffracted beam is observed at the instant when the crystal is correctly oriented to satisfy the Bragg condition for a certain set of planes.

(3)   *Debye-Scherrer method:* Powder (or polycrystalline) sample, fixed inci-

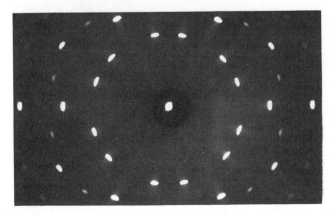

Fig. 13–16(c).   *Laue picture of Mg crystal. Note hexagonal symmetry.* [*Courtesy of C. S. Barrett,* Structure of Metals (*McGraw-Hill, New York, 3rd ed.*).]

dent angle, fixed wave length. The Bragg condition is satisfied for different planes by some of the randomly oriented grains in the sample.

13–8   THE LAUE METHOD

We may construct a simple example of Laue diffraction by a simple cubic crystal, considering only two dimensions. Let us find the reflections of white radiation from the sets of planes shown in Fig. 13–17. That is, let us calculate the direction of the emergent beams and the wave lengths of the diffracted radiation, assuming the incident direction is e_i. Notice that the angle ϕ which the diffracted beam makes with the incident direction is

$$\phi = 180° - 2\theta$$

(1) $\theta_1 = 90°$ $d_1 = a$

   $\phi_1 = 0$ $\lambda_1 = 2\dfrac{a}{n}$

(2) $\theta_2 = 45°$ $d_2 = a/\sqrt{2}$

   $\phi_2 = 90°$ $\lambda_2 = \dfrac{2a}{n\sqrt{2}}\dfrac{1}{\sqrt{2}} = \dfrac{a}{n}$

For the set (3), it is harder to find d geometrically, although it is of course a solvable problem. It is easier to appeal to the following trick: if there are N atoms in the crystal, its total volume is Na^3, since with each atom is associated a little cube of side a. The volume can also be obtained as the sum of all the little parallelopipeds (Fig. 13–18) of sides a (perpendicular to the paper), l, and d, so that $Na^3 = Na\,l\,d$, or $d = a^2/l$. The length l is easier than d to compute geometrically; in this case, it is obviously

$$l = a\sqrt{2^2 + 1^2} = a\,\sqrt{5}$$

(3) $\theta_3 = \tan^{-1} 2/1 = 63.4°$ $d_3 = a/\sqrt{5}$

   $\phi_3 = 53˘$ $\lambda_3 = \dfrac{2a}{n\sqrt{5}}\dfrac{2}{\sqrt{5}} = \dfrac{4}{5}\dfrac{a}{n}$

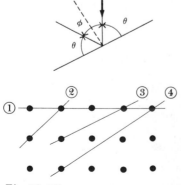

Fig. 13–17

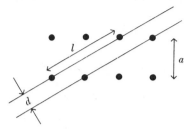

Fig. 13–18

(4) $\theta_4 = \tan^{-1} 3/2 = 56.3°$ $d_4 = a/\sqrt{13}$

$\phi_4 = 67°$ $\lambda_4 = \dfrac{2a}{n\sqrt{13}}\dfrac{3}{\sqrt{13}} = \dfrac{6}{13}\dfrac{a}{n}$

Diffracted beams will be found in many other directions, especially if the 3-dimensional problem is considered. Calculation of the intensity (as opposed to the direction) of each beam is a much more difficult problem, which will not be considered at all. It may be noted, however, that the diffracted wave lengths become shorter for the more closely spaced planes. Since there must be a shortest wave length λ_{min} contained in the incident radiation—otherwise the beam would contain infinite energy—there is also a shortest wave length that can be diffracted,

$$\lambda \geq \lambda_{min}$$

(determined by the x-ray source, rather than by the crystal structure). For typical radiation, we will see later that $\lambda_{min} \approx \frac{1}{4}$ Å. The number of "orders" of reflection (values of n) which can be obtained from the set of planes (2), for example, is $n_{max} = a/\lambda_{min}$. If $a \approx 3$ Å, $n_{max} \approx 12$. For more closely spaced planes, fewer orders can be reflected and the intensity of the reflection is weaker.

From diffraction angles determined with the Laue method, the structure and the orientation of the specimen can be deduced, but not the unit cell dimension a, since it is impossible (or rather, inordinately difficult) to measure the wave lengths of the diffracted beams. The other two methods do yield the value of a, if the wave length of the monochromatic x-ray source is known.

PROBLEMS

13–1. Show that the proportion of the total volume actually occupied by hard spheres in contact is

$$\pi/6 = 0.52 \quad \text{for simple cubic}$$
$$\sqrt{2}\pi/6 = 0.74 \quad \text{for fcc or hcp}$$

13–2. Locate the tetragonal interstitial sites in the hcp structure, recalling that they are at the center of 4 symmetrically placed nearest neighbor atoms of the structure. (If half of these are occupied by another type of ion, one obtains the "wurtzite" structure, named for a second modification of ZnS.)

13–3.   Calculate the percentage of contraction to be expected when α-iron transforms to γ-iron.

13–4.   In the *Handbook of Chemistry and Physics*, look up the structures of oxides and sulfides of divalent metals. Is there any regularity in those which have NaCl structure in contrast to one of the ZnS structures?

13–5.   Look up the density of Cu and calculate the side of the unit cell. What is the diameter of a Cu atom?

13–6.   Look up the densities of all the alkali metals. Calculate the diameters of the atoms.

13–7.   Look up the densities of the alkali earth metals and calculate their diameters. Compare them with the alkali metal in the same row of the periodic table (Prob. 13–6).

13–8.   According to our interpretation, if the ions Na^+, K^+, Cl^-, Br^-, have well defined diameters, one should find $a_{NaBr} + a_{KCl} = a_{KBr} + a_{NaCl}$. Calculate the side of the unit cell from the densities and check this relation.

13–9.   Calculate the sum of the Cs^+ and Cl^- diameters from the density of CsCl.

13–10. Calculate the sum of the Zn^{++} and S^{--} diameters from the density of zincblende. Would a volume change be expected when the structure changes to wurtzite? (See Prob. 13–2.)

13–11. In x-ray diffraction work, x-rays of wave length 1.54 Å (emitted by a copper-target x-ray tube), are commonly used. What is the smallest angle at which these x-rays could be reflected from NaCl, where the nearest neighbor distance is 2.81 Å? How many other orders of reflection would there be from the same set of planes?

13–12. In the Laue method, suppose "white" x-ray radiation is incident normal to a cube face of an NaCl crystal. Calculate some angles at which reflected radiation would be observed.

13–13. If white radiation were incident on an NaCl crystal normal to a plane through a *face diagonal* (such as the plane (2) in Fig. 13–17), rather than normal to a cube face as in Prob. 13–12, calculate some angles at which reflected radiation would be observed.

REFERENCES

C. Zwikker, *Physical Properties of Solid Materials* (Pergamon Press, 1954), Ch. II.

A. J. Dekker, *Solid State Physics* (Prentice-Hall, 1957), Ch. 1.

C. Kittel, *Introduction to Solid State Physics* (John Wiley & Sons, 1956, 2nd ed.), Ch. 2.

R. C. Evans, *An Introduction to Crystal Chemistry* (Cambridge, 1948).

R. W. James, *X-Ray Crystallography* (Methuen, 1953, 5th ed.).

14/mechanical and thermal properties of crystals

The kind of structure assumed by a particular substance is determined by the law of forces between the atoms. We shall next investigate the physical structure of a crystal, as opposed to the mere geometrical arrangement of the atoms. Symmetry of the interatomic forces can lead to symmetry in the crystal: the spherically symmetric noble gas atoms crystallize in the fcc close packed structure, whereas unsymmetrical organic molecules usually have crystal structures of much lower symmetry. The actual force laws between the atoms are quite complicated and depend on the electronic structure of the atoms, which can only be understood quantum mechanically. The attempt to predict these forces theoretically will therefore be deferred, and at this point we will simply assume *a law of force between the atoms and see what macroscopic properties of the crystal we can calculate on this basis. Conversely, we can regard the macroscopic properties as giving empirical information about the microscopic force laws, which should later be explained by a quantum mechanical theory of atomic structure. In this program we shall not be much concerned with fine distinctions between different crystal structure types but will concentrate on an example—the ionic crystal—which is particularly simple.*

The atoms are still assumed at first to remain at their equilibrium positions, which assumption amounts to holding the crystal at the absolute zero of temperature, as we shall learn later in this chapter. We shall allow the equilibrium positions to be displaced, however, by the application of external forces, in considering the elastic moduli. Afterwards, we shall consider the vibrations about the equilibrium positions which occur at all temperatures above absolute zero, and shall calculate the heat capacity and other thermal properties of the crystal.

14–1   INTERATOMIC FORCES

The general form of the interatomic force law has already been discussed in Section 7–2, in connection with the van der Waals equation of state. In order to have a condensed phase (e.g., a liquid) there have to be attractive forces, and for it to have a non-zero volume there have to be repulsive forces in addition. We even obtained in Section 8–3 quantitative information about the repulsive forces from the mean free path, determined through the measurement of transport processes in the gas, though this did not depend strongly on the attractive forces. The interatomic force law (force field) which acts between the atoms of a solid is identical to that between the same atoms when they are in the gaseous phase. (This is not strictly true in metals or ionic materials, since the atoms themselves are somewhat modified—ionized—in the solid.) The important difference here is not in the force law, but in the fact that in the gas the atoms spend most of their time far apart, where the forces are weak, but in the condensed phase they are always close together, where the forces are strong. We are presently interested in the same picture as before (Fig. 14–1(a)), but on a different scale (Fig. 14–1(b)).

In fact, our attention will be restricted to the region near the distance $r = d_0$ where the repulsive force and the attractive force are equal (the net force is zero), or where the potential energy has a *minimum*. This separation will be related to the nearest neighbor distance in the crystal, the equilibrium separation of the atoms. If only forces between nearest neighbors are important, as in a solid noble gas, the nearest neighbor distance will be equal to the separation at the potential energy minimum; but if longer range forces between more distant neighbors are important, as they are in ionic crystals, then the equilibrium distance will be slightly modified.

In order to draw any quantitative conclusions, it is necessary to have an analytical expression for the potential energy curve. An empirical expression which has the right shape was proposed long ago (1907) by G. Mie,

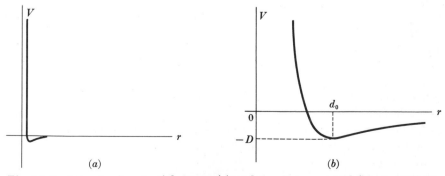

Fig. 14–1. *Interatomic potential energy* (a) *at large distances, and* (b) *at small distances.*

20 years before it was possible to say much about the theoretical shape. The *Mie potential* is in the form of two power laws:

$$V(r) = -\frac{A}{r^m} + \frac{B}{r^n} \quad n > m \tag{14-1}$$

The constants A and B are positive, and it is necessary to have $n > m$ so that the positive term will dominate (approach ∞ faster) as r goes to zero and vanish faster as r goes to infinity, thus assuring that the force is attractive for large r and repulsive for small r. Other expressions have been proposed subsequently, based on better theoretical understanding, but they do not give much better agreement with experiment and they are harder to handle algebraically, so we shall work with the Mie potential.

The analysis of transport processes in gases has already shown us that the repulsive exponent is large, say of the order of $n = 10$. This fact justifies our discussion of crystal structure in terms of the packing of hard spheres (for which $n = \infty$). The spheres are not quite ideally hard, however, and we intend to relate this fact to the compressibility of the real solid. The kinetic theory of gases did not yield much information about the attractive exponent m. We are therefore fortunate that there is one case in which we can predict m without appeal to a quantum mechanical theory. An *ionic crystal*, such as NaCl, is assumed to be constructed of Na^+ and Cl^- ions, rather than of Na and Cl atoms. The validity of this assumption can be justified quantum mechanically, but its real justification lies in agreement between the effects that we shall calculate on the basis of it and the observed properties of NaCl crystals. With this assumption, the attraction between the Na^+ ions and the Cl^- ions is just the electrostatic coulomb attraction e^2/r. Thus, for a monovalent ionic crystal, we have (in cgs units)

$$A = e^2 \quad m = 1 \tag{14-2}$$

(In mks units, $A = e^2/4\pi\epsilon_0$.) The theory can actually be developed generally for other types of binding, but it is most useful for the ionic binding, and so we will henceforth restrict our attention mainly to it.

14-2 MOLECULAR BINDING

Before discussing the application of Eqs. 14-1 and 14-2 to the problem involving an enormous number of atoms (or ions) held together in a crystal, it will be advantageous to digress for a moment, in order to discuss first the simpler problem of two atoms held together in a diatomic molecule. For definiteness, we can think of an NaCl molecule, which can exist in sodium chloride vapor. We shall assume that the potential energy of interaction is of the form given by Eq. 14-1 and compute the energy difference between the stable equilibrium state of the molecule (when the potential energy is a minimum) and the state when the two ions are separated infinitely far from one another. (See Fig. 14-1(b).) This energy, called the *dissociation energy D* of the molecule, can be measured experimentally and compared with our theoretical calculation.

First, we must calculate $V(d_0)$ from the Mie potential, Eq. 14–1. To do so, we shall eliminate the unknown parameter B, in terms of the empirically known parameter d_0. We use the fact that V has its minimum at $r = d_0$ (Fig. 14–1(b)):

$$\left. \frac{dV}{dr} \right]_{r=d_0} = 0$$

Differentiating $V(r)$ with respect to r, and setting the result equal to zero for $r = d_0$, we find

$$B = \frac{m}{n} A d_0^{n-m} \tag{14–3}$$

or

$$V(r) = -\frac{A}{d_0^m}\left[\left(\frac{d_0}{r}\right)^m - \frac{m}{n}\left(\frac{d_0}{r}\right)^n\right] \tag{14–4}$$

This expression contains the constant d_0, which is measurable as the internuclear distance in the molecule, in place of the constant B. The potential minimum is then

$$V(d_0) = -\frac{A}{d_0^m}\left(1 - \frac{m}{n}\right) \tag{14–5}$$

Specializing to the monovalent ionic diatomic molecule, by using Eq. 14–2,

$$V(d_0) = -\frac{e^2}{d_0}\left(1 - \frac{1}{n}\right) \tag{14–6}$$

The energy is just the coulomb energy $-e^2/d_0$, modified by the factor $(1 - 1/n)$ involving the repulsive potential. The dissociation energy of the molecule D is then defined as

$$D \equiv -V(d_0)$$

Equation 14–6 predicts a relation between the dissociation energy D and the internuclear distance d_0. In order to compare this prediction with experiment, we must know the repulsive exponent n. As we have already seen, n is large—about 10. The repulsive contribution to the energy is therefore small, of the order of 10%, so that it does not make too much difference exactly what value we use for n. In fact, for reasons to be seen later, we shall use $n = 9$, but the difference between $n = 9$ and $n = 10$ would result in only a 1% difference in D. Both d_0 and D can be inferred from the infrared spectrum of NaCl vapor. The experimental value is $d_0 = 2.5$ Å, so that from Eq. 14–6,

$$D = \frac{4.8^2 \times 10^{-20}}{2.5 \times 10^{-8}} \frac{8}{9} = 8.1 \times 10^{-12} \text{ erg} = 5.1 \text{ eV}$$

for NaCl. This result is in close agreement (within about 4%) of the experimental value, thus justifying our theoretical treatment. In order to avoid confusion, we should emphasize that D is the energy to dissociate the molecule into ions,

$$NaCl \rightarrow Na^+ + Cl^-$$

Frequently the dissociation energy is defined instead as the energy to dissociate the molecule into neutral atoms,

$$NaCl \rightarrow Na + Cl$$

The ionization energy required in the intermediate step,

$$Na + Cl \rightarrow Na^+ + Cl^-$$

depends on the electronic structure of the atoms, and will not be considered until Chapter 22.

14–3   CRYSTAL BINDING ENERGY

As the first and simplest application to a solid, we will calculate what is usually regarded as a *chemical* rather than a physical property of a solid, namely the *binding energy*. The binding energy means the energy which must be supplied (in the form of heat usually) in order to disperse the crystal into ions all infinitely far apart from each other. (It is measurable in terms of the heat of vaporization of the solid, the dissociation energy of NaCl, and ionization energy of Na and Cl.) Clearly it is related to the difference in potential energy when the ions are at their equilibrium separation and when they are at ∞. In fact, it is something like the total number of ions N times the potential energy minimum $V(d_0)$.

Let us return to the potential energy of interaction between two atoms (or ions), Eq. 14–1; in the solid where many atoms are present it is important to take into account the interaction between a given atom and all of the other atoms. This interaction may involve not only the nearest neighbors, but also more distant neighbors, especially in the case of the long range coulomb force acting between ions. In NaCl, for example, a given Na^+ ion has both a repulsive and an attractive interaction with its 6 nearest neighbor Cl^- ions. It also has an appreciable coulomb interaction with its 12 next nearest neighbor Na^+ ions, although the short range repulsive interaction is very small since these ions are not in "contact." Even the coulomb interaction does not build up to an extraordinarily large value, however, because it not only falls off with increasing distance but in addition there is an alternating positive and negative contribution from successive shells of Na^+ and Cl^- ions. In short, the potential energy of a given ion interacting with all of the other ions can be written, instead of Eq. 14–1,

$$V'(r) = -\alpha \frac{A}{r^m} + \beta \frac{B}{r^n} \tag{14–7}$$

where r is the separation between nearest neighbors. The constants α and β, which take into account the interactions with all the neighbors, can be expected to be not very different from unity, and they could be calculated exactly for any given crystal structure. When we add up all these gradually diminishing contributions, we find that they are in sum not very much different from the contribution of one neighbor.

Now the calculation of the crystal binding energy can proceed just like that of the binding energy for a molecule. First we eliminate the coefficient of the repulsive potential by introducing the nearest neighbor separation d instead. (We will see below that the equilibrium separation d in the crystal is somewhat different from d_0, that in the diatomic molecule.) Differentiating Eq. 14–7,

$$\frac{dV'}{dr}\bigg]_{r=d} = 0$$

we find

$$\beta B = \frac{m}{n}\, \alpha A d^{n-m} \tag{14-8}$$

Inserting this expression into Eq. 14–7,

$$V'(r) = -\alpha \frac{A}{d^m}\left[\left(\frac{d}{r}\right)^m - \frac{m}{n}\left(\frac{d}{r}\right)^n\right] \tag{14-9}$$

This is the energy of interaction between a given ion and all of the other ions. At the potential energy minimum it becomes

$$V'(d) = -\alpha \frac{A}{d^m}\left(1 - \frac{m}{n}\right) \tag{14-10}$$

The binding energy U for one mole is then

$$U = -N_0 V'(d)$$

where N_0 is Avogadro's number. There are $2N_0$ ions in a mole of molecules, but then a factor $\frac{1}{2}$ is inserted in order to avoid counting each pair of ions twice. Thus the binding energy is

$$U = \alpha N_0 \frac{A}{d^m}\left(1 - \frac{m}{n}\right) \tag{14-11}$$

Specializing to the monovalent ionic case by using Eq. 14–2,

$$U = \alpha N_0 \frac{e^2}{d}\left(1 - \frac{1}{n}\right) \tag{14-12}$$

This result is essentially N_0 times the molecular binding energy Eq. 14–6, except for the factor α and the slightly different equilibrium separation d in place of d_0. The constant α is called the *Madelung constant*, and its value for the NaCl structure has been computed to be $\alpha = 1.748$ . . . . The values of the Madelung constant for other ionic crystal structures are shown in Table 14–1.

Our theoretical result may be compared with the value of 183 kcal/mole

Table 14–1

	Structure	Madelung Constant α
NaCl	Sodium chloride	1.748
CsCl	Cesium chloride	1.763
ZnS	Zincblende	1.638

for NaCl obtained by calorimetry. The number of molecules per unit volume is $1/2d^3$. (d^3 is the volume associated with one ion in the NaCl structure; the number of molecules is $\frac{1}{2}$ the number of ions.) Therefore the density is

$$\rho = M/2d^3N_0$$

where M is the molecular weight. Using $N_0 = 6.02 \times 10^{23}$ mole^{-1}, $\rho = 2.16$ g/cm^3, $M = 58.4$ g/mole, we find $d = 2.81 \times 10^{-8}$ cm. Then with $n = 9$, we get $U = 184$ kcal/mole, in very good agreement with the experimental value. This good agreement is actually what justifies the assumption that the binding is ionic in the NaCl crystal. The binding energy of 184 kcal/mole = 8.0 eV/molecule is somewhat greater than the binding energy of a single molecule calculated in the last section.

By comparing Eq. 14–3 with Eq. 14–8, we see that the equilibrium separation in the solid should be somewhat different from that in the isolated molecule:

$$d = d_0\left(\frac{\beta}{\alpha}\right)^{1/(n-m)}$$

In fact d turns out to be slightly greater than d_0, as follows. Since the repulsive force is short range, we might expect that only the 6 nearest neighbor interactions would contribute, so that $\beta \cong 6$, accounting for the repulsive interaction of these 6 nearest neighbors. The Madelung constant is $\alpha = 1.748$, smaller than β because the positive and negative long range coulomb interactions partly cancel when distant neighbors are taken into account. Thus

$$d \cong d_0(6/1.748)^{1/3} = 1.16d_0$$

The experimental values give $d = (2.8/2.5)\, d_0 = 1.12\, d_0$, again in fairly good agreement with the theory.

A *divalent* ionic crystal should have a much larger binding energy than a monovalent one, because in place of Eq. 14–2 we have

$$A = (2e)^2 = 4e^2$$

For example, CaS has the NaCl structure and nearly the same lattice constant as NaCl (within 1%), so that its binding energy should be 4 times larger, or 732 kcal/mole. No experimental value is available, but the large binding energies of alkali earth oxides and sulfides are evidenced by their very high melting points.

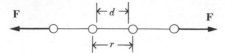

Fig. 14–2

14–4   ELASTIC MODULUS

Next we want to show that this same model of the interatomic force implies that Hooke's law holds for the solid material and gives a reasonable value for the elastic modulus. To do so, let us consider a particular *line* of atoms running all the way through the crystal. We will apply an external force to either end of the line and pull all the atoms further apart. The separation of each pair of atoms will be increased from $r = d$ to $r = d + x$ (Fig. 14–2). At this larger separation, the potential energy is higher (Fig. 14–3), and there is an attractive force exerted between each pair of atoms. To hold the system in equilibrium, the external force must just balance this interatomic attractive force. We therefore must first calculate the force from the Mie potential energy.

The force is obtained by differentiating Eq. 14–9, the expression for the potential energy:

$$F(r) = -\frac{dV'}{dr} = -\alpha m A \left[\frac{1}{r^{m+1}} - \frac{d^{n-m}}{r^{n+1}} \right]$$

Specializing to the monovalent ionic crystal with $A = e^2$, $m = 1$,

$$F(r) = -\alpha e^2 \left[\frac{1}{r^2} - \frac{d^{n-1}}{r^{n+1}} \right]$$

In this force, we substitute (Fig. 14–3)

$$r = d + x = d(1 + \epsilon) \qquad \text{where} \qquad \epsilon \equiv x/d$$

is the *strain*. It is not only the microscopic strain of the bond between two atoms, but is also the macroscopic strain of the whole line of atoms, since

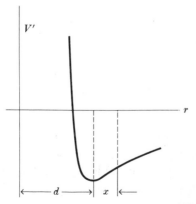

Fig. 14–3. *Displacement from equilibrium separation.*

if we increase the separation of each pair of atoms in the chain by 1%, say, then the length of the whole chain increases by 1% too. With this substitution, the force in terms of ϵ becomes

$$F = - \frac{\alpha e^2}{d^2} \left[(1 + \epsilon)^{-2} - (1 + \epsilon)^{-n-1} \right] \qquad (14\text{--}13)$$

Unfortunately, this force does not appear to be a linear function of the strain, so that we have not derived Hooke's law. Recall, however, that Hooke's law holds only for *small* strains, and our intention was to limit the discussion to small strains at this point. Therefore it is legitimate to expand F in a power series (Taylor series) in ϵ, and keep only the lowest order term. Making this expansion (or using the binomial theorem),

$$F \cong - \frac{\alpha e^2}{d^2} \left[1 - 2\epsilon - 1 + (n + 1)\epsilon \right]$$

$$F \cong - \frac{\alpha(n - 1)e^2}{d^2} \, \epsilon \qquad (14\text{--}14)$$

Having obtained Hooke's law, in order to find the elastic modulus we have only to express the stress instead of the force. Since the cross sectional area of the line of atoms under consideration is d^2, the stress is

$$S \cong F/d^2$$

Then

$$S \cong - \frac{\alpha(n - 1)e^2}{d^4} \, \epsilon$$

and the coefficient is the elastic modulus. (The minus sign is there because we are considering the internal stress, i.e., the force per unit area with which the material resists the applied stress, rather than the applied stress itself which is equal and opposite to it.) This coefficient indeed turns out to be of approximately the right order of magnitude.

The above calculation shows why Hooke's law holds and is the same for tension and compression, and it gives a qualitative estimate of Young's modulus. It is not accurate enough for quantitative purposes, however. The reason is that the calculation was based on a consideration of $V'(r)$, where r was supposed to be the nearest neighbor distance between any pair of ions. Now when a tensile stress is applied, the distance between ions in the direction parallel to the stress is increased, but in the perpendicular directions the distance is not increased by the same amount. Indeed, in general the interionic distance in the perpendicular directions is *decreased*. Thus an accurate calculation of Young's modulus is fairly difficult.

It is possible, however, to make a straightforward calculation of the response to a hydrostatic pressure, because then the interionic distances all decrease in the same proportion. We shall not carry through this calculation, but merely quote the result, which gives the *bulk modulus* β (not to be confused with the constant β in Eq. 14–7). The result is

$$\beta = \gamma \, \frac{\alpha(n-1)e^2}{d^4} \tag{14–15}$$

This result is the same as the one which we derived, except for the numerical constant γ. The value of γ is characteristic of the structure type, and some values are listed in Table 14–2.

Table 14–2

Structure	γ
Sodium chloride	1/18
Cesium chloride	$1/8\sqrt{3}$
Zincblende	$1/16\sqrt{3}$

Returning to the case of NaCl, and using the values of the Madelung constant α and n and d which were previously given for NaCl, Eq. 14–15 gives $\beta = 2.9 \times 10^{11}$ dyne/cm², in agreement with the experimental value, when it is extrapolated to $T = 0$. The numerical factor $1/18$, which appears in the accurate calculation of the bulk modulus, is rather different from 1, but our crude calculation nevertheless gave the correct dependence on the quantities α, n, e, and d. (Young's modulus is not very far from the bulk modulus in numerical value.) In fact, this expression, Eq. 14–15, gives the best way to determine the exponent n. The bulk modulus is essentially proportional to n, whereas the binding energy Eq. 14–12 contained n as a small contribution.

Our simple model can give good quantitative agreement with two properties of the crystal which at first sight do not seem to be very closely related—the chemical binding energy and the elastic moduli. It has also explained Hooke's law, and the fact that the tensile modulus is equal to the compressive modulus in all materials. These latter two facts resulted simply because we used the first order approximation to the interatomic force, and this approximate force law is linear in the displacement and symmetric about the equilibrium position.

14–5   THERMAL VIBRATIONS

At any temperature above absolute zero, the atoms of a solid will not all be at rest at their equilibrium separations, as has hitherto been assumed, but they will move around with a thermal motion, like the atoms in a gas. In fact, we will find that, just as in the case of a gas, the average kinetic energy is

$$\tfrac{1}{2}m\overline{v^2} = \tfrac{3}{2}kT$$

The character of the motion will prove to be quite different from that in the gas, however. In the solid, the atoms merely vibrate back and forth about their equilibrium positions, instead of making long free flights only occasionally interrupted by collisions. In the gas, the analysis of the problem was simplified because we could completely neglect the interactions

between the atoms to a good approximation (except during the brief collisions). In a solid, the interaction cannot be neglected—the atoms are
constantly "colliding" with their neighbors—but nevertheless the problem
becomes quite simple when we regard each atom as vibrating individually
about its fixed equilibrium position. In a liquid, we are not helped by either
of these simplifications—the atoms are close together and in constant interaction, yet at the same time they are all milling around and can wander far
from their initial positions. This is why we leave the problem of the liquid
out of consideration. In this section, we will first estimate the frequency at
which the atoms vibrate, and then in the following sections we will calculate some thermal properties of the solid—its heat capacity and thermal
expansion coefficient.

In order to estimate the vibrational frequency, let us return to Eq. 14–14,
and replace ϵ by x/d. Then

$$F \cong - \left[\frac{\alpha(n-1)e^2}{d^3} \right] x \tag{14–16}$$

The interatomic force is seen to be approximately of the form of the harmonic oscillator force, and so we can use the theory of the harmonic oscillator to write down the vibrational frequency. We recall, however, that a
more accurate calculation of the elastic constant introduces a numerical
factor which is not negligible. Furthermore, in the present case we should
seek the frequency of a single ion when all the other ions are held fixed,
whereas in the elastic modulus calculation, all the interionic distances were
assumed to increase by the same fraction. To compound the difficulty, in
reality the other ions are not fixed, but all the ions are vibrating simultaneously, and the relative distances are changing in a complex way. Therefore
we shall content ourselves with reverting to a simpler problem for our frequency calculation, namely the problem of the vibrational frequency of the
diatomic molecule. This problem can be carried through with some exacti-
tude, and it will yield the result referred to in Section 4–4.

In order to calculate the vibrational frequency for the molecule, it is
necessary to calculate the force from Eq. 14–4 instead of Eq. 14–9. The result is the same as Eq. 14–13, except for the absence of α and the occurrence of d_0 in place of d. When the expansion which led to Eq. 14–14 or Eq.
14–16 is carried out, we obtain instead

$$F \cong - \left[\frac{(n-1)e^2}{d_0^3} \right] x = - Kx$$

where

$$K \equiv \frac{(n-1)e^2}{d_0^3} \tag{14–17}$$

This approximation amounts to approximating the potential energy (Fig.
14–1(b)) by a parabola for r close to d_0, which gives the linear restoring

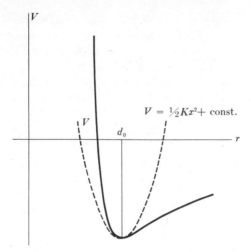

Fig. 14–4. Approximation of interatomic potential energy by an harmonic oscillator potential.

force of the harmonic oscillator (Fig. 14–4). Then we can use the result which was found for the harmonic oscillator in Eq. 4–10:

$$\nu = \frac{1}{2\pi}\sqrt{\frac{K}{m}} = \frac{1}{2\pi}\sqrt{\frac{(n-1)e^2}{md_0^3}}$$

If we insert the values previously used for n and d_0 in NaCl, and for m use the reduced mass, we obtain

$$\nu = 1.13 \times 10^{13} \text{ sec}^{-1} \qquad \text{(NaCl)}$$

This value is within 1% of the experimental one and completely vindicates our use of the Mie potential and its approximation by a parabola for small vibrations.

Returning to the case of the crystal, we may assume that the atomic vibration frequency in the solid will be of roughly the same order of magnitude. This elastic vibration is actually related to the propagation of *sound* in the crystal, since it represents a displacement of the medium. The frequency, however, is orders of magnitude greater than the highest frequency which can be observed by acoustic means. But it can be observed by an interaction with *light* in an ionic crystal. Because the ions carry charges, the alternating electric field of a light wave will set them into forced vibration (Fig. 14–5). If the frequency of the light is the same as the natural fre-

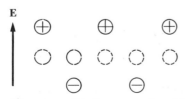

Fig. 14–5. Displacement of positive and negative ions in an electric field.

quency of the vibration, "resonance" occurs, with a maximum amplitude of vibration and a maximum absorption of light. The light whose frequency is 10^{13} sec^{-1} has a wave length of

$$\lambda = \frac{c}{\nu} = 3 \times 10^{-3} \text{ cm} = 30\mu$$

(A micron μ is 10^{-6} m $= 10^{-4}$ cm $= 10^4$ Å.) Light of wave length 30μ, or 300,000 Å, lies very far in the *infrared*. Therefore we should expect an ionic crystal to have a strong infrared absorption band. This band (called "reststrahlen" in the literature) is observed; in NaCl it occurs at 61μ. Although this agreement is no better than our crude argument deserves, it gives additional confidence in the usefulness of our model. In any case, it ought to be emphasized that the discrepancy stems not primarily from an inadequacy of the Mie potential, but from our failure to account for the simultaneous motion of all the ions. This failure can be remedied by an analysis of the so-called "normal modes" of vibration, but we cannot carry it out now. Indeed, the assumption that each ion vibrates about its own equilibrium position with a fixed frequency is still adequate for many purposes, even though we have had some difficulty in making a precise calculation of what that effective frequency is.

14–6   HEAT CAPACITY

Having estimated the frequency of atomic vibration in a solid, we will next calculate the *amplitude* of vibration to be expected at any temperature T. If we still assume that the displacement from equilibrium is small, i.e., the amplitude of vibration is small, we can use the parabolic potential as an approximation, so that the energy is related to the amplitude as for the harmonic oscillator, Eq. 4–2,

$$E = \tfrac{1}{2}KA^2$$

Actually, the total energy E is not constant for a given atom, which is constantly exchanging energy with its neighbors. What we want is the *average thermal energy* $\bar{E}$, and we can calculate it using the Boltzmann distribution, Eq. 9–21,

$$\bar{E} = \frac{\int Ee^{-E/kT}\, dv_x\, dv_y\, dv_z\, dx\, dy\, dz}{\int e^{-E/kT}\, dv_x\, dv_y\, dv_z\, dx\, dy\, dz}$$

Since, for the harmonic oscillator,

$$E = \tfrac{1}{2}mv_x{}^2 + \tfrac{1}{2}mv_y{}^2 + \tfrac{1}{2}mv_z{}^2 + \tfrac{1}{2}Kx^2 + \tfrac{1}{2}Ky^2 + \tfrac{1}{2}Kz^2$$

we get a term in $\bar{E}$ just as in the case of the ideal gas, Eq. 9–24,

$$kT \frac{\displaystyle\int_{-\infty}^{\infty} \xi^2\, e^{-\xi^2}\, d\xi}{\displaystyle\int_{-\infty}^{\infty} e^{-\xi^2}\, d\xi} = \tfrac{1}{2}kT$$

for each of the terms $\frac{1}{2}mv_x^2$, etc. But here, in addition, we get $\frac{1}{2}kT$ for each of the terms $\frac{1}{2}Kx^2$, etc., which have exactly the same functional form. The result is that

$$\bar{E} = 3kT \tag{14--18}$$

for the assembly of oscillators. This is another example of the *Law of Equipartition of Energy:* with each degree of freedom (component of position or velocity) is associated an average thermal energy $\frac{1}{2}kT$—here there are 6 degrees of freedom in this sense.

The total *thermal energy* for one mole of atoms is

$$U_T = N_0\bar{E} = 3RT \tag{14--19}$$

since $R = N_0k$. The *heat capacity* per mole (at constant volume) is

$$C = dU_T/dT = 3R = 6 \text{ cal/mole-deg} \tag{14--20}$$

for all solids. This result is the classical law of Dulong and Petit, which was first discovered empirically. As in the case of a gas, the heat capacity of a solid is independent of the details of the interatomic force law and of the mass of the atoms, because of the equipartition of energy law. (In particular, it does not depend on the frequency of the atomic vibration.) It is twice as large as that of a monatomic gas, however, since not only is the kinetic energy increased by a rise in temperature but also the potential energy. (In the gas, the potential energy is about zero, but for the harmonic oscillator the average potential energy equals the average kinetic energy.) As in the case of ideal gases, the heat capacity of ideal solids is the same for all materials, so long as it is referred to one mole of the material.

We can now check whether our assumption of small vibrations is realistic. At room temperature (300°K),

$$U_T = 3RT = 1800 \text{ cal/mole} = 1.8 \text{ kcal/mole}$$

so that the thermal energy is only about 1% of the binding energy U (Fig. 14–6). The amplitude of vibration is a correspondingly small fraction

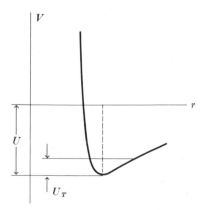

Fig. 14–6. Thermal energy U_T.

of the equilibrium interatomic distance. Even though our approximations are well justified, nevertheless the Dulong and Petit law fails. Surprisingly, it fails disastrously not at high temperatures, where the vibration amplitude becomes larger, but at very low temperatures: the specific heat of all substances goes to zero as T approaches zero. (See Fig. 14–7.) This failure of the law of equipartition was considered one of the most disappointing failures of the Boltzmann principle, but ironically it was not the statistical principle which was at fault. Really this was one of the earliest known *failures of classical mechanics.* An essentially correct theory of heat capacity at low temperature (Fig. 14–7) was given by the genius of Einstein (1907), as soon as the quantum idea was put forward in another connection by Planck. (See Chapter 18 for this quantum mechanical calculation.)

14–7 THERMAL EXPANSION COEFFICIENT

Next we will try to estimate the thermal expansion coefficient. Here, for the first time, we will find that the first order approximation, which treats the interatomic force as a harmonic oscillator, is not good enough. The reason is that the parabolic potential would predict *no* thermal expansion at all. Because the potential is symmetrical, the mean position would be unchanged, no matter how great the amplitude of vibration. Thus no matter how large the thermal vibrations, the average separation of the atoms would not increase. It is true that the expansion coefficient is rather small for solids, but it is not exactly zero, and so we must proceed to the next order of approximation. The real potential is unsymmetrical (Fig. 14–8), so that as the amplitude of vibration (thermal energy) increases, the mean position is displaced toward the right, corresponding to larger average separations between the atoms.

In order to take this asymmetry into account, let us carry our power series expansion of Eq. 14–13 beyond the harmonic term which is linear in x. When the first *anharmonic* term in the force is included, one terminates the power series expansion with

$$F \cong - K_1 x + K_2 x^2$$

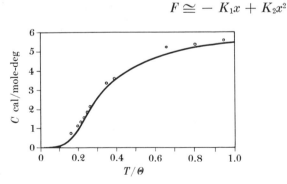

Fig. 14–7. *Heat capacity of diamond as a function of temperature. The curve is calculated theoretically in Section 18–6, where* Θ *is defined. The value of* Θ *for diamond is* 1320°K. [*After A. Einstein*, Ann. Physik **22,** 180 (1907).]

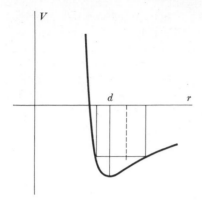

Fig. 14–8. *Asymmetry in potential energy which leads to thermal expansion.*

The coefficient K_1 has already been found in Eq. 14–17 to be approximately (replacing d_0 by d)

$$K_1 \approx \frac{(n-1)e^2}{d^3}$$

The calculation of K_2, by carrying the power series expansion to one more term, will be left as a problem (Prob. 14–16). When this term is included, the particles spend more time at greater separations, the higher the average energy.

Very roughly, the thermal expansion can be found as follows. Take the time average of the force; this must be zero, as the particle has no average acceleration (or else it would move away from its lattice position).

$$\bar{F} = 0 = -K_1\bar{x} + K_2\overline{x^2}$$

Therefore the mean displacement of the particle is

$$\bar{x} = \frac{K_2}{K_1}\overline{x^2}$$

Now using for the time average of the square displacement the value given by the equipartition law,

$$\tfrac{1}{2}K_1\overline{x^2} = \tfrac{1}{2}kT$$

we have

$$\bar{x} = \frac{K_2}{K_1{}^2}kT$$

Dividing by d to get the strain, and dividing by T to get the expansion coefficient,

$$\alpha \approx \frac{kK_2}{dK_1{}^2}$$

(The thermal expansion coefficient is not to be confused with the Madelung constant. We use the same symbol α for both in order to abide by established convention.)

Inserting the appropriate numbers, one finds that this expression agrees in order of magnitude with the experimental value for NaCl,

$$\alpha = 4 \times 10^{-5} \text{ deg}^{-1}$$

The classical theory predicts that α is independent of temperature and at higher temperatures it very nearly is. Like the heat capacity, however, α vanishes at $T = 0°K$, a fact which can only be understood quantum mechanically.

PROBLEMS

14–1. Compute the crystal binding energies and compare with the experimental values given for the following:

(a)
	LiCl	NaCl	KCl	RbCl	
	198	183	164	160	kcal/mole

(b)
	NaCl	NaBr	NaI	
	183	173	166	kcal/mole

14–2. The Madelung constant for the CsCl structure has the value 1.763. Calculate the binding energy of CsCl and compare with the experimental value of 155 kcal/mole.

14–3. Calculate the binding energy of AgCl and AgBr (NaCl structure) and compare with the respective experimental values 206 and 202 kcal/mole.

14–4. The Madelung constant for the cubic ZnS structure is 1.638. Calculate the binding energy of CuCl, which has this structure. The experimental value is 222 kcal/mole.

14–5. The binding energy and the elastic modulus can be calculated from the general form of the Mie potential, Eq. 14–9, without specializing to the ionic crystal case where the attractive potential is the coulomb potential. (a) Show that for a *monatomic* crystal the binding energy is

$$U = \frac{1}{2} N_0 \alpha \frac{A}{d^m} \left(1 - \frac{m}{n} \right)$$

(b) Show that the elastic modulus is

$$\beta = \gamma \frac{\alpha A m (n - m)}{d^{m+3}}$$

14–6. For the alkali metals, it is possible to give a crude justification of the Mie potential with $A = e^2$, $m = 1$, $n = 2$ (by considering the quantum mechanical behavior of the conduction electrons). Calculate the binding energy and bulk modulus for Na metal (bcc), assuming $\alpha \approx 6$. (See Prob. 14–5.) The experimental values are 144 kcal/mole (of which 118 kcal/mole is the ionization energy of Na) and 0.5×10^{11} dyne/cm². (For this structure, the factor γ in Prob. 14–5 should be $1/8\sqrt{3}$.)

14–7. For the rare gas atoms, the attractive potential can be shown theoretically to obey an inverse sixth power law. Below 84°K, argon is a solid with fcc structure. (a) Evaluate the expression for the binding energy of argon, assuming $m = 6$ and $n = 12$. (See Prob. 14–5.) Since the r^{-6} potential falls off very rapidly, only nearest neighbors need to be considered in the attractive term; justify a value of 12 for α. Is the repulsive contribution to the binding energy greater or less than for NaCl? From the experimental value $U = 0.9$ kcal/mole, calculate the constant A. ($d = 3.84$ Å.) (b) Evaluate the expression for the bulk modulus of argon (Prob. 14–5). (For this structure, the factor γ should be $1/9\sqrt{2}$.) Evaluate the expression using the value of A from (a).

14–8.   The "Morse potential"

$$V(r) = -\frac{e^2}{r} + \frac{e^2 b}{d_0^2} \exp\left(-\frac{r - d_0}{b}\right)$$

gives a slightly better representation of the interionic potential than the Mie potential. Again d_0 is the equilibrium separation (in a molecule) and b is another parameter (distance).

(a) Show that the equilibrium separation does come at $r = d_0$. (b) Evaluate $V(d_0)$. From knowledge of the contribution by the repulsive term to this energy, estimate the value of b. (c) Approximate the interionic force by a linear expression in $x = r - d_0$ and find the frequency of small oscillations about $r = d_0$.

14–9.   What is the force constant for the HCl molecule if the vibrational frequency is 9×10^{13} sec^{-1}?

14–10.   According to the Herzfeld–Mayer theory of melting, a solid will melt when the amplitude of vibration is so large that the atoms travel past $r = r_m$, where the potential energy $V'(r)$ has an inflection point and the attractive force, $F'(r) = -dV'(r)/dr$, starts to decrease (see figure below). For solid krypton, in the Mie potential let $m = 6$, $n = 9$.

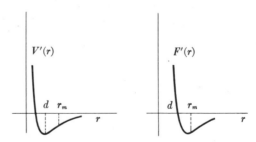

(a) Calculate the value of r_m in terms of d. (b) Expand the force expression and obtain the harmonic oscillator force constant. (c) Derive an expression for the melting temperature T_m by equating the average energy of an oscillator with amplitude $(r_m - d)$ to kT_m.

14–11.   Would the law of Dulong and Petit apply to glasses as well as crystals? Why?

14–12.   Calculate the amplitude of oscillation in NaCl at its melting point (801°C). Assume the harmonic oscillator relation between amplitude and energy. What is the ratio of the amplitude to the nearest neighbor distance?

14–13.   Look up the specific heats near room temperature of the following (in the *Handbook of Physics and Chemistry*) and convert to molar heat capacity:

$$\text{Na} \quad \text{Cu} \quad \text{Au} \quad \text{KCl}$$

14–14.   For a few materials the Dulong and Petit law fails even at room temperature (although it holds at higher temperatures). Look up the specific heats of Be and C (diamond), and compare with the value of 6 cal/mole-deg.

14–15.   Look up the specific heat of elements and, for as many as possible, tabulate the values above and below the melting point. Show the percentage change on melting. Give a qualitative explanation why it is small.

14–16.   Expand the force derived from the Mie potential (Eq. 14–13) to the term in x^2.

14–17.   Using the same values for the constants used to compute the binding energy and elastic modulus of NaCl, calculate its thermal expansion coefficient from the result of Prob. 14–16.

REFERENCES

A. J. Dekker, *Solid State Physics* (Prentice-Hall, 1957), Ch. 5.

C. Kittel, *Introduction to Solid State Physics* (John Wiley & Sons, 1956, 2nd ed.), Ch. 3.

15/imperfections in solids

Many of the properties of solids which are of the greatest practical importance depend on deviations from the "ideal" structure described up until now. By deviations is meant more than mere tiny oscillatory motions of the atoms about their equilibrium positions. There are more serious departures from the ideal rule, "one site, one atom (or molecule)." First, some of these deviations will be tabulated and then the consequences of two kinds of them will be calculated in more detail.

It is important to point out that "imperfections" (or "defects," as some kinds of them are called) is not used in a perjorative sense. It is completely natural for crystals to contain such differences from the previously described "ideal" structure, and indeed in certain cases they are intentionally added because they impart valuable properties to the material. As we shall see, a certain number of each kind of defect is present in thermal equilibrium at any temperature above absolute zero. Not all specimens are in thermal equilibrium, of course, and so the number actually present may be greater or less than the equilibrium number. Some properties, like diffusion of matter and plastic deformation, could not exist in the absence of the defects. Others, like electrical and thermal conductivity, depend on them to a greater or lesser extent in different kinds of materials. Even those properties discussed in the two preceding chapters can be indirectly modified slightly by the presence of imperfections. Therefore, although they may seem somewhat accidental, their study is extremely important for a genuine understanding of the properties of real solids.

15–1 TYPES OF IMPERFECTIONS

The most important kinds of imperfections—i.e., deviations from the perfect, infinite crystal structure—can be displayed in the following scheme:

Disorder		*Impurities*	
Lattice defects	$\Big\{$ Vacancies Interstitials	Solutions	$\Big\{$ Substitutional Interstitial

Dislocations
Grain boundaries, surfaces

Precipitates

Those listed under Disorder do not involve the presence of any foreign matter, whereas material containing Impurities is not chemically pure material. Reading downward, the imperfections are listed in order of increasing extension. Lattice defects and solutions involve single atoms and so are centered about a single *point*. Dislocations involve a long *line* of atoms. Grain boundaries and surfaces refer to the interior or exterior *surface* which bounds a particular crystal. Finally, material forming a precipitate occupies a certain *volume* in the crystal.

Impurities refer to atoms of a different species from those which nominally constitute the host crystal. They may either be dispersed on an atomic scale, in solution, or else segregated into relatively large aggregations called precipitates. In the latter case, they usually have much less effect on the properties of the material, since the situation is essentially like a mixture of the two materials (one present in a small amount). Impurities in solution may either occupy a normal atom site, as a substitute for the atom which should be there, or they may occupy an interstice between normal atom sites (Fig. 15–1). Lattice defects refer to analogous imperfections in which no foreign atom is involved: a vacancy is a site which is not occupied by any atom at all, and an interstitial atom refers to an atom of the correct species which is located at an interstitial site instead of at a normal atom site. Dislocations are disruptions of the lattice which extend beyond a single point, and they will be described more precisely later. Grain boundaries have already been mentioned in Section 13–1.

Impurities are inevitably present to some extent in all chemical preparations. Although no macroscopic sample of material is ever strictly pure, sometimes the impurities present have no measurable effect on the properties of the material. In other cases, however, they have an effect, out of all proportion to their concentration, on the mechanical or electrical behavior of the sample. For example, the enormous differences between wrought iron, steels, and cast iron depend on differences in carbon con-

Fig. 15–1. Interstitial atom, vacancy, and substitutional and interstitial impurities.

centration of a few per cent. As a second example, a fraction of a per cent of arsenic, say, can change the electrical conductivity of germanium by many orders of magnitude; the whole transistor technology depends on effects of this kind. Important as the effects of impurities may be, however, they will not be considered further at this point, since their presence is usually predetermined, either accidentally or intentionally. Lattice defects and dislocations have equally important and more inevitable effects on the properties of the material, which will be considered in more detail here.

First, self-diffusion occurs in solids as in gases. The diffusion coefficient is generally much smaller for solids, but it becomes appreciable at higher temperatures, and it is responsible for many of the changes which occur during the annealing and aging of materials. These effects are of great technological importance at present, because materials are subjected to very high temperatures in nuclear reactors and rocket propulsion systems. Diffusion of foreign atoms is important in corrosion and other solid state chemical reaction problems, and it provides the practical means of "doping" semiconductors with controlled amounts of impurities in order to produce solid-state electronic devices. In addition, ionic crystals evidence an ionic conductivity, like that of a liquid electrolyte. This can be regarded as a forced diffusion of the charged ions under the influence of an applied electric field.

These related effects are utterly incomprehensible in a crystal model, such as we have considered up to this point, in which the atoms (or ions) are permitted to make only small excursions from fixed equilibrium positions. One kind of "lattice defect" in the perfect crystal structure which would permit atoms to wander over long distances would be to allow some of the atoms to move into *interstitial* positions and to jump from one interstitial position to a neighboring one. A second possibility would be to introduce some vacant atom sites. These lacunae in the completely regular arrangement of the atoms allow the atoms to be shuffled around as in a puzzle. It is convenient to look at the migration of the *vacancies* as units, even though it might seem more "realistic" to describe the events as the jumping of a neighboring atom into the vacant site, followed by the jumping of another neighbor into the newly vacant site, etc. (Some other possible mechanisms for migration of the atoms have been suggested theoretically, but they do not seem to be important in nature.)

15-2   CONCENTRATION OF LATTICE DEFECTS

In order to analyze the defects quantitatively, let us fix first upon the interstitials for definiteness; the extension of the analysis to the vacancies will be obvious. In order to discuss diffusion by the mechanism of interstitials, we must first ask how many of them there will be in the crystal. (If none, then there is no diffusion.) The statistical answer, at least in the thermal equilibrium situation, is given, as always, by the *Boltzmann principle*.

Suppose there are n interstitial atoms per unit volume. Let the number of normal atoms per unit volume be n_0. We assume $n \ll n_0$. Then, according to the Boltzmann principle, the probability of finding an atom at an interstitial site, instead of a normal site, is an exponential function, which can be calculated somewhat as in the derivation of the Saha equation (Eq. 10–3): in thermal equilibrium,

$$n/n_0 \propto e^{-w/kT} \tag{15-1}$$

where w is the difference in energy between the interstitial state and the normal state, i.e., the work required to take the atom from its normal site and to put it into an interstitial site. In the case of lattice defects, the pre-exponential factor is very difficult to calculate. Therefore we shall set it equal to 1, even though it is found experimentally to be rather large in many cases—perhaps 100. If we write $W = N_0 w$ for one mole of defects instead of one atom (one mole of anything means just Avogadro's number of the things, even defects), then

$$n/n_0 \approx e^{-W/RT} \tag{15-2}$$

where $R = N_0 k$ is the gas constant per mole.

How big this ratio is numerically depends strongly on W, i.e., on how hard it is to get an atom into the interstitial state. Suppose first that the work W were roughly comparable with the binding energy, so that it is roughly as difficult to force the atom into an interstitial site as to take it away to infinity. Then, for $W \approx 200$ kcal/mole and for $RT \approx 2$ kcal/mole at the relatively high temperature of $1000°K$,

$$\frac{W}{RT} \approx 100 \qquad \frac{n}{n_0} \approx e^{-100} \approx 10^{-43}$$

Thus, in this case the number of interstitials would be essentially zero, for all practical purposes. On the other hand, if W were only 1/10 of the binding energy, then

$$n/n_0 \approx e^{-10} \approx 10^{-4}$$

a small, but not negligible, number. (If W were only 1/100 of the binding energy, n and n_0 would be of the same order of magnitude, and our picture of an essentially perfect crystal with a few defects would break down.) Therefore, in order for diffusion (or ionic conductivity) to occur by the interstitial mechanism, we must expect W to be of the order of 1/10 the binding energy, but still about 10 times the thermal vibration energy RT.

The number of interstitials can depend as dramatically on T as on W. If the relative number is 10^{-4} at $1000°K$, at half that temperature it will be 10^{-8}, so that the diffusion coefficient is 10,000 times smaller. For this reason, diffusion effects are usually only significant at comparatively high temperatures. (We repeat, in this analysis some oversimplifications have been made, and the ratio n/n_0 contains a pre-exponential factor which is not exactly 1, but the above order-of-magnitude arguments are still correct.)

In an ionic crystal, the situation is slightly modified because the interstitials and vacancies have an electric charge. It is true that *all* the ions of the perfect crystal have an electric charge too, but because positive and negative charges are present in equal numbers, the volume of the crystal is (macroscopically) neutral. In order to preserve the neutrality when defects are present, positive and negative defects must occur in equal numbers. A positive ion (cation) interstitial obviously represents an excess positive charge; a cation vacancy, on the other hand, represents a negative charge, since a positive charge is missing. Likewise a negative ion (anion) vacancy represents a positive charge.

There are various possibilities for satisfying the neutrality condition. If cation interstitials and vacancies occur together (Fig. 15–2(a)), the defects are called *Frenkel defects*, after J. Frenkel, who suggested them (1926). Anion interstitial-vacancy pairs are also called Frenkel defects, although these do not occur commonly. When cation vacancies and anion vacancies occur together (Fig. 15–2(b)), the defects are called *Schottky defects*, after W. Schottky (1930). A fourth type, cation-anion interstitial pairs, is conceivable, but it is not known to exist in any actual crystals.

Letting n_+ be the number per unit volume of lattice defects representing an excess positive charge $+e$ (cation interstitials or anion vacancies) and n_- the number with a negative charge $-e$ (anion interstitials or cation vacancies), Eq. 15–1 for the thermal equilibrium number is modified to be

$$n_+ n_- / n_0^2 = e^{-w/kT} = e^{-W/RT} \tag{15–3}$$

(Here n_0 is the number of normal anions or cations, i.e., the number of molecules per unit volume, and is nearly constant.) This equation is derived in a similar way to the Saha equation, Eq. 10–3, for positive and negative ions in a gas. The energy w is here the energy required to form the defect pair (interstitial-vacancy or vacancy-vacancy) from the perfect crystal, whether it is a Frenkel or a Schottky pair. Only the pre-exponential factor is different from that in the Saha equation, because the particles are not free particles. Normally, in order to have charge neutrality with monovalent ions,

$$n_+ = n_- \tag{15–4}$$

so that

$$n_+/n_0 = n_-/n_0 = e^{-w/2kT} = e^{-W/2RT} \tag{15–5}$$

(a)   (b)

Fig. 15–2. *An ionic crystal containing* (a) *Frenkel defects, and* (b) *Schottky defects.*

In any given crystal, both Frenkel and Schottky defects could in principle exist together. The energy of formation W is likely to be smaller for one than for the other, however, and so the kind with the larger energy of formation will be present in much smaller numbers and can usually be neglected. Equations 15–3 and 15–4 are written with a notation which is applicable to either Frenkel or Schottky defect pairs, but not both simultaneously. To consider both at once, separate symbols would be needed for anion interstitials and cation vacancies, and an equation of the form of Eq. 15–3 would be written for both Frenkel and Schottky pairs.

In certain circumstances, the defects may be present in much larger numbers than the thermal equilibrium number we have calculated. An example is in *radiation damage*, which occurs when a material is bombarded with high energy neutrons, for instance. The neutrons collide with atoms in the solid and knock them bodily from their normal site to an interstitial site. Radiation damage can very seriously modify the properties of a solid. In fact, under sufficiently heavy radiation doses, the material may simply crumble. The damaged crystal, however, is not in equilibrium, and it can usually be restored to its normal condition by annealing. "Annealing" means holding the specimen at an elevated temperature for an extended time. Since, as we shall see, the atoms are able to move around at high temperatures, annealing allows them to return to their equilibrium positions.

Another example of a non-equilibrium concentration is in ionic crystals which contain an *aliovalent impurity* (i.e., an impurity ion whose valence is different from that of the ions of the host crystal). Such an impurity also affects the electrical neutrality condition, Eq. 15–4, and modifies the thermal equilibrium defect concentrations. For example, if $CaCl_2$ is added to NaCl, the Ca^{++} ion occupies one cation site, while the two Cl^- each occupy an anion site (Fig. 15–3). Thus one cation site is left vacant, so that the cation vacancy concentration is increased by the addition of the impurity. To see this analytically, the electrical neutrality condition becomes

$$n_i + n_+ = n_- \tag{15–6}$$

where n_i is the number per unit volume of Ca^{++} impurity ions, each with an excess positive charge of $+e$. Equation 15–3 still holds, however, for the numbers of lattice defects n_+ and n_- as defined there. When it is solved simultaneously with Eq. 15–6, one obtains new values for the defect concentrations in place of Eq. 15–5. At low temperatures the result is $n_- \approx n_i$,

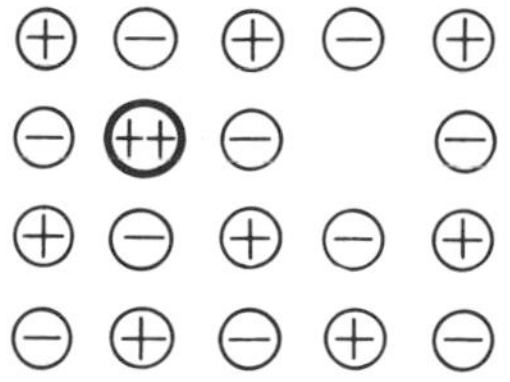

Fig. 15–3. Divalent impurity in an ionic crystal with accompanying vacancy.

while at high temperatures Eq. 15–5 still holds approximately. (See Prob. 15–7.) The boundary between "low" and "high" temperatures occurs when

$$e^{-W/2RT} \approx n_i/n_0$$

15–3　DIFFUSION

As we have already said, the self-diffusion coefficient in a solid may be expected to be proportional to the defect concentration, since the atoms in the perfect crystal may not leave their normal positions (by definition of the perfect crystal). In fact, in order to calculate the diffusion coefficient, it will be most convenient to regard the defects as a separate "tagged" species, and to calculate first a diffusion coefficient for them. Let us again fix our attention on interstitials for definiteness.

In addition to the concentration of interstitials, another factor also enters into the diffusion coefficient. Unless the interstitials can move from one site to the next, there would still be no diffusion, no matter how many (immobile) interstitials were present. The frequency with which the atom makes the jump from one site to the next is also given by the Boltzmann principle. The atom's energy is a minimum at the interstitial site (not an absolute minimum, which occurs at a normal lattice site, but a relative minimum when no normal site is available). To move to the next interstitial site, it must squeeze through a tight-fitting region, where its energy is greater, by an amount E/N_0 say. (See Fig. 15–4.)

It tries to make the jump ν_0 times per second, where ν_0 is its vibration frequency. The probability that it has, due to a thermal fluctuation, the

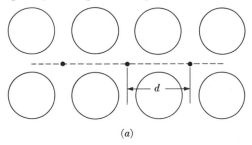

(a)

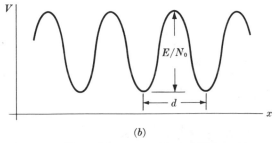

(b)

Fig. 15–4. Potential energy of interstitial atom.

extra energy needed to surmount the potential energy "hump" between it and the neighboring site is exp $(- E/RT)$. Then the *jump frequency*, or the number of successful jumps per second, is

$$\nu \cong \nu_0 e^{-E/RT} \qquad (15\text{–}7)$$

The energy E is called the *activation energy* for motion.

We have previously seen (Section 14–5) that ν_0 is about 10^{13} sec^{-1}. Again, if E is of the order of 10 kcal/mole (1/20 the binding energy), then at 1000°K, about one vibration in 100 will result in a completed jump. The jump frequency is about 10^{11} sec^{-1}, and again it decreases rapidly as the temperature is lowered. Since at each jump the atom travels a distance of the order of the lattice distance a, it has a velocity of the order of

$$\bar{\bar{v}} \approx a\nu$$
$$\approx 10 \text{ m/sec at } 1000°K \qquad (15\text{–}8)$$

The rate at which it makes any net progress is actually much smaller than this, of course, because each time the jump is in a random direction. (See Fig. 15–5.) The average speed with which the atom moves around in the lattice has been designated $\bar{\bar{v}}$ in Eq. 15–8, in order to distinguish it from the average speed $\bar{v}$ of the atom's vibrational motion, during its dwelling time at one site. The latter is approximately the same as the rms speed of the oscillation, and this is just the same as the rms speed would be in a gas at the same temperature: according to the discussion preceding Eq. 14–18, the average kinetic energy in the solid is $\frac{3}{2}kT$, as in a gas, so that $(\overline{v^2})^{1/2} = \sqrt{3kT/m}$. Therefore $\bar{v}$ is of the order of a hundred times greater than $\bar{\bar{v}}$, even at its largest.

The calculation of the diffusion coefficient D_d for the defects (interstitials) can now proceed just as in the case of a gas (Section 8–5). We suppose that their density is $n - \Delta n$ on one side of a plane and $n + \Delta n$ on the other. The flux across the plane per unit area is

$$J = \tfrac{1}{2}\bar{\bar{v}}(n - \Delta n) - \tfrac{1}{2}\bar{\bar{v}}(n + \Delta n) = - \bar{\bar{v}} \, \Delta n$$

Since the positions on either side of the plane between which the atoms are jumping are separated by a distance of about a, then $\Delta n \cong a \, dn/dx$, and

$$J = - \bar{\bar{v}}a \, dn/dx$$

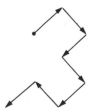

Fig. 15–5. Random displacements in diffusion.

By comparison with the definition of the diffusion coefficient (Eq. 8–28), we have

$$D_d \cong \bar{\bar{v}} a \qquad (15\text{–}9)$$

(Actually we have ignored another numerical factor in the derivation, which would equal 1/6 if the sites formed a simple cubic array: the interstitial would have the choice of 6 different directions for its jump, only one of which would be "right.") Equation 15–9 is formally identical to the expression for a gas, Eq. 8–29, since a corresponds to the mean free path L. In the crystal the diffusion is much slower, however. Not only is the "mean free path" much shorter, but also the atom pauses for a relatively long time between each jump; in the gas the collisions are of negligible duration.

To calculate the self-diffusion coefficient for the material, we note that the atoms which happen to be in interstitial positions are the only ones which can move. If we could watch an atom which was really tagged (say a radioactive isotope), we would see it diffuse with coefficient D_d when it happened to be in an interstitial position, but the fraction of the time (probability) that it was interstitial would be only equal to the concentration of interstitials n/n_0 given by Eq. 15–2. Therefore the actual *self-diffusion coefficient* is

$$D = D_d\, n/n_0 \qquad (15\text{–}10)$$

We must emphasize that in a solid the diffusion occurs only through diffusion of *defects*. That is why the defect concentration n/n_0 occurs in Eq. 15–10.

Substituting in Eq. 15–9 from Eqs. 15–8 and 15–7, we obtain

$$D_d \cong a^2 \nu_0 e^{-E/RT} \qquad (15\text{–}11)$$

and finally, using Eq. 15–2,

$$D \cong a^2 \nu_0 e^{-(W+E)/RT} \qquad (15\text{–}12)$$

The pre-exponential factor may be expected to have the approximate value

$$a^2\nu_0 \cong (3 \times 10^{-8})^2 \times 10^{13} \approx 0.01 \text{ cm}^2/\text{sec}$$

For many materials, the value of $(W+E)/RT_m$ at the melting temperature T_m is between about 10 and 20. (Both T_m and $W+E$ tend to be larger in crystals with large binding energy.) Thus at the melting point, D is between 10^{-7} and 10^{-11} cm²/sec for many solids.

Incidentally, D changes only by about one order of magnitude when the crystal *melts*, in contrast to a change of several orders of magnitude in the liquid–vapor transition. This fact suggests approaching the description of a *liquid* near its freezing point from the standpoint of a solid with an extremely high defect concentration. In the opposite extreme, near the critical point, we have previously (Chapter 7) suggested a model in which the liquid was similar to an extremely dense gas. Both models seem to have some qualitative usefulness, although neither has had much quantitative success.

15-4   IONIC CONDUCTIVITY

In an ionic crystal, because the lattice defects carry an effective charge, they give rise to an electrical conductivity σ, related to the diffusion coefficient by the Einstein relation (Eq. 10–12), just as in the case of an ionized gas. Ionic conductivity in solids is not of great practical importance; it is similar to semiconduction (Chapter 26), but in the materials which are important in semiconductor electronics, it is electrons rather than ions which are the charge carriers. It is nevertheless of considerable interest, because it is the means by which most of the experimental information about lattice defects was originally obtained, the electrical charge giving a handle on the defects which does not exist in other kinds of materials. Electrical conductivity measurements are among the easiest kinds of experimental measurements, and the influence of aliovalent impurities on the defect concentrations (Eq. 15–6) provides an additional possibility for controlled experiments, through "doping" with known amounts of impurity.

In discussing the application of the Einstein relation, we must recall that in an ionic crystal at least two kinds of defects must be present, in order to preserve electrical neutrality. In the pure crystal, the two kinds are present in equal numbers (Eq. 15–4). Nevertheless, one of the pair usually makes a negligible contribution to the conductivity (and diffusion). Each has its own activation energy for motion, E_+ and E_-, and one of these is likely to be appreciably greater than the other, leading according to Eq. 15–7 to a much smaller jump frequency. Thus, for example, if $E_+ > E_-$, the current is carried mainly by n_-, and according to Eq. 10–17 its mobility is

$$\mu_- = (-e/kT)D_-$$

By Eq. 10–16,

$$\sigma_- = n_-(-e)\mu_- = \frac{e^2}{kT} n_- D_-$$

Using Eq. 15–11, with $D_d = D_-$, we can write

$$\sigma_- \cong (e^2 a^2 \nu_0 n_0/kT) \frac{n_-}{n_0} e^{-E_-/RT} = \sigma_0(n_-/n_0)e^{-E_-/RT} \qquad (15\text{–}13)$$

(We should note that the conductivity σ_- is proportional to $n_- D_-$, where D_- is the defect diffusion coefficient. Then, by Eq. 15–10, the conductivity is proportional to the overall self-diffusion coefficient D for that species of ion which is the more mobile.)

The numerical value of the coefficient σ_0 at 1000°K is about

$$\sigma_0 \equiv (e^2 a^2 \nu_0 n_0/kT) \approx 10^2 (\text{ohm-cm})^{-1}$$

a moderately high value (comparable with graphite). Again, the factors we have ignored can contribute an additional factor, which may be more than 100. It should be remembered, however, that both the fraction of defects (n_-/n_0) and the exponential $\exp(-E_-/RT)$ are much less than one, so that ionic conductors are in general rather poor conductors.

As in Section 15–2, two temperature ranges must be distinguished when the crystal contains impurities (and all crystals contain some concentration, however small, of impurities accidentally present). At high temperature, in the so-called *intrinsic region*, (n_-/n_0) is given by Eq. 15–5, so that Eq. 15–13 becomes

$$\sigma_- \cong \sigma_0 e^{-(W/2+E_-)/RT} \tag{15–14}$$

On the other hand, at low temperature we have from Eq. 15–6 $n_- \approx n_i$, where n_i/n_0 is the impurity concentration, so that

$$\sigma_- \cong \sigma_0 (n_i/n_0) e^{-E_-/RT} \tag{15–15}$$

These two regions are clearly shown experimentally, in Fig. 15–6, for NaCl of normal purity. In the intrinsic region the slope of the curve is $(\tfrac{1}{2}W + E_-)$, and at lower temperatures (below about 550° C) it is equal to E_-. This fact suggests how the intentional addition of impurities can be used to determine the values of W and E_- separately.

As examples, we may consider first NaCl. Schottky defects predominate in all of the alkali halides, and in NaCl the Na^+ vacancy is more mobile than the Cl^- vacancy at all temperatures up to the melting point. The conductivity is therefore described by Eqs. 15–14 and 15–15 in the intrinsic and

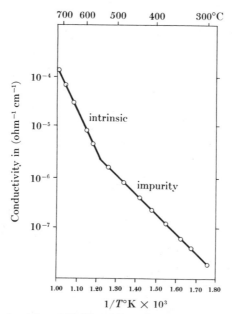

Fig. 15–6. *Ionic conductivity of NaCl as a function of temperature.* [*After H. W. Etzel and R. J. Maurer*, J. Chem. Phys. **18**, *1003 (1950)*.]

impurity-controlled (or extrinsic) regions, respectively. From the measured slopes of the curve, the values are found to be for NaCl

$$\tfrac{1}{2}W = 23 \text{ kcal/mole} = 1.0 \text{ eV/molecule}$$
$$E_- = 20 \text{ kcal/mole} = 0.9 \text{ eV/molecule}$$

In AgCl, cation Frenkel defects predominate, with the Ag^+ interstitial more mobile. Here the situation is a little more complicated: at high temperature the Ag^+ interstitials (n_+) account for most of the conductivity. As the impurity-controlled region is approached at lower temperatures, the Ag^+ vacancy (n_-) concentration levels off at the impurity concentration, as in NaCl: $n_- \approx n_i$. The interstitial concentration, on the other hand, is depressed according to Eq. 15–3: at any temperature, if the vacancy concentration is enhanced, the interstitial concentration must be depressed, since their product is constant. Thus at first the conductivity drops below the intrinsic line, when the concentration of the more mobile interstitials decreases. At still lower temperatures, the interstitial contribution becomes negligible, in spite of their higher mobility, and the conductivity is described by the vacancy line, Eq. 15–15, as in NaCl. The experimental values for AgCl are

$$\tfrac{1}{2}W = 16 \text{ kcal/mole} = 0.7 \text{ eV/molecule}$$
$$E_- = 9 \text{ kcal/mole} = 0.4 \text{ eV/molecule}$$
$$E_+ = 2 \text{ kcal/mole} = 0.1 \text{ eV/molecule}$$

The smaller values in AgCl as compared with NaCl correspond to its lower melting temperature.

15–5 PLASTIC DEFORMATION

Another example of a practically important effect which cannot be explained by the perfect crystal model is *plastic deformation*. For most crystals, Hooke's law holds only up to strains of the order of 0.1%. Beyond this point, the strain increases more rapidly with stress, and a *permanent set* is introduced—i.e., when the stress is removed, the specimen does not completely return to its original dimensions (Fig. 15–7). Deformation beyond the so-called *yield point*, where the permanent set first occurs, is called

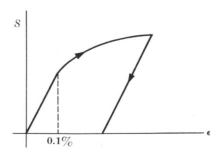

Fig. 15–7. Stress-strain diagram showing permanent set in a plastic deformation.

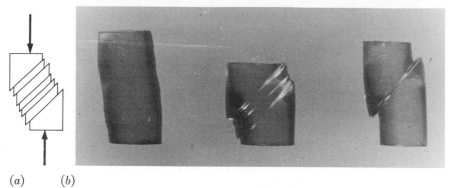

(a)   (b)

Fig. 15–8. (a) *Slip as a result of compression.* (b) *Single crystal AgBr cylinders deformed in compression. Slip occurred on one, a few, and many sets of slip planes, respectively.*

"plastic" deformation as opposed to elastic deformation. Plastic deformation in crystals is generally observed to occur by *slip*, in which the deformation is limited to a shear in certain directions of the crystal structure, even if the applied stress is in another direction (Fig. 15–8).

It is possible to imagine how such slip could occur even in a perfect crystal. One would have only to slide one plane of atoms across the neighboring plane (Fig. 15–9). Since this would presumably be easiest in a certain direction in the crystal lattice, the preference for certain slip directions is also explained. The trouble is that quantitatively this explanation comes out entirely wrong.

Using such a model, the predicted yield point can readily be estimated by considering the interatomic forces. The potential energy of the crystal as the two halves are relatively displaced across some plane will vary so that there is a minimum when the planes are in register; it will increase to a maximum and then have another minimum when the displacement is equal to the interatomic distance d, when the planes will again be in register (Fig. 15–10). The corresponding force is shown by the dashed line. For any reasonable shape of the potential energy curve, the maximum value of the force occurs for a relative displacement of the order of $d/4$. As soon as the

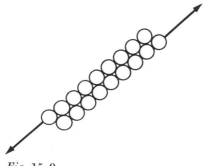

Fig. 15–9

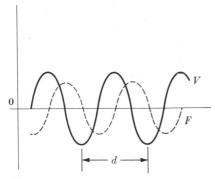

Fig. 15–10

force applied to the crystal exceeds this value, plastic deformation should occur. Therefore, the strain at the yield point would be $(d/4)/d$, or about 25%. Instead the observed strain at the yield point is of the order of 0.1%. Put in another way, in terms of the stress $S = G\epsilon$, the calculated yield stress is about $G/4$, but the experimental yield stress is about $G/1000$. Thus it is very much easier to produce plastic deformation than our model predicts.

15–6 DISLOCATIONS

A new type of crystal imperfection, the *dislocation*, was first proposed theoretically in order to explain the ease of producing slip. The dislocation is most easily visualized by removing part of an entire plane of atoms of the crystal, as shown schematically in cross section in Fig. 15–11. The partial plane removed is perpendicular to the page in Fig. 15–11(b). The dislocation itself is the distorted region of the lattice along the edge of the missing plane. The imperfect region of the lattice is centered along a *line*, rather than about a *point* as in the case of impurities and lattice defects. The line is perpendicular to the page in Fig. 15–11(c), and is marked by ⊥. To move the dislocation line one atom spacing to the left or right could be imagined to be rather easy, since only a single line of atoms has to be squeezed past another line, rather than squeezing all the atoms in a plane past at once. Furthermore, if the dislocation is moved all the way across the crystal to the right, a slip of one atomic spacing has been produced to the left (Fig. 15–12). (If the dislocation were moved across to the left, the step would be

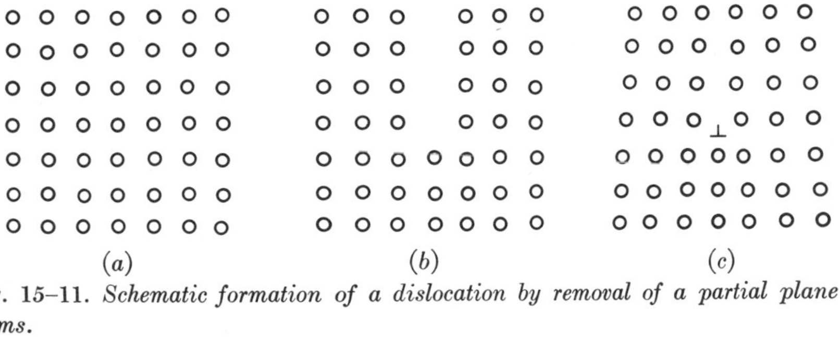

```
 o o o o o o o        o o o    o o o        o o o o o o
 o o o o o o o        o o o    o o o        o o o o o o
 o o o o o o o        o o o    o o o        o o o o o o
 o o o o o o o        o o o    o o o        o o o ⊥ o o o
 o o o o o o o        o o o o o o o         o o o o o o o
 o o o o o o o        o o o o o o o         o o o o o o o
 o o o o o o o        o o o o o o o         o o o o o o o
       (a)                  (b)                   (c)
```

Fig. 15–11. *Schematic formation of a dislocation by removal of a partial plane of atoms.*

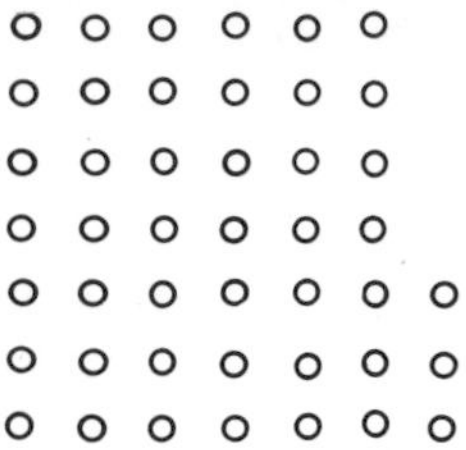

o   o   o   o   o   o
o   o   o   o   o   o
o   o   o   o   o   o
o   o   o   o   o   o
o   o   o   o   o   o   o
o   o   o   o   o   o   o
o   o   o   o   o   o   o

Fig. 15–12

on the left side instead.) Therefore the way slip is supposed to occur is by moving many dislocations through the crystal, each one requiring a comparatively small force to move it. The mathematical theory of dislocations is quite complicated and will not be considered at all.

Dislocations were at first purely hypothetical structures, but quite recently they have been observed by rather direct means. The greatly magnified photograph in Fig. 15–13 shows etch pits on the surface of a lithium fluoride crystal. Each etch pit reveals where a dislocation intersects the surface of the crystal. How the dislocations are produced in the first place, however, is still something of a mystery. One can estimate that the energy required to form one would be of the same order as for a vacancy, per atomic length. Since they are millions of atomic lengths long, by the Boltzmann principle the equilibrium number of them would be essentially zero.

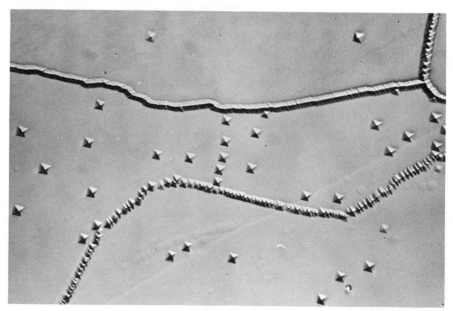

Fig. 15–13. *The surface of a lithium fluoride crystal that has been chemically etched, magnified about 500 times. Each etch pit reveals a dislocation.* [Courtesy of J. J. Gilman and W. G. Johnston, Dislocations and Mechanical Properties of Crystals, *Ed. by Fisher, Johnston, Thomson, and Vreeland* (John Wiley & Sons, New York, 1957).]

It is probable that some are grown into the crystal when it is originally produced (and in fact may be involved in the mechanism of its growth), but they can also be generated in the existing crystal by an applied stress, in a way which is not yet completely understood.

Like the "point defects" (impurities and lattice defects), dislocations have an enormous influence on the properties of real crystals. For example, internal friction of a vibrating material is at least partly due to the damped back-and-forth motion of dislocations. Even when one is primarily interested in effects which can occur in the perfect crystal, it is important to be aware that imperfections could profoundly modify the effects when they are measured in real crystals.

PROBLEMS

15-1.   Suppose a cubic crystal contains a substitutional impurity in a concentration of 0.1% (normal for "chemically pure" materials). What is the average distance between impurity atoms, measured in units of the interatomic distance? (*Hint:* Each cube containing a thousand atoms contains on the average one impurity.)

15-2.   Very pure germanium used in manufacturing semiconductor devices contains only one part in 10^9 of impurities which affect the electrical conductivity. What is the average distance between impurities?

15-3.   Assuming the classical law of Dulong and Petit, how would the presence of a substitutional impurity affect the molar heat capacity? Why?

15-4.   Consider the diffusion of a vacancy in a fcc structure. (*a*) Starting with the vacancy at one corner of a unit cell, what is the minimum number of jumps required to reach an adjacent corner? What is the minimum number of jumps to reach a corner diagonally across a cube face? (*b*) What are the respective probabilities of reaching those two corners in the minimum number of jumps? (*Hint:* Consider what fraction of all possible jumps leads to the desired goal.)

15-5.   Suppose a thin evaporated film of AgBr is sandwiched between two Ag metal films. Use Eq. 8-32 to estimate how long a time would be required for Ag atoms to diffuse from one side to the other, if the AgBr film is 10^{-4} cm thick, and the temperature is 150°C. The diffusion coefficient of Ag in AgBr at this temperature is 10^{-10} cm^2/sec. Make the same calculation for a slab of AgBr 1 cm thick.

15-6.   Repeat the calculation of Prob. 15-5 for room temperature. The "activation energy" $W + E$ in Eq. 15-12 is 18 kcal/mole.

15-7.   Solve Eqs. 15-3 and 15-6 for the defect concentrations (n_-/n_0) and (n_+/n_0) in terms of the impurity concentration (n_i/n_0). Obtain the approximate forms for large and small values of (n_i/n_0).

15-8.   What is the jump frequency of an Na$^+$ vacancy in NaCl at its melting point (801°C)? at room temperature? at liquid nitrogen temperature (78°K)?

15-9.   Calculate the mobility of Na^+ vacancies in NaCl at the melting point; at room temperature; and at liquid nitrogen temperature.

15-10.   What would be the conductivity at room temperature of NaCl containing 1 ppm (part per million) of divalent cation impurities?

15-11.   The measured diffusion coefficient of K in KCl at 600°C is 2×10^{-10} cm^2/sec, and the measured conductivity is 3×10^{-6} $(ohm\text{-}cm)^{-1}$. (H. Witt, *Z. Physik* **134**, 117 (1953).) Check how well the Einstein relation is satisfied. Suggest mechanisms which could lead to discrepancies with this relation.

REFERENCES

A. J. Dekker, *Solid State Physics* (Prentice-Hall, 1957), Ch. 7.

J. Frenkel, *Kinetic Theory of Liquids* (Dover, 1946), Ch. I.

L. V. Azároff, *Introduction to Solids* (McGraw-Hill, 1960), Ch. 5.

F. Seitz, *The Physics of Metals* (McGraw-Hill, 1943).

III

QUANTUM MECHANICS

The interaction of atoms according to the laws of classical mechanics has been seen to lead to the understanding of many properties of matter, in both the gaseous and solid forms. We have not yet considered, however, the internal structure of the atoms themselves. From the Rutherford scattering experiment we know that they consist of massive positively charged nuclei surrounded by electrons. In considering plasmas, we saw that an electron can be removed from the atom, and interact with the remaining positive ion. In certain types of solids, interactions of positive and negative ions accounted for the observed properties of the crystal. But the stability of an atom or ion has not yet been explained. One might suppose that it would follow from the theory of planetary motion developed in Chapter 5; this supposition will be tested in Chapter 18 and found wanting. Classical mechanics predicts certain elliptical orbits for electrons moving in the coulomb field of nuclei. In Chapter 18 we shall see that although these orbits are of some use in picturing the structure of an atom, if taken literally they give rise to unsurmountable difficulties.

A correct description of the behavior of electrons under all possible circumstances requires an essentially new physical theory—quantum mechanics. Quantum mechanics bears certain similarities to classical mechanics and gives the same results for sufficiently massive particles (e.g., entire atoms, except at very low temperatures), but its basic concepts and mathematical methods are profoundly different. In its most "physical," least abstract form, quantum mechanics is a wave theory. The seeming paradox of using a wave theory to describe a particle will be resolved in Chapter 20. Before that, some aspects of the wave-like behavior of electrons will be recounted and the needed type of wave theory will be inferred. The problem will also be illuminated by considering a parallel, or perhaps one should say inverse, problem, namely, some particle-like aspects of light, which classically is described by an electromagnetic wave. As a preliminary, the formal theory which describes wave propagation will be presented (Chapter 16), in order to provide the necessary mathematical tools.

16/the wave equation

In this chapter, the mathematical equation which describes wave propagation
will be developed and some solutions of it will be derived. Formally, these will
serve as the basis for our subsequent discussion of quantum mechanics. In order to introduce the mathematical problem in a more familiar physical context,
however, we shall first consider sound waves. Mathematically, the problem of
sound waves is completely identical to the problem of light waves or even of
quantum mechanical "particle" waves. Physically, our description of sound
waves is completely classical, and has nothing to do with quantum mechanics.
In fact, it might serve as an interesting and satisfying completion of our classical mechanical theory of continuous media (solid or gaseous).

We have already described deformations of solids (compression, expansion,
or shear) and gases (compression or expansion) in terms of the macroscopic
equations of state, and have sought to explain the observed parameters of the
deformation (the elastic moduli) in terms of the microscopic interactions between the atoms which constitute the matter. The problem treated, however, was
a purely static one, in which the matter was assumed to be in equilibrium with
external forces. If the external forces are instead applied very rapidly, a pulse,
or wave, of deformation can be made to travel through the matter; and if the
forces vary periodically in time, the resulting periodic wave which is propagated through the medium is the familiar transmission of sound. In this chapter, the mathematical description of the wave motion will be developed from the
macroscopic point of view.

In the case of a crystal, the wave could also be considered from a microscopic
point of view as a description of the vibration of the atoms about their equilibrium positions. This, in fact, provides a much more nearly correct description of the vibrational motion of the atoms than the one we have given, because

*in our simplified treatment an atom was assumed to move in the potential en-
ergy well due to neighboring atoms which are held fixed, but in reality all of the
atoms are moving simultaneously. This microscopic description of the collective motions of the atoms will not be pursued, however, and it should be admitted again that the primary motive for presenting a rather detailed mathematical
formulation of wave motion is in its application to quantum mechanics, which
formally can be represented in a very similar way. It must be re-emphasized,
of course, that the present chapter is purely classical, in that nothing is involved
beyond an application of Newton's second law to a new physical situation.*

16-1   THE VIBRATING STRING

A familiar situation in which wave motion occurs is in the vibration of a
stretched string, as for example a guitar string. Since this example of wave
motion is most easily visualized, we begin with an analysis of it. The string
is assumed to be perfectly flexible and uniform, and under a constant tension (force) F. We choose a coordinate system with x-axis along the string
when it is at rest and assume that its motion is in a plane, the xy-plane.
We let the variable Ψ describe the displacement in the y-direction of the
string from its rest position, and in general Ψ will be different at each position x and at every time t. Our aim is to write the equation of motion
$\mathbf{F} = m\mathbf{a}$ for each little piece of the string. If we consider one small element
of the displaced string, of length dx, its mass will be

$$dM = \mu dx \qquad (16\text{--}1)$$

where $\mu \equiv M/L$ is the linear density, M and L being the total mass and
length of the string. The acceleration in the y-direction is

$$a_y = \ddot{\Psi} \qquad (16\text{--}2)$$

It remains only to calculate the force F_y in the y-direction which is causing the motion. From Fig. 16–1, the force at one end of the element of string
is $F \sin \alpha$. We must now make the assumption that the displacement Ψ,
and therefore the angle α, is *small*, small enough to use the approximation
$\sin \alpha \approx \tan \alpha$. Then

$$\sin \alpha \approx \tan \alpha = d\Psi/dx \equiv \Psi'(x)$$

where the ' is used to denote the derivative of Ψ with respect to the position x. With this simplifying assumption, the y-component of the force is

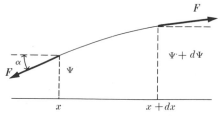

Fig. 16–1

seem to vary along the string proportionally to its slope, $F_y = F\Psi'(x)$, even though the total force vector has the constant magnitude F.

What is needed for the equation of motion, however, is not F_y, but the *net* force acting on the element of the string (Fig. 16–1). The net force in the y-direction dF_y is the difference between the values of F_y at the two ends of the element,

$$dF_y = F[\Psi'(x + dx) - \Psi'(x)]$$

Now assuming that dx is small, a Taylor series expansion of the function $\Psi'(x + dx)$ can be used:

$$\Psi'(x + dx) = \Psi'(x) + \frac{d\Psi'(x)}{dx}\, dx + \ldots = \Psi'(x) + \Psi''(x)dx + \ldots$$

Then the net force is

$$dF_y \cong F\Psi''(x)dx \tag{16–3}$$

proportional to the *second* derivative of Ψ.

We are now ready to write the y-component of the equation of motion for the element of string. Combining Eqs. 16–1 to 16–3,

$$F\Psi''dx = \mu dx\ddot{\Psi}$$

Since Ψ is a function of the *two independent variables* x and t, the differentiations with respect to space and time should be represented by partial derivatives. Therefore, the equation of motion for the string can finally be written as

$$u^2 \frac{\partial^2 \Psi}{\partial x^2} = \frac{\partial^2 \Psi}{\partial t^2} \qquad u \equiv \sqrt{F/\mu} \tag{16–4}$$

This equation is called the *wave equation;* it is a *partial differential equation,* which asserts a relation between the partial derivatives of the dependent variable Ψ, just as an ordinary differential equation asserts a relation between the ordinary derivatives of a function of a single variable. Finding a solution to the equation consists in finding a function $\Psi = \Psi(x,t)$ whose derivatives satisfy the equation. Note that the new constant u which is introduced in Eq. 16–4 must have the dimensions of velocity; we shall see below that u is the velocity of propagation of a wave.

The analysis of a partial differential equation is a much more difficult mathematical problem than the analysis of an ordinary differential equation, and it is not possible to write down something analogous to the "general solution" of an ordinary second order differential equation containing two arbitrary constants; in fact, solutions to the wave equation containing two arbitrary *functions* can be found. Instead, we shall derive some solutions of a particular kind—infinitely many of them—and we will see that these are enough for all practical purposes. In this approach it is important to notice that the equation is *linear,* i.e., no squares or higher powers of Ψ or its derivatives occur, so that just as with an ordinary equation the sum of two or more solutions is again a solution. Equations which are non-linear are very intractable, and it was just so that the equation would come out linear that we assumed that the displacement was small. If sin α had been retained instead of the approximation tan α, it would still be easy to write down the differential equation, but it would be much harder to solve it.

16–2 SOLUTIONS OF THE WAVE EQUATION

In order to generate some solutions to the equation, let us assume that each element of the string moves up and down harmonically with time, but with an amplitude and phase which depend on position, so that we look for solutions of the form

$$\Psi(x,t) = \psi(x)e^{i\omega t} \tag{16–5}$$

This function is like the complex form of the solution to the harmonic oscillator equation (with no damping) discussed in Section 4–3, with ω the angular frequency of the motion. The difference is that now the "amplitude" $\psi(x)$ depends on position x, instead of being a constant A. To see if a function of the form given by Eq. 16–5 can satisfy the wave equation, we must compute the derivatives of $\Psi(x,t)$ and substitute them into Eq. 16–4. Since

$$\frac{\partial^2 \Psi}{\partial x^2} = \psi''(x)e^{i\omega t} \qquad \frac{\partial^2 \Psi}{\partial t^2} = -\omega^2 \psi(x)e^{i\omega t}$$

the trial solution will satisfy the wave equation, provided that $\psi(x)$ satisfies the ordinary differential equation

$$\psi''(x) + \kappa^2 \psi(x) = 0 \qquad \kappa \equiv \omega/u \tag{16–6}$$

This type of equation is called the *Helmholtz equation*, and it is formally identical to the harmonic oscillator equation in that it says that the second derivative of a function plus a positive constant times the function itself equals zero. We have thus reduced the problem of finding solutions for the partial differential equation Eq. 16–4 to the simpler problem of finding solutions for the ordinary differential equation Eq. 16–6, which the amplitude function must satisfy. The frequency ω is completely arbitrary—it is not determined by the equation of motion (although we shall see later what does determine it). But once ω is chosen, then κ is specified, since u is physically determined by the mass and tension of the string.

Solutions of Eq. 16–6 can be written down immediately, by analogy with the solutions of the harmonic oscillator equation. We could consider the real solutions

$$\psi(x) = \sin \kappa x, \cos \kappa x$$

or the complex solutions

$$\psi(x) = e^{\pm i\kappa x} = \cos \kappa x \pm i \sin \kappa x$$

Let us consider the latter solutions first, so that from Eq. 16–5 the complete solution to the wave equation is of the form

$$\Psi(x,t) \,=\, e^{i(\omega t \pm \kappa x)} \,=\, e^{i\kappa(ut \pm x)}$$

In order to interpret these complex solutions, we must take either the real or the imaginary part (since they satisfy the differential equation separately), for example the real part

$$\Psi(x,t) \,=\, \cos\,(\omega t \pm \kappa x) \,=\, \cos\,\kappa(ut \pm x)$$

At a fixed instant, Ψ varies like cos κx; at a fixed position, Ψ varies like cos ωt (Fig. 16–2). Therefore we see that ω and κ are related to the *frequency* and *wave length* of the wave:

$$\omega = 2\pi\nu \qquad \kappa = 2\pi/\lambda \qquad\qquad (16\text{--}7)$$

From the second form of the solution, cos $\kappa(ut \pm x)$, the meaning of u can be seen. Suppose we look at a certain value of the displacement, say a peak of the wave, for which the cosine is 1, or the argument of the cosine is 0. Then at any time t the position where the peak occurs is determined by $ut \pm x = 0$, or $x = \mp ut$. With the upper sign, the peak travels to the left with velocity u, and with the other choice of sign it travels to the right with velocity u, which is called the *phase velocity* of the wave. The phase velocity is determined by the physical situation ($\sqrt{F/\mu}$ for the string). The constant ω is arbitrary, but once it has been chosen κ is determined by $\kappa = \omega/u$. Therefore, a wave of any frequency whatever can be propagated on the string, but the wave length is determined by the frequency:

$$u = \omega/\kappa = \lambda\nu \qquad\qquad (16\text{--}8)$$

Such waves are called *travelling waves*, to distinguish them from the standing waves, which will be considered in the next section.

We seem, in fact, to have obtained a great many solutions to the problem, since sines and cosines (or complex exponentials) can be put together in any combination, and the frequency is arbitrary. The reason there are so many solutions is that we have not yet specified the problem completely; when a unique physical problem is stated, the mathematical equations which describe it must have a unique solution.

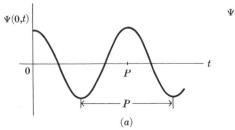

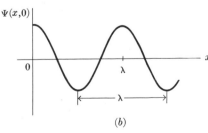

(a)   (b)

Fig. 16–2

16-3 BOUNDARY CONDITIONS

To specify a particular physical situation, the conditions at the ends of the string must also be described, by giving some *boundary conditions*. For example, the most common situation is when the ends of the string are tied down so they cannot move. That is, the displacement Ψ is 0 at the ends $(x = 0, x = L)$, at all times; mathematically expressed,

$$\Psi(0,t) = \Psi(L,t) = 0 \qquad (16\text{-}9)$$

We must pick solutions—out of all those which satisfy the wave equation— which also satisfy Eq. 16–9. To consider this case, let us substitute $\Psi(x,t) = \psi(x) \cos \omega t$ into the wave equation. Then $\psi(x)$ must satisfy the Helmholtz equation, and it will be convenient to use the real solutions:

$$\Psi(x,t) = (A \sin \kappa x + B \cos \kappa x) \cos \omega t = \psi(x) \cos \omega t$$

From the first boundary condition $\Psi(0,t) = B(\cos \omega t) = 0$, so that $B = 0$. Then from the second condition $\Psi(L,t) = (A \sin \kappa L) \cos \omega t = 0$, so that either $A = 0$ or $\sin \kappa L = 0$. Since $A = 0$ gives $\Psi(x,t) \equiv 0$, this solution describes a string at rest, and so is not very interesting. The other possibility, $\sin \kappa L = 0$, requires that $\kappa L = n\pi$, with $n = 1, 2, 3, \ldots$. We then get the infinitely many solutions

$$\Psi = \Psi_n = A_n \cos \omega_n t \sin \kappa_n x = A_n \cos \omega_n t \, \psi_n(x) \qquad (16\text{-}10)$$

where

$$\psi_n \equiv \sin \kappa_n x \qquad \kappa_n = n\pi/L \qquad \omega_n = u\kappa_n \qquad n = 1, 2, 3, \ldots$$

and each A_n is an arbitrary constant.

All of the solutions Eq. 16–10 satisfy both the wave equation Eq. 16–4 and the boundary conditions Eq. 16–9. These solutions describe *standing waves* on the string. Since $\kappa_n = 2\pi/\lambda_n$, we have $\lambda_n = 2L/n$, so that the length of the string must be an integral number of half wave lengths. (See Fig. 16–3.) Now the string can vibrate only with certain frequencies and their corresponding wave lengths.

Still, infinitely many different motions are possible, and to specify which motion actually occurs, some *initial conditions* must be imposed at $t = 0$. Suppose we deform the string into a certain shape, $\Psi(x,0) = f(x)$, and release it from rest, $\dot{\Psi}(x,0) = 0$. The second condition is automatically satis-

Fig. 16–3. Standing waves on a string.

fied because we chose the cos ωt solutions; if we wanted to have an initial velocity, sin ωt solutions could be included, but there is no point in complicating the problem this way now. If the initial shape is one of the functions $A_n \sin \kappa_n x = f(x)$, then we merely choose that solution—but this is not very likely. A more realistic initial configuration might be that of Fig. 16–4, if the string is "plucked." Because the wave equation is linear, other more complicated initial shapes can be obtained from sums of solutions,

$$\Psi(x,t) = \sum_{j=1}^{N} A_j \sin \kappa_j x \cos \omega_j t$$

$$\Psi(x,0) = \sum_{j=1}^{N} A_j \sin \kappa_j x$$

Indeed, one might hope that by letting N go to infinity and using *infinite series* of solutions, arbitrary initial conditions could be satisfied:

$$f(x) = \sum_{j=1}^{\infty} A_j \sin \kappa_j x = \sum_j A_j \psi_j \qquad (16–11)$$

Such series, called *Fourier series*, can be shown to converge and to be twice differentiable under rather general conditions, and in the next section we will see how to calculate the appropriate coefficients A_j.

Our outline of a method for obtaining a mathematical solution to the wave equation is now complete. It may be compared with the solution of the problem of the motion of a particle. In that case, the physical situation is described by an ordinary differential equation; of the infinitely many solutions to the equation, that unique one which describes what actually happens is picked out by imposing initial conditions on the position and velocity. In contrast, for a continuous medium like the string, the physical situation is described by a partial differential equation, which must be supplemented by some boundary conditions for a complete description. A unique solution is obtained by imposing initial conditions on the position and velocity at each point of the medium (given by functions, rather than numbers).

It is useful for our later purposes to review part of what we have done from a somewhat more abstract and sophisticated point of view. Let us rewrite the Helmholtz equation, Eq. 16–6, as

$$\frac{d^2}{dx^2}\psi = \alpha\psi \qquad (\alpha \equiv -\kappa^2) \qquad (16–12)$$

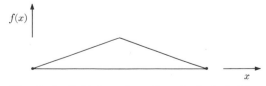

$f(x)$

x

Fig. 16–4. Initial configuration of plucked string.

To complete the specification of the problem, some boundary conditions were added, $\psi(0) = \psi(L) = 0$. (Cf. Eq. 16–9.) As a result, the "permissible" solutions to the problem are

$$\psi = \psi_n \equiv \sin \kappa_n x \qquad (16\text{–}13)$$

corresponding to

$$\alpha = \alpha_n \equiv -\kappa_n{}^2$$

The permissible values α_n are called *eigenvalues*, and the corresponding solutions ψ_n are called *eigenfunctions*. ("Eigen" is German for "characteristic.") The sophisticated way of looking at this "eigenvalue problem" is the following: in general the *differential operator* d^2/dx^2 maps a function ψ into some other function; if this other function is a constant multiple $\alpha\psi$ of ψ, then ψ is an eigenfunction and α is an eigenvalue. The discrete set of eigenvalues (Eq. 16–13) stems from the imposition of boundary conditions. The initial condition can be satisfied by expanding the initial configuration in an infinite series of the eigenfunctions (Eq. 16–11). We describe the solution to the Helmholtz equation in this abstract way—not because it casts any light on the vibrations of strings—but because these properties are not peculiar to the Helmholtz equation but can be shown to apply to all such equations which arise in physics. We shall have occasion to consider some others in quantum mechanics. Note that for the vibrating string, the eigenvalues are related to the possible wave lengths of the standing waves on the string, and the corresponding wave functions describe the shape of the string in that particular mode of vibration.

16–4   FOURIER SERIES

In this section we shall explain in more detail how the series expansion of Eq. 16–11 can actually be carried out. We shall not have occasion to make use of the results, but the method is very important in physical problems.

As an aid in calculating the coefficients, notice that the functions $\sin \kappa_j x$ have the following interesting property:

$$\int_0^L dx \, \sin \kappa_j x \, \sin \kappa_k x = \begin{cases} 0 & j \neq k \\ L/2 & j = k \end{cases}$$

This relation is very easily proved (Prob. 16–4), if we write the integrands

$$\sin \kappa_j x \, \sin \kappa_k x = \tfrac{1}{2}[\cos(\kappa_j - \kappa_k)x - \cos(\kappa_j + \kappa_k)x]$$
$$\sin^2 \kappa_j x = \tfrac{1}{2}[1 - \cos 2\,\kappa_j x]$$

If the product of two functions integrated over their domain vanishes, they are said to be *orthogonal*, and a set of functions like $\{\sin \kappa_j x\}$, each of which is orthogonal to every other one, is called an *orthogonal set*. It is convenient to define a new set of functions,

$$\phi_j(x) \equiv \sqrt{2/L} \, \sin \kappa_j x$$

so that

$$\int_0^L dx\ \phi_j(x)\ \phi_k(x) = \begin{cases} 0 & j \neq k \\ 1 & j = k \end{cases} \qquad (16\text{--}14)$$

The functions ϕ_j are said to be *normalized*, by the *normalizing* factor $\sqrt{2/L}$, and the set $\{\phi_j\}$ is called an *orthonormal set*, meaning that it is both orthogonal and normalized. We may try to represent the initial configuration $f(x)$ in terms of this orthonormal set, just as in Eq. 16–11:

$$f(x) = \sum_{j=1}^{\infty} c_j\ \phi_j(x) \qquad (16\text{--}15)$$

From the orthonormal property of the set $\{\phi_j\}$ it is easy to calculate the c_j. To calculate the coefficient c_k, multiply both sides of this expression by ϕ_k, and integrate both sides, integrating the series term by term:

$$\int_0^L dx\ f(x)\ \phi_k(x) = \int_0^L dx \sum_{j=1}^{\infty} c_j\ \phi_j(x)\ \phi_k(x)$$

$$= \sum_{j=1}^{\infty} c_j \int_0^L dx\ \phi_j(x)\ \phi_k(x) = c_k$$

Because of the orthonormality of the ϕ_j, the only non-vanishing term on the right is c_k, so that

$$c_k = \int_0^L dx\ f(x)\ \phi_k(x) \qquad (16\text{--}16)$$

If the coefficients of the Fourier series are calculated in this way, then the solution

$$\Psi(x,t) = \sum_{j=1}^{\infty} c_j\ \phi_j(x)\ e^{i\omega_j t} \qquad \text{(real part)}$$

satisfies the differential equation, the boundary conditions, and the initial conditions. (In order rigorously to justify the validity of the solution, a number of mathematical questions concerning the convergence, differentiability, integrability, etc., of the series would have to be answered affirmatively; suffice it to say here that they can be, under conditions which subsume all practical cases. The initial conditions can therefore be satisfied by calculating the appropriate coefficients c_j.)

The set of eigenfunctions of the Helmholtz equation (with suitable boundary conditions) is an orthonormal set. Other functions can be expressed as a linear combination of (an infinite number of) these eigenfunctions, in much the same way that an arbitrary vector can be expressed as a linear combination of orthonormal basis vectors. The set of orthonormal functions is therefore called a *basis* for a "vector space of functions." A given orthonormal set of functions is said to "span" a certain space of functions—namely all those functions which can be represented as linear combinations of the basis functions. The assertion made above can then be rephrased to say that the eigenfunctions of the Helmholtz equation span a function space which is large enough to contain all the functions ordinarily encountered in physical problems. The reason for making the statement in this general form is that one can show that for a large class of differential equations the eigenfunctions constitute such an orthonormal set of functions (though not necessarily sine functions). We shall find these mathematical ideas particularly important to the understanding of the quantum mechanical theory (Chapter 20).

16–5   WAVES IN THREE DIMENSIONS

Before leaving the wave problem, we wish to indicate the extension to a *three-dimensional* medium, and consider an application to the propagation of sound waves. For the string, the restoring force was related to the variation of displacement by F, and the inertia was represented by μ, giving a wave velocity $u = \sqrt{F/\mu}$. For a three-dimensional solid, the corresponding restoring stress is related to the variation of displacement (strain) by the shear modulus G, and the inertia depends on the density ρ. Making similar approximations, the wave equation is obtained with phase velocity $u = \sqrt{G/\rho}$. Or for a compressional wave, Young's modulus E appears in place of G. For a compressional wave in a fluid (liquid or gas), where the stress can only be a hydrostatic pressure, the bulk modulus β appears. These expressions for the phase velocity could also be arrived at with dimensional analysis (up to a multiplicative constant), since only these combinations of elastic moduli and densities have the correct dimensions of a velocity. The first two waves are called *transverse*, because the displacements are perpendicular to the direction of propagation of the wave, and the last two *longitudinal*, because the displacement and propagation directions are the same. The generalization of the wave equation for the displacement Ψ is

$$u^2 \left(\frac{\partial^2 \Psi}{\partial x^2} + \frac{\partial^2 \Psi}{\partial y^2} + \frac{\partial^2 \Psi}{\partial z^2} \right) = \frac{\partial^2 \Psi}{\partial t^2} \tag{16–17}$$

The equation may be abbreviated

$$u^2 \nabla^2 \Psi = \ddot{\Psi}$$

where ∇ is the same vector differential operator as was used previously (Eq. 1–4) to express the gradient of a scalar function; here ∇^2 means $\nabla \cdot \nabla$, and is called the *Laplacian* operator.

The wave equation can be reduced to a three-dimensional Helmholtz equation

$$\nabla^2 \psi + \kappa^2 \psi = 0 \qquad \kappa \equiv \omega/u \tag{16–18}$$

by substituting $\Psi(x,y,z,t) = \psi(x,y,z)e^{i\omega t}$. The Helmholtz equation has solutions of the form

$$e^{i\kappa_x x}, \quad e^{i\kappa_y y}, \quad e^{i\kappa_z z}$$

These describe waves in the x-, y-, or z-directions. A more general solution to the Helmholtz equation is given by

$$\psi(\mathbf{r}) = e^{i\mathbf{K} \cdot \mathbf{r}} \tag{16-19}$$

The corresponding solution to the wave equation is

$$\Psi(\mathbf{r},t) = e^{i(\omega t - \mathbf{K} \cdot \mathbf{r})} = e^{i\kappa(ut - \mathbf{s} \cdot \mathbf{r})} \qquad \mathbf{\kappa} = \kappa\mathbf{s} = \kappa_x \mathbf{e}_x + \kappa_y \mathbf{e}_y + \kappa_z \mathbf{e}_z$$

At a given instant t, the wave has the same phase at all those points $\mathbf{r}$ which satisfy $\mathbf{s} \cdot \mathbf{r} =$ const. This solution describes a *plane wave* propagating in an arbitrary direction $\mathbf{s}$, because every point on the plane $\mathbf{r} \cdot \mathbf{s} =$ const perpendicular to the unit vector $\mathbf{s}$ (or $\mathbf{\kappa}$) at a given instant t has the same phase. (Cf. Fig. 13–13.)

Many other forms of solutions of Eq. 16–18 could be found. A particularly interesting one has spherical symmetry. Suppose there is a solution $\psi(r)$ which depends only on $r = \sqrt{x^2 + y^2 + z^2}$, but not on the other spherical coordinates θ and ϕ. Then, changing to spherical coordinates, we obtain

$$\frac{\partial \psi}{\partial x} = \frac{\partial \psi}{\partial r}\frac{\partial r}{\partial x} - \frac{\partial \psi}{\partial r}\frac{x}{r} \qquad \frac{\partial^2 \psi}{\partial x^2} = \frac{1}{r}\frac{\partial \psi}{\partial r} + x \frac{\partial r}{\partial x}\frac{\partial}{\partial r}\left(\frac{1}{r}\frac{\partial \psi}{\partial r}\right)$$

$$= \frac{1}{r}\frac{\partial \psi}{\partial r} + \frac{x^2}{r}\left(\frac{1}{r}\frac{\partial^2 \psi}{\partial r^2} - \frac{1}{r^2}\frac{\partial \psi}{\partial r}\right)$$

$$\frac{\partial^2 \psi}{\partial x^2} + \frac{\partial^2 \psi}{\partial y^2} + \frac{\partial^2 \psi}{\partial z^2} = \frac{3}{r}\frac{\partial \psi}{\partial r} + \frac{r^2}{r}\left(\frac{1}{r}\frac{\partial^2 \psi}{\partial r^2} - \frac{1}{r^2}\frac{\partial \psi}{\partial r}\right)$$

$$= \frac{\partial^2 \psi}{\partial r^2} + \frac{2}{r}\frac{\partial \psi}{\partial r} = \frac{1}{r^2}\frac{\partial}{\partial r}\left(r^2 \frac{\partial \psi}{\partial r}\right)$$

Thus the Helmholtz equation (Eq. 16–18) for this spherically symmetric case can be written

$$\frac{1}{r^2}\frac{\partial}{\partial r}\left(r^2 \frac{\partial \psi}{\partial r}\right) = -\kappa^2 \psi \tag{16-20}$$

It is easily verified that

$$\psi(r) = \frac{e^{-i\kappa r}}{r} \tag{16-21}$$

satisfies this equation. This solution is called a *spherical wave*, since the surfaces of constant phase are spheres ($r =$ const). It propagates outward with a spherical wave front, but with an amplitude which falls off as $1/r$ (Fig. 16–5). This decrease in amplitude is necessary to conserve energy, as we shall see later in this section. The solution describes the radiation of a wave from a point source.

To examine the energy contained in the wave in more detail, let us first return to the standing waves or travelling waves on a string. In either case,

270 QUANTUM MECHANICS

a given point on the string moves up and down with simple harmonic motion. If, for example, a travelling wave is described by

$$\Psi(x,t) = A \sin (\omega t - \kappa x)$$

at a given position we can write $-\kappa x = \phi = $ const. The solution $A \sin (\omega t + \phi)$ is just the same as the solution of the harmonic oscillator problem (Eq. 4–6). The average kinetic energy $d\overline{T}$ of a length dx of the string is therefore

$$d\overline{T} = \tfrac{1}{2}(dM)\overline{v^2} = \tfrac{1}{2}(\mu \, dx) \, A^2\omega^2 \, \overline{\cos^2 (\omega t + \phi)}$$

since $v = \dot{\Psi} = A\omega \cos (\omega t + \phi)$. Since the average value of $\cos^2$ is $\tfrac{1}{2}$, we can write the density of kinetic energy along the string as

$$\frac{d\overline{T}}{dx} = \tfrac{1}{4}A^2\omega^2\mu$$

The average kinetic energy of a harmonic oscillator is one half the total energy (cf. Prob. 4–2), and so the total *energy density* is

$$\frac{dE}{dx} = \tfrac{1}{2}A^2\omega^2\mu$$

In the travelling wave this energy is propagated in the x-direction with velocity $u = \omega/\kappa$. For example, the position of maximum kinetic energy (node) or maximum potential energy (antinode) moves with the wave form travelling at the velocity u.

In three dimensions, the energy density is likewise proportional to the square of the amplitude of the wave, but now the energy and mass are re-

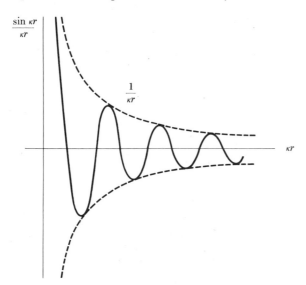

Fig. 16–5. Spherical wave.

ferred to unit volume rather than unit length. For a plane wave, the energy density is

$$\frac{dE}{dV} = \frac{1}{2}A^2\omega^2\rho \qquad (16\text{-}22)$$

where ρ = mass per unit volume. This energy is propagated with the travelling wave form. The flux of energy (i.e., the power) which passes through a unit area parallel to the wave front (or perpendicular to the propagation direction) is

$$I = u\frac{dE}{dV} \qquad (16\text{-}23)$$

where u is the velocity of propagation. (The proof of this relation is just the same as the proof for particle flux leading to Eq. 7-3.) The energy flux per unit area I is called the *intensity* of the wave, and it is proportional to the square of the amplitude. We now see exactly why the amplitude of a spherical wave must decrease like $1/r$ in Eq. 16-21: the total energy flowing through a sphere of radius r surrounding the source is proportional to the surface area of the sphere, or to r^2, and to the intensity I. Thus in order for the total energy flow to be independent of r, the intensity I must be proportional to $1/r^2$. For all kinds of waves (not only sound waves), the intensity is proportional to the square of the amplitude, and the same energy conservation argument holds, provided a negligible amount of energy is absorbed by the medium through which the wave is propagating

16-6   SOUND WAVES

In order to make an immediate physical application of some of the wave theory we have developed, let us consider the propagation of sound. Since most of the sounds we hear propagate through air, let us first treat the medium as an ideal gas. The *velocity* with which the sound waves propagate is

$$u = \sqrt{\beta/\rho} \qquad (16\text{-}24)$$

where β is the bulk modulus and ρ is the density of the gas. In Section 12-3, we calculated the bulk modulus to be, from $PV = RT$,

$$\beta_T = P$$

where the subscript T means that the temperature is held constant. Furthermore, according to Eq. 7-6, the density of an ideal gas is given by

$$\rho = (M/RT)\,P$$

Substituting these quantities into Eq. 16-24, the pressure of the gas cancels, and we find

$$u = \sqrt{RT/M}$$

where M is the (average) molecular weight.

This formula, which was first derived by Isaac Newton, gives a result which is a disappointing 15% smaller than the measured velocity of sound. The difficulty was later resolved by Laplace, who pointed out that the successive compressions and rarefactions of the gas in the wave occur so rapidly, and the thermal conductivity of the gas is so small, that the temperature does not really remain uniform. Instead, the gas is *adiabatically* compressed and expanded at each point. Thus we ought to use the *adiabatic bulk modulus* β_S to describe the relation between the pressure and volume changes, in place of the isothermal bulk modulus β_T. (The ideal gas law can still be used for the average density ρ, since these changes are extremely small.) The adiabatic modulus is obtained by applying the definition

$$\beta \equiv -V\frac{dP}{dV}$$

to the adiabatic gas law

$$PV^\gamma = \text{const}$$

Differentiating this equation,

$$\frac{dP}{dV} = -\gamma\frac{P}{V} \tag{16-25}$$

Then

$$\beta_S = \gamma P$$

and

$$u = \sqrt{\gamma RT/M} \tag{16-26}$$

To evaluate Eq. 16–26 we need to know γ for air. In the derivation of the adiabatic gas law, γ enters as the ratio of specific heats at constant pressure and constant volume, c_P/c_V. Since, in addition, the relation $c_P - c_V = R$ holds for ideal gases, for a diatomic gas $c_V = \frac{5}{2}R$ (Table 9–1), $c_P = \frac{7}{2}R$, and $\gamma = \frac{7}{5}$. The experimental value for air is very close to this theoretical value (1.402). Then at 273°K (0°C) Eq. 16–26 gives $u = 332$ m/sec, in very good agreement with the experimental value.

It is interesting to look at Eq. 16–26 in another way. Dividing numerator and denominator by Avogadro's number, we can write the speed of sound

$$u = \sqrt{\gamma kT/m}$$

By comparison, according to Eq. 9–18 the average speed $\bar{v}$ of a molecule in the gas is

$$\bar{v} = \sqrt{8kT/\pi m}$$

This comparison shows that for any ideal gas, at any temperature (or pressure), the speed at which a sound wave propagates is slightly less than the average speed of the chaotic molecular motion:

$$u \cong \frac{3}{4}\bar{v}$$

It could hardly be greater, since the information about a local compression in the gas is communicated to a neighboring volume element by the motions of the molecules. This fact is related to the very violent disturbance which is produced in a gas when something moves through it with *supersonic* velocities. Such a disturbance, called a *shock wave*, has very different properties from a sound wave. For aircraft, it introduces a "sound barrier" to flight at supersonic velocities. The sound barrier is independent of pressure according to Eq. 16–26; it nevertheless depends on altitude because the temperature or the average molecular speed decreases with altitude (at first). At 30,000 ft, u might be about 10% smaller than at sea level.

The *power* transmitted by a sound wave is given by combining Eqs. 16–22 and 16–23:

$$I = \tfrac{1}{2}uA^2\omega^2\rho$$

A more convenient form of this expression results if we replace the maximum displacement A by the maximum pressure difference (ΔP). The bulk modulus relates (ΔP) to the volume strain,

$$dP = -\beta\frac{dV}{V} \qquad (\Delta P) = \beta\frac{\Delta V}{V}$$

and in a plane wave the volume strain is just the same as the linear strain. The latter, according to the definition of Eq. 12–1, is $d\psi/dx$, which can be calculated from the displacement

$$\psi = A \sin \kappa x$$

to be

$$d\psi/dx = A\kappa \cos \kappa x$$

The maximum strain is therefore $A\kappa$ $(= 2\pi A/\lambda)$, so that

$$A = (\Delta P)/\beta\kappa$$

Inserting this expression into I, and recalling that $\omega/\kappa = u$ (Eq. 16–8) and $\beta = u^2\rho$ (Eq. 16–24), we have finally

$$I = \tfrac{1}{2}\frac{(\Delta P)^2}{u\rho} \tag{16–27}$$

The maximum pressure difference in an acoustic wave is normally a very small fraction of atmospheric pressure $(1.013 \times 10^6 \text{ dyne/cm}^2)$, so that the assumption of small amplitude made in deriving the wave equation is well satisfied. Acoustical pressure differences are expressed in *microbars*, where 1 microbar $\equiv 1$ dyne/cm^2 $(\cong 10^{-6} \text{ atm})$; intensity is generally expressed in watt/cm^2. About the faintest sound detectable by the human ear (a very sensitive detector) involves a pressure difference of 0.0003 microbar. At standard conditions $\rho = M/V = 29/22.4 \times 10^3 = 1.29 \times 10^{-3}$ g/cm^3 for air, and $u = 332$m/sec $= 3.32 \times 10^4$ cm/sec. Inserting these values into Eq. 16–27, we find a corresponding intensity $I \cong 10^{-9}$ erg/cm^2-sec =

10^{-16} watt/cm². The loudest sound which the ear can tolerate is some 10^{12} times more intense, corresponding to a pressure difference 10^6 times greater (300 microbars = 0.0003 bar $\cong$ 0.0003 atm). Because sound intensities span such an enormous range, they are usually expressed on a logarithmic scale.

Sound transmission in *liquids* is also of considerable practical interest because of the importance of underwater acoustics (sonar, etc.). For water, the bulk modulus is about 2.2×10^{10} dyne/cm² and the density is about 1 g/cm³. Thus the sound velocity is 1500 m/sec, or more than 4 times the velocity in air. Both β and ρ are larger for a condensed phase than for a gas, but in general the difference in β is greater, so that the velocity is higher. The power transmission in a liquid is still given by Eq. 16–27, since the gas law was not used anywhere in its derivation. For a given power transmitted, the pressure difference is much larger for an acoustic wave in water than for one in air. Acoustic waves in *solids* are chiefly of interest with respect to standing waves, which describe the vibrations of beams, plates, etc. The analysis of these standing waves can become quite complicated in practical engineering situations, because of the complexity of the boundary conditions imposed by irregularly shaped objects.

The standing wave vibrations in solids are of interest in *physics* primarily at ultrasonic frequencies, above the audible range (i.e., above about 20 kc). As was mentioned earlier in this chapter, a standing wave vibration is a vibration of the atoms of the solid when looked at microscopically, and this model (the Debye model) gives a better account of thermal vibrations than the model in which each atom vibrates in a fixed potential well (the Einstein model), which was assumed in Section 14–5. It is interesting to compare the energy of these thermal vibrations with the energy in an ordinary sound. In Eq. 14–19 we saw that the thermal energy near room temperature is $3RT \approx 2000$ cal/mole. Since the typical molar volume of a heavy solid is $V = M/\rho \approx 20$ cm³/mole, the corresponding energy density is 100 cal/cm³ ≈ 400 joule/cm³. By contrast, for the loudest sound intensity the ear can tolerate, $I \approx 10^{-4}$ watt /cm² and a velocity $u \approx 5000$ m/sec typical of solids, we find an energy density of $10^{-4}/5 \times 10^3 \times 10^2 = 2 \times 10^{-10}$ joule/cm³, about 10^{12} times smaller than that of the thermal vibrations. The reason that we do not *hear* the vibrations of a hot object is that the overwhelming number of the standing wave modes are at ultrasonic frequencies, ranging up to the highest frequency of the order of 10^{13} sec^{-1} which was estimated in Chapter 14. Just how the vibrational energy is distributed among all these modes of vibration—i.e., the *frequency spectrum* of a solid— is a problem which is currently receiving considerable attention in solid state physics. At higher frequencies, *dispersion* occurs because of the discrete atomic structure of the vibrating medium. (Dispersion means that the propagation velocity depends on the frequency, or wave length.) It is fortunate for the appreciation of music that dispersion is absent in the audible range in air, because otherwise low notes would be heard before or after high notes when the hearer was at a distance from the musicians.

The mathematical theory of wave propagation which has been sketched here is actually not limited to elastic deformations but underlies a wide range of physical phenomena. In particular, it describes the propagation of light and other radiation. (In this case, what is "displaced" is an electric or magnetic field.) The spreading of the wave fronts can in general also be described in terms of "beams" shining in the directions s, which are perpendicular to the wave fronts. The properties of the medium are entirely described by the phase velocity u. The velocity may vary from point to point in the medium, in which case phenomena such as *refraction* occur, or it may depend on the frequency of the wave, in which case *dispersion* occurs. In all cases, when the wave passes through apertures whose dimensions are of the order of the wave length, interference effects lead to *diffraction*. These effects are common to all types of waves. Diffraction, especially, is characteristic of wave motion, and it was the discovery of the diffraction of light which defeated the corpuscular theory of light in the early nineteenth century.

PROBLEMS

16–1.   Derive a partial differential equation that applies for *large* displacements of a stretched string. (*Hint:* Do not replace $\sin \alpha$ by $\tan \alpha$, but express $\sin \alpha$ in terms of $d\Psi/dx$.)

16–2.   Show that any function of the form

$$\Psi(x, t) = f(\xi), \quad \xi \equiv x + ut$$

is a solution of the wave equation, where f can be any function, so long as it is differentiable twice. Note that another solution is obtained if u is replaced by $-u$. Interpret these solutions.

16–3.   Prove that two sinusoidal travelling waves of equal amplitude propagating in opposite directions combine to give a standing wave.

16–4.   Prove that the set of functions $\{\sin \kappa_j x\}$ is an orthogonal set.

16–5.   Suppose

$$f(x) = (H/L)x \qquad \text{for } 0 \leq x \leq L$$

Expand in a Fourier sine series, calculating the coefficients c_k. Plot the sum of the first few terms, to see how fast the partial sums approach $f(x)$.

16–6.   Suppose the initial displacement of a string is a parabola,

$$f(x) = x(L - x)/100 \, L \qquad \text{for } 0 \leq x \leq L$$

Expand $f(x)$ in a Fourier sine series. How does the coefficient of the fundamental term in the series compare with $f(L/2)$? Plot $f(x)$ and the first term of the series.

16–7.   A banjo string has a density of 3.7×10^{-3} g/cm, and a length of 65 cm. What tension will tune it to D above middle C (294 cps)? How large is u?

16–8.   Find the temperature change in an ideal gas caused by a compression from P_0 to P_1. (*Hint:* Eliminate V from the adiabatic law and the equation of state.) What is ΔT, assuming $\Delta P \equiv P_1 - P_0$ is small? What is ΔT for a wave in air whose intensity is 10^{-4} watt/cm² at STP?

16–9.   Calculate du/dT from Eq. 16–26. How much does the sound velocity change for a 1°C temperature change at 20°C?

16–10. The velocity of sound in He at 0°C is 970 m/sec. Calculate γ for He and compare with the theoretical value.

16–11. Suppose a 20-watt amplifier drives a loudspeaker with 1% efficiency, and the speaker radiates uniformly into π steradians (i.e., $\frac{1}{4}$ of the entire sphere). How far away could one just barely hear it?

16–12. Suppose a plane wave propagates in air and in water with the same intensity. Find the ratio of the peak pressures.

16–13. Calculate the displacement amplitude A in a 1-kc sound wave of intensity 10^{-4} watt/cm² for both air and water.

16–14. *Cavitation* can occur in a sound wave in water if the total pressure is negative—i.e., if the pressure amplitude (ΔP) exceeds the average pressure P. Calculate the intensity I and amplitude A for $\Delta P = 2$ atm.

16–15. Prove Eq. 16–23.

REFERENCES

R. J. Stephenson, *Mechanics and Properties of Matter* (John Wiley & Sons, 1960, 2nd ed.), Ch. 9.

R. A. Waldron, *Waves and Oscillations* (D. Van Nostrand, 1964).

R. H. Stuart, *An Introduction to Fourier Analysis* (Methuen, 1962).

17/light corpuscles

In the early nineteenth century, the discovery of the interference and diffraction of light proved that light was a wave phenomenon, and the corpuscular theory of light was abandoned. In the twentieth century, the discovery of some new effects—notably the Compton scattering of light and the photoelectric emission of electrons—"proved" that light was a corpuscular (or particle) phenomenon. This time, however, the response could not be so direct as simply to abandon the wave theory of light, because interference and diffraction experiments can still be performed in the twentieth century. The correct response, which was made, was to invent a new theory that would somehow combine the necessary features of both the wave and the corpuscular theories. The invention was developed over the first quarter of the century by many people, from Planck and Einstein to Schrödinger and Heisenberg, and gave the foundation for the present theory of quantum mechanics.

This chapter describes the analysis of the Compton and photoelectric effects in terms of collisions involving light particles, or photons. It may seem that it does not make much sense to regard light as a wave at one moment and as a particle at the next moment, and that is correct—it does not make sense. The reason is that to "make sense" in common parlance usually means to obey the laws of classical mechanics and here we are dealing with something which does not obey them. It was necessary to construct a new mechanics—quantum mechanics—which is obeyed. With it as a basis, it is possible to derive all these phenomena consistently and rigorously, in which context they do "make sense." The presentation of a formal theory will be deferred, however, until some of its consequences have been analyzed and compared with experiment.

17–1   COMPTON SCATTERING

The most unambiguous (although historically not the first) manifestation of the corpuscular nature of light is the Compton scattering of photons, in which a photon makes an elastic collision with an electron at rest. In the collision, which can be analyzed in the ordinary way (Chapter 6) using momentum and energy conservation, the incident photon loses part of its energy to the electron. As will be seen, it is not feasible to observe the effect with visible light, but only in the case of much shorter wave length radiation, i.e., x-rays or γ-rays. The Compton scattering accounts for part of the attenuation of a beam of x-rays or γ-rays as it penetrates through matter. Therefore we consider a collision (Fig. 17–1)

$$\gamma + e \rightarrow \gamma' + e$$

in which an incident photon with momentum $\mathbf{p}_1$ collides with an electron at rest ($\mathbf{p}_2 = 0$), imparting momentum $\mathbf{p}_2'$ to the electron and itself moving off with momentum $\mathbf{p}_1'$. Conservation of momentum (Eq. 6–2) requires that

$$\mathbf{p}_1 = \mathbf{p}_1' + \mathbf{p}_2'$$

In order to write down the energy conservation condition, the relativistic expression, Eq. 3–17,

$$E = \sqrt{(cp)^2 + (mc^2)^2} \qquad (17\text{–}1)$$

must be used, where m represents the rest mass of the particle. The photon always travels with the velocity of light c (since it *is* light), and a particle which always has velocity c must have *zero rest mass:* from Eq. 3–18,

$$E = \frac{mc^2}{\sqrt{1 - v^2/c^2}}$$

If $v = c$, the denominator on the right vanishes. Therefore, if the energy is to be finite, the numerator must also vanish, so that the mass is exactly zero, $m = 0$. For a zero rest mass particle, the energy and momentum are related by the very simple expression, obtained by putting $m = 0$ in Eq. 17–1,

$$E = cp \qquad (17\text{–}2)$$

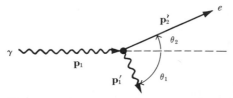

Fig. 17–1. *Compton scattering of a photon by an electron.*

The electron, of course, has a non-zero rest mass. Then the energy conservation condition is

$$cp_1 + m_2c^2 = cp_1' + \sqrt{(cp_2')^2 + (m_2c^2)^2} \qquad (17\text{-}3)$$

Let us solve the energy and momentum equations by eliminating the variables which refer to the electron, so that we can see what happens to the photon. (Having done so, the electron recoil momentum could be found from $\mathbf{p_2}' = \mathbf{p_1} - \mathbf{p_1}'$, of course.) Squaring the momentum relation $\mathbf{p_2}' = \mathbf{p_1} - \mathbf{p_1}'$,

$$p_2'^2 = p_1^2 + p_1'^2 - 2\mathbf{p_1}\cdot\mathbf{p_1}' = p_1^2 + p_1'^2 - 2p_1p_1' \cos \theta_1$$

Squaring the energy relation, Eq. 17-3, after transposing cp_1',

$$(cp_1)^2 + (cp_1')^2 + (m_2c^2)^2 - 2c^2p_1p_1' + 2m_2c^3(p_1 - p_1') = (cp_2')^2 + (m_2c^2)^2$$

Inserting $p_2'^2$ into this expression, almost everything cancels, and we are left with

$$m_2c(p_1 - p_1') = p_1p_1'(1 - \cos \theta_1)$$

Dropping the subscripts, we have the result for the momentum p' of a photon scattered at an angle θ,

$$\frac{1}{p'} - \frac{1}{p} = \frac{1}{mc}(1 - \cos \theta) \qquad (17\text{-}4)$$

where m is the electron mass, and p is the original momentum of the photon.

In terms of photon *energy*, $E = cp$, Eq. 17-4 becomes

$$\frac{1}{E'} - \frac{1}{E} = \frac{1}{mc^2}(1 - \cos \theta) \qquad (17\text{-}5)$$

or if $\Delta E \equiv E - E'$,

$$\frac{\Delta E}{E'} = \frac{E}{mc^2}(1 - \cos \theta)$$

Thus the final photon energy E' will be smaller than the incident energy E, depending on the angle θ at which the photon is scattered. The energy loss ΔE (relative to the final photon energy E') depends on the scattering angle θ as shown in Fig. 17-2, rising from zero for a clean miss ($\theta = 0$), to

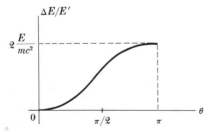

Fig. 17-2. *Photon energy loss as a function of angle for Compton scattering, relative to final photon energy.*

twice the original photon energy E (relative to the electron rest energy mc^2) for direct back scattering ($\theta = \pi$). The relative decrease in the scattered photon energy thus depends on the scattering angle and is large only if the incident photon energy is comparable with the electron rest energy. Since the rest energy of the electron is

$$mc^2 = 0.511 \text{ MeV} = 511{,}000 \text{ eV}$$

(cf. Section 6–3), the difference is inappreciable unless E is of a similar order of magnitude. That is why the effect is observed with x-rays (typically 0.05 to 0.25 MeV) and γ-rays (typically 0.1 to 2 MeV).

This deduction from the requirements of energy and momentum conservation tells the conditions under which the scattering *could* happen; it does not tell the probability with which it *does* happen. The latter question (the calculation of the collision *cross section*) will not be answered here, although the cross section can be shown to be appreciable. The result of such a calculation is something of the order of a cross section resulting from an *electron radius* of

$$e^2/mc^2 = 2.8 \times 10^{-13} \text{ cm}$$

This number is called the "classical radius of the electron."

If we want to look at light sometimes as a beam of particles (photons) with energy E and momentum p, and sometimes as waves with frequency ν and wave length λ, it is essential to make a well-defined connection between these two pictures, or else we would not have a consistent view of nature. The connection is that the photon energy is proportional to the wave frequency,

$$E = h\nu \qquad (17\text{–}6)$$

where h is a universal constant called *Planck's constant* (since it was first introduced by Max Planck in connection with black-body radiation, as will be described later). As a corollary, the photon momentum is related to the wave length by

$$p = h/\lambda \qquad (17\text{–}7)$$

since $p = E/c$ and $\nu = c/\lambda$. In terms of $\omega = 2\pi\nu$ and $\kappa = 2\pi/\lambda$,

$$E = \hbar\omega \qquad p = \hbar\kappa \qquad (17\text{–}8)$$

where $\hbar \equiv h/2\pi$. The constant $\hbar$ (read h-cross or h-bar) is often used instead of h, when a factor of 2π can thereby be eliminated. The numerical value of h must be determined by experiment. It could be determined by the Compton scattering experiment, among others, as follows.

Substituting $p = h/\lambda$ into Eq. 17–4,

$$\lambda' - \lambda = (h/mc)(1 - \cos\theta) \qquad (17\text{–}4')$$

This equation gives the predicted wave length of the scattered radiation, using the particle model of the collision and the connection Eq. 17–7 between the two pictures. The quantity h/mc is called the *Compton wave length* of the electron. It has the value, determined from Compton scattering experiments with x-rays at known wave lengths,

$$h/mc = 0.0243 \text{ A}$$

This value, with $m = 0.91 \times 10^{-27}$ g and $c = 3 \times 10^{10}$ cm/sec, gives

$$h = 6.63 \times 10^{-27} \text{ erg-sec}$$

or

$$\hbar = 1.054 \times 10^{-27} \text{ erg-sec}$$

It is worth emphasizing that an analysis of the Compton effect using the wave theory of light does not work. Classically, an electromagnetic wave would set an electron into synchronous oscillation, and the oscillating electron would reradiate light of the same frequency. The appearance of light of a lower frequency can be understood only with the particle picture. This discrepancy raises a disturbing question: how do you know which theory to use? The answer is that there exists one correct theory—quantum electrodynamics—which gives the right answer for all known experiments involving photons and electrons. Its application is very difficult, however, so that it is still worthwhile to be able to make a simple calculation on the basis of the wave picture or the particle picture. Knowing which to use depends partly on intuition and prior knowledge, but in general the particle picture works at high energy (short wave length) and the wave picture works at long wave length (low energy). In the Compton effect, for example, the particle picture is essential only for high energy photons, because for low energy (low compared with the electron rest energy) the result is the same as with the wave picture (no measurable wave length shift). Conversely, in the diffraction of light, the wave picture is essential only at long wave length, because for short wave length (short compared to the size of the aperture) the particle picture gives the same answer (no measurable diffraction). Similar criteria will be seen to apply to the other effects that will be discussed.

17-2   ELECTRON-POSITRON PAIR PRODUCTION

Another mechanism by which a beam of γ-rays is attenuated as it passes through matter is electron *pair production*. The photon may be, in such an event, *annihilated*, with the simultaneous creation of an electron and *positron* (a particle with the same mass as the negative electron, but with positive charge—a "positive electron"):

$$\gamma \rightarrow e^- + e^+$$

(See Fig. 17-3.)

Energy conservation requires that

$$E_\gamma = cp_\gamma = \sqrt{(cp_-)^2 + (mc^2)^2} + \sqrt{(cp_+)^2 + (mc^2)^2} \qquad (17\text{-}9)$$

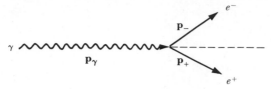

Fig. 17–3. *Electron-positron pair creation by a photon.*

For $p_- = p_+ = 0$, the right-hand side of this equation has its smallest possible value, and

$$E_\gamma = 2mc^2 = 1.02 \text{ MeV}$$

If the electron and positron have any momentum at all, the photon energy must be correspondingly greater. Therefore, the rest energies of the particles impose an absolute *threshold* energy below which the process cannot occur at all.

Seemingly, however, γ-rays with energy greater than the threshold energy, 1.02 MeV, could be annihilated in free space by pair creation, even if no matter were present. Thus even a vacuum would be "opaque" to these γ-rays. Nevertheless, this process does not occur, because in it momentum could not be conserved. From the energy conservation equation, Eq. 17–9, $p_\gamma > p_- + p_+$. (If m were 0, it would imply that $p_\gamma = p_- + p$; but actually $m > 0$.) On the other hand, from the momentum equation

$$\mathbf{p}_\gamma = \mathbf{p}_- + \mathbf{p}_+$$

one has

$$p_\gamma \leq p_- + p_+$$

since a side of a triangle is less than the sum of the other two sides (Fig. 17–4). Pair creation therefore does not occur in vacuum; but if the heavy nucleus of an atom is nearby, the nucleus can carry away the excess momentum without taking much energy $(E = p^2/2M)$, and the process will occur. Pair production is thus an important mechanism for absorption of γ-rays in matter, for γ-rays with energies greater than 1.02 MeV, becoming more important as the energy increases. At smaller energies the absorption is due entirely to the Compton effect and the photoelectric effect (Section 17–3).

The inverse to this pair-production process can also occur, in which a positron and electron are *annihilated* and a photon is produced, a nearby

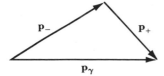

Fig. 17–4

Fig. 17–5. *Photoelectric absorption of a photon by an electron.*

nucleus taking the excess momentum. It is much more likely, however, that the annihilation will produce *two* photons which share all the momentum. (See Prob. 17–4.) (The inverse of this latter process could occur too, without the presence of other matter, but it is very unlikely that two photons should collide with each other, because of the smallness of their cross section, and such a process has never been observed.)

17–3   THE PHOTOELECTRIC EFFECT AND GAMMA RAY ABSORPTION

A third mechanism by which photons are attenuated in matter is the *photoelectric effect.* In this process, as in pair production, the photon is totally annihilated or absorbed, not merely scattered as in the Compton effect; but it is absorbed by an electron which is already present in some matter, and the electron gets the entire energy of the photon (Fig. 17–5). Energy conservation requires

$$E_\gamma + mc^2 = \sqrt{(cp)^2 + (mc^2)^2} \qquad (17\text{--}10)$$

Again, as in the case of pair production, momentum cannot be conserved at the same time, but the excess momentum can be taken up by a nearby nucleus. These three processes together account for the interaction of γ-rays with matter. To calculate their cross sections is a difficult problem, which has been solved with some accuracy. Compton scattering and pair production are important only at high energy, the latter only above 1 MeV.

In order to relate the cross sections for the three processes which have been discussed to the penetrating power of γ-rays, we may return to the analysis of Section 6–4. Suppose a beam of photons is incident on a slab of material of thickness dx (Fig. 17–6). Some photons will be annihilated by pair production or the photoelectric effect, and some will be scattered by the Compton effect. In any case the number of photons which come out of

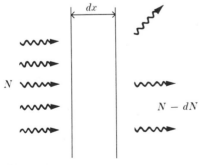

Fig. 17–6

the slab *in the beam* will be smaller than the number which entered. According to Eq. 6–11, the probability that a photon is removed from the beam is

$$d\Pi = n\sigma \, dx$$

where n is the number per unit volume of scattering centers, and σ is the total integrated cross section. ("Total" here means it is the sum of the individual cross sections for the three processes under consideration, and "integrated" means the cross sections are integrated over all scattering angles.) Thus if N photons are incident on the slab, a fraction dN/N is lost, with

$$dN/N = -\, d\Pi = -\, n\sigma \, dx \tag{17–11}$$

(Cf. Eq. 8–4.) Integrating Eq. 17–11,

$$N = N_0 e^{-n\sigma x} \tag{17–12}$$

where N is the number of photons reaching a depth x, and N_0 (the arbitrary constant of integration) is the number incident at $x = 0$.

We can also express this result in terms of the *intensity* of the γ-ray beam. Since the intensity refers to the energy per unit time carried by the beam through a unit area (cf. Eq. 16–23), and since each photon carries a "quantum" of energy $E_\gamma = h\nu$, the intensity is

$$I = \frac{Nh\nu}{At} \tag{17–13}$$

where A is the area through which N photons pass in time t. That is, the intensity is $h\nu$ times the photon flux per unit area. In view of this proportionality between I and N, Eq. 17–12 can be rewritten

$$I = I_0 e^{-\mu x} \qquad \mu \equiv n\sigma \tag{17–14}$$

The quantity μ (dimensions cm^{-1}) is called the *absorption coefficient*. Equation 17–14 expresses the very important fact that all electromagnetic radiation (including visible light) is attenuated exponentially as it passes through matter. Thus, a thickness twice as great does not absorb twice as much radiation (although that is approximately true for thin layers, as may be seen by expanding the exponential in a power series). Instead, if a given layer transmits 1/10 of the incident radiation, a layer twice as thick transmits only 1/100.

The absorption coefficient μ can be measured experimentally by interposing different thicknesses of absorber in a beam and measuring the transmitted intensity. In fact, this is an important experimental method for measuring γ-ray energies, since μ depends on photon energy, as well as on the kind of absorbing material. The total absorption coefficient for Pb is shown in Fig. 17–7 as a function of energy, together with the individual contributions of each of the three processes. The importance of the Compton effect decreases gradually with energy and that of pair production increases. At low energies the photoelectric effect becomes strongly dominant. At still lower energies a fourth effect, the coherent scattering of x-rays (the Bragg reflection discussed in Section 13–6), becomes significant. In addition, at certain photon energies, there is a small amount of absorption by atomic *nuclei*, but this absorption will not be mentioned further until Chapter 29.

The relative importance of the different processes depends strongly on the kind of material. Because the atomic nucleus is involved in pair production and the photoelectric effect (in order to conserve momentum), the cross sections for these processes depend in a relatively complex manner on the scattering atoms—in particular on the atomic number Z. (The atomic cross sections are proportional to Z^2 and Z^5, respectively.) The Compton effect, on the other hand, can occur for free electrons, and so the atomic cross section is simply the number of electrons per atom Z, times the cross section for one electron,

$$\sigma = Z\sigma_e \tag{17–15}$$

Because the photoelectric effect depends on Z^5 it is much more important in heavy elements, and this is why Pb is used for γ-ray and x-ray shielding. In light elements the Compton effect is generally most important. In Pb the Compton effect is dominant between 1 and 10 mc^2 (Fig. 17–7), but in Al, for example, it dominates between 0.1 and 30 mc^2 (50 keV to 15 MeV).

In order to consider a simple numerical example, let us estimate the absorption constant for Al in the region where the Compton scattering dominates. To calculate the number n of atoms per unit volume, we recall that the density ρ is nm, where m, the mass of an atom, is the molecular weight M divided by Avogadro's number N_0. Therefore,

$$n = \rho N_0/M \tag{17–16}$$

Using Eqs. 17–14 to 17–16, we obtain the absorption coefficient for Compton scattering,

$$\mu = \rho \sigma_e N_0 Z/M \tag{17–17}$$

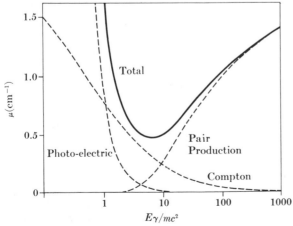

Fig. 17–7. *Absorption coefficients for γ-rays in Pb, as a function of photon energy.*

As stated in Section 17–1, the "radius" of an electron is about 3×10^{-13} cm (or about 100,000 times smaller than an atom), so that

$$\sigma_e \approx 10^{-25} \text{ cm}^2 = 0.1 \text{ barn}$$

where 1 barn $\equiv 10^{-24}$ cm^2 is a conventional unit for cross sections. Inserting $\rho = 2.7$, $N_0 = 6 \times 10^{23}$, $Z = 13$, and $M = 27$ into Eq. 17–17,

$$\mu \approx 0.1 \text{ cm}^{-1} \text{ for Al}$$

a result which we expect to be valid in the vicinity of 1 MeV. To calculate the wave length of a 1 MeV γ-ray, $E_\gamma = h\nu = hc/\lambda$, so that

$$\lambda = hc/E_\gamma = 6.6 \times 10^{-27} \times 3 \times 10^{10}/10^6 \times 1.6 \times 10^{-12} \cong 10^{-10} \text{ cm}$$
$$= 0.01 \text{ Å}$$

The tabulated value of μ at $\lambda = 0.01$ Å (from the *Handbook of Chemistry and Physics*, for example) is 0.16 cm^{-1}, giving some confidence in our model. It is interesting to note in Eq. 17–17 that, for an element, $M \cong A$, the mass number, and for light elements $A \cong 2Z$. Thus for Compton scattering in light elements we can write

$$\mu/\rho \cong \tfrac{1}{2}\sigma_e N_0 \approx 0.1 \text{ cm}^2/\text{g}$$

The quantity μ/ρ, called the *mass absorption coefficient*, should be roughly the same for all light elements, although dependent on γ-ray energy. Experimentally, at 0.01 Å, it is 0.058 ± 0.001 cm^2/g for C, Al, Fe, Cu, and Sn (and 0.071 for Pb). Because of the usefulness of μ/ρ, one often expresses the "thickness" of a scattering foil in Eq. 17–14 in terms of $x\rho$ g/cm^2.

We may remark that photons of wavelength 0.01 Å are able to "see" the internal structure of atoms whose diameter is about 1 Å, in the sense that they are scattered by the individual component electrons. This fact exemplifies an important generality, namely that radiation, in order to probe a structure, must have a wave length which is smaller than the dimensions of the structure. It is just this necessity which drives men, in order to investigate smaller and smaller objects, to devise means for producing higher and higher energy (shorter wave length) probes. In the other extreme, radiation of wave length long compared to the atomic size, for example visible light (5000 Å), is scattered by the atom as a whole. Since the size of the atom is some 3×10^{-8} cm, the cross section may be expected to be of the order of 10^{-15} cm^2, or some 10^{10} times greater than the electronic cross section. The absorption coefficient, according to Eq. 17–14, is also correspondingly bigger. A γ-ray absorption coefficient of 0.1 cm^{-1} means that in a 10-cm thickness the transmitted intensity is $e^{-1} \approx 1/3$ of the incident intensity. Light elements, like aluminum, are therefore rather transparent to γ-rays. Visible light, however, with an absorption coefficient roughly 10^9 times greater, is cut down to $1/e$ in a few Ångstroms, so that it penetrates only a few atomic layers. The opacity of aluminum is thus accounted for. Why some other materials, such as glass, quartz, diamond, etc., are transparent to visible light, can only be understood after more subtle aspects of their structure are examined in Chapter 25. Overlooking such subtleties, we may expect a large interaction cross section for photons with wave length in the visible region.

We shall next concentrate our attention on the photon-electron interaction which occurs in this low energy region. It is interesting for both practical and theoretical reasons: many important technological devices operate in this range; moreover, a great deal has been inferred about the structure of the atoms from their response to a more gentle barrage of low energy photons (Chapter 18). In the next section, we treat the photoelectric effect in this low energy region.

17-4 PHOTOEMISSION OF ELECTRONS

Of the three effects we have considered—the Compton, pair-production, and photoelectric effects—only the last occurs with low energy photons, down in the ultraviolet and visible regions of the electromagnetic spectrum. As has been stated, the photoelectric effect involves the whole atom in the interaction, because of the necessity of momentum conservation, and even more so when the wave length is long compared to the atomic size. Indeed, in solid metals the electrons belonging to a large number of atoms all interact together. (A similar collective interaction of all the electrons accounted for coherent x-ray scattering, or Bragg reflection, although there the reason was obvious because we were considering the wave picture of the electromagnetic radiation.) Nevertheless, the net result of the photoelectric effect is that a photon goes in and an electron comes out, so that for our present purposes it is still not too gross an oversimplification to say that the photon knocks out the electron.

In focusing our attention on this low energy region, two differences occur. First, the electron can be treated nonrelativistically: for visible (green) light, the photon energy, which is transferred to the electron, is only about 2 eV, compared with the electron rest energy of 511,000 eV. Second, at the lower energies involved, the electron cannot necessarily be treated as totally "free" and at rest. In particular, the electrons in the atoms of a gas or in a solid are *bound* in the atom, essentially in the same sense as the atoms are bound in a solid—i.e., work must be supplied in order to remove them. We are going to see later that the binding energy of the electrons in isolated atoms (called the ionization energy) varies from a few eV up to the order of 100,000 eV for the most tightly bound electrons in heavy atoms; and that the binding energy for the most loosely bound electrons in a metal (called the *work function*) is also a few eV. When a bound electron absorbs a photon, part of the photon energy is used to overcome the binding energy and remove the electron from the atom or solid, and only the remainder appears as kinetic energy of the electron.

Including all these modifications, Eq. 17-10 becomes

$$E_\gamma + mc^2 + p_0^2/2m - V_0 = mc^2 + p^2/2m,$$

where p_0 and $-V_0$ are, respectively, the momentum and potential energy of the electron inside the material. Writing $W \equiv V_0 - p_0^2/2m$ for the work function or ionization energy,

$$E_\gamma = p^2/2m + W$$

where $p^2/2m$ is the kinetic energy of the freed electron. (See Fig. 17–8.) After the electron gets out, its total energy is kinetic energy, $E = p^2/2m$. Furthermore, E_γ is related to the frequency of the light (in its wave aspect) by Eq. 17–6,

$$E_\gamma = h\nu$$

so that the electrons come out with energy E,

$$E = h\nu - W \qquad (17\text{–}18)$$

Actually, in the case of photoelectric emission from a solid, this energy is the *maximum* possible energy, and electrons with lower energy appear too. Some of them were more tightly bound or had smaller kinetic energy, and others lost some energy in collisions on the way out. The highest energy electrons which are ejected, however, obey this relation, Eq. 17–18.

The relation can be tested experimentally by shining a light of frequency ν on a material and measuring the retarding electrical potential which will prevent any electrons from leaving; this potential is equal to the maximum energy E, in eV, with which electrons come out. The relation between E and ν is well confirmed, with the same value of h as quoted in Section 17–1. Furthermore, the electron *energy* is independent of the *intensity* of the light I, depending only on the frequency (i.e., the photon energy), a result which is incomprehensible on the basis of the wave picture of light. These relations are shown in the graphs of Fig. 17–9. Historically, the idea of photons was invented (Einstein, 1905) in order to explain this experiment. On the basis of this idea, the relations are quite natural: the electron energy depends on the photon energy (light frequency), and the electron current depends on the photon current (light intensity).

Photoelectric emission is of considerable practical importance, since photoelectric tubes are among the most useful *detectors* of visible and ultraviolet light. In this application, the photoemitting surface is made negative,

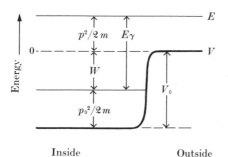

Inside   Outside

Fig. 17–8. *Energy relations in photoelectric emission at the surface of a solid.*

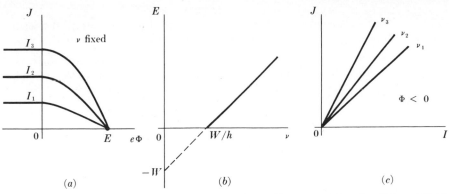

Fig. 17-9. (a) Photocurrent J as a function of retarding potential Φ, for different light intensities I. (b) Maximum electron energy E as a function of frequency ν of the light. (c) Saturation photocurrent as a function of light intensity, for different frequencies.

and the ejected electrons are collected by an anode. The anode current is proportional to the intensity of the light (for a given frequency), since the number of ejected electrons is proportional to the number of incident photons. Let it be emphasized that the maximum electron energy is independent of intensity and related to frequency of the light, but the number of electrons is related to the intensity (and also to the frequency). No current can be obtained for frequencies $\nu < W/h$, according to Eq. 17–18, since the electrons would not come out with positive kinetic energy (i.e., not at all). The limitation thus imposed on phototubes makes them useless for most of the infrared spectral region, because all known materials have work functions which are greater than about 1 eV, corresponding to a wave length of about 12,000 Å.

The effects we have considered account for the interaction between high energy photons and electrons with complete success—indeed down to the region of 1 eV. (The same approach is applicable to the interaction of photons with other charged particles such as mesons and protons.) At much lower frequencies, e.g., radio and power frequencies, the wave approach is usually satisfactory. The range of photon energies *slightly* less than the electron binding energy is especially interesting, because it reveals something about the quantum mechanics of the electrons, and that is the area we look at next.

PROBLEMS

17–1. Find the largest energy loss by Compton scattering of a 1.33-MeV γ-ray (emitted by Co⁶⁰).

17–2. Calculate the photon energy for a 0.25 Å x-ray, the Na-D line (5890 Å), a 1400-kc radio wave, and 60-cycle ac. Calculate the wave length of a 1.33-MeV γ-ray.

17–3.   Show that momentum could not be conserved in the photoelectric effect without a nucleus to carry off the excess momentum.

17–4.   Suppose a positron and electron at rest annihilate each other, producing two γ-ray photons. Find the energy and possible directions of the two γ's.

17–5.   Pair production can also take place in the field of an electron as well as a nucleus (although this process is not very important in γ-ray absorption). Show that the γ-ray threshold energy is 4 mc^2. (*Hint:* At threshold, all 3 particles move off together.)

17–6.   The *half-value thickness* $x_{1/2}$ is defined as the thickness of absorber which will reduce the intensity of an incident beam of γ-rays to one-half its original value. Show that $x_{1/2} = (\ln 2)/\mu$.

17–7.   For Pb, the cross section for γ-ray absorption is 0.153 barn. How many centimeters of Pb would reduce the intensity to 1/16 of its incident value?

REFERENCES

F. K. Richtmyer, E. H. Kennard, and T. Lauritsen, *Introduction to Modern Physics* (McGraw-Hill, 1955, 5th ed.), Ch. 3, 8.

M. Born, *Atomic Physics* (Hafner, 1951, 5th ed.), Ch. 4.

I. Kaplan, *Nuclear Physics* (Addison-Wesley, 1963, 2nd ed.), Ch. 15.

18/emission and absorption of light

In the last chapter, we showed that in certain circumstances light has to be described as a particle—a photon—rather than as a wave, when the light interacts with a free electron. (At least the electron was free after the interaction.) Now we shall consider the interaction between light and a bound electron. Incidentally, the reason for concentrating on the interaction between light and matter, rather than on the unobstructed propagation of light through the vacuum, is that light can be observed only when it interacts with something; the pure propagation of light through space can be described equally well as the spreading of a wave or as the flight of particles. In describing the interaction with bound electrons, the light will again be treated as a particle of energy $E_\gamma = h\nu$, but its corpuscular nature need not be reemphasized. Instead, attention will be focussed on the implications of the emission and absorption of photons with respect to the possible mechanical states of the bound electrons. It will develop that (under certain circumstances) the electron states cannot be described by classical mechanics, just as classical electromagnetic wave theory fails to describe the light.

The absorption of a photon which is to be discussed here is similar to the photoelectric effect already described, except that the electron which absorbs it, instead of being knocked free of the atom or solid, remains bound, but "excited"; i.e., the electron has higher energy than it had before, but its energy is still less than that required to escape to infinity. Emission of a photon is the inverse process—an excited electron loses some of its energy and a photon is created. Conservation of energy requires that when the electron emits a photon which carries away energy $h\nu$, its own energy decrease by the same amount. Therefore, from the observed features of emission spectra (emitted intensity as a function of frequency), inferences about the electronic energy can be made. In contrast to the free electron, which was treated classically (although relativisti-

cally), *the bound electron will be seen to be capable of changing its energy only in discrete "quanta." The mechanical theory which is designed to calculate these quanta (nonrelativistically in the present context) is "quantum mechanics." The emission of light by electrons will be discussed first for the electrons in isolated atoms, as in a gas, and secondly for electrons in a condensed phase, such as a liquid or solid.*

18–1   SPECTRUM AND ENERGY LEVELS OF ATOMIC HYDROGEN

The emission spectrum of a gas (i.e., the distribution of light intensity as a function of frequency) is a *line spectrum*, in which the light energy is concentrated in narrow frequency (or wave length) regions (Fig. 18–1), at least so long as the emission is by individual atoms rather than molecules. It is called a line spectrum because when the image of an illuminated slit is dispersed by a prism or grating, bright lines of the different colors are seen (Fig. 18–2). The separation of the bright lines occurs in a very complicated pattern for most atoms, but for the simplest atom—hydrogen—the pattern is fairly simple. The wave lengths of the lines can be described very accurately by the formula

$$\frac{1}{\lambda} = R\left(\frac{1}{n^2} - \frac{1}{m^2}\right) \qquad n, m = 1, 2, 3, \ldots \qquad m > n \qquad (18\text{–}1)$$

The constant R is called the *Rydberg constant*, and its experimental value is

$$R = 109,700 \text{ cm}^{-1}$$

When $n = 2$, the different values of m give a series of lines in the visible part of the spectrum known as the *Balmer series*. For $m = 3, 4, 5, 6$, the wave lengths of the familiar red, green, blue, and violet lines of hydrogen result. For $n = 1, m = 2, 3, 4, \ldots$, the *Lyman series* occurs in the ultraviolet. The so-called *Lyman alpha* light ($n = 1, m = 2$), with wave length 1216 Å, happens to be very intense in space, but it is strongly absorbed by the earth's atmosphere. For all atoms, those frequencies (and only those) which can be emitted can also be absorbed.

The photon of frequency ν which is emitted carries away an energy (Eq. 17–6) $E_\gamma = h\nu$, or $E_\gamma = hc/\lambda$. Combining this relation between the

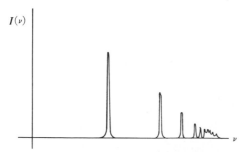

Fig. 18–1. Intensity distribution in a line spectrum.

photon energy and the wave length of the light with the empirical expression for the allowed wave lengths, Eq. 18–1, we have

$$E_\gamma = hcR\left(\frac{1}{n^2} - \frac{1}{m^2}\right) \qquad (18\text{–}2)$$

In order to *conserve energy*, the photon energy E_γ must be equal to the difference between the electron energy before the emission E' and the electron energy after the emission E:

$$E_\gamma = E' - E = \frac{hcR}{n^2} - \frac{hcR}{m^2}$$

We may write

$$E_\gamma = E_m - E_n \qquad (18\text{–}3)$$

if we define E_n by

$$E_n \equiv -\frac{hcR}{n^2} \qquad n = 1, 2, 3, \ldots \qquad (18\text{–}4)$$

It is natural to assume that

$$E' = E_m \qquad E = E_n$$

That is, one is led to the conclusion that the electron can have infinitely many different energy values, E_n, but not any arbitrary energy. The possible electron energies form a discrete set, indexed by the integer n. Conservation of energy requires this restriction on the possible electron energy states, in order to explain the observed spectrum of photons emitted from hydrogen with energies $h\nu$.

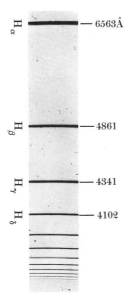

H_α —— 6563Å

H_β —— 4861

H_γ —— 4341

H_δ —— 4102

Fig. 18–2. Emission spectrum of the hydrogen atom Balmer series. [Courtesy of G. Herzberg, Atomic Spectra and Atomic Structure (Dover, New York, 1944).]

The constant hcR must have the dimensions of energy; if the measured values of the constants are inserted, we obtain

$$E_n = -\frac{13.6}{n^2} \text{ eV} \tag{18–5}$$

The energies can be shown by an *energy level diagram*, with the energy on a vertical scale (and nothing on the horizontal scale). The smallest possible energy is E_1, which is 13.6 eV below $E = 0$ (Fig. 18–3). The level E_2 is only $\frac{1}{4}$ as far below zero, etc. The lowest level E_1 is called the *ground state*, and the others are called *excited states*. We see that there are infinitely many bound excited states, i.e., states with $13.6 \text{ eV} < E < 0$. The changes in electron energy, or *transitions* between states, which result in the emission of a photon can be symbolized on the same diagram, by drawing arrows from the initial to the final electron states. The length of the arrow is equal to the photon energy (hc/λ). The transitions which give the strongest lines in the Lyman and Balmer series are shown, with the wave lengths in Å. Similar series which end at the levels E_3 and E_4 are called the Paschen and Brackett series, respectively, and lie in the infrared. Transitions in the opposite direction would correspond to absorption of light of the same wave lengths.

18–2   THE BOHR ATOM

The quantum mechanical theory which predicts these allowed energy levels for the hydrogen atom will be presented in Chapter 21, but at this point it is worthwhile to compare, and contrast, these results with the predictions of

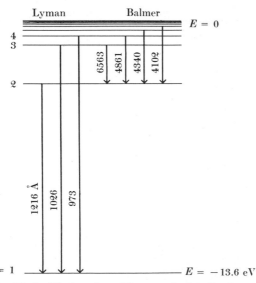

Fig. 18–3. *Electron transitions producing the first two series of lines in the hydrogen atom spectrum.*

classical mechanics. The hydrogen atom consists of an electron and a proton which are attracted to each other by the coulomb force, with potential energy $V = - e^2/r$, since the electron has charge $- e$ and the proton $+ e$. (In mks units, there would be an additional factor of $4\pi\epsilon_0$ in the denominator, and this factor would carry through the following calculation, so that e^2 would have to be replaced by $e^2/4\pi\epsilon_0$ wherever it occurs.) The proton is 1836 times heavier than the electron, so that, like the sun in the planetary system, it remains nearly at rest while the electron revolves around it. The electron orbits are just those which were calculated for the inverse square law force, with $K = e^2$, and all the previous results (Section 5–3) can be applied. In particular, the total energy in an orbit with semimajor axis a is (Eq. 5–12)

$$E = - K/2a = - e^2/2a$$

If only the energies $E_n = - hcR/n^2$ are allowed according to Eq. 18–4, then only the corresponding values of

$$a = a_n = (e^2/2hcR)n^2$$

give possible orbits. To each allowed energy E_n would correspond the allowed classical orbits with semimajor axis a_n.

It is instructive to calculate the *angular momentum* in the allowed orbits. In general the total energy can be written (Eq. 5–4)

$$E = \tfrac{1}{2}m\dot{r}^2 + \frac{L^2}{2mr^2} - \frac{e^2}{r}$$

where L is the angular momentum (like E, a constant of the motion). For given E, L is largest for the circular orbit, and we may begin with this case. Then $\dot{r} = 0$, $r = a$, and

$$E = \frac{L^2}{2ma^2} - \frac{e^2}{a} = - \frac{e^2}{2a}$$
$$L^2 = me^2a$$

(Cf. Eq. 5–7.) Inserting the allowed values of a, the allowed values of L are given by

$$L = (me^4/2hcR)^{1/2}n \qquad n = 1, 2, 3, \ldots$$

The angular momentum can only assume values which are integral multiples of a constant. When evaluated in terms of the measured values of the other fundamental constants, that constant is

$$(me^4/2hcR)^{1/2} = 1.054 \times 10^{-27} \text{ g cm}^2 \text{ sec}^{-1}$$

The constant has exactly the same numerical value as $\hbar (= h/2\pi) = 1.054 \times 10^{-27}$ erg-sec. The numerical equality is not an accident of the cgs system of units, however, because the dimension g cm^2 sec^{-1} is easily shown to be the same as erg-sec. Therefore, we find that

$$L = n\hbar \qquad n = 1, 2, 3, \ldots \qquad (18\text{–}6)$$

This simple result can be taken (Bohr, 1913) as the basis of the semi-classical theory of the *Bohr atom*. While the theory is not really correct, it is nevertheless worth remembering, because the correct hydrogen atom energy levels can be derived from it (working the above argument backwards) in an elementary and pictorial way: putting $L = n\hbar$ into $a = L^2/me^2$ for a circular orbit,

$$a_n = a_0\, n^2 \qquad a_0 \equiv \hbar^2/me^2 \tag{18-7}$$

a_0 being called the *Bohr radius* for the electron; then from $E = -e^2/2a$,

$$E_n = -\frac{e^2}{2a_0}\frac{1}{n^2} = \frac{-me^4}{2\hbar^2}\frac{1}{n^2} \tag{18-8}$$

The Rydberg constant is given as a combination of other fundamental constants, by comparing Eqs. 18-4 and 18-8:

$$R = me^4/4\pi\hbar^3 c \tag{18-9}$$

Indeed, if the *quantization of angular momentum* (Eq. 18-6) is taken seriously as a basis for the Bohr theory, some further correct conclusions can be drawn from it. We have derived the energy of the nth level from the condition that in the *circular* orbit of this energy the angular momentum should be $L = n\hbar$. Other *elliptical* orbits of the same energy but smaller angular momentum are also possible. (Cf. Fig. 5-8.) They have the same major axis but higher eccentricity. If we demand that for these, too, the angular momentum should be an integral multiple of $\hbar$, then for each E_n there are exactly n possible orbits, having angular momentum

$$L = k\hbar \qquad k = 1, 2, 3, \ldots, n \qquad (k \le n) \tag{18-10}$$

The one with $k = n$ is the circular orbit, and the others are more eccentric (Fig. 18-4). Thus for $n = 1$, there is just one orbit of energy E_1; for $n = 2$, there are two of energy E_2; etc.

The fact that there are actually n energy states (orbits) all with exactly the same energy E_n is conventionally described by saying that the nth level is *n-fold degenerate*. To separate the degenerate levels on the energy level diagram, the levels for different k are usually displaced sideways (Fig. 18-5). The levels for $k = 1, 2, 3$, etc., are also designated by the letters s, p, d, f, g, etc. (alphabetical order after f), respectively. This designation is a vestige of an old spectroscopic terminology, but since it is always used, not

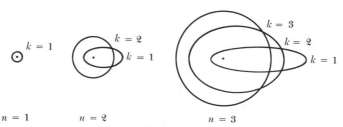

Fig. 18-4. *Bohr orbits of the electron in a hydrogen atom.*

only with reference to atomic and molecular states but also for nuclear and other elementary particles, it must be learned. The degenerate levels are slightly split (one says that the "degeneracy is removed") when relativistic and other small effects are taken into account (as will be done in part later). Then the photon energies in the transition from one value of n to another are slightly different, depending on the values of k, and the existence of the eccentric orbits is revealed by a fine structure of the emitted spectral lines.

18-3   EXCITATION AND IONIZATION OF HYDROGEN-LIKE SYSTEMS

The Bohr theory can be successfully applied not only to hydrogen, but also to other one-electron systems, such as the ions He$^+$, Li^{++}, Be^{+++}, etc.—the so-called *hydrogen-like ions*. These systems differ only in that the electron moves around a nucleus of charge $+Ze$, where Z, the *atomic number*, is 2 for He, 3 for Li, etc. For these ions it is merely necessary to put Ze^2 wherever e^2 appears in the above results. The radius a_n is smaller by the factor $1/Z$, and the energy E_n is multiplied by Z^2, for each integral value of n. All these results agree with experiment. The He$^+$ spectrum is just like that of the H atom, except that all the energy differences (and photon frequencies) are larger by 2^2, so that the corresponding wave lengths are shorter by a factor of 4.

The energy $E = 0$ corresponds to the escape energy, with which the electron can just escape to infinity, and for an atom or ion the difference $0 - E_1 = -E_1\,(E_1 < 0)$ is called the *ionization energy*. For $E > 0$, the electron is in an unbound hyperbolic orbit, and excitation into one of these unbound orbits ("free" electron) is the photoelectric effect which was described previously. The ionization energy of H is observed to be 13.6 eV, and that of He$^+$ is $4 \times 13.6 = 54.4$ eV. The size of the H atom in the ground state is given by the Bohr radius,

$$a_0 = \hbar^2/me^2 = 0.53 \text{ Å}$$

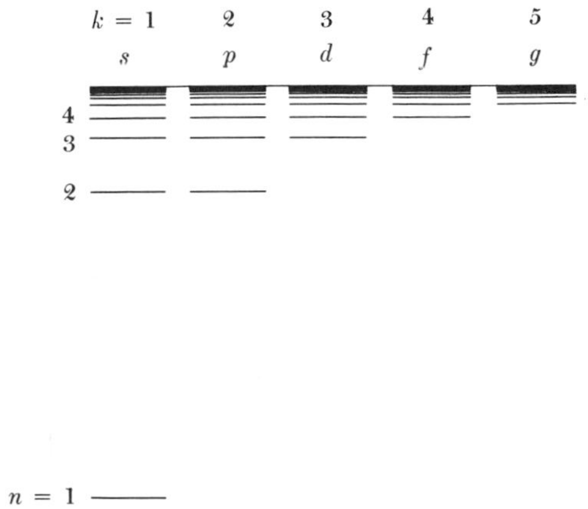

Fig. 18–5. Degeneracy of energy levels of the Bohr atom.

The diameter of 1 Å is approximately what is observed from collision experiments or the separation between H atoms in molecules. The He$^+$ ion is half this size.

When an absorbed photon has energy smaller than the ionization energy, excitation of the atom occurs; if the photon energy is greater, the photoelectric effect is observed and the atom is ionized. The excitation or ionization can result from collisions with other electrons or atoms as well as with photons. After excitation, the atomic electron decays back to the ground state with the emission of light. Electron collisions give rise to spark, arc, or gas discharge spectra; collisions with atoms account for the light emitted by flames.

The proportion of electrons which are in an excited state in equilibrium is determined by the Boltzmann principle. Thus the number of atoms in the state E_n is proportional to

$$\exp\left[-\,(E_n - E_1)/kT\right]$$

For the H atom $(E_n - E_1)$ is not less than 10.2 eV; since at room temperature kT is only 0.025 eV, the number of excited atoms is very small except at high temperatures. In a gas discharge or plasma, the electrons are often at a much higher temperature than the atoms (they are not in equilibrium), and the electrons cause appreciable excitation even though the atoms do not heat up the walls of the tube inordinately. When the atom is excited by collisions with electrons, the electrons can lose only discrete amounts of energy corresponding to the difference between atomic energy levels; this effect can also be observed (Franck-Hertz, 1914). Recent results of such an experiment are shown in Fig. 18–6.

Let us emphasize again, however, that although the classical theory of electron orbits can be doctored up to give a fairly consistent picture of observed phenomena, it is not really satisfactory. The quantization of angular momentum is tacked on to the theoretical structure in a completely unnatural way. Furthermore, the theory encounters hopeless difficulties if

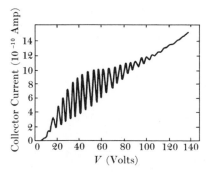

Fig. 18–6. *Franck-Hertz experiment in Hg vapor. The electrons accelerated by the applied electric field can lose energy in a collision with an Hg atom only when they have the 4.9 eV necessary to excite the atom to its lowest excited state. The successive minima in the electron current are separated by 4.9 volts. [After J. W. Dewdney, Am. J. Phys.* **27,** *645 (1959).]*

one tries to apply it to atoms with more than one electron. Therefore, the discussion of atomic spectra will be dropped for the present, until the correct quantum mechanical theory has been presented.

18–4   BLACK-BODY RADIATION

The spectrum of light emitted by an incandescent solid affords a second example in which the quantization of electron energy levels produces observable effects. The electrons in a hot solid emit a continuous spectrum of frequencies (photon energies) rather than a discrete line spectrum, but nevertheless we shall see that the shape of the spectrum cannot be understood unless the electron energy levels themselves form a discrete, discontinuous set. Here we shall be dealing with the harmonic oscillator force instead of the inverse square law force, and the separation of the levels E_n will be characteristically different; but the restriction of the electron to a countable number of states will be analogous.

The radiation we are discussing is that which makes a toaster glow red, or the hotter filament in a light bulb look white. Even a radiator, which is relatively cold, emits infrared radiation (felt as heat). The measured spectrum of such *thermal radiation* is a continuous distribution with a single wide peak (Fig. 18–7). It is found that the peak lies at a frequency ν_p which is proportional to the absolute temperature T, and that the total intensity is proportional to the fourth power of T (Stefan's law):

$$\nu_p \propto T \qquad \int_0^\infty I d\nu = \sigma T^4 \qquad (18\text{–}11)$$
$$\sigma = 5.67 \times 10^{-5} \text{ erg cm}^{-2} \text{ sec}^{-1} \text{ deg}^{-4}$$

The fact that the light shifts to higher frequency (shorter wave length) and becomes brighter as the temperature increases makes the color a good guide to the temperature. For example, machinists, in tempering steel, can estimate the temperature to within about 100° C by visually observing the color. The total intensity and the spectral distribution depend significantly on the material, however, and in particular on the surface of the material.

It is possible to abstract from the particular material if one considers the radiation which is emitted into the inside of a cavity (Fig. 18–8) entirely surrounded by the material at temperature T. This *cavity radiation* is in

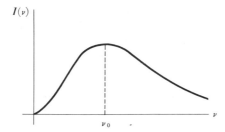

Fig. 18–7. Intensity distribution of black-body radiation.

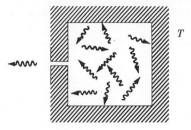

Fig. 18–8. *Cavity radiation contained in a furnace at temperature* T. *Black-body radiation can be observed escaping from a small hole.*

equilibrium with the walls of the cavity and it can be described by giving its energy density (energy per unit volume) $dU/dV \equiv u$ as a function of the radiation frequency. The intensity $I(\nu)$ is proportional to $u(\nu)$, just as for a plane wave (Eq. 16–23), even though here the waves are propagating in all directions. (Here of course we are using u to denote the energy density, and not the velocity of propagation, which is c.) That the energy distribution $u(\nu)$ is independent of the material of the cavity walls follows from the transitive property of *equilibrium:* if the radiation is in equilibrium with one material, which is in equilibrium with a second material (i.e., at the same temperature), then the radiation is in equilibrium with the second material; and, therefore, the quality of the radiation depends only on the temperature. The radiation in the cavity could be regarded as a *gas of photons*, which is in equilibrium with the walls of its container. Like any gas of atoms, its properties do not depend on what the container is made of. In fact, it can be shown on very general (thermodynamical) grounds that

$$u = \nu^3 f(\nu/T) \qquad (18\text{–}12)$$

where f is some function which remains to be determined. Equation 18–12 is known as *Wien's law.*

The two properties which were mentioned in Eq. 18–11 both follow immediately from Wien's law: differentiating Eq. 18–12 with respect to ν,

$$\frac{du}{d\nu}\bigg|_{\nu=\nu_p} = 0 = 3\nu^2 f + \frac{\nu^3}{T} f'$$

$$3f\left(\frac{\nu_p}{T}\right) + \frac{\nu_p}{T} f'\left(\frac{\nu_p}{T}\right) = 0$$

The solution to this equation will be $\nu_p/T = \text{const}$, where the constant depends on the particular form of f. In addition, integrating Eq. 18–12 with respect to ν,

$$\int_0^\infty I\, d\nu \propto \int_0^\infty u\, d\nu = \int_0^\infty \nu^3 f\left(\frac{\nu}{T}\right) d\nu = T^4 \int_0^\infty \left(\frac{\nu}{T}\right)^3 f\left(\frac{\nu}{T}\right) d\left(\frac{\nu}{T}\right)$$

$$= \text{const } T^4$$

giving Stefan's law.

Finally, one may ask how cavity radiation could be observed, if it is supposed to be contained entirely inside a cavity. The answer is that it will not be perturbed too much if a small peep hole is made in the cavity wall. The radiation which comes out of the peep hole is typical of the cavity radiation contained inside. Incidentally, the cavity radiation is also called *blackbody radiation*, because it is emitted from the hole, whose "surface" is ideally black, in the sense that it would absorb all radiation which fell on it. Any material window across the hole would act as a filter which would modify the cavity radiation more or less, and so the surface of a hot material body is only an approximation to the ideal black body.

18-5   HARMONIC OSCILLATOR ENERGY LEVELS

In order to determine the detailed form of $u(\nu)$ (or of the function f in Wien's law), one could make a statistical analysis of the photon gas, much as one does for a material gas in order to determine its equation of state. For our present purpose, however, it will be more germane to consider the matter with which the cavity radiation is in equilibrium. The photons in the cavity are continually emitted and absorbed by electrons in the material of the walls. Since $u(\nu)$ is independent of the material, we may use any model we like to describe the walls; let us assume (following Planck) that the electrons in the walls are harmonic oscillators of frequency $\nu = \omega/2\pi$, $\omega = \sqrt{K/m}$. Oscillators of all possible frequencies are assumed to be present, and each one is in equilibrium with the photons of the corresponding frequency. This model does not actually correspond very closely to the real electronic structure of the solid, but, as indicated, that is irrelevant.

Intuitively, it is evident that, for any given frequency ν the average energy of the oscillators $\overline{E_\nu}$ and the energy density $u(\nu)$ of the photons which are in equilibrium with them will increase together:

$$u(\nu) \propto \overline{E_\nu}$$

In fact, the proportionality factor can be calculated by equating the rate of emission of radiation by an oscillating electron to the rate of absorption of radiation with which it is in resonance. The result may be quoted,

$$u = \frac{8\pi\nu^2}{c^3} \overline{E_\nu} \tag{18-13}$$

although we do not need to make explicit use of the proportionality factor in the present argument. The factor ν^2 will be seen to follow from Wien's law. The important point is in the calculation of the average energy $\overline{E_\nu}$.

The average energy has already been computed using the classical theory; the result for a one dimensional harmonic oscillator is (Section 14-6)

$$\overline{E_\nu} = kT \tag{18-14}$$

(independent of ν), according to the equipartition of energy law. In the present context, the result gives nonsense when extended to high frequencies: the energy density would be given by the *Rayleigh-Jeans law*,

$$u = \frac{8\pi\nu^2}{c^3} kT \qquad (18\text{--}15)$$

in agreement with Wien's law if $f(x) \propto 1/x$. At low frequencies the Rayleigh-Jeans law agrees with experiment, but $u(\nu)$ would be higher and higher at higher frequencies (Fig. 18–9), and so the total energy in the cavity would be infinite. This paradox even has a name, the *ultra-violet catastrophe;* fortunately the "catastrophe" does not really occur.

The correct computation depends on recognizing that when a photon of energy $h\nu$ is emitted by an oscillator whose natural frequency is ν, in order to conserve energy the electron must make a transition in which its energy suddenly decreases by just this amount. The simplest assumption (made by Max Planck in 1900, before the idea of photons had been invented) is that the harmonic oscillator has energy levels

$$E_n = nh\nu \qquad (18\text{--}16)$$

Thus a transition $E_n \to E_{n-1}$ creates a photon of energy $E_n - E_{n-1} = nh\nu - (n-1)h\nu = h\nu$. If these discrete energies are the only allowed levels, the average energy can be calculated using the *Boltzmann principle*, but a sum must be used instead of an integral; the significant modification is not in the method of computing the average, but in the discreteness of the energy states:

$$\overline{E_\nu} = \frac{\sum\limits_{n=0}^{\infty} E_n e^{-E_n/kT}}{\sum\limits_{n=0}^{\infty} e^{-E_n/kT}} = \frac{\sum nh\nu e^{-nh\nu/kT}}{\sum e^{-nh\nu/kT}} \qquad (18\text{--}17)$$

This is the weighted average of the E_n's, with each value of E_n weighted by the Boltzmann factor $\exp(-E_n/kT)$ giving the probability of that energy state; the denominator is the normalizing factor.

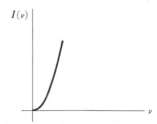

Fig. 18–9. Black-body spectrum according to the Rayleigh-Jeans law. It agrees with experiment (Fig. 18–7) at low frequency, but fails at high frequency.

Although these infinite series look rather forbidding, the summation can be evaluated in closed form by a trick which sometimes works when exponential functions are involved. Writing $\beta = 1/kT$, Eq. 18–17 becomes

$$\overline{E}_\nu = \frac{\sum nh\nu e^{-nh\nu\beta}}{\sum e^{-nh\nu\beta}} = -\frac{d}{d\beta}\ln \sum e^{-nh\nu\beta} = -\frac{d}{d\beta}\ln \sum_{n=0}^{\infty}(e^{-h\nu\beta})^n$$

Using the summation formula for geometric series, we obtain

$$\overline{E}_\nu = -\frac{d}{d\beta}\ln\frac{1}{1-e^{-h\nu\beta}} = \frac{h\nu e^{-h\nu\beta}}{1-e^{-h\nu\beta}} = \frac{h\nu}{e^{h\nu\beta}-1}$$

so that

$$\overline{E}_\nu = \frac{h\nu}{e^{h\nu/kT}-1} \tag{18–18}$$

Then

$$u = \frac{8\pi h\nu^3/c^3}{e^{h\nu/kT}-1} \tag{18–19}$$

This energy distribution function, called the *Planck radiation law*, is in good agreement with experiment (and is consistent with Wien's law). For low frequencies, $h\nu \ll kT$,

$$e^{h\nu/kT} \cong 1 + h\nu/kT$$
$$\overline{E}_\nu \cong kT$$

The energy density u agrees with the classical calculation, Eqs. 18–14 and 18–15, and is in agreement with experiment at the low frequency limit. In the high frequency limit, $h\nu \gg kT$, on the other hand,

$$\overline{E}_\nu \cong h\nu e^{-h\nu/kT} \tag{18–20}$$

and from Eq. 18–13,

$$u \cong \frac{8\pi h\nu^3}{c^3}e^{-h\nu/kT}$$

so that u goes to zero with increasing ν, as it must. In between there is a maximum, at a frequency which is derived from Eq. 18–19 by solving a (transcendental) equation as outlined for the general form of Eq. 18–12. The result for the frequency ν_p at the peak of the intensity distribution is

$$h\nu_p = 5.0\ kT \tag{18–21}$$

From this relation, we find, for example, that for $T = 6000°\text{K}$, $\lambda_p = c/\nu_p = 4700$ Å. The sun's surface temperature is roughly 6000°, and that is presumably related to the fact that our eyes are most sensitive to green light. We also find that for $T = 2000°\text{K}$, $\lambda_p = 14,000$ A, in the infrared, and that is why incandescent lamps are such inefficient sources of visible light.

18-6   HEAT CAPACITY OF SOLIDS

To digress for a moment, our calculation of the average energy of a *quantized oscillator* yields a bonus, in that we can clear up a point which in Section 14–6 had been left up in the air, namely the fact that the specific heat of solids always vanishes as the absolute zero of temperature is approached. Recall that if an *atom* in a crystal is treated as a 3-dimensional harmonic oscillator of frequency ν, its average energy is

$$\bar{E} = 3\overline{E_\nu}$$

The total thermal energy (Eq. 14–19) of a mole of atoms is

$$U_T = N_0\bar{E}$$

and

$$C_V = dU_T/dT$$

Using the expression Eq. 18–18 just derived for a quantized oscillator,

$$U_T = 3N_0 \frac{h\nu}{e^{h\nu/kT} - 1} = 3RT \frac{(h\nu/kT)}{e^{h\nu/kT} - 1}$$

$$C_V = \frac{3N_0 h\nu}{(e^{h\nu/kT} - 1)^2} \frac{h\nu}{kT^2} e^{h\nu/kT} = 3R \frac{(h\nu/kT)^2 e^{h\nu/kT}}{(e^{h\nu/kT} - 1)^2} \qquad (18\text{--}22)$$

Again for $kT \gg h\nu$,

$$\overline{E_\nu} \cong kT$$
$$U_T \cong 3RT$$
$$C_V \cong 3R$$

in accordance with the Dulong-Petit law. But at low temperatures (Eq. 18–20), $kT \ll h\nu$,

$$\overline{E_\nu} \cong h\nu \, e^{-h\nu/kT}$$

The reason the average energy is so small is that the oscillator cannot have energy kT, because there is no allowed energy state there; the first excited state is much higher ($h\nu$), and so it is in the ground state most of the time. Then the thermal energy and molar heat capacity at low temperatures are

$$U_T \cong 3N_0 h\nu \, e^{-h\nu/kT} = 3RT \frac{h\nu}{kT} e^{-h\nu/kT}$$

$$C_V \cong 3R\left(\frac{h\nu}{kT}\right)^2 e^{-h\nu/kT} \qquad (18\text{--}23)$$

a result first derived by Einstein.

This value of C_V now approaches 0 when T approaches 0, as it should (Fig. 18–10). If the lattice vibrations are treated more correctly as waves (cf. Section 16–6), then the quantum calculation gives $C_V \propto T^3$ at low temperature, which is in closer agreement with experiment. Equation 18–22 gives a good fit to experimental data down to about $\frac{1}{3}$ of the classical value, but at lower temperatures Eq. 18–23 predicts much too small a value of heat capacity. The transition from classical to quantum behavior occurs when $kT \approx h_\nu$ (the energy level separation), or when

$$T \approx T_E \equiv \frac{\hbar\omega}{k} = \frac{\hbar}{k}\sqrt{\frac{K}{m}} \qquad (18\text{–}24)$$

Thus, for example, the Dulong-Petit law should hold down to a lower temperature for Pb than for Al (assuming the force constants K are about the same), since Pb atoms are much heavier, and indeed it does.

To *summarize* the most important results which have been implied in this chapter, a bound particle (as opposed to a free particle) can only assume energies which belong to a discrete set of energy levels. Among these levels, there is a lowest one, called the ground state. This conclusion has here been drawn for two important force laws—the inverse square law and the harmonic force, but will be found to be true in general (Chapter 20). The ground state energies are, respectively,

$$E_1 = -K/2a_0 = -mK^2/2\hbar^2$$

and

$$E_0 = 0$$

For the harmonic oscillator,

$$E_1 = h\nu = \hbar\sqrt{K/m}$$

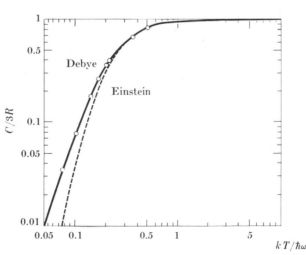

Fig. 18–10. *Theoretical heat capacity curves. (Cf. Fig. 14–7.) The Einstein curve is given by Eq. 18–22. The Debye curve (Section 16–6) gives even better agreement with experiment at low temperature.*

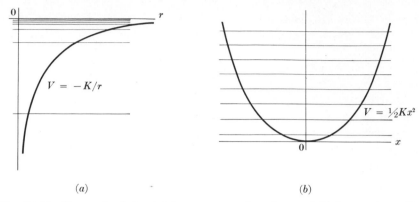

$Fig.$ 18–11. $Energy\ levels\ for$ (a) $inverse\ square\ force\ law\ and$ (b) $harmonic\ oscillator$
$potentials.$

gives the energy of the first excited state. The complete energy level
schemes are given by, respectively,

$$E_n = E_1/n^2$$

and

$$E_n = nE_1$$

These are illustrated in Fig. 18–11, together with the potential energy
curves which give rise to them. (The quantum mechanical theory of the
harmonic oscillator gives

$$E_n = (n + \tfrac{1}{2})h\nu \tag{18–25}$$

The energy levels are still separated by $h\nu$, the only difference being that
the ground state energy is $\tfrac{1}{2}h\nu$ instead of 0.) We have assumed these
energy level schemes so that the photons created in (energy-conserving)
transitions between states would agree with experimental emission spectra.
The discrete levels have no foundation in classical mechanics, and later
we will have to formulate an entirely new theory of quantum mechanics
to account for them.

PROBLEMS

18–1.   Show that angular momentum has the same dimensions as Planck's constant (erg-sec).

18–2.   Find the velocity of the electron in the Bohr orbit $n = 1$. Express the result in terms of v/c.

18–3.   A μ^--meson can be bound to a proton to form an "atom," just like an electron. The meson mass is 207 times the electron mass while its charge is
the same as that of the electron. Find the Bohr radius and ionization potential for this atom.

18–4.   Applying the quantum condition on angular momentum, $L = n\hbar$, find the allowed energy levels of a rigid rotator with moment of inertia I; calculate the frequency of the light emitted in the transition $n \rightarrow n - 1$. Evaluate the frequency for the H_2 molecule, assuming the separation between the nuclei to be 1 Å.

18–5.   Calculate the wave lengths in the Paschen series.

18–6.   In Eq. 18–8, the reduced mass should really have been used. Calculate the reduced mass for hydrogen and deuterium, and find the resulting shift of the red line (in Å).

18–7.   What fraction of H atoms would be in the first excited state at 300°K? 3000°K?

18–8.   What is the wave length corresponding to the peak of the black-body radiation spectrum at 300°K?

18–9.   Suppose a sphere of gas, radius 1 m, is at a temperature of 1,000,000°K Calculate the total power radiated and the peak wave length, assuming the radiation is in equilibrium with the gas. (In a fusion reactor, the gas pressure is kept low so that equilibrium between the atoms and photons will *not* be attained.)

18–10. Estimate the temperature $T_E = (\hbar/k) \sqrt{K/m}$ above which the specific heat of Al approaches the classical value, assuming a reasonable value for the force constant K.

18–11. A positron and an electron can form a bound hydrogen-like system called positronium. Calculate the positronium energy levels. If electron-positron annihilation takes place from the positronium ground state, how much is the γ-ray energy calculated in Problem 17–4 altered.

18–12. A particle of mass m is moving in a circular orbit in a simple harmonic oscillator potential, $V = \frac{1}{2} Kr^2$. With an elastic radial force, $F = - Kr$, and a radial acceleration, $a = - v^2/r$ (circular motion), we have

$$Kr = mv^2/r$$

Imposing the Bohr condition,

$$L = mvr = nh$$

calculate the allowed energy levels. (A. D. Crowell, *Am. J. Phys.* 32, 643 (1964).)

18–13. Calculate the allowed energy levels for the circular hydrogen atom orbits with the same procedure as in the previous problem.

18–14. The expression given in Eq. 18–3 is not completely correct when the recoil kinetic energy, $p^2/2M$, of the atom is taken into account. Instead we get

$$h\nu + p^2/2M = E_m - E_n.$$

Express $h\nu$ in terms of $E_m - E_n$ and M. Calculate the wave length of the light emitted in the $n = 3$ to $n = 2$ transition in hydrogen with and without the atomic recoil term.

REFERENCES

R. B. Leighton, *Principles of Modern Physics* (McGraw-Hill, 1959), Ch. 2.

F. K. Richtmyer, E. H. Kennard, and T. Lauritsen, *Introduction to Modern Physics* (McGraw-Hill, 1955, 5th ed.), Ch. 4, 5, 9.

M. Born, *Atomic Physics* (Hafner, 1951, 5th ed.), Ch. 5, 8.

G. Herzberg, *Atomic Spectra and Atomic Structure* (Dover, 1944), Ch. 1.

19/electron waves

Light, in certain circumstances, such as diffraction by an aperture, can be understood only as a wave phenomenon. Yet other experiments cannot be explained except by treating it as corpuscular photons (Chapter 17). It seems like an obvious expression of a natural duality to suggest that electrons, *which are "normally" regarded as corpuscles, should under suitable circumstances exhibit* wave-like *properties. (We have tried to set up this suggestion so that it would seem natural; when it was first made by de Broglie in 1924, it seemed rather wild.) In fact, the relations* $E = h\nu$, $p = h/\lambda$, *which relate the energy and momentum of a photon to the frequency and wave length of a light wave, might be inverted to represent (one hopes) the frequency and wave length of an electron of energy* E *and momentum* p:

$$\nu = E/h \qquad \lambda = h/p$$

The only question is whether the predicted wave properties are actually observed, and the answer is that they are (Davisson and Germer, 1927; G. P. Thomson, 1928). Indeed these wave-like aspects of the electron (or other microscopic particle such as a neutron or proton) not only substantiate a philosophically attractive duality, but they also provide the key to understanding the non-classical quantization of electron energy levels which has been discussed in Chapter 18.

19–1 ELECTRON OPTICS

As a preliminary to the presentation of the quantum theory of the electron, and without minimizing its profoundly revolutionary aspects, it may be well to point out that the possibility of describing a phenomenon in terms of the propagation of waves, or alternatively in terms of the trajectories of particles, does not necessarily involve utterly outlandish contradictions. In the case of light, for over 100 years, so long as only the phenomena of *geometrical optics* were known, only a subjective preference could dictate a choice between the description in terms of the spreading of a wave front or the path of a ray (everywhere normal to the wave front). Before 1900 a theory of particle mechanics in which the particle trajectories were treated as the normals to "wave fronts" was highly developed (Hamilton, Jacobi, and others). Analogous to the geometrical optics of light, it was conceived only as an elegant and powerful formulation, which was entirely equivalent to Newton's laws of motion.

The Hamilton-Jacobi formulation of mechanics is much too abstruse to develop here. Nevertheless, it is instructive to investigate a simple example of a particle trajectory in which the similarity to geometrical optics will be clear. Consider a (non-relativistic) electron moving in a potential field V with total energy E,

$$E = p^2/2m + V = \text{const}$$

Suppose in particular that V is constant ($V = V_1$) below the x-axis and constant but smaller ($V = V_2$, $V_2 < V_1$) above the x-axis, with a narrow transition region (Fig. 19–1) in between, where a force ($= -dV/dy$) acts on the electron. The electron is accelerated in the y-direction, but not in the x-direction, so that p_x remains constant, but p increases. Since $p_x = p \sin \theta$, one has from Fig. 19–1,

$$p_1 \sin \theta_1 = p_2 \sin \theta_2 \tag{19–1}$$

This equation for the trajectory of the electron may be compared with the relation which describes the path of a ray of light, according to geometrical optics, when the ray passes from a medium with index of refraction n_1 into a medium with index n_2, $n_2 > n_1$. The optical result is *Snell's law*,

$$n_1 \sin \theta_1 = n_2 \sin \theta_2 \tag{19–2}$$

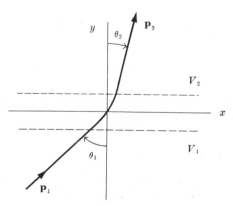

Fig. 19–1. Refraction of an electron beam at a potential energy step.

To draw a correspondence between the particle trajectory and geometrical optics, one is led by a comparison of Eqs. 19–1 and 19–2 to assume that the "index of refraction" for the electron is proportional to its momentum,

$$n \propto p \tag{19–3}$$

Since $p = \sqrt{2m(E - V)}$, the refractive index of the "medium" can then be described as a function of position by

$$n \propto \sqrt{2m(E - V)} \tag{19–4}$$

This simple example actually provides a rough proof of the validity of Eq. 19–4 for an arbitrarily varying potential V: any arbitrary potential could be approximated as the limit of a sequence of step-wise changes across thin transition layers. The electron refractive index therefore varies with position (since V varies with position), as in an *inhomogeneous refractive medium*. Furthermore, the "medium" is *dispersive*, since at any given position the refractive index varies with the energy E of the electrons (analogous to the variation of n with the frequency of light). This optical theory of electron rays has very great practical usefulness in *electron optics*, where it is always used in the design of lenses for electron guns in cathode ray tubes, electron microscopes, etc.

19–2   ELECTRON DIFFRACTION

The optical theory of the electron is completely equivalent to the classical Newtonian theory of particle trajectories, and which point of view one adopts is merely a matter of convenience for the problem at hand. Nevertheless, if one took the optical theory really seriously and considered the "wave length" of the electron, in optics $\lambda = \lambda_0/n$. One would therefore assume that

$$\lambda \propto 1/n \propto 1/p$$

where the second proportionality depends on Eq. 19–3. In fact, formally, we could write

$$\lambda = h/p \tag{19–5}$$

The proportionality constant h is something that would have to be determined experimentally, since its magnitude is not predicted by the above considerations.

Recall that geometrical optics is the limit of short wave lengths, where light casts sharp shadows, and that uniquely wave-like phenomena such as diffraction can be observed only with long wave lengths. One then sees from Eq. 19–5 that if the proportionality constant h were exactly zero, the "wave length" of the electron would be merely an artifice (being always zero) and the classical theory (geometrical optics) would always hold. But if h is different from zero, for sufficiently slowly moving (low energy) electrons, some diffraction effects should be observable.

312 QUANTUM MECHANICS

Electron diffraction has been observed, and the measured value of h in Eq. 19–5 is the same as Planck's constant. (Cf. Eq. 17–7.) The fact that h is non-zero means that classical mechanics fails; the fact that h is small means that its failure is difficult to observe, so that it went unnoticed until the present century. To understand how small h is, recall that it (or rather $\hbar$) is the smallest unit of angular momentum. The smallest particle that can be seen (in an optical microscope) has a radius of about 10^{-4} cm; such a particle, with an angular momentum of $\hbar$, would be rotating with an angular velocity of about one revolution every 20 years.

To see how long the electron wave lengths actually are, let us rewrite Eq. 19–5 as

$$\lambda = h/\sqrt{2m(E - V)} \qquad (19\text{–}6)$$

Now let $E = 0$, so that the zero of V is chosen where the electron is at rest. Since $V = -e\Phi$, where Φ is the electrostatic potential, we have

$$\lambda = (h/\sqrt{2me})/\sqrt{\Phi} = 12.3/\sqrt{\Phi}\ \text{Å} \qquad (\Phi \text{ in volts}) \qquad (19\text{–}7)$$

If the potential Φ is the accelerating potential of the electron in volts, then Φ is equal to the electron's kinetic energy in electron volts. It is very difficult practically to form an electron beam with Φ less than about 100 volts, because of space charge and thermal effects. Therefore, the longest

Fig. 19–2(a). Electron diffraction by a graphite crystal. Note hexagonal symmetry. (Cf. Fig. 13–16(c).) [Courtesy of R. B. Leighton, Principles of Modern Physics *(McGraw-Hill, New York, 1959).]*

wave length electron beam which can be easily produced has a wave length of about 1 Å.

The diffraction of light was discovered rather late in the history of its investigation because its wave length is short (5000 Å). The diffraction of electrons (Fig. 19–2) was also discovered late because the wave length of electrons is even shorter. The discovery was made, however, only 15 years after that of the diffraction of light of equal wave length—i.e., of x-rays. The experimental method of observing electron diffraction is similar to that for x-ray diffraction: an electron beam is diffracted by a crystal. To observe a beam transmitted through the crystal, a very thin specimen is required: in the case of x-rays, the cross section for effects (such as the photoelectric effect) other than coherent scattering (i.e., diffraction) is relatively small, whereas for an electron beam the cross section for ionization is large and the beam is not very penetrating.

The diffraction experiments of Davisson and Germer furnished unambiguous confirmation of the wave nature of the electron. Once the reality of the electron waves is established, their existence finally provides a sound basis for understanding the quantized energy levels of the electron. (Cf. Eq. 18–8.) The discrete set of electron states follows from a wave theory of the electron in just the same way that the wave theory of the

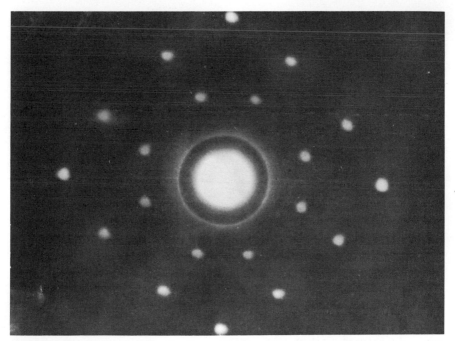

Fig. 19–2(b). *Neutron diffraction by an NaCl crystal. Note four-fold symmetry.* (*Cf. Fig. 13–16(a).*) [*Photograph by E. O. Wollan and C. G. Shull, reprinted from H. Semat,* Introduction to Atomic and Nuclear Physics (*Holt, New York, 1962*).

vibrating string led to a discrete set of possible states of vibration—
the various harmonics. A crude application of the electron wave idea to the
hydrogen atom can predict the correct energy levels: suppose the electron
has momentum p in a circular orbit of radius r. If the electron has a wave
length λ, the existence of a well-defined wave requires that the circumference of the orbit should be exactly equal to an integral number of wave
lengths,

$$2\pi r = n\lambda$$

(See Fig. 19–3.) Since

$$\lambda = h/p$$

then

$$rp = L = n\hbar$$

As we have already seen, according to Eq. 18–6, the correct energy levels
result from this quantum condition on the angular momentum. A more
precise formulation of the wave theory of the electron and some deduc-
tions from it will be given in the next chapter, and it will be applied more
rigorously to the hydrogen atom in Chapter 21.

19–3   THE HEISENBERG UNCERTAINTY PRINCIPLE

Before treating the formal theory, we may consider a consequence of the
wave-particle effects which has had very profound and far-reaching philosophical repercussions, namely the Heisenberg uncertainty principle. The
principle asserts that there exists an inherent limitation on the precision
with which physical measurements can be made, or an unavoidable uncertainty in the results of observations. What is meant is not merely the
ordinary practical limits of error in measurement, which, by taking sufficient pains or by spending enough money on instrumentation, could in
general be reduced below any predetermined level (i.e., could be made to
approach zero). The uncertainty referred to here is a much more profound
one, which is inherently contained in the fundamental laws of nature. Suppose one measures the x-coordinate of a particle within a precision Δx, and
simultaneously measures the x-component of its momentum with a pre-

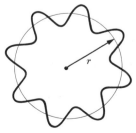

Fig. 19–3

cision Δp. Then the uncertainty principle states that in a *simultaneous measurement*, the *minimum* errors of measurement are related by

$$\Delta x\, \Delta p \approx \hbar \qquad\qquad (19\text{--}8)$$

The principle imposes no limitation on the precision Δx with which the position can be measured (practical considerations aside); the restriction is in that, the more precisely one tries to measure the position, then the greater uncertainty one introduces into the *simultaneous* knowledge of the momentum, and vice versa. The quantum mechanical laws of nature imply an inherent limitation on the information one can have about a particle.

The relation of the uncertainty principle to the wave-corpuscle effects which have been considered can best be illustrated by giving a couple of examples. One could, for instance, determine the x-coordinate of a beam of electrons, moving in the y-direction with momentum p, by causing them to pass through a slit (Fig. 19–4). If Δx is the width of the slit, the uncertainty in this measurement of x is Δx, since one does not know through which part of the slit a particular electron passes. Suppose that before encountering the slit, the electrons have an x-component of momentum which is exactly zero; but when they pass through the slit (i.e., as a result of the measurement of x), the beam suffers diffraction. Some of the electrons are diverted outside the geometrical shadow of the slit, so that they must have acquired an x-component of momentum Δp, of an uncertain amount determined by the width of the diffraction pattern. If, for definiteness, we call the "width" of the diffraction pattern the angle α at which the first minimum of intensity occurs, then, as for the diffraction of light, $\sin \alpha = \lambda/\Delta x$ (Fig. 19–5). Furthermore, since Δp is the corresponding x-component of momentum, $\sin \alpha = \Delta p/p$ (Fig. 19–4). Finally, using the connection $\lambda = h/p$ from Eq. 19–5,

$$\Delta x\, \Delta p \approx h$$

(Since only the order of magnitude is under consideration, one could write as well $\Delta x\, \Delta p \approx \hbar$.) Consequently, in trying to determine the particle position by forcing it through a slit, one unavoidably introduces an uncertainty

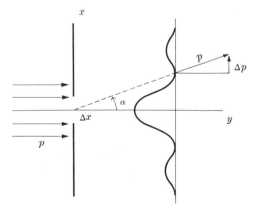

Fig. 19–4. Single slit diffraction pattern.

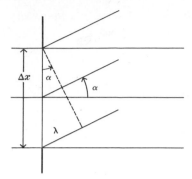

Fig. 19–5

into the momentum because of *diffraction* of the wave, which effect is greater the narrower the slit.

An alternative approach to the observation of the position of a particle is to observe the light which is scattered by the particle, with a microscope if the particle is small. The uncertainty in the position of the particle Δx is now determined by the size of the diffraction pattern of the light, which will be smaller for shorter wave length light. Ultraviolet light is sometimes used in miscroscopy, and attempts have been made to construct x-ray microscopes, but in principle there is no reason why one should not use gamma rays. (The so-called *gamma-ray microscope* is a hypothetical instrument, for the purpose of this example.) When the photon is scattered into the microscope, the particle recoils, and if it was originally at rest it acquires an x-component of momentum Δp, of an uncertain amount determined by the change in photon momentum. The resolving power of a microscope can be shown to be $\Delta x \approx \lambda/\sin \alpha$ (Fig. 19–6). If p is the momentum in the y-direction of the incoming photons (Fig. 19–7), the maximum x-component of momentum of the photons which are scattered into the microscope is $p \sin \alpha$, so that momentum conservation requires that $\Delta p = p \sin \alpha$. Again using $p = h/\lambda$,

$$\Delta x \, \Delta p \approx h$$

In locating the particle by scattering short wave length light off it, the inescapable momentum uncertainty is simultaneously produced by the mo-

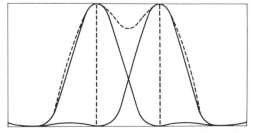

Fig. 19–6. *Criterion for resolution of two diffraction patterns.*

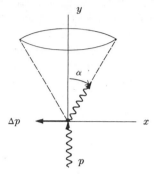

Fig. 19–7. The "gamma-ray microscope."

mentum transfer from the photon, which effect is greater the shorter the
wave length of the light.

19–4 MEASURABILITY IN QUANTUM MECHANICS

In both of the above examples, there is an *interaction with the observer*, which
absolutely cannot be reduced beyond certain limitations, because of the
dual particle-wave nature of either the "particle" (e.g., electron) or of the
light which interacts with it. Classically, the electron would experience no
diffraction, so that a slit could without penalty be made as narrow as desired; and the momentum transferred by the light would not come in
packets (photons), so that for however short a wave length the momentum
could be reduced to tolerable limits by decreasing the light intensity. Quantum mechanically, however, the very act of making the observation of
position perturbs the particle's momentum, and vice versa, so that the
attainable precision of these simultaneous measurements shows an inter-
relationship, which is described by the Heisenberg principle, Eq. 19–8.

This irreducible perturbation of a particle's behavior by the act of making
a measurement on it has led to the re-examination of some concepts which
were accepted without question in classical mechanics. For example, to assign an empirical meaning to the notion of the *trajectory* of a particle, it
should be possible in principle to make arbitrarily accurate measurements of
both its position and velocity, arbitrarily close together (Fig. 19–8). That

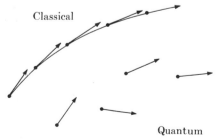

Fig. 19–8. Observation of a "trajectory."

corresponds with what we mean when we *see* a macroscopic particle follow a certain trajectory. To extend the concept of trajectory to microscopic particles, a similar series of observations should be possible; but the uncertainty principle shows that it is not. Certain philosophers therefore choose to say that it is *meaningless* to talk about the "trajectory" of an electron. Indeed, it is questionable whether the notion of a "particle" itself can be given a precise meaning which would coincide with the macroscopic concept.

Quantum mechanics, especially the results expressed by the uncertainty principle, has had an enormous influence on contemporary philosophy, particularly in emphasizing the importance of *testability* as a requirement for empirical meaningfulness. But the uncertainty principle also often plays a very useful practical role in that, judiciously employed, it permits certain order-of-magnitude quantum mechanical calculations to be made in a very simple way. It has, of course, negligible significance for macroscopic particles. Even a particle of radius 10^{-4} cm, if its position were determined to within 10^{-6} cm, would acquire an uncertainty in its velocity of only about 1 mm per century. This example shows again that h is a very small quantity, from any macroscopic point of view. When it comes to electrons, or even atoms, however, the limitation imposed by the uncertainty principle is severe. We could, for example, compute the uncertainty in velocity of an electron which is confined (i.e., known to be) within a region the size of the Bohr radius (so that its uncertainty in position is this much). Putting $\Delta x = a_0 = \hbar^2/me^2$, $\Delta p = m\Delta v$, from

$$\Delta x \, m\Delta v \approx \hbar$$

we find

$$\frac{\Delta v}{c} \approx \frac{e^2}{\hbar c} = \frac{1}{137} \tag{19-9}$$

Thus, a measurement of the electron's speed would yield a result which might, with appreciable probability, be anything between zero and a few percent of the velocity of light, the average value being about $c/137$. A number of similar examples will be cited later in the appropriate context.

The uncertainty principle has been discussed above as an induction from experiments (in our case two, but actually more) in which the wave aspect of the electron or the particle aspect of the photon came to the fore. It can also be deduced as a rigorous consequence of the quantum mechanical theory to be presented hereafter. We are not going to carry out that derivation in detail; but merely by recasting the principle into a slightly different form, it will be apparent that it depends solely on the properties of waves. Writing $p = h/\lambda = \hbar\kappa$, $\Delta p = \hbar\Delta\kappa$, the uncertainty principle is

$$\Delta x \, \Delta\kappa \approx 1 \tag{19-10}$$

In this form, only the coordinate and the wave number of the wave enter, not any properties of the particle or physical constants. As a matter of fact,

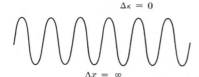

$$\Delta\kappa = 0$$

$$\Delta x = \infty$$

Fig. 19–9

this relation can be shown mathematically to hold for any type of wave whatever, regardless of quantum mechanics. For example, for an exact sinusoidal wave, $\sin \kappa x$, with a definite wave number $\kappa (\Delta\kappa = 0)$, the wave is spread out uniformly along the entire x-axis, so that $\Delta x = \infty$ (Fig. 19–9). On the other hand, if the wave disturbance is localized within a region Δx, it obviously cannot be represented as a single sinusoidal wave (Fig. 19–10); instead, this function can be represented mathematically by means of a Fourier series, in which it can be proved that the sum is over a sequence of functions $\sin \kappa x$ with a range $\Delta\kappa$ of κ of the order of $\Delta\kappa \approx 1/\Delta x$. (Actually, an integral, called the Fourier integral, must be used rather than the sum, so we shall not prove this mathematical theorem.)

Furthermore, since the relation is simply a mathematical consequence of a wave theory, it must hold in the same form for the time part of the wave:

$$\Delta t \, \Delta\omega \approx 1 \qquad (19\text{--}11)$$

This analogous mathematical relation can be recast back into a physical statement by using the other wave-particle connection $E = h\nu = \hbar\omega$. Thus

$$\Delta t \, \Delta E \approx \hbar \qquad (19\text{--}12)$$

This relation likewise can often be used to facilitate a rough physical calculation of the spread in an energy state, knowing the uncertainty in the time at which the particle was in that state, or vice versa.

We have now hopefully prepared the ground for a formal description of the quantum mechanical theory, by emphasizing the importance of the wave aspects of the electron, as well as of light. Although we began our discussion of quantum phenomena with a description of photons, and although historically the particle aspects of light were appreciated before the wave aspects of the electron, we shall nevertheless restrict the formal develop-

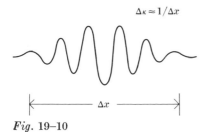

$$\Delta\kappa \approx 1/\Delta x$$

$$\Delta x$$

Fig. 19–10

ment of the quantum theory to electrons rather than photons. The reason for this restriction is that electrons can frequently be treated nonrelativistically, whereas photons are always relativistic (since they always have velocity c). Nonrelativistic quantum mechanics is a relatively simple and fully developed theory, as is classical relativity theory, but the synthesis of these two great revolutions in our basic conception of the universe, not unexpectedly, proves to be a more challenging problem. Accordingly we shall present in the following chapter a rigorous (although not complete) description of the wave formulation of quantum mechanics for the nonrelativistic electron (or other particle with non-zero rest mass).

PROBLEMS

19–1.   Suppose a beam of 100-eV electrons is incident on a material at an angle $\theta_1 = 30°$ from the normal. If the potential energy is lower inside by $V_0 = 20$ volts (cf. Fig. 17–8), calculate the angle of the refracted beam, θ_2. (This effect has to be taken into account in electron diffraction experiments.)

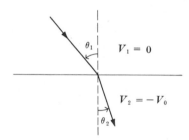

19–2.   What is the energy of an electron whose wave length is of the order of the nuclear diameter, say 10^{-12} cm?

19–3.   At what energy (and wave length) would an electron and a photon of the same energy have the same wave length?

19–4.   What is the wave length of a 100-eV proton?

19–5.   What is the energy of a 2-Å wave length neutron? At what temperature would its thermal equilibrium energy have this value?

19–6.   Suppose an electron is confined to a region of about 1 Å. What is the uncertainty in momentum? To what energy does this correspond? (This is about the energy with which an electron is bound in an atom.)

19–7.   Suppose an electron is confined to a region of about 10^{-12} cm. What is the uncertainty in momentum? To what energy does this correspond? (This is much greater than the binding energy in a nucleus, so there are no electrons inside nuclei.)

19–8.   Suppose a beam of electrons with wave length 10^{-3} cm passes through a slit 10^{-2} cm wide.
(a) What is the momentum and energy of the beam?
(b) Approximately what angular spread is introduced because of diffraction by the slit?

(c) At what temperature would random thermal energy kT equal the electron beam energy of (a)? (This is about the lowest temperature ever reached, so that this experiment would be extremely difficult.)

19-9. Suppose an electron initially has a velocity of 10^8 cm/sec. Consider the effect of observing its position with an accuracy of 10^{-7} cm every 10^{-13} sec in an attempt to plot its trajectory.

19-10. The time during which a system is in an excited state is related to its uncertainty (spread) in energy by Eq. 19-12. If Π is the probability to be in the excited state, $\Pi = e^{-t/\tau}$, where τ is the lifetime. One knows the system was excited only on observing the emitted radiation, so $\Delta t \approx \tau$. The uncertainty in energy ΔE is revealed by the spread in energy of the emitted photons.

(a) The lifetime of an excited state of an atom is typically of the order of 10^{-8} sec. Find the minimum line width in Å of a spectral line in the visible spectrum.

(b) The pulse from a ruby laser (6300 Å) lasts of the order of a millisecond. Find the width of the line in Å and in cycles per second.

(c) The lifetime of an excited state of a nucleus is typically about 10^{-12} sec. Find the uncertainty (in MeV) of the emitted γ-ray energy.

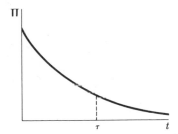

19-11. Suppose a parallel beam of 40-keV electrons is diffracted by a slit of width $0.6~\mu$. At what angle would the first minimum in the diffraction pattern appear? (A similar experiment has actually been carried out by G. Möllenstedt and C. Jönsson, *Z. Physik* **155**, 472 (1959).)

REFERENCES

M. Born, *Atomic Physics* (Hafner, 1951, 5th ed.), Ch. 4.

F. K. Richtmyer, E. H. Kennard, and T. Lauritsen, *Introduction to Modern Physics* (McGraw-Hill, 1955, 5th ed.), Ch. 6.

W. Heisenberg, *The Physical Principles of the Quantum Theory* (Dover, 1930), Ch. 1, 2.

20/wave mechanics

On the basis of what has been said about electron waves, we are now in a position to formulate a precise wave theory of the electron (or other particle), which will form a new foundation for mechanics to replace Newton's law of motion $\mathbf{F} = \mathbf{ma}$. We have seen that the acceleration $\mathbf{a}$ of a particle along its path cannot retain its classical meaning in quantum mechanics—even the "path" has no meaning—and the force $\mathbf{F}$ will play little role. The description of the environment of the particle is given instead by the potential energy V and that is why it has been emphasized heretofore. The only thing that is salvaged is the mass m, which will still be taken as one of the defining properties of the particle. We already know enough about the electron waves so that the required wave equation can be written down immediately. Once this theory has been concocted, its validity depends on the agreement between the predicted results and experiment. Without exception, it has been successful in replacing (or including) classical mechanics in the entire realm of atomic, molecular, and macroscopic physics. (To what extent it in turn will be replaced or modified in order to include a description of very high energy phenomena in elementary particle physics is presently an open question.)

20-1 THE SCHRÖDINGER EQUATION

In order to write down the wave equation for the electron, we may recall the wave equation in one dimension, Eq. 16–4,

$$\frac{\partial^2 \Psi}{\partial t^2} = u^2 \frac{\partial^2 \Psi}{\partial x^2} \quad \Psi = \Psi(x,t)$$

and its spatial part, Eq. 16–6,

$$\frac{d^2\psi}{dx^2} + \kappa^2\psi = 0 \qquad \kappa \equiv \omega/u$$

obtained by inserting the time dependence of the form $\exp(-i\omega t)$,

$$\Psi(x,t) = \psi(x)e^{-i\omega t}$$

Since $\kappa = 2\pi/\lambda$, and, as we have seen in Eq. 19–6, $\lambda = h/\sqrt{2m(E - V)}$, it follows that

$$\kappa = \sqrt{2m(E - V)}/\hbar$$

Inserting this value, one obtains the nonrelativistic wave equation for the electron,

$$\frac{d^2\psi}{dx^2} + \frac{2m}{\hbar^2}(E - V)\psi = 0 \qquad (20\text{--}1)$$

the so-called *time-independent Schrödinger equation*. The equation describes, as we shall see, all the stable states of electrons or other particles, and covers the entire range of effects we intend to analyze. Let us emphasize again that, although the form of the equation is a very plausible inference from the electron wave experiments we have considered, its general validity rests on confirmation by consistent agreement between its consequences and experiment, even in cases which have so far not been considered at all. (Note that κ is not constant, except for a free electron, because V varies with x. Whether this is the right equation when V is a rapidly varying function of position can be decided only by its success in predicting experimental results.)

Although we plan to limit our attention to the time-independent Schrödinger equation, for a complete basis of the quantum theory, it is necessary to have also a time-dependent equation. Our analogue approach is not quite enough in this respect. For a non-relativistic free electron,

$$E = p^2/2m$$

or, substituting $E = \hbar\omega$ and $p = \hbar\kappa$,

$$\omega = \left(\frac{\hbar}{2m}\right)\kappa^2 = \left(\frac{\hbar\kappa}{2m}\right)\kappa$$

This relation is in contrast to the simple proportionality

$$\omega^2 = u^2\kappa^2 \qquad \omega = u\kappa$$

which obtains in the wave equation. What is evidently required is an equation containing only the *first* derivative with respect to time, but still the second derivative with respect to position, since each differentiation of the exponential functions brings down a factor of ω or κ. (An extreme relativistic equation can be of the same order in x and t, since $E = cp$.)

The time independent equation can be written

$$E\psi = -\frac{\hbar^2}{2m}\frac{d^2\psi}{dx^2} + V\psi$$

Clearly this equation results from

$$i\hbar\frac{\partial\Psi}{\partial t} = -\frac{\hbar^2}{2m}\frac{\partial^2\Psi}{\partial x^2} + V\Psi \qquad (20\text{-}2)$$

by substituting

$$\Psi(x,t) = \psi(x)e^{-i\frac{E}{\hbar}t} = \psi(x)e^{-i\omega t}$$

The latter partial differential equation, which is called the *time-dependent Schrödinger equation*, is the fundamental equation of the complete quantum mechanical theory, but since we shall not enter into any calculations which require its use, no further mention of it need be made. The physical effects we have considered can all be understood in terms of solutions of the time-independent equation, for example $\exp(i\kappa x)$. The *propagation* of the wave is described by a solution of the time-dependent equation, like $\exp i(-\omega t + \kappa x)$, but the phase velocity of this wave has no direct physical significance; in particular, it is *not* the velocity of the particle, which is related to the wave *length: $v = p/m = h/m\lambda = \hbar\kappa/m$.*

20-2   THE PROBABILITY INTERPRETATION OF $|\psi|^2$

The solution of the time-independent Schrödinger equation, for a given potential energy function V which describes the physical situation, is now merely the mathematical problem of obtaining solutions $\psi(x)$ to the differential equation. In order to have a precise solution to a physical problem, however, it is essential not only to obtain the mathematical function $\psi(x)$, but also to have some precise instructions for translating ψ into physical terms—i.e., we must know what ψ means. This definite prescription for interpreting ψ is still lacking, although we have tacitly assumed in a vague way that where the waves go is somehow where the electrons go too. For example, in the electron diffraction experiment it was assumed that the diffraction pattern of the wave would determine the intensity distribution of the diffracted electron beam, in the same way that a diffraction pattern of a light wave could be interpreted as describing the intensity of a flux of photons. But what would happen if a single electron went through the slit, that is, how ψ would determine where the electron would land, has not even been considered as yet.

The interpretation of ψ that is now almost universally accepted is the following:

$$|\psi(x)|^2 dx$$

is the probability that, if a measurement of the x-coordinate of the particle is made, the result of the measurement will be a number between x and $x + dx$. This statement may be abbreviated to say that $|\psi(x)|^2 dx$ is the probability of *observing* the electron in the interval between x and $x + dx$, so that $|\psi|^2$ itself is a *probability density*. Like any probability function, it must be *normalized*,

$$\int_{-\infty}^{+\infty} |\psi(x)|^2 dx = 1 \qquad (20\text{-}3)$$

as the probability of finding the particle *somewhere* on the x-axis is unity. (The normalization is simply accomplished by multiplying the solution to the Schrödinger equation by an appropriate constant normalizing factor.) If $|\psi|^2$ is a probability density, what is the interpretation of the wave function ψ itself? The answer is that ψ has no direct interpretation at all—i.e., no physical meaning is attached to ψ, only to $|\psi|^2$. Note that the probability density is analogous to the energy density, or intensity, of a classical wave, since that is also proportional to the square of the amplitude (Eq. 16–22).

The interpretation of the wave function has been stated in a somewhat cumbersome way, but it is important to do so, because this interpretation can resolve the paradox of regarding the electron as a wave and as a particle. If one does an experiment to measure whether an electron is observed in a certain element of space Δx, the experiment can have one of only two possible results: either the electron is found there or it is not. The probability that it *will* be found there is predicted by

$$\int_{x}^{x+\Delta x} |\psi|^2 dx$$

The electron is not in any sense "smeared out" the way the wave function is smeared out. When a measurement is made on it, either all of it is observed or none of it is observed, never part of it, so in that sense it is a particle. What is a wave is the wave function ψ, the square of which describes the probability of the various possible outcomes of an experiment. This interpretation again emphasizes the importance of attaching empirical meaning only to statements which can be tested. The question of where the electron "is" when one is not observing it has no meaning, and it avails nothing to ask it. When not observed, the wave function may be spread out in space, according to a solution of the Schrödinger equation; when the electron is observed, it is found to be in a certain region, and the wave function is thereby modified by the act of observation, according to the uncertainty principle.

The probability density $|\psi|^2$ is formally identical to the distribution functions $f(x)$ which were considered in kinetic theory, but the intended meaning is much different. Those distribution functions were interpreted as labor saving devices for dealing with large numbers of particles, but there was no question that one could in principle imagine following each particle along its own trajectory. The quantum mechanical probability distribution, on the other hand, is supposed to be all one can know, no matter how much labor one is willing to imagine, and the trajectory of the particle has no meaning. Some people (notably Einstein) have hoped that the quantum theory with this interpretation would prove to be only a stop-gap theory, an approximation like kinetic theory, and some serious attempts are still being made to reinterpret or reconstruct it. Most physicists, however, eventually reconcile themselves to using the techniques and results of the quantum theory with this probability interpretation, and do not brood too much about where the electrons are when one cannot see them.

20-3   PHYSICAL QUANTITIES AS OPERATORS

We have been discussing the physical meaning that we ascribe to the wave function ψ, or rather its absolute value squared, $|\psi|^2$. Let us now turn to those factors in the Schrödinger equation that multiply or "operate on" ψ. In discussing them, we shall see that ψ contains information not only about the position of the particle, but also about its other physical properties, such as its momentum, kinetic energy, etc. If we write the equation in the form

$$E\psi = \left[-\frac{\hbar^2}{2m} \frac{d^2}{dx^2} + V(x) \right]\psi$$

and compare it to the classical equation

$$E = T + V$$

it appears that the differential *operator*, $-\dfrac{\hbar^2}{2m} \dfrac{d^2}{dx^2}$, must somehow be identified with the kinetic energy T. The potential energy, on the other hand, is (in most cases) simply a "multiplicative operator," or just a function multiplying ψ, so as to transform it into the new function $V(x)\psi(x)$. Later in this chapter we shall find that physical quantities other than the kinetic energy, such as the linear momentum $\mathbf{p}$ and the angular momentum $\mathbf{L}$, are also represented in quantum theory by differential operators. Physicists have in fact adopted as a postulate the idea that *to every measurable physical quantity there corresponds a quantum mechanical operator*. This is an idea which has no analog in classical particle mechanics and one that it may take you a while to get used to. What it means in terms of physical measurements will be explored in this section and in more detail in Section 20-7.

In what follows operators will be denoted by "sans serif" letters. Thus T, p, and L will be defined as the operators corresponding to T, $\mathbf{p}$, and $\mathbf{L}$ (kinetic energy, momentum, and angular momentum) respectively. For motion in one dimension we have already found that

$$\mathsf{T} \equiv -\frac{\hbar^2}{2m} \frac{d^2}{dx^2} \tag{20-4}$$

Suppose we know the wave function $\psi(x)$ of a particle. Do we then know the numerical value which would be obtained in a measurement of the particle's kinetic energy for example? Or if the answer to that question is no, what are the possible results of such a measurement, and what is the probability that a given value of the kinetic energy would be observed if we actually measured it? It is clear that if ψ_1 were an eigenfunction (Section 16–3) of the operator T, such that ψ_1 satisfied the equation

$$\mathsf{T}\psi_1 \equiv -\frac{\hbar^2}{2m}\frac{d^2\psi_1}{dx^2} = T_1\psi_1$$

where T_1 is a constant (the eigenvalue), then Schrödinger's equation would become

$$\psi(E - V - T_1) = 0$$

This equation could only be satisfied if the kinetic energy $T \equiv E - V$ were equal to T_1. The wave function yields, in other words, a unique value for the kinetic energy when it is an eigenfunction of the corresponding operator T, and a measurement of the kinetic energy could have only one result, namely the eigenvalue. It is a basic assumption of quantum mechanics that such is the case for each operator corresponding to a physical variable, provided the wave function is an eigenfunction of that operator. One further postulates that *the only possible results of measurements of a physical quantity are the eigenvalues of the corresponding operator*, a postulate which is confirmed by the success of quantum mechanics in predicting results in agreement with experiments. The question of which eigenvalue one might expect to measure for the physical quantity when the wave function is not an eigenfunction of the corresponding operator will be explored further in Section 20–7.

Having introduced the kinetic energy operator T, let us turn next to the total energy operator, called the *Hamiltonian operator*, which is defined by

$$\mathsf{H} \equiv \mathsf{T} + \mathsf{V} \equiv -\frac{\hbar^2}{2m}\frac{d^2}{dx^2} + V(x) \tag{20–5}$$

It is evident that the problem of solving the time-independent Schrödinger equation,

$$\mathsf{H}\psi = E\psi \tag{20–6}$$

is just the eigenvalue problem for the operator H. We will now solve this equation for some simple cases.

20–4   FREE PARTICLE

The simplest possible wave function is that of a *free particle*, that is, a particle moving in the absence of any potential. With $V = 0$, the Schrödinger equation (Eq. 20–1) becomes

$$-\frac{\hbar^2}{2m}\frac{d^2\psi}{dx^2} = E\psi$$

or

$$\psi'' + \kappa^2\psi = 0 \qquad \kappa \equiv \sqrt{2mE}/\hbar \tag{20–7}$$

which is the familiar Helmholtz equation, the differential equation for a harmonic oscillator. Equation 20–7 is exactly the same as the equation for the displacement of a stretched string, Eq. 16–6. The general solution is

$$\psi = A \cos \kappa x + B \sin \kappa x \qquad (20\text{–}8)$$

where A and B may be complex numbers. A special solution is obtained with $B = iA$:

$$\psi = A e^{i\kappa x}$$

Since $\sqrt{2mE}$ is the magnitude p of the momentum for a free particle, we can equally well write

$$\psi = A e^{ipx/\hbar} \qquad (20\text{–}9)$$

Note that since

$$\psi'(x) = \frac{ip}{\hbar} \psi(x)$$

or

$$\frac{\hbar}{i} \frac{d}{dx} \psi = p\psi$$

the operator corresponding to the x-component of the momentum must be

$$\mathsf{p}_x \equiv \frac{\hbar}{i} \frac{d}{dx} \qquad (20\text{–}10)$$

The special solution given in Eq. 20–9 is seen to be not only an eigenfunction of the Hamiltonian operator (i.e., a solution of Schrödinger's equation), but also an eigenfunction of the momentum operator, p_x. This particular wave function therefore describes a particle which has exactly the momentum p in the positive x-direction, in the sense that if a measurement of the particle's momentum were made, that would always be the result. Similarly, the wave function $\psi = A e^{-ipx/h}$ describes a particle with momentum p in the negative x-direction. From Eqs. 20–4 and 20–10 we see that the momentum and kinetic energy *operators* are related by the same equation which holds between the classical quantities,

$$\mathsf{T} = \mathsf{p}^2/2m$$

The function given in Eq. 20–9 is complex. It is important to admit this complex solution, since we have just seen that it is the wave function for a particle with a definite momentum p. At first, the idea of a complex wave function may seem perplexing; but since the only physically meaningful quantity is the square of the absolute magnitude, $|\psi(x)|^2$, which is always real and positive, no difficulty ensues. With a wave function, Eq. 20–9, corresponding to a definite momentum p, we find in fact that

$$|\psi|^2 = |A e^{ipx/\hbar}|^2 = |A|^2$$

which is not only real, but also independent of x. All positions x are therefore equally probable, in accord with the uncertainty principle ($\Delta x = \infty$

for $\Delta p = 0$). Note that it is not necessary to restrict E or p in any way in the wave function for a free particle, since there are no boundary conditions to satisfy. The energy levels of a free particle are in other words *not* quantized. In this respect, it is similar to *travelling* waves on a string.

20–5   PARTICLE IN A BOX

The second example that we consider is that of a particle moving between two walls at $x = 0$ and $x = L$, which we represent mathematically by a potential

$$V(x) = 0 \quad \text{for} \quad 0 \le x \le L \qquad V(x) = \infty \text{ for } \quad x > L \quad \text{or} \quad x < 0$$

Fig. (20–1). Between 0 and L, the particle is like a free particle, but it is confined to just this region. With $V(x) = \infty$, the only solution to the Schrödinger equation is $\psi = 0$. Since $\psi(x)$ must be continuous, the wave function in the region $0 \le x \le L$ must satisfy the boundary conditions, $\psi(0) = \psi(L) = 0$. Our problem is then formally identical to the one of finding the standing waves on a string of length L (Chapter 16). Since $V = 0$ for $0 \le x \le L$, our equation is the same as for the free particle,

$$\psi'' + \kappa^2\psi = 0 \qquad \kappa \equiv \sqrt{2mE}/\hbar.$$

The solutions to this problem have already been obtained in Eq. 16–10 or Eq. 16–13:

$$\psi_n(x) = A_n \sin \kappa_n x$$
$$\kappa_n = n\pi/L \qquad n = 1, 2, 3 \ldots \qquad (20\text{–}11)$$

For a given wave function, we could also write the solution as $\psi_n = A_n \sin \kappa_n x = \tfrac{1}{2}iA_n[e^{-i\kappa_n x} - e^{+i\kappa_n x}]$. The standing wave is then seen to be the difference of two eigenfunctions of the momentum operator corresponding to the eigenvalues $\pm p_n$, where $p_n = \hbar\kappa_n = \hbar n\pi/L$. The meaning of this fact will be examined in detail in Section 20–7, but now we can see intuitively that the presence of the two waves travelling in opposite directions corresponds to the classical back-and-forth motion the particle would have in this potential well (being reflected at the walls).

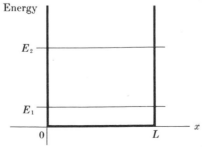

Fig. 20–1. The lowest allowed energy levels for a particle in a box.

Since

$$\kappa = \sqrt{2mE}/\hbar \qquad \text{or} \qquad E = \hbar^2\kappa^2/2m$$

the allowed energy levels are

$$E_n = \frac{1}{2m}\left(\frac{\pi\hbar}{L}\right)^2 n^2 \qquad n = 1, 2, 3, \ldots \qquad (20\text{--}12)$$

Only the wave functions corresponding to these energies will fit between $x = 0$ and $x = L$. If L gets very large, the energy levels go closer together, until in the limit as $L \to \infty$ we recover the free particle result of a continuum of allowed energies. On the other hand, for L small, the energies and momenta are widely separated. In the lowest energy level, the particle can have an x-component of the momentum equal to $+p_1$ or $-p_1$. With the uncertainty in the x-component of the momentum equal to $\Delta p = 2p_1 = 2\pi\hbar/L$, we see that Δp is large when $\Delta x = L$ is small, in agreement with the Heisenberg uncertainty principle.

From the expression for E_n it can be seen that the wave function corresponding to the lowest energy, or the *ground state*, has no nodes ($n = 1$), the next higher energy state (or the first excited state) has one node ($n = 2$), the second excited states two nodes ($n = 3$), and so forth (Fig. 20–2). These qualitative features carry over to more complicated potential functions and it is easy to see why: the more nodes, the more rapidly the wave function curves, and the larger the curvature or second derivative.

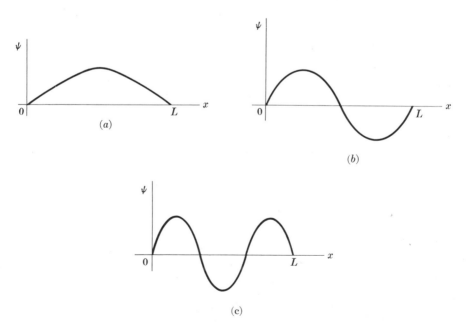

Fig. 20–2. The wave functions for the ground state and the lowest excited states of a particle in a box.

Since the second derivative of the wave function is proportional to the kinetic energy, it follows that the wave function with more nodes per unit length is the one of higher energy.

20-6 POTENTIAL WELL

We have seen how the boundary conditions $\psi(0) = \psi(L) = 0$ lead to quantized energy levels. Let us next examine what happens when the potential walls at $x = 0$ and $x = L$ are not infinite, but finite (Fig. 20–3). We will now choose the arbitrary constant in the potential energy function such that $V = 0$ for $x < 0$ and for $x > L$. For $0 \leq x \leq L$ the potential is negative (a "square well" potential), $V = - V_0$, and we will assume that there is a bound particle in this potential well with negative total energy $0 > E > - V_0$ (Fig. 20–3). (See discussion of bound particles in potential wells in Chapter 3.) For $0 \leq x \leq L$ the Schrödinger equation takes the form

$$-\frac{\hbar^2}{2m}\frac{d^2\psi}{dx^2} = (E - V)\psi = (V_0 - |E|)\psi$$

or

$$\psi'' + \kappa_1^2\psi = 0 \qquad \kappa_1^2 \equiv \frac{2m(V_0 - |E|)}{\hbar^2} \tag{20–13}$$

This equation is of the same form as those in the previous two examples. The general solution is, Eq. 20–8,

$$\psi = A \cos \kappa_1 x + B \sin \kappa_1 x \tag{20–14}$$

In the regions $x < 0$ and $x > L$ the kinetic energy is clearly negative:

$$T \equiv E - V = - |E|$$

In classical mechanics the kinetic energy, $T \equiv \frac{1}{2}mv^2$, can never be negative; or to put it differently, the particle could never penetrate into the regions $x < 0$ or $x > L$. One might expect the same result in wave mechanics, i.e., $\psi = 0$ for $x < 0$ or $x > L$, which would make the probability of finding the particle in these regions equal to zero. We will, however, reach a different conclusion. The quantum mechanical kinetic energy, according to Eq. 20–1, is

$$T \equiv E - V = - \frac{\hbar^2}{2m}\frac{d^2\psi/dx^2}{\psi} \tag{20–15}$$

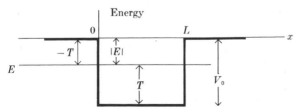

Fig. 20–3

and it is perfectly possible for this term to be negative, i.e., for ψ'' to have the same sign as ψ.

Defining κ_2 by

$$\kappa_2{}^2 \equiv 2m\,|E|/\hbar^2$$

the Schrödinger equation for $x < 0$ and $x > L$ can be written

$$\psi'' - \kappa_2{}^2\psi = 0 \tag{20-16}$$

The solution to this equation is clearly

$$\psi = Ce^{-\kappa_2 x} + De^{+\kappa_2 x}$$

For $x > L$ we must have $D = 0$ in order that the normalization condition, Eq. 20–3, can be satisfied. If D were not equal to zero, ψ and the probability density $|\psi|^2$ would approach infinity at large x, a situation which is physically impossible. Hence

$$\psi = Ce^{-\kappa_2 x} \qquad x > L \tag{20-17}$$

For $x < 0$ we have $C = 0$ for the same reason:

$$\psi = De^{+\kappa_2 x} \qquad x < 0 \tag{20-18}$$

We see that although the wave function does not vanish completely in the classically forbidden regions $x < 0$ and $x > L$, it does decay exponentially with a decay constant $\kappa_2 \equiv \sqrt{2m\,|E|}\,/\hbar$. The penetration into these regions is therefore largely limited to a distance of the order of $\kappa_2{}^{-1}$.

Nevertheless there is a finite probability that the particle will be observed in the regions where its kinetic energy is negative. What does this mean? Actually the uncertainty principle helps us out of the dilemma, since in order to localize the particle within a distance $\Delta x \approx \kappa_2{}^{-1}$ below $x = 0$ or above $x = L$, the momentum becomes uncertain by $\Delta p \approx \hbar/\Delta x \approx \hbar\kappa_2$, and the energy uncertain by

$$\Delta E \approx (\Delta p)^2/2m \approx \hbar^2\kappa^2{}_2/2m = |E|$$

With $\Delta E \approx |E|$ we can no longer say that the kinetic energy is negative, so the paradox is resolved: in order to observe the particle in the classically forbidden regions, enough energy is imparted in the measurement process to free the particle. This is not to say, however, that the classical and quantum mechanical situations are identical. The wave function ψ can penetrate through a finite potential "barrier" where T is negative, and come out on the other side (Fig. 20–4). This wave-mechanical "tunneling"

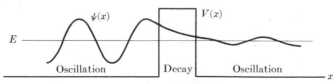

Fig. 20–4. The wave function penetrating a potential barrier.

has been observed to take place for electrons in tunnel diodes and "thin film" devices, and for α-particles in α-decay. Classically this tunneling through a region of negative kinetic energy could of course not occur.

Let us return to the particle in the "square well" potential. With the solutions given in Eqs. 20–14, 20–17, and 20–18, we know how the wave function behaves for all x. So far, however, the four constants A, B, C, and D have not been determined, and the energy E has not been restricted in any way. What are the restrictions on the wave function? We no longer have $\psi = 0$ at $x = 0$ and $x = L$, but we must be able to demand that the kinetic energy be finite everywhere, though not necessarily continuous. If T is finite, ψ'' must also be finite, Eq. 20–15, which in turn demands that ψ' as well as ψ be continuous. Matching ψ and $d\psi/dx$ at both $x = 0$ and $x = L$ gives us 4 equations and the normalization integral, Eq. 20–3, a 5th equation, relating the constants A, B, C, and D, and the energy E. This set of equations will determine all five quantities including the energy. There turn out to be more than one solution if the well is sufficiently deep and wide, leading to several allowed energy levels. The details of the solutions will not be worked out here, but it is clear from our previous argument that the lowest energy solution will be the one with the smallest curvature or no nodes, the first excited state will have one node, etc. (Fig. 20–5). As V_0 increases, the exponential tails get smaller and smaller until with $V_0 = \infty$ they disappear, so that we recover our earlier result for infinite walls.

It is only when V is piecewise constant that the solutions to the Schrödinger equation can be written as simple sinusoidal and exponential functions of x. For more complicated potential functions, the solutions become more difficult to calculate. Often they can only be obtained numerically. The qualitative features of the solution will remain the same for all potential wells, however. This may be seen from Eq. 20–15. In the classically inaccessible regions where T is negative, $d^2\psi/dx^2$ will always have the same sign as ψ itself (e.g., $d^2\psi/dx^2$ is positive where ψ is positive). You can see that with ψ finite, this is possible only if ψ damps to zero (Fig. 20–6). Wherever T is positive, on the other hand, the Schrödinger equation tells us that the sign of $d^2\psi/dx^2$ is opposite to that of ψ itself, i.e.,

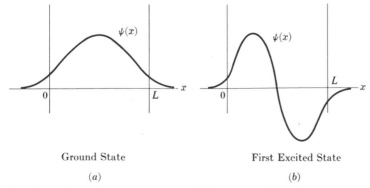

Ground State

(a)

First Excited State

(b)

Fig. 20–5. Wave functions of a particle in a potential well.

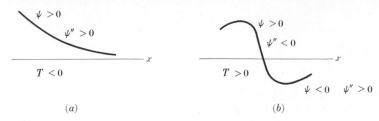

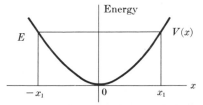

Fig. 20–6. Where $T < 0$, ψ and ψ'' have the same sign and ψ damps to zero. Where $T > 0$, ψ and ψ'' have opposite signs and ψ oscillates.

where ψ is positive it is concave down, where ψ is negative it is concave up (Fig. 20–6). The wave function is therefore oscillatory where $E - V > 0$. No matter what functional form $V(x)$ takes, we have this general result: when $T = E - V(x)$ is positive in a finite region only, the wave function oscillates in that region and damps to zero outside it. Furthermore, as we have already argued, the less $\psi(x)$ curves (or the fewer the nodes) in the oscillatory region, the lower the energy.

As an example of a potential that is not piecewise constant, take the simple harmonic oscillator potential,

$$V = \tfrac{1}{2}Kx^2$$

If $V(x_1) = E$ (Fig. 20–7), the wave function will oscillate from $-x_1$ to x_1; it will damp for $|x| > x_1$, in the classically inaccessible region where $T < 0$. The ground state wave function will behave as indicated in Fig. 20–8(a), while a highly excited state will take the form shown in Fig. 20–8(b). A detailed calculation would show that the allowed energy levels are

$$E_n = (n + \tfrac{1}{2})\hbar\sqrt{K/m} \qquad n = 0, 1, 2, \ldots$$

while the wave function of the nth level is a product of a damping term, $\exp(-\text{const } x^2)$ and a polynomial in x of degree n. Since $\sqrt{K/m} = \omega$ is the natural frequency of the classical oscillator, this is the result which was quoted previously (Eq. 18–25).

20–7   EXPECTED VALUES OF MEASUREMENTS

Let us return to the question of what value to assign to a physical variable when the wave function is *not* an eigenfunction of the corresponding operator. We discussed the probable outcome of position measurements in

Fig. 20–7. The harmonic oscillator potential.

Section 20–2. The position "operator" is of course a simple multiplicative operator, but for all the wave functions $\psi(x)$ that we have considered so far,

$$x \cdot \psi \neq \text{constant} \cdot \psi,$$

i.e., ψ is *not* an eigenfunction of the operator x. In that case we cannot predict the exact result of a position measurement. We only know the probability $|\psi(x)|^2 dx$ that the particle be observed between x and $x + dx$. If we measured the positions of particles with identical wave functions repeatedly, the distribution of measured positions should agree well with $|\psi(x)|^2$. The average value of the measurements would then equal the so-called *expectation value* of x, defined by

$$\bar{x} = \int_{-\infty}^{\infty} dx \ x|\psi|^2 = \int_{-\infty}^{\infty} dx \ \psi^* x \psi \qquad \psi^* = \text{complex conjugate of } \psi$$

(Note that this is perfectly consistent with the way we calculated averages with the distribution function in kinetic theory.)

The latter expression for $\bar{x}$ has been written because it has general validity for any physical variable G with its corresponding operator G; i.e.,

$$\bar{G} = \int_{-\infty}^{\infty} dx \ \psi^* G \psi \qquad\qquad (20\text{–}19)$$

is the expectation value of G. That this is the correct way to calculate the average of the measured G values has to be verified by experiments, as

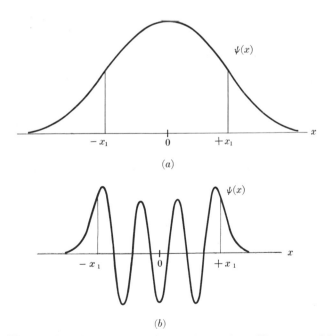

Fig. 20–8. *The wave functions of a particle in a harmonic oscillator potential in* (a) *the ground state and* (b) *an excited state.*

indeed it has been. When ψ_1 is an eigenfunction of G,

$$\mathsf{G}\psi_1 = G_1\psi_1$$

$\bar{G}$ is easily calculated,

$$\bar{G} = \int_{-\infty}^{\infty} dx\, \psi_1{}^*\mathsf{G}\psi_1 = \int_{-\infty}^{\infty} dx\, \psi_1{}^*G_1\psi_1 = G_1 \int_{-\infty}^{\infty} dx\, |\psi_1|^2 = G_1$$

The expectation value is equal to the eigenvalue, as it must be if every measurement of G yields G_1 as suggested in Section 20–3.

As an example of another expectation value calculation, we will now evaluate $\bar{p}_x$ with one of the wave functions discussed in Section 20–5 and given by Eq. 20–11,

$$\psi = \begin{cases} A \sin \kappa_n x & 0 \le x \le L \\ 0 & x < 0 \quad x > L \end{cases}$$

The wave function is normalized if $A = \sqrt{2/L}$, as was shown in Eq. 16–14. We have

$$\bar{p}_x = \int_{-\infty}^{\infty} dx\, \psi^*\mathsf{p}_x\psi = \int_{-\infty}^{\infty} dx\psi^*\frac{\hbar}{i}\frac{d}{dx}\psi = \frac{2}{L}\frac{\hbar}{i}\kappa_n \int_0^L dx\, \sin \kappa_n x \, \cos \kappa_n x$$

$$= \frac{\hbar\kappa_n}{iL} \int_0^L dx\, \sin 2\kappa_n x = -\frac{\hbar}{2iL}\left[\cos(2\kappa_n L) - \cos(0)\right] = 0$$

Note that $\cos(2\kappa_n L) = 1$ since $2\kappa_n L = n(2\pi)$, Eq. 20–11. The expectation value of p_x is seen to be equal to zero. Yet we know that the energy eigenvalue is $E_n = \frac{1}{2m}\left(\frac{n\pi\hbar}{L}\right)^2$, Eq. 20–12, corresponding to $p_x{}^2 = (n\pi\hbar/L)^2$, or $p_x = \pm n\pi\hbar/L$. What this must mean is that a measurement is as likely to yield $p_x = -n\pi\hbar/L$ as $p_x = +n\pi\hbar/L$, for a mean value $\bar{p}_x = 0$. This view is supported by the fact that $\psi(x)$ is a linear combination of $e^{i\kappa_n x}$ and $e^{-i\kappa_n x}$,

$$\psi = \sqrt{2/L} \sin \kappa_n x = \frac{\sqrt{2/L}}{2i}\left[e^{i\kappa_n x} - e^{-i\kappa_n x}\right]$$

as shown in Section 20–5. Since

$$\frac{\hbar}{i}\frac{d}{dx}e^{\pm i\kappa_n x} = \pm \kappa_n \hbar e^{\pm i\kappa_n x} = \pm \frac{n\pi\hbar}{L} e^{\pm i\kappa_n x}$$

we see that ψ is a linear combination (with equal amplitudes) of two eigenfunctions of p_x with eigenvalues $\pm n\pi\hbar/L$.

The preceding example is in line with the following general quantum mechanical result. Let $\{\psi_n\}$ be the set of orthonormal eigenfunctions of a quantum mechanical operator G corresponding to a physical quantity G:

$$\mathsf{G}\psi_n = G_n\psi_n$$

Then any wave function ψ can be written as a linear combination (with perhaps an infinite number of terms) of the eigenfunctions ψ_n,

$$\psi = \sum_n a_n \psi_n$$

(Here some of the eigenvalues G_n corresponding to the eigenfunctions ψ_n may be numerically equal.) The interpretation given to the coefficients a_n is that $|a_n|^2$ represents the probability that a measurement of the physical quantity G will yield the eigenvalue G_n. So far no experiment has contradicted this interpretation. Calculating the expectation value, we find

$$\bar{G} = \int_{-\infty}^{\infty} dx\, \psi^*(x) \mathsf{G}\psi(x) = \int_{-\infty}^{\infty} dx \sum_n a_n^* \psi_n^*(x) \mathsf{G} \sum_m a_m \psi_m(x)$$

$$= \sum_n \sum_m a_n^* a_m G_m \int_{-\infty}^{\infty} dx\, \psi_n^*(x)\psi_m(x) = \sum_n a_n^* a_n G_n$$

$$= \sum_n |a_n|^2 G_n$$

where we have noted, Eq. 16–14, that for an orthonormal set

$$\int_{-\infty}^{\infty} dx\, \psi_n^*(x)\psi_m(x)$$

is equal to zero for $n \neq m$ and equal to 1 for $n = m$. It is clear that the interpretation of $|a_n|^2$, as the probability that a measurement of G will yield G_n, is perfectly consistent with the above result for the mean value of the measurements:

$$\bar{G} = \sum_n |a_n|^2 G_n$$

20-8   WAVE MECHANICS IN THREE DIMENSIONS

We have introduced wave mechanics in a one-dimensional context in order to isolate the new physical ideas as much as possible from purely mathematical difficulties. Most physical problems, of course, are not even approximately one dimensional. To deal with motion in a world with three spatial dimensions, such as that of the electron in the field of a nucleus, we must develop a three dimensional wave mechanics. Since we found that $\mathsf{p}_x \equiv \dfrac{\hbar}{i}\dfrac{d}{dx}$ is the operator for the x-component of the momentum, we would expect the operator for the momentum *vector* to be

$$\mathsf{p} \equiv \frac{\hbar}{i}\nabla \tag{20-20}$$

This would lead to a kinetic energy operator

$$\mathsf{T} = \frac{1}{2m}\mathsf{p}^2 = -\frac{\hbar^2}{2m}\nabla^2 \tag{20-21}$$

where ∇^2 is the same operator introduced into Eq. 16–17, and to a three dimensional Schrödinger equation,

$$\left[-\frac{\hbar^2}{2m}\nabla^2 + V(\mathbf{r})\right]\psi(\mathbf{r}) = E\psi(\mathbf{r}) \qquad (20\text{-}22)$$

The wave function describing a particle is now a function of all three space coordinates, and its probability interpretation must be adjusted accordingly. The expression $|\psi|^2\,dx\,dy\,dz$ is to be understood as the probability that the particle, if observed, would be found within the volume element $dx\,dy\,dz$ centered on the point (x,y,z). In other words, $|\psi|^2$ is now a probability per unit volume rather than per unit length. This interpretation requires $\psi(\mathbf{r})$ to be normalized as follows:

$$\int_{-\infty}^{\infty} dx \int_{-\infty}^{\infty} dy \int_{-\infty}^{\infty} dz\,|\psi(\mathbf{r})|^2 = 1 \qquad (20\text{-}23)$$

with the expectation value of a physical quantity G given by

$$\bar{G} = \int_{-\infty}^{\infty} dx \int_{-\infty}^{\infty} dy \int_{-\infty}^{\infty} dz\,\psi^*\mathsf{G}\psi \qquad (20\text{-}24)$$

rather than by the one dimensional expression in Eq. 20–19.

In one-dimensional problems the angular momentum of a particle has no importance. For motion in three dimensions, however, we know from classical mechanics (Chapter 3) that the angular momentum is an important quantity, and judging by Bohr's quantization rules (Chapter 18), we might expect it to be even more important in wave mechanics. The classical relation,

$$\mathbf{L} = \mathbf{r} \times \mathbf{p}$$

suggests that the quantum mechanical angular momentum operator should be

$$\mathbf{L} = \mathbf{r} \times \mathbf{p} = \mathbf{r} \times \frac{\hbar}{i}\boldsymbol{\nabla} \qquad (20\text{-}25)$$

i.e.,

$$\mathsf{L}_z = x\frac{\hbar}{i}\frac{\partial}{\partial y} - y\frac{\hbar}{i}\frac{\partial}{\partial x} \qquad \text{etc.}$$

For motion in a central potential, $V(|\mathbf{r}|) = V(r)$, such as the coulomb potential, it is advantageous to work with spherical coordinates r, θ, and ϕ. Their relations to the rectangular coordinates (Fig. 20–9) are given by

$$
\begin{aligned}
x &= r\sin\theta\cos\phi \\
y &= r\sin\theta\sin\phi \\
z &= r\cos\theta
\end{aligned}
\qquad (20\text{-}26)
$$

When the components of $\mathbf{L}$ are expressed in terms of spherical coordinates, we find that they are independent of r. The results for L_x and L_y are rather complicated combinations of derivatives with respect to θ, and ϕ, the precise form of which can be calculated from Eqs. 20–25 and 20–26, but

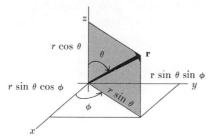

Fig. 20–9. The relations between rectangular and spherical coordinates.

which will not concern us here. The expression for L_z is quite simple, however:

$$L_z = \frac{\hbar}{i} \frac{\partial}{\partial \phi} \qquad (20\text{--}27)$$

One also finds

$$L^2 = -\hbar^2 \left[\frac{1}{\sin \theta} \frac{\partial}{\partial \theta} \sin \theta \frac{\partial}{\partial \theta} + \frac{1}{\sin^2 \theta} \frac{\partial^2}{\partial \phi^2} \right] \qquad (20\text{--}28)$$

For wave functions of definite total angular momentum we must have

$$L^2 \psi_l(\mathbf{r}) = L_l^2 \psi_l(\mathbf{r})$$

where L_l^2 is the eigenvalue. We are not going to solve this equation but merely discuss some of the requirements that we must impose on the solutions in order that they be admissible. One requirement is that ψ be finite (more precisely that $\int \int \int dx\, dy\, dz\, |\psi|^2 = 1$). The solutions to the above equation show a great tendency to blow up at $\theta = 0$ or $\theta = \pi$. In fact, the only solutions that do not blow up are those for which the constant L_l^2 takes on the special values $l(l + 1)\,\hbar^2$, where l is a non-negative integer $l = 0, 1, 2, \ldots$. Again, we see that angular momentum is quantized, but here it is not an assumption as in the Bohr theory, but the result of a

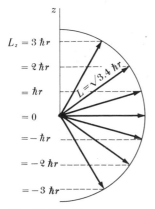

Fig. 20–10. The quantization of angular momentum.

necessary physical restriction on the mathematical form of the wave function. (The result is slightly different from that of the Bohr theory, which is incorrect. The Bohr theory had the values $l^2\hbar^2$ instead of $l(l+1)\hbar^2$.)

The square of the total angular momentum L^2 can take on the values

$$L^2 = L_l^2 = l(l+1)\hbar^2 \tag{20-29}$$

With a particular value for l, what are the permissible values of *one component* of the angular momentum vector, say L_z? The answer is to be found in the solutions to the eigenvalue problem:

$$\mathsf{L}_z \psi_m = L_{z_m} \psi_m$$

The constant L_{z_m} is traditionally denoted by $m\hbar$, so that, using Eq. 20–27,

$$\frac{\hbar}{i} \frac{\partial}{\partial \phi} \psi_m = m\hbar \psi_m \tag{20-30}$$

The solution to this equation is obviously $\psi_m = C(r,\theta)e^{im\phi}$, where $C(r,\theta)$ is an arbitrary function of r and θ. The requirement that the wave function be single-valued, i.e., that it should be unaltered when ϕ is increased by 2π or multiples thereof, is fulfilled only if m is an integer. Since $L_z^2 < L^2$, it follows that $m^2 < l(l+1)$. With m and l both integers, the maximum value of m is therefore l, and its minimum value $-l$. In other words the z-component of L can take on only the values $m\hbar$, where m is one of the $2l+1$ integers $-l$, $-l+1$, . . . , 0, . . . , $l-1$, l. One also finds, when ψ is an eigenfunction of L_z so that this component of the angular momentum has a definite value $m\hbar$, that ψ cannot at the same time be an eigenfunction of L_x or L_y, i.e., the other components do not have definite values, although their expectation values can of course be calculated. Similarly, when ψ is an eigenfunction of L_x, the eigenvalues are again integral multiples of $\hbar$, but now ψ cannot be an eigenfunction of L_z nor of L_y. This kind of symmetry must of course obtain, since the designation of the "z" axis is completely arbitrary.

Having expressed the angular momentum operators in terms of spherical coordinates, let us do the same for the kinetic energy operator. Again, we omit the algebra and merely give the result:

$$\begin{aligned}
\mathsf{T} &= -\frac{\hbar^2}{2m}\nabla^2 = -\frac{\hbar^2}{2m}\left[\frac{\partial^2}{\partial x^2} + \frac{\partial^2}{\partial y^2} + \frac{\partial^2}{\partial z^2}\right] \\
&= -\frac{\hbar^2}{2m}\frac{1}{r^2}\frac{\partial}{\partial r}r^2\frac{\partial}{\partial r} + \frac{L^2}{2mr^2}
\end{aligned} \tag{20-31}$$

We have already proved in Eq. 16–20 that when there is no angular dependence, $(-\hbar^2/2m)\nabla^2$ is given by the first term in the above expression. The present result is to be compared with the classical result, Eq. 3–27 or Eq. 3–28,

$$T = \frac{1}{2m}p_r^2 + \frac{L^2}{2mr^2} \qquad \text{where} \qquad p_r = m\dot{r}$$

The term $-\dfrac{\hbar^2}{2m}\dfrac{1}{r^2}\dfrac{\partial}{\partial r}r^2\dfrac{\partial}{\partial r}$ clearly represents the kinetic energy due to the radial motion, while $L^2/2mr^2$ corresponds to the kinetic energy of the angular motion.

20-9 POSTULATES OF QUANTUM MECHANICS

In this chapter we have introduced the basic ideas of quantum mechanics, which are fundamental to all of modern physics. Because of their great importance and their assumed unfamiliarity to the reader, a summary of these new concepts is presented in this section.

The fundamental postulates of wave mechanics are:

1. The state of a physical system is defined by a wave function, $\psi(x,y,z)$, which must be single-valued, continuous (with a continuous first derivative), and normalizable: $\displaystyle\int_{-\infty}^{\infty} dx \int_{-\infty}^{\infty} dy \int_{-\infty}^{\infty} dz\, \psi^*\psi = 1.$

2. To every observable quantity G there corresponds a quantum mechanical operator G.

3. The only possible results of a measurement of the physical quantity G are the eigenvalues G_n of the corresponding operator G:

$$\mathsf{G}\psi_n = G_n\psi_n$$

4. The expectation value (expected mean of a series of measurements on identical systems) of an observable G when a system is in a state represented by the (normalized) wave function ψ is

$$\bar{G} = \int_{-\infty}^{\infty} dx \int_{-\infty}^{\infty} dy \int_{-\infty}^{\infty} dz\, \psi^*\mathsf{G}\psi$$

The prescription for finding the quantum mechanical operator corresponding to a classical physical quantity is very simple: if the classical quantity is a function of the position $\mathbf{r}$ and the momentum $\mathbf{p}$, the quantum mechanical operator is the same function but with the momentum $\mathbf{p}$ replaced by $\dfrac{\hbar}{i}\boldsymbol{\nabla}$. A few simple examples to illustrate this prescription are given in Table 20–1.

TABLE 20–1

Classical Quantity	Quantum Mechanical Operator
$\mathbf{r}$	$\mathbf{r}$
$\mathbf{p}$	$\dfrac{\hbar}{i}\boldsymbol{\nabla}$
$\mathbf{L} = \mathbf{r} \times \mathbf{p}$	$\mathsf{L} = \mathbf{r} \times \dfrac{\hbar}{i}\boldsymbol{\nabla}$
$E = p^2/2m + V(r)$	$\mathsf{H} = -\dfrac{\hbar^2}{2m}\nabla^2 + V(r)$

According to Postulate 3 the only possible energies of a system are the eigenvalues E_n of the energy operator (the Hamiltonian operator) H:

$$\mathsf{H}\psi_n = E_n\psi_n$$

i.e., the eigenvalues obtained by solving the Schrödinger equation. We have already seen (Sections 20–5 and 20–6) how the imposition of suitable boundary conditions consistent with the restrictions on the wave function listed in Postulate 1 can lead to *discrete* energy spectra or the *quantization* of energy. No matter how complicated the physical system, the program for finding the allowed energy states is always the same: first we write down the Hamiltonian operator for the system and next we solve the Schrödinger equation. In the next chapter we shall see that the eigenvalues of the Hamiltonian operator for the hydrogen atom are precisely those energy levels (Eq. 18–5) deduced from the hydrogen emission spectrum.

PROBLEMS

20–1. Normalize (as in Eq. 20–3) the ground state wave function ψ_1 for a particle in a box (Eq. 20–11).

20–2. With the wave function in Problem 20–1, calculate the probability of finding the particle between

(a) $x = 0$ and $x = L/2$.
(b) $x = L/4$ and $x = 3L/4$.
(c) What is the expectation value of x?

20–3. Repeat Problem 20–2 with the wave function ψ_8 (Eq. 20–11).

20–4. With a square potential well of finite depth, Fig. 20–3, the wave function is given by Eqs. 20–14, 20–17, and 20–18. Write down the equations which, when solved, determine the constants A, B, C, and D as well as the energy eigenvalues.

20–5. Show that the functions

$$\psi_1(x) = C_1 \exp\!\left(\frac{-x^2\sqrt{mK}}{2\hbar}\right)$$

and

$$\psi_2(x) = C_2\, x\, \psi_1(x)$$

satisfy the Schrödinger equation with $V(x) = \tfrac{1}{2}\,Kx^2$.
What are the energy eigenvalues?
Calculate the expectation values of x^2 for the two cases.

20–6. Calculate the spacing for the energy levels in a harmonic oscillator with a frequency of 440 cps.

20–7. The commutator of the operators p and x is defined to be $\mathsf{px} - \mathsf{xp}$. It is denoted by $[\mathsf{p}, \mathsf{x}]$. Compute the result of this operator when acting on an arbitrary wave function ψ.

20-8.   Calculate the ground state energy of a neutron confined to a one-dimensional "box" of length 10^{-12} cm. (This is approximately the diameter of a nucleus).

20-9.   Prove that the expressions for L_z in Eqs. 20–25 and 20–27 are identical. *Hint*: Start with Eq. 20–27 and recall that

$$\frac{\partial \psi}{\partial \phi} = \frac{\partial \psi}{\partial x}\frac{\partial x}{\partial \phi} + \frac{\partial \psi}{\partial y}\frac{\partial y}{\partial \phi} + \frac{\partial \psi}{\partial z}\frac{\partial z}{\partial \phi}$$

20-10. Derive the expressions for L_x and L_y in spherical coordinates.

REFERENCES

R. B. Leighton, *Principles of Modern Physics* (McGraw-Hill, 1959), Ch. 2–4.

F. K. Richtmyer, E. H. Kennard, and T. Lauritsen, *Introduction to Modern Physics* (McGraw-Hill, 1955, 5th ed.), Ch. 6.

D. Bohm, *Quantum Theory* (Prentice-Hall, 1951), Parts I, II, and III.

C. W. Sherwin, *Introduction to Quantum Mechanics* (Holt, 1959), Ch. 1–5.

W. Heisenberg, *The Physical Principles of the Quantum Theory* (Dover, 1930), Ch. 1–4.

IV

ELECTRONIC STRUCTURE
OF MATTER

In the last few chapters the laws of quantum mechanics have been introduced. With this introduction behind us, we are now in a position to apply the wave mechanical theory to the study of the electronic structure of atoms, molecules, and solids.

In quantum mechanics it is futile to attempt a calculation of the precise "trajectories" or orbits of the electrons in an atom. The uncertainty principle embodies this futility. What one can hope to do is to calculate correctly (and thereby "explain") the electronic energy levels deduced from observed emission spectra. We will find that this can be done. Just as in the case of the square well potential, discrete allowed energy levels follow in a natural way from the boundary conditions that must be imposed on the wave function.

The fine details of the observed spectra, however, can only be understood in terms of electron "spin"; i.e., the electron is found to possess an intrinsic angular momentum, as though it were spinning on its own axis, in addition to its orbital angular momentum $\mathbf{L}$. The idea of spin, introduced for the first time in Part IV, occupies a very fundamental position in contemporary physical theory, and has an enormous number of important practical consequences.

We will also gain some understanding of how the electrons distribute themselves among the permissible energy levels and how atoms combine into aggregated forms such as solids. The periodicity in the chemical properties of the elements arises in a natural way. Because of the great complexity of the systems under study, some of the considerations will necessarily be of a qualitative nature. Indeed, exact theoretical calculations of most of these effects have not yet been achieved. What we do intend to demonstrate is that the quantum mechanical ideas, developed and applied to some simple systems in Part III, are capable of yielding a consistent picture of all these more complex systems.

21/the hydrogen atom

The hydrogen atom constitutes the simplest atomic system, and as such it has played a crucial role in the history of modern physics as a testing ground for atomic theories. Hydrogen has a single negatively charged electron bound to its positively charged nucleus, called a proton, and its relatively simple emission spectrum can be understood in terms of allowed energy levels given by the formula (Eq. 18–5),

$$E_n = -13.6/n^2 \text{ eV} \qquad n = 1, 2, 3, \ldots$$

Any comprehensive theory of the electronic structure of matter would have to explain why these and only these energy levels are permitted. We have seen that the simple Bohr theory (Chapter 18) does this, but only by pulling out of a hat the quantization of angular momentum, Eq. 18–10,

$$L = k\hbar \qquad k = 1, 2, 3, \ldots$$

We will now show that the Schrödinger equation predicts the same energy spectrum as the Bohr theory. This will involve a rather lengthy mathematical calculation. Furthermore, the quantization of angular momentum in wave mechanics can be seen (Eq. 20–29) to arise quite naturally through a restriction of the wave function to finite values.

21-1 THE SCHRÖDINGER EQUATION FOR HYDROGEN

In Chapter 3 we showed that a classical two-particle problem was identical to the problem of a single particle with a "reduced mass" moving in a stationary central force field, the distance from the force center being the interparticle distance. A similar result can be proved quantum mechanically. Since the mass of the proton m_p is 1836 times the electron mass m_e, the reduced mass is very close to the mass of the electron, so close that we will ignore the difference in what follows. The difference is real, however. Thus "heavy hydrogen," or deuterium, with a nuclear mass about twice that of ordinary hydrogen, has an energy spectrum that differs slightly in a way precisely accounted for by the change in the reduced mass (Prob. 18–6).

The potential energy of an electron in the coulomb field of a nucleus is

$$V(r) = -\frac{Ze^2}{r} \qquad (21\text{-}1)$$

where $+Ze$ is the charge on the nucleus. For hydrogen $Z = 1$, of course, but we will carry the Z along, since the results for $Z > 1$ will be of interest when we discuss the heavier elements and the origin of x-rays. The Schrödinger equation for the electron is then, according to Eqs. 20–22 and 20–31,

$$-\frac{\hbar^2}{2m}\frac{1}{r^2}\frac{\partial}{\partial r}r^2\frac{\partial \psi}{\partial r} + \frac{1}{2mr^2}\mathsf{L}^2\psi - \frac{Ze^2}{r}\psi = E\psi \qquad (21\text{-}2)$$

We may try to simplify this equation in a way which is analogous to the classical procedure used in Section 5–2. If the wave function ψ corresponds to a state of definite angular momentum, we have, by Eq. 20–29,

$$\mathsf{L}^2\psi = l(l+1)\hbar^2\psi$$

This expression, when substituted in the Schrödinger equation, leaves us with an ordinary differential equation in r, since no derivatives with respect to θ or ϕ appear. If the wave function $\psi(r,\theta,\phi)$ is now written in the form

$$\psi(r,\theta,\phi) = R(r)Y(\theta,\phi) \qquad (21\text{-}3)$$

it is clear that $Y(\theta,\phi)$ will factor out, with the result

$$-\frac{\hbar^2}{2m}\frac{1}{r^2}\frac{d}{dr}r^2\frac{dR}{dr} + \left[\frac{l(l+1)\hbar^2}{2mr^2} - \frac{Ze^2}{r}\right]R = ER \qquad (21\text{-}4)$$

This equation, like Eq. 5–4, contains the constant angular momentum $L^2 = l(l+1)\hbar^2$. Those negative energy solutions to Eq. 21–4 which satisfy the proper boundary conditions at $r = 0$ and $r = \infty$ will yield the allowed energies of the electron in the hydrogen atom.

One can show that the lower energy states are those corresponding to small angular momentum quantum numbers l. This is perhaps most easily seen by combining the kinetic energy of the angular motion with the potential energy to form an "effective potential" $V'(r)$ for the radial motion, similar to Eq. 5–5:

$$V'(r) = -\frac{Ze^2}{r} + \frac{l(l+1)\hbar^2}{2mr^2} = \frac{e^2}{r}[-Z + l(l+1)a_0/2r] \qquad (21\text{-}5)$$

where $a_0 \equiv \hbar^2/me^2$ is the Bohr radius, Eq. 18–7. We can readily determine the value of r corresponding to the minimum of this potential:

$$0 = \frac{d}{dr}\,V'(r) = \frac{e^2}{r^2}\,[Z - l(l+1)a_0/r]$$

or

$$r = a_0 l(l+1)/Z \tag{21-6}$$

The "bottom" of the effective potential well is therefore (Fig. 21-1)

$$V'\left(\frac{a_0 l(l+1)}{Z}\right) = \frac{Ze^2}{a_0 l(l+1)}\,[-Z + l(l+1)a_0/2a_0 l(l+1)Z^{-1}]$$

$$= -\frac{Z^2 e^2}{2a_0 l(l+1)}$$

Since the total energy must exceed $V'(r)$ by the kinetic energy of the radial motion, it is clear that

$$E > -\frac{Z^2 e^2}{2a_0 l(l+1)} = -\frac{13.6 Z^2}{l(l+1)}\,\text{eV} \tag{21-7}$$

The maximum possible binding energy, $|E|$, is seen to decrease rapidly with increasing l. Consequently, the ground state wave function should be sought among the $l = 0$ solutions to the Schrödinger equation.

21-2   WAVE FUNCTIONS AND ENERGY LEVELS WITH $l = 0$

If we define γ by

$$\gamma \equiv \sqrt{-2mE}/\hbar = \sqrt{2m|E|}/\hbar \tag{21-8}$$

and set $l = 0$, the Schrödinger equation, Eq. 21-4, can be written

$$\frac{d^2 R}{dr^2} + \frac{2}{r}\frac{dR}{dr} + \frac{2Z}{a_0 r}\,R = \gamma^2 R \tag{21-9}$$

Let us first see what we can infer by looking at the equation when r is extremely large.

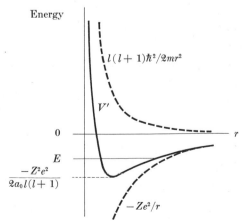

Fig. 21-1. *The effective potential of an electron in a coulomb field.*

For very large r the two terms containing the factor $\frac{1}{r}$ can be ignored, in which case the differential equation simplifies greatly:

$$\frac{d^2R}{dr^2} \cong \gamma^2 R$$

an equation of the same mathematical form as Eq. 20–16. The general solution of this approximate equation is

$$R \cong Ae^{-\gamma r} + Be^{+\gamma r}$$

for

$$r \to \infty$$

The wave function is clearly not normalizable unless B vanishes, since otherwise it would approach infinity with r. We must insist, therefore, that the hydrogen wave functions approach $Ae^{-\gamma r}$ for large r. This does not mean that A is completely constant, only that its variation in r is slow compared to that of $e^{-\gamma r}$ for large r.

Let us next look at the equation with smaller values of r, in the region where the kinetic energy $T = E - V$ is positive. This is the region $0 \le r \le r_1$, with r_1 determined by (Fig. 21–2)

$$E = -\frac{Ze^2}{r_1}, \text{ or } r_1 = Ze^2/|E|$$

It is clear that this region where the wave function is oscillatory (cf. Section 20–6) gets smaller as the binding energy $|E|$ gets larger, i.e., it is smallest for the ground state of the atom. We might expect therefore that the radial wave function corresponding to the ground state would have no nodes: if we tried to force a wave function with one or more nodes inside the same minimum r_1, it would curve more rapidly and therefore raise the energy. In fact one would argue that the more nodes in R, the less $|E|$ and the larger r_1 would have to be. We will find that this is indeed true. It is also true that an infinite (but discrete) set of energy levels is possible in the hydrogen atom. This is because $V(r)$ falls off so slowly that it is always possible to get in one more oscillation or one more node in the wave function by increasing r_1 (decreasing $|E|$) sufficiently. In a potential with a

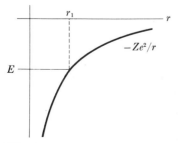

Fig. 21–2

finite depth and range this is not possible, and there is only a finite number of bound energy levels.

Since the potential is of the form r^{-1}, one is tempted to try a polynomial in r multiplied by $e^{-\gamma r}$ as a solution to the Schrödinger equation. Such a solution would exhibit the correct behavior $e^{-\gamma r}$ for very large r; and if the polynomial is of degree d, it will have a possible d zeros or nodes. Our trial solution is

$$R_n = \sum_{i=0}^{n-1} C_i r^i e^{-\gamma r} \qquad n \geq 1 \qquad (21\text{-}10)$$

where the C_i's are constants. The function R_n has $d = n - 1$ nodes. We take the first and second derivatives of R_n in Eq. 21-10 and substitute the resulting expressions into the Schrödinger equation, Eq. 21-9,

$$\frac{d^2 R_n}{dr^2} + \frac{2}{r}\frac{dR_n}{dr} + \frac{2Z}{a_0 r} R_n = \gamma^2 R_n$$

This will give a relation which the coefficients C_i must satisfy in order for R_n actually to be a solution. The result is

$$\sum_{i=0}^{n-1} C_i e^{-\gamma r} \left\{ r^{i-1}\left[\frac{2Z}{a_0} - 2\gamma(i+1)\right] + r^{i-2} i(i+1) \right\} = 0 \quad (21\text{-}11)$$

In order to determine the values of the C_i's which will make this equation hold for all r, we must rewrite the equation collecting all the coefficients of each power of r. The sum over the last term in Eq. 21-11 may be rewritten as follows, by setting the dummy index i equal to $j + 1$ (i.e., by renaming the summation index):

$$\sum_{j=-1}^{n-2} C_{j+1} e^{-\gamma r} r^{j-1} (j+1)(j+2)$$

Since the $j = -1$ term in the sum vanishes due to the factor $j + 1$, the sum really starts with $j = 0$. Also, since $C_n = 0$, by Eq. 21-10, we may as well extend the sum from $j = n - 2$ to $j = n - 1$. With $\Sigma_{j=-1}^{n-2}$ thus changed to $\Sigma_{j=0}^{n-1}$, and now substituting i for the dummy index j again, the sum over the last term in Eq. 21-11 becomes

$$\Sigma_{i=0}^{n-1} C_{i+1} e^{-\gamma r} r^{i-1} (i+1)(i+2)$$

We can now combine the two terms, since the summation and the power of r are the same in each term. Equation 21-11 may then be written

$$\Sigma_{i=0}^{n-1} D_i r^{i-1} e^{-\gamma r} = 0$$

where

$$D_i \equiv C_i 2\left[\frac{Z}{a_0} - \gamma(i+1)\right] + C_{i+1} (i+1)(i+2) \qquad (21\text{-}12)$$

If this sum is to vanish for *all* values of r, each coefficient D_i must be equal to zero individually:

$$D_i = 0 \qquad i = 0, 1, \ldots, n - 1 \qquad (21\text{-}13)$$

or from Eq. 21-12,

$$C_{i+1} = C_i \frac{2[\gamma(i + 1) - Z/a_0]}{(i + 1)(i + 2)} \qquad (21\text{-}14)$$

This is a *recursion formula* for the coefficients of the polynomial in Eq. 21-10. From this relation C_1 is given in terms of C_0, C_2 in terms of C_1 and hence in terms of C_0, and so forth. With all coefficients C_i for $i > 0$ expressed in terms of C_0, C_0 itself can be calculated from the normalization integral, Eq. 20-23, so that the trial solution, Eq. 21-10, is completely determined.

If we let i get very large, we see from Eq. 21-14 that

$$C_{i+1}/C_i \cong 2\gamma/i$$

This would be found to be precisely the ratio of the coefficients in the infinite series expansion of $e^{2\gamma r}$. We cannot permit i to become infinite therefore, because then R would behave like $e^{2\gamma r}e^{-\gamma r} = e^{\gamma r}$ for large r, which is clearly inadmissible: we can let n in our series expression for R_n get as large as we please, but it must remain a finite integer.

The fact that the series must terminate for some finite integer n will now be seen to lead to a definite allowed value of energy corresponding to that particular n. Our polynomial factor in R_n terminates with r^{n-1}, i.e., C_n vanishes,

$$C_n = 0 \qquad (21\text{-}15)$$

where n, as we have just argued, must be finite. If we set $i = n - 1$ in our expression for D_i, Eq. 21-12, we find that by Eq. 21-13,

$$0 = D_{n-1} = C_{n-1}2[Z/a_0 - \gamma n] + C_n n(n + 1)$$

Since $C_n = 0$ (Eq. 21-15) and $C_{n-1} \neq 0$ by assumption, it follows that

$$\gamma = \gamma_n = Z/na_0 \qquad (21\text{-}16)$$

Recalling the definition of γ, Eq. 21-8, this condition on γ implies

$$E = E_n = -\frac{\hbar^2}{2ma_0^2}\frac{Z^2}{n^2} = -\frac{e^2}{2a_0}\frac{Z^2}{n^2} = -\frac{me^4}{2\hbar^2}\frac{Z^2}{n^2} = -\frac{13.6Z^2}{n^2}\text{eV} \qquad (21\text{-}17)$$

where n is any finite integer greater than or equal to 1 (see Eq. 21-10), $n = 1, 2, 3 \ldots$.

These are precisely the energy levels we arrived at with the Bohr theory. The way in which the energy levels are obtained, however, is quite different here. The quantization, as in our earlier examples of wave mechanics, follows from the boundary conditions on the wave function. We demanded that ψ should vanish at $r = \infty$, which led to the requirement that the series in R_n be a finite polynomial. This in turn led to the allowed energy levels as the eigenvalues E_n corresponding to the eigenfunctions R_n. In comparison, the Bohr rules seem rather arbitrary. The real power of wave mechanics, however, is not seen until one turns to more complicated systems, such as an atom with more than one electron. For such systems the Bohr theory cannot predict the correct energy levels, whereas wave mechanics does give the observed levels in all cases where the mathematical problem has been solved with sufficient accuracy. As you may imagine, after having followed through the simplest case ($l = 0$) for the simplest atom (hydrogen), the mathematical problem is rather formidable.

Let us look at the wave function for the ground state and the first excited state in some detail. For the ground state, $n = 1$, we have (Eq. 21–15) $C_1 = 0$ and, by Eq. 21–10,

$$R_1 = C_0 e^{-\gamma_1 r} = C_0 e^{-Zr/a_0} \tag{21--18}$$

As expected, this wave function has no nodes. For the first excited state, $n = 2$, $C_2 = 0$ (Eq. 21–15), and from Eq. 21–14 with $i = 0$, and Eq. 21–16 with $n = 2$,

$$C_1 = C_0 \frac{2[\gamma_2 - Z/a_0]}{1 \times 2} = - C_0 \frac{Z}{2a_0}$$

This leads, by Eq. 21–10, to

$$R_2 = C_0 \left(1 - \frac{Zr}{2a_0} \right) e^{-Zr/2a_0} \tag{21--19}$$

or a wave function with one node located at $r = 2a_0/Z$. With $n = 3$ we would find two nodes, with $n = 4$ three nodes, and so forth.

For each function the constant C_0 is determined by the normalization integral, Eq. 20–23, which for spherically symmetric wave functions, $\psi = R(r)$, may be written

$$\int_0^\infty 4\pi r^2 dr \, |R|^2 = 1 \tag{21--20}$$

The functions R_1 and R_2 are plotted in Fig. 21–3.

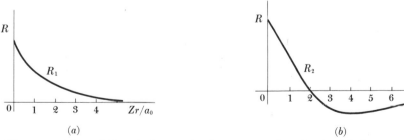

Fig. 21–3. *The radial variation of the electron wave function for* (a) *the ground state and* (b) *the first excited state of the hydrogen atom.*

Since $|\psi|^2$ represents the probability per unit volume, the probability of finding the electron between r and $r + dr$ must be equal to

$$4\pi r^2 dr \, |\psi|^2$$

To determine the most probable radial distance of the electron, we would therefore have to plot $r^2 R_n^2$, *not* just R_n^2. In Fig. 21–4 we show the radial probability density $(rR_n)^2$ for $n = 1$ and $n = 2$. It is clear that for $n = 2$ the electron is on the average further away from the proton ($\bar{r}$ larger), which means that it is less tightly bound ($\overline{V} \propto \overline{(1/r)}$ smaller).

21–3   WAVE FUNCTIONS AND ENERGY LEVELS WITH $l > 0$

With $l > 0$, we have an additional term $[l(l + 1)\hbar^2/2mr^2]R$ in the wave equation, Eq. 21–4. Since this term is also a simple power in r, one might again expect a solution in the form of a polynomial in r multiplied by $e^{-\gamma r}$. This is in fact so. The only difference is that the lowest power in the polynomial is now found to be r^l. The higher l becomes, therefore, the smaller R is for small r, and the less likely it is to find the electron near the origin (i.e., the nucleus). This result, which agrees with the classical orbit, can be understood qualitatively from the shape of the effective potential $V'(r)$ (Fig. 21–1). When the repulsive part of $V'(r)$, $l(l + 1) \, \hbar^2/2mr^2$, is increased, the electron is pushed further out, as the crossing point of V' and E moves out to larger r. In fact the bottom of the potential well occurs at $a_0 l(l + 1)/Z$ (Eq. 21–6), so that the average electron-nuclear separation is roughly proportional to l^2.

The allowed energy levels can be obtained as for $l = 0$ by demanding that the power series solution in r terminate after a finite number of terms. Since the procedure here is the same as with $l = 0$, we will simply give the result:

$$E_n = - \frac{e^2}{2a_0} \frac{Z^2}{n^2} \qquad n = l + 1, l + 2, \ldots \qquad (21\text{–}21)$$

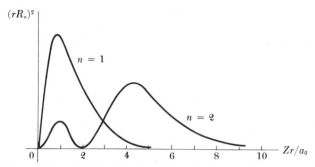

Fig. 21–4. *The radial probability density of the electron in the* n = 1 *and the* n = 2 *states in hydrogen.*

These energy levels are the same as for $l = 0$, but with the restriction $n \geq l + 1$. With E_n as given, this restriction follows immediately from our result for the minimum of $V'(r)$, Eq. 21-7,

$$E_n = - \frac{Z^2 e^2}{2a_0 n^2} > - \frac{Z^2 e^2}{2a_0 l(l + 1)}$$

or

$$n^2 > l(l + 1)$$

With n and l both positive integers, this requires $n \geq l + 1$ in agreement with Eq. 21-21.

We therefore see that there is only one ground state wave function. It has $l = 0$ and $n = 1$, i.e., it is constant in θ and ϕ and has no nodes radially. By having the wave function curve as little as possible we are able to concentrate it very close to the nucleus, where the potential energy is large and negative. For the first excited state we have a tie between the $l = 0$, $n = 2$ wave function, which is constant in θ and ϕ but has one node in the radial direction, and the $l = 1$, $n = 2$ wave function, which curves in the angular directions, but has no nodes radially. With $n > 2$ the wave functions wiggle even more, with $|\psi|^2 r^2$ peaking farther and farther away from the nucleus as n increases, leading to less and less binding energy.

If we plot the allowed energy levels for $l = 0, 1, 2, 3 \ldots$, according to Eq. 21-21, we get the level scheme given in Fig. 21-6. This figure is identical to Fig. 18-5 obtained from the Bohr theory, of course, since the Bohr theory was able to give the correct energy levels for the hydrogen atom. It is sometimes confusing that the s-levels are those with $k = 1$ but $l = 0$, the p-levels with $k = 2$ but $l = 1$, etc. Since the square of the angular momentum in wave mechanics is $l(l + 1)\hbar^2$ while in the Bohr theory it is $k^2\hbar^2$, this

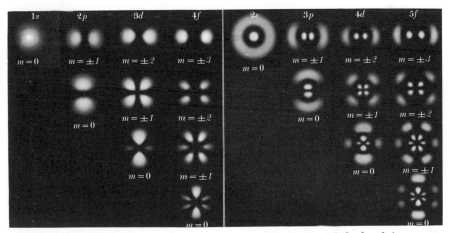

Fig. 21-5. An illustration of the electron probability density of the low-lying energy states in the hydrogen atom. [Courtesy of R. B. Leighton, Principles of Modern Physics (McGraw-Hill, New York, 1959).]

result would be different whatever identification between k and l were used. Unfortunately the conventional identification is $k = l + 1$, rather than $k = l$. This source of confusion is unimportant, however, because the quantum number k never occurs in wave mechanics and need not be used at all. The letters s, p, d, etc., *are* used; they stand for $l = 0, 1, 2$, etc.

We have seen that the imposition of boundary conditions on the solutions of an eigenvalue equation generally leads to a discrete (denumerable) set of eigenfunctions with their corresponding eigenvalues. For example, we have referred to the energy eigenvalues of H for the hydrogen atom problem (Eq. 21–21), the eigenvalues of L^2 (Eq. 20–29), and the eigenvalues of L_z (Eq. 20–30). In each case, the eigenvalues and eigenfunctions are indexed by a set of integers—n, l, and m, respectively, in the three cases mentioned. These integers are called *quantum numbers*. It may happen that one wave function is indexed by more than one quantum number, if it is simultaneously an eigenfunction of more than one operator. We have just encountered such a case: in a central force field where angular momentum is conserved, energy eigenfunctions can be chosen which are also eigenfunctions of the angular momentum operators (i.e., energy and angular momentum are both constants of the motion). Then n, l, and m must all be specified in order to designate a unique wave function. In one-dimensional problems, the single energy quantum number is enough, as we saw in the case of a particle in a box in Section 20–5 and the harmonic oscillator in Section 20–6·

In the hydrogen atom problem, the three quantum numbers n, l, m have individual names. The quantum number n is called the *principal quantum number*. The eigenvalue of L^2 is specified by l, called the *azimuthal quantum number*, or the orbital angular momentum quantum number. The integer m, which specifies the eigenvalue of L_z, is called the *magnetic quantum number*, for a reason which will be explained below. Sometimes it is called the orbital magnetic quantum number, and denoted m_l, in order to distinguish it from the spin magnetic quantum m_s, which is to be introduced in Section 22–3 of the next chapter. In order to specify a hydrogen atom wave function, all three numbers must be given, and so we should

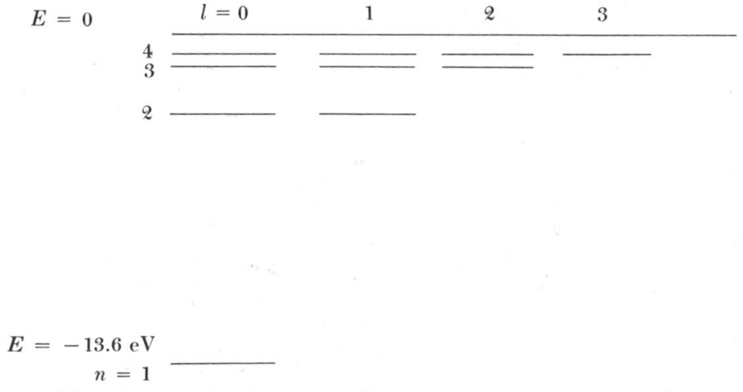

$E = 0$ $l = 0$ 1   2   3

$E = -13.6$ eV
$n = 1$

Fig. 21–6. Allowed energy levels vs. angular momentum quantum numbers in the hydrogen atom.

write the wave functions as $\psi_{nlm}(r,\theta,\phi)$. The only wave functions which we considered explicitly in Section 21–2 were those with l and m zero, $l = m = 0$. These depended only on the radial function R, so that

$$\psi_{n00} \propto R_n$$

It may happen that different eigenfunctions correspond to energy eigenvalues which are numerically the same. We have met this case in the hydrogen atom problem: the energy levels, according to Eq. 21–21, depend only on the principal quantum number n, so that eigenfunctions ψ_{nlm} and $\psi_{nl'm'}$, which have the same n but different azimuthal and magnetic quantum numbers, belong to the same energy level. Such a case is termed *degeneracy*. A degenerate energy level is one to which more than one distinct wave function corresponds. Thus all the hydrogen atom energy levels except the lowest one are degenerate. (This statement will have to be modified slightly after we discuss the electron spin in Section 22–3.) One also speaks of "degenerate wave functions" when the eigenfunctions correspond to the same energy level. In one dimensional problems, we saw that no degeneracy occurred for bound particles (Sections 20–5 and 20–6). For an unbound particle, however, degeneracy can occur in one dimension. For the free electron (Section 20–4), the eigenfunctions exp $(+ i\kappa x)$ and exp $(- i\kappa x)$ both correspond to the same energy $\hbar^2\kappa^2/2m$.

All central potentials $V(r)$ have the property that the energy eigenvalues are independent of the quantum number m, since the force does not single out any particular z-direction, being spherically symmetric. The energy levels must therefore not depend on the component of angular momentum along the arbitrarily chosen z-axis, and so the levels are degenerate for different values of m. The energy independence of l that we have found in the hydrogen atom energy levels, however, is a peculiarity of the r^{-1} or coulomb potential. For a different r-dependence of the potential, the degeneracy in l would be removed, i.e., wave functions with different l but the same n would no longer have the same energy. For example, an electron in a *heavy* atom (containing many other electrons) sees the nuclear coulomb field distorted by the electric fields of all the other electrons. The energy eigenvalues then depend on both n and l; the energy levels of heavy atoms will be investigated further in the next chapter (cf. Fig. 22–1). If the spherical symmetry of the central potential is destroyed, the degeneracy in m is also removed. Such a perturbation of the potential could be accomplished by applying a small external magnetic field in the z-direction, in which case the energy levels that we have discussed are split into a number of sublevels, as we shall see in the following chapter. It is because a magnetic field splits the levels for different m that m is called the magnetic quantum number.

In summary: the Schrödinger equation predicts the same energy levels for the hydrogen atom as the Bohr theory (Chapter 18). In the Schrödinger theory, however, the energy eigenvalues emerge as a natural consequence of the boundary conditions on the wave function. The real superiority of the Schrödinger wave mechanics is best seen, however, in more complicated atomic systems, where it can again predict the correct energy levels while the Bohr theory fails. Unfortunately, because of the mathematical complexity, we shall be forced to discuss the atoms with more than one electron in qualitative rather than quantitative terms.

PROBLEMS

21-1.   Normalize the $l = 0$ wave functions with $n = 1$ and $n = 2$ (Eqs. 21–18 and 21–19).

21-2.   Calculate the expectation values of the potential energy, $-e^2/r$ (see Eq. 20–24), for the two states represented by the wave functions in Prob· 21–1.

21-3.   Calculate the expectation values of the electron radial coordinate r with the two wave functions in Prob. 21–1. Express your answers in terms of the Bohr radius a_0.

21-4.   Show that

$$\psi = Cre^{-r/2a_0} \cos \theta$$

is an eigenfunction of L^2 and determine the quantum number l. Show that the function also satisfies the hydrogen atom Schrödinger equation, Eq. 21–2. What is the energy eigenvalue?

21-5.   Normalize the wave function in Prob. 21–4.

21-6.   With the wave function of the two preceding problems calculate the expectation values of

   (a) r (b) $-e^2/r$ (c) L_z (d) p_z.

21-7.   Find the wave function R_3 for the electron in a hydrogen atom with quantum numbers $l = 0$, $n = 3$. Plot $(R_3r)^2$ as a function of r. Where is its maximum (the most probable distance of the electron from the nucleus)?

21-8.   Show that the two wave functions $\psi = Cre^{-r/2a_0}e^{\pm i\phi} \sin \theta$ satisfy the Schrödinger equation for the hydrogen atom, Eq. 21–2. Determine the quantum numbers n and l. What is the principal difference between these wave functions and the one in Prob. 21–4?

21-9.   The visible spectrum extends from about 3800 Å to 7700 Å. Find all the transitions in hydrogen which give rise to visible photons.

21-10.   Compare the $n = 2 \rightarrow n = 1$ transition in hydrogen and the $n = 4 \rightarrow n = 2$ transition in singly ionized helium. Calculate the photon energies in the two transitions using the reduced mass but ignoring the atomic recoil.

REFERENCES

R. B. Leighton, *Principles of Modern Physics* (McGraw-Hill, 1959), Ch. 5.

W. Heitler, *Elementary Wave Mechanics* (Oxford, 1946), Ch. 3.

D. Bohm, *Quantum Theory* (Prentice-Hall, 1951), Ch. 14, 15.

C. W. Sherwin, *Introduction to Quantum Mechanics* (Holt, 1959), Ch. 4.

22/many-electron atoms

It is to be expected that the problem of calculating the energy levels in an atom with many electrons should be extremely difficult. Even in classical mechanics the dynamics of a system containing more than two particles gets so complicated that one must resort to numerical methods in order to calculate the particle trajectories. (The mechanics of the solar system is a good example.) Nevertheless, in the many-electron atom there is a simplifying feature that makes it possible to arrive at a number of conclusions that are at least qualitatively correct: the atomic nucleus, because its charge is bigger and its mass very much bigger than that of an individual electron, gives the system a well-defined center. *In an isolated system of particles at rest, the center of mass does not move (Chapter 3). Since a typical nucleus carries all but about 2×10^{-4} of the total mass of the atom, the nucleus is always so close to the center of mass that the extent of its motion is quite negligible. The electrons may therefore be considered to move about a nucleus which is at rest. Furthermore, since the force between the nucleus of a many-electron atom and an electron is larger than the force between any two electrons, it is reasonable (as a first approximation) to neglect the electron-electron interactions. In this "one-electron approximation" each electron moves* independently *in the common coulomb potential of the nucleus. This approximation represents a great simplification indeed.*

22-1 THE ONE-ELECTRON APPROXIMATION

In general a system of Z electrons must be described by a Z-electron wave function, $\psi(1, 2, 3, \ldots, Z)$, where 1 is intended to denote the coordinates of particle 1, 2 the coordinates of particle 2, etc. The Schrödinger equation for the many-electron wave function is formally identical to the one-electron equation, Eq. 20–6, but the many-electron Hamiltonian operator is a sum of the kinetic and potential energy terms for each electron. The probability intrepretation associated with $|\psi|^2$ is analogous to that of the many-particle distribution function briefly discussed at the end of Chapter 9. Thus $|\psi(1, 2, 3\ .\ .\ .)|^2$ gives the joint probability of finding particle 1 with the coordinates 1, particle 2 at 2, particle 3 at 3, etc. Actually the previous statement is in need of a rather subtle modification. What we should say is that $|\psi(1, 2, 3\ .\ .\ .)|^2$ gives the probability of finding one electron at 1, one electron at 2, one electron at 3, etc. Since the electrons are completely *indistinguishable*, there is no way of knowing whether the particle at 1 is electron number 1, 2, or 3. In fact we must give up trying to label the individual electrons altogether. The consequences of this indistinguishability will be explored further in the next section and again in Chapter 26.

For a system of non-interacting particles the joint probability of finding one particle at 1 and another at 2, etc., must be just the product of the independent single-particle probabilities of finding a particle at 1 and a particle at 2. A suitable many-particle wave function is therefore simply a product of single-particle wave functions, each satisfying the single-particle Schrödinger equation,

$$\psi(1, 2, \ldots, Z) = \psi(1)\psi(2) \ldots \psi(Z)$$

The Schrödinger equation for a single electron moving in the coulomb field of a nucleus has already been solved (Chapter 21). The allowed energy levels were found to be, by Eq. 21–17,

$$E_n = -\frac{13.6Z^2}{n^2}\ \text{eV} \tag{22-1}$$

If there were no interactions between the Z electrons, each electron would occupy one of the energy levels given by this equation. The *state of the many-electron atom* is then determined in the one-electron approximation if we can specify how many of the Z electrons occupy each of the allowed one-electron energy levels. The lowest energy state, or the ground state, of the atomic system would clearly be the state in which each of the Z electrons is in the $n = 1$ one-electron energy level, $E_1 = -13.6Z^2$ eV. Then $|E_1|$ would be the energy needed to tear loose one electron from the atom, the so-called *ionization energy*, which would be proportional to Z^2. Actually one finds (Table 22–2) no such increase in the ionization potential with increasing Z.

For example, for Hg, with $Z = 80$, we would expect the ionization energy to be $13.6 \times 80^2 = 87,000$ eV. The actual measured value is about 10 eV (Table 22–2). This huge discrepancy is in part removed when we take into account the *Pauli exclusion principle* (Section 22–2), which states that only *one* electron may occupy any given one-electron energy state. This means that not all of the 80 electrons of Hg can be put into the $n = 1$ level, but most of them must go into higher levels, and so the 80th electron is much easier to remove from the atom. In applying the Pauli principle, we must take into account the hitherto neglected fact that the electron possesses an intrinsic *spin angular momentum* (Section 22–3), whose value enters into the specification of the state of the electron. When these revisions are made we find (Section 22–4) that the last Hg electron will fit into the $n = 6$ energy level. The predicted ionization energy is then $87,000/6^2 = 2400$ eV. While the agreement is improved, this value is still a long way from the experimental 10 eV. Quantitative agreement can be obtained only by taking into account the electron-electron repulsive forces, which are neglected in the one-electron approximation.

We have just seen that the one-electron approximation, in which the mutual repulsion of the electrons is ignored, is incapable of giving quantitative results for a many-electron problem. Nevertheless, the one-electron approximation serves as a very convenient starting point. We may still express the state of a heavy atom by stating how many electrons are in each of the one-electron energy levels, taking into account the electron spin and the Pauli principle—i.e., by specifying the *occupation numbers* for each of the one-electron states. The important fact we have to remember is that the energy levels corresponding to these states are shifted from the values we calculated for hydrogen (Chapter 21) because of the mutual repulsion of the electrons. This repulsion is taken into account in a qualitative way in Section 22–4.

22-2 THE PAULI EXCLUSION PRINCIPLE

Consider a two-electron system in the one-electron approximation discussed in the previous section, i.e., the approximation in which the repulsive force between the two electrons is ignored. Let a stand for the quantum numbers (n, l, m) of one of the electrons and b for the corresponding quantum numbers of the other electron. The wave function of the first mentioned electron will be denoted by ψ_a and that of the other electron by ψ_b. The two-particle wave function corresponding to particle 1 (with coordinates abbreviated by **1**) occupying state a and particle 2 occupying state b would then be the product $\psi_a(\mathbf{1})\,\psi_b(\mathbf{2})$. However, we do not know that it is particle 1 that is in state a; it might equally well be particle 2, in which case the two-electron wave function would be $\psi_a(\mathbf{2})\,\psi_b(\mathbf{1})$. How then do we write the correct two-particle wave function $\psi(\mathbf{1}, \mathbf{2})$ in terms of the one-particle functions ψ_a and ψ_b?

Since the two particles are indistinguishable, we must require that there should be no observable change when the two particles are formally interchanged. The probability density $|\psi(\mathbf{1}, \mathbf{2})|^2$ must therefore be equal to the density with the particles permuted, $|\psi(\mathbf{2}, \mathbf{1})|^2$, or

$$\psi(\mathbf{2}, \mathbf{1}) = \pm\,\psi(\mathbf{1}, \mathbf{2}) \qquad (22\text{--}2)$$

Neither the function $\psi_a(\mathbf{1})\,\psi_b(\mathbf{2})$ nor the function $\psi_a(\mathbf{2})\,\psi_b(\mathbf{1})$ possesses the required symmetry given by Eq. 22–2. We must therefore try to construct a wave function which will describe one particle in state a and one particle in state b, and yet have the necessary symmetry when the names of the two particles are interchanged. Since $\psi_a(2)\ \psi_b(1)$ results from $\psi_a(1)\ \psi_b(2)$ when the coordinates 1 and 2 are interchanged, and vice versa, clearly the sum of these two functions

$$\psi_a(1)\ \psi_b(2) + \psi_a(2)\ \psi_b(1)$$

is unchanged, and therefore satisfies Eq. 22–2 with the $+$ sign. It is easy to see that the difference,

$$\psi_a(1)\ \psi_b(2) - \psi_a(2)\ \psi_b(1)$$

likewise satisfies Eq. 22–2 with the $-$ sign. These two combinations of one-particle wave functions are therefore the only ones which are permissible for indistinguishable particles, satisfying Eq. 22–2.

The linear combination $\psi_a(1)\ \psi_b(2) - \psi_a(2)\ \psi_b(1)$ is called *antisymmetric* and $\psi_a(1)\ \psi_b(2) + \psi_a(2)\ \psi_b(1)$ is called *symmetric* under the interchange of the particles. There is no a priori way of deciding which of these two possibilities should be used for the electrons. Actually one finds empirically (as we shall see below) that the wave functions for electrons (and for many other particles such as protons and neutrons) are *antisymmetric* under the interchange of any two particles. Thus the proper two-electron wave function in the one-electron approximation is

$$\psi(1, 2) = \psi_a(1)\ \psi_b(2) - \psi_a(2)\ \psi_b(1) \qquad (22\text{–}3)$$

Symmetrical wave functions, on the other hand, must be used to describe assemblies of photons, π-mesons, and other mesons.

Let us now investigate the probability of having both of the electrons in the *same* state, i.e., we set b equal to a. Then, by Eq. 22–3,

$$\psi(1, 2) = \psi_a(1)\ \psi_a(2) - \psi_a(2)\ \psi_a(1) \equiv 0$$

We therefore conclude that the probability of the two electrons being in the same state a is identically equal to zero. This is the content of the Pauli exclusion principle: *no two electrons can be in the same quantum mechanical state.* Since we have argued that we know all that we can know about a particle when we know its wave function, this means that no two electron wave functions can be identical. We have seen that with a central potential the ϕ dependence of the wave function, $e^{im\phi}$ (Eq. 20–30), is determined by the quantum number m. Similarly, with m given, l determines the θ dependence of the function, Eqs. 20–28 and 20–29, and with l given, the r dependence is specified by the number of radial nodes, or by n, since $n - (l + 1)$ gives the number of nodes. The three quantum numbers n, l, and m therefore completely specify the spatial dependence of the electron wave function. (It turns out that the electron has one more degree of freedom, however; the direction of its *"intrinsic angular momentum"* or *"spin,"* and the modifications required by this new variable, will be discussed in the following section.)

The Pauli principle is expressed in its most general form by saying that the many-particle wave function is *antisymmetric*—i.e., it changes sign when two particles are interchanged. To say that electrons, protons, and neutrons obey the Pauli principle is equivalent to saying that they have antisymmetric wave functions. In the one-particle approximation to a many-particle problem, we have seen that the Pauli principle implies that no two particles may occupy the same one-particle state, and it is in this sense that it is called the "exclusion" principle. All of our subsequent discussion will be based on the one-particle approximation, but it is important to see how the Pauli principle arises in a fundamental way out of the indistinguishability of elementary particles. Particles such as photons and mesons which do not obey the Pauli principle have a corresponding restriction, in that their wave functions must be symmetric. This restriction does not, however, involve any "exclusion" in a one-particle approximation.

22-3 ELECTRON SPIN

The fact that an electron possesses an intrinsic angular momentum, as though it were spinning on its axis, was first deduced by Uhlenbeck and Goudsmit (1926) from the observed splitting of some spectral lines into *"spin multiplets."* How the electron spin produces this splitting will be discussed in the next chapter; suffice it to say here that the observed multiplicity is consistent with a spin angular momentum operator **S**, whose square, when acting on any electron wave function ψ, yields

$$\mathbf{S}^2\psi = s(s + 1)\hbar^2\psi, \qquad (22\text{-}4)$$

with $s = \frac{1}{2}$. Equation 22-4 is formally the same as Eq. 20-29, except that s is always $\frac{1}{2}$. As in the case of the orbital angular momentum, one finds (this is not obvious and you will have to take our word for it) that a given component of **S**, say $\mathbf{S}_z$, can only have the eigenvalues $m_s\hbar$, with m_s having the minimum value of $-s$ (i.e., $-\frac{1}{2}$) and the maximum value of $+s$ (i.e., $+\frac{1}{2}$). The possible eigenvalues of **S**z, like those of **L**z, differ by integral numbers of $\hbar$, which restricts m_s to the two values $-\frac{1}{2}$ and $+\frac{1}{2}$. Since s is always $\frac{1}{2}$, the dependence of the wave function on the spin-coordinate is determined by the value of m_s. With the spatial dependence of the wave function completely characterized by n, l, and m, only the value of m_s must be given in order to have a unique specification of the state of the electron.

We have introduced spin as an operator in order to maintain consistency with our general characterization of quantum mechanical observables as operators. In what follows, however, we shall not be concerned with the explicit mathematical form of the operator **S**, nor with the explicit way in which ψ depends on the spin variable or the quantum number m_s. It will be sufficient to bear in mind that every electron state depends, in addition to the quantum numbers discussed in Section 21-3, on the quantum number m_s, which can assume only the two possible values $\pm \frac{1}{2}$. The pictorial interpretation of this quantum number is that the electron possesses an intrinsic spin angular momentum, whose z-component can assume the values $m_s\hbar$, i.e., $+ \frac{1}{2}\hbar$ or $- \frac{1}{2}\hbar$. One often describes these two states as "spin up" and "spin down," respectively, meaning that the electron has a z-component of spin angular momentum lying in the $+ z$-direction or $- z$-direction, respectively. For every state we have previously discussed, we must now consider in addition whether the electron spin points up or down.

The observable consequences of electron spin, some of which indeed led to the introduction of the spin concept in the first place, will be considered in greater detail below. Here we may note the changes in our previous theory which are occasioned by the role of the spin quantum number m_s. First, the discussion of the required symmetry of wave functions and the Pauli principle in the last section must be slightly modified. We must understand the subscripts a and b to serve as abbreviations for *four* quantum numbers—n, l, m, m_s—instead of three; and the designations 1 and 2 must include a spin variable as well as the three position variables r, θ, ϕ. Thus Eq. 22–2 shall hold when *all* the electron coordinates, including spin, are interchanged. Furthermore, the Pauli principle, as expressed in Eq. 22–3, shall imply that *no two electrons in an atom can have the same set of four quantum numbers* n, l, m, m_s. It can very well happen that two electrons possess the same spatial wave function if the antisymmetry in the total state is produced by different values of m_s. For example, two electrons could have the ground state wave function Eq. 21–18, provided one has spin up ($m_s = + \frac{1}{2}$) and one has spin down ($m_s = - \frac{1}{2}$). In all the one-electron states previously described, the Pauli principle allows us to place two electrons, with opposite spin.

The existence of spin also affects the occurrence of degeneracy. The energy of an electron in certain cases may be independent of the orientation of its spin angular momentum m_s, just as it is independent of the z-component of orbital angular momentum m in a central potential field. All the states of the hydrogen atom are doubled: for each spatial wave function there is one state with spin up and another with spin down. Even the ground state with $l = 0$, $m = 0$, is degenerate, because m_s can be either $+ \frac{1}{2}$ or $- \frac{1}{2}$. The electron states in one-dimensional problems are also degenerate, corresponding to the two possible spin orientations. If a small magnetic field is applied, however, the spin degeneracy, like the orbital degeneracy in m, is lifted. The consequent splitting of energy levels in a magnetic field manifests itself in the emitted spectra. Henceforth when we refer to the *state* of an electron, we shall mean its spatial wave function plus its spin orientation. When we refer to the *wave function*, we shall usually mean only the spatial part which depends on the variables r, θ, ϕ or x, y, z. Thus to each distinct wave function there correspond two states, with spin up and down. An energy level is degenerate if more than one state corresponds to it.

There is an intimate connection between the spin of a particle and the symmetry of its states. All particles which have spin $s = \frac{1}{2}$ obey the Pauli principle, i.e., they have antisymmetric states. The above-mentioned particles which do not obey the Pauli principle, having symmetric states, have spin 0 or 1. This connection is very far-reaching, so that integral spin is always associated with symmetric states, and half-integral spin ($\frac{1}{2}$, $\frac{3}{2}$, etc.) is associated with antisymmetric states. For our present purposes, however, we need only note that electrons, protons, and neutrons all have spin $\frac{1}{2}$ and obey the Pauli principle.

22-4   THE SHELL STRUCTURE OF ATOMS

Let us try to imagine what happens if we add electrons one by one until we have a total of Z electrons around a nucleus of charge Ze, or in other words a neutral atom. If there were no interactions between the electrons, each electron would move independently of all the others in the potential $V = -\dfrac{Ze^2}{r}$, which means that the allowed energy levels of each electron are just those already calculated for a single electron, Eq. 22–1. Without the Pauli principle the ground state of the atomic system would clearly be the state in which each of the Z electrons was in the ground state of energy $-Z^2 \times 13.6$ eV. For $Z > 2$ this is not possible, however, according to the Pauli principle. With $n = 1$, we must have $l = 0$ (Eq. 21–21) and hence $m = 0$ (Section 20–8), so that according to the Pauli principle only two electrons, corresponding to the two possible values of m_s, can occupy this level.

For larger values of n, the energy levels can hold more than two electrons. With the 2 values of m_s and the $2l + 1$ values of m (Section 20–8), it follows that $2(2l + 1)$ electrons with the same value of l can be put in a common energy level. Since for given n, l can take on the values 0, 1, . . . , $n - 1$, Eq. 21–21, the total number of different combinations of the three quantum numbers, l, m, and m_s for a given n must be equal to the sum of n terms:

$$\sum_{l=0}^{n-1} 2(2l + 1) = 2 \left[1 + 3 + 5 + \ldots + 2n - 1 \right]$$
$$= 2 \frac{n[1 + (2n - 1)]}{2} = 2n^2$$

In the $n = 1$ level we would then be able to put 2 electrons, as we have already seen, in the $n = 2$ level 8, in the $n = 3$ level 18, in the $n = 4$ level 32, and so forth. This scheme would mean that we would have atoms with filled levels or *filled shells* at $Z = 2$, $Z = 2 + 8 = 10$, $Z = 10 + 18 = 28$, $Z = 28 + 32 = 60$, and so forth.

These filled-shell atoms should be very different from those with Z one or two higher. The additional one or two electrons would have to go into the next higher shell (higher n) and the binding energy of the outermost electron, or the ionization potential, would be much smaller than for the closed-shell atoms. One would also expect that the atoms with closed shells plus one electron, such as those with $Z = 3$ and $Z = 11$, would have a great deal in common. In particular we would expect them to display similar chemical properties and similar optical spectra, since, as we will see later, the outermost electrons are the ones largely responsible for chemical and optical properties. The atoms with closed shells plus two electrons would also be expected to be much alike, and so forth, leading to a certain periodicity among the elements.

Such a periodic structure has long been known to the chemists, who have investigated these similarities over the years. The elements with closed shells present a tightly bound structure relatively immune to the influence of other atoms. These are the inert or noble gases, He, Ne, A, Kr, and Xe, chemically inert and with high ionization potentials. The atoms with closed shells plus one extra electron are the alkali metals, Li, Na, K, Rb, and Cs, which have low ionization potentials, readily sharing the outermost loosely bound "valence" electron with other atoms. They are especially ready to share the electron with hydrogen or the halogens F, Cl, Br, and I, which have an atomic structure consisting of a closed shell minus one electron.

The two first closed shells do in fact occur with $Z = 2$ (He) and $Z = 10$ (Ne), as we predicted. The next noble gases, however, are not those next in our list with $Z = 28$ (Ni) and $Z = 60$ (Nd), but rather argon with $Z = 18$, krypton with $Z = 36$, and xenon with $Z = 54$. How can we understand this discrepancy? We shall find the answer in a failure of the one-electron approximation, namely the *screening effect* of the electrons. It is clear that the energy levels cannot be given correctly by $E_n = -\dfrac{Z^2}{n^2} \, 13.6$ eV, Eq. 22–1, when the effects of the mutual interaction of the electrons on each other are considered. An electron in the third shell, for instance, will see the coulomb field of the nucleus reduced or "screened" by the ten electrons in the two innermost shells. One might expect that the energy level for this electron would be better described by substituting $(Z - 10)^2$ for Z^2 in the formula for E_n. Actually, the screening is not complete, since the wave function of an electron in the third shell partially penetrates the inner shells. There is evidence from x-ray energies (Chapter 23) that the best approximation to the $n = 3$ energy level is obtained by substituting $(Z - 8.2)^2$ for Z^2. This would clearly raise the energy level substantially above the value given by

$$E_3 = -\, 13.6 \, \frac{Z^2}{3^2} \, \text{eV}$$

There are also important differences in the energy levels within a group of electrons with the same value of n, in contrast with our previous assumption: the electrons with large angular momenta are screened more effectively than those with small angular momenta. This can be understood qualitatively from the l-dependence of $V'(r)$, Eq. 21–5 and Fig. 21–1, which shows that the higher the l value, the farther away the electron is on the average from the nucleus. This same effect is seen classically in Fig. 18–4. The high-l electrons will therefore see a smaller effective nuclear charge, which raises their energy levels in relation to the low-l electrons with the same value of n. We can then display the energy level dependence for a typical many-electron atom as in Fig. 22–1, which may be compared with the corresponding level scheme (Fig. 21–6) for hydrogen. It is clear that this rearrangement of energy levels can lead to a different shell structure from the one we arrived at previously. It is conceivable, for instance, that the $n = 3, l = 2$ level is raised up to or above the $n = 4$, $l = 0$ level. Similarly, the $n = 4, l = 2$ level may be raised above the $n = 5, l = 0$ level; the $n = 4, l = 3$ and $n = 5, l \geq 2$ levels beyond the $n = 6, l = 0$ level; and so forth.

If this is the case, the first two shells would be unaltered, containing 2 and 8 electrons, respectively, therefore accounting for the noble gases $He(Z = 2)$ and $Ne(Z = 10)$. The third shell, however, would consist of the $n = 3, l = 0$ and $n = 3, l = 1$ sublevels, accommodating only $2 + 6 = 8$ electrons. This would explain why argon $(Z = 18)$ is a noble gas. The fourth shell would contain the $n = 3, l = 2$ and the $n = 4, l = 0$, and $l = 1$ sublevels with 10, 2, and 6 electrons, respectively, for a total of 18, which when added to the argon core of 18 electrons predicts a noble gas at $Z = 36$. Krypton $(Z = 36)$ is indeed a noble gas. A fifth shell would be made up of the $n = 5, l = 0$, and $l = 1$ and the $n = 4, l = 2$ levels, which like the fourth shell can accommodate 18 electrons. When the fifth shell is filled we are therefore up to $Z = 54$ or the noble gas xenon. The corresponding alkali metals with one electron outside the closed shells are $Li(Z = 3)$, $Na(Z = 11)$, $K(Z = 19)$, $Rb(Z = 37)$, and $Cs(Z = 55)$. The halogens with closed shells minus one electron are similarly $F(Z = 9)$, $Cl(Z = 17)$, $Br(Z = 35)$, and $I(Z = 53)$. With considerations of this kind we can understand the entire periodic table of the elements (Table 22–1)

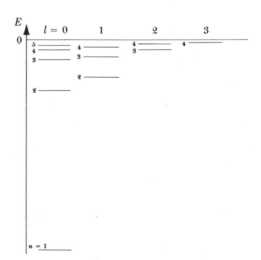

Fig. 22–1. *Allowed energy levels vs. angular momentum quantum numbers in a typical many-electron atom.*

in terms of the Pauli principle and the reordering of the hydrogen-like energy levels through partial screening of the nucleus by the electrons in the inner shells.

22–5   THE PERIODIC TABLE

It is clear that if we could designate the n, l, m, and m_s values of each electron in the atom, the electron state would be completely specified. We have seen, however, that the m and m_s quantum numbers do not affect the energy levels (ignoring small magnetic effects to be discussed later). For that reason it is conventional to describe the *electron configuration* by counting how many electrons occupy each energy level corresponding to the various possible combinations of the n and l quantum numbers. It is furthermore conventional to express n in terms of its numerical value, but l in terms of letters of the alphabet, as has already been mentioned in connection with Fig. 18–5. The code is quite simple: the $l = 0$, 1, 2, 3, 4, 5 . . . levels are denoted by s, p, d, f, g, h . . . and so on, in alphabetical order beyond f. The historical origin of the first 4 letters will be understood when we discuss the optical spectra of atoms (Chapter 23).

The number of electrons with a common n and l combination is given by a superscript. Thus $1s^2$ indicates 2 electrons in the $n = 1$, $l = 0$ level (s-level) and so describes the configuration of helium, while $1s^2 2s^1$ describes the lithium ($Z = 3$) configuration with one electron in the $n = 2$, $l = 0$ level added to the helium shell. (Actually when there is only one electron with a given n and l, the superscript 1 is usually omitted.) The noble gas neon ($Z = 10$) has the ground state configuration $1s^2 2s^2 2p^6$, argon ($Z = 18$) $1s^2 2s^2 2p^6 3s^2 3p^6$, etc. The configurations of all the naturally occurring elements are listed in Table 22–2.

In filling the atomic shells to form the various elements, as in Table 22–2, the level $n + 1$, l is always higher than n, l, and is therefore filled afterward. Furthermore, as was explained in Section 22–4, the level n, $l + 1$ is always higher than n, l, because of the smaller penetration by the higher angular momentum electrons. These regularities, however, are not enough to specify the order in which the levels are filled in the presence of screening. A simple rule which does enable one to remember this order is the following: the level $n + 1$, $l - 1$ is filled immediately after the level n, l. For example, this rule gives the sequence (Table 22–2) $3d$, $4p$, $5s$ going from Sc($Z = 21$) to Sr($Z = 38$). After $5s$ ($l = 0$) the rule cannot be applied, because there is no $l = -1$ level. We then begin again with the lowest n level still empty—in this case $4d$ since there is no $3f$ level. The next sequence is $4d$, $5p$, $6s$. We are again stopped and begin again with $4f$, getting $4f$, $5d$, $6p$, $7s$. The next sequence begins with $5f$ since there is no $4g$. Although this rule is useful if one wants to be able to construct the general form of the periodic table from memory, it has no very deep significance.

In particular, there are minor deviations from the general order specified by the rule. These discrepancies arise because the ordering of the energy levels is to some extent a function of how many electrons occupy them. Thus $Ca(Z = 20)$ has the $4s$ level below the (empty) $3d$ level, while for $Zn(Z = 30)$ with a full $3d$ level the order is reversed. (See Table 22–2.) This effect accounts for the monovalent metals Cu, Ag, Au in group IB of the periodic table and for the divalent metals Zn, Cd, Hg in group IIB. In Cu the $4s$ and $3d$ levels are close enough that Cu sometimes exhibits a valence of 2 instead of 1. Other less prominent anomalies of a similar kind occur at Cr, Nb, and Pt. The rule is temporarily violated at La $(Z = 57)$, where one electron goes into $5d$ before the $4f$ shell is filled, forming the rare earths; a similar violation occurs at Ac, where 1 electron goes into $6d$ before $5f$ is filled. The order of filling always returns to normal, however, when a p-shell is filled to form a noble gas.

22–6 THE QUANTUM NUMBERS OF THE ELECTRON STATE

We have specified the electron configuration of many-electron atoms in terms of the occupation numbers for the various n, l energy levels; and by means of this configuration we have been able to understand the principal features of the periodic table. It is not really possible to go further and specify the values of m and m_s for each individual electron, because the one-electron states are not strictly eigenfunctions of the Hamiltonian operator when the electron-electron interactions (screening) are taken into account. Nevertheless something further can be said about the angular momentum of the electrons, in order to specify the state of the atom more precisely. This specification has meaning only because it gives rise to observable effects, which become apparent mainly in the optical spectra of the atoms (Chapter 23).

The empirical justification for specifying further quantum numbers stems from the observation that the n, l energy levels are themselves split into relatively closely spaced sublevels, and transitions between them produce the spectral lines to be described in the next chapter. The energy differences, or level splitting, occur because a rotating electric charge produces a magnetic dipole moment, like a current loop. This magnetic dipole can interact with an applied magnetic field, as has already been mentioned. In addition, the magnetic dipole associated with the orbital angular momentum can interact with the magnetic dipole associated with the electron spin. These two effects can split the electron configuration into sublevels which are manifested by fine structure in the optical spectra. Although the electron configuration defined by n and l determines the gross features of optical spectra and the chemical periodic table, the fine details of spectra depend on magnetic effects associated with the electron angular momentum. Since it is not realistic to try to specify values of m and m_s for each electron, we must seek other ways in which the angular momentum of the electrons in an atom can be described. The purpose of this section is to present some exact and some approximate ways of describing the angular momentum.

Knowing the l and s quantum numbers of each electron does not, of course, tell us how the individual orbital angular momentum vectors and spin vectors add up to give a *total angular momentum* of the system as a whole. We can, however, define a total angular momentum operator $\mathbf{J}$ for the system of Z electrons by

$$\mathbf{J} \equiv \sum_{i=1}^{Z} (\mathbf{L}_i + \mathbf{S}_i) \qquad (22\text{-}5)$$

where $\mathbf{L}_i$ and $\mathbf{S}_i$ represent the orbital angular momentum operator and spin operator of the ith electron. It is possible to show rigorously that an isolated system of particles will always have a wave function ψ which is an eigenfunction of $\mathbf{J}^2$. This quantum mechanical result is analogous to the classical conservation of total angular momentum for a system of particles (Eq. 3–30). The total angular momentum is therefore an important physical quantity. It is quantized in the usual way (cf. Eqs. 20–29 and 22–4) for an angular momentum,

$$\mathbf{J}^2\psi = J(J + 1)\hbar^2\psi \qquad (22\text{-}6)$$

where J is an integer 0, 1, 2, etc., for an even number of electrons; and a half-integer $\frac{1}{2}$, $\frac{3}{2}$, etc., for an odd number of electrons. If J is known we have some information on how the individual angular momenta add up, but even with the vector sum given, there are many different ways in which the individual vectors can combine to yield this resultant vector.

One possibility is that the orbital angular momentum and the spin of each individual electron add up to a definite value, in the sense that the wave function ψ of the system is an eigenfunction of each operator $\mathbf{J}_i$, defined by •

$$\mathbf{J}_i \equiv \mathbf{S}_i + \mathbf{L}_i \qquad (22\text{-}7)$$

That is,

$$\mathbf{J}_i^2\psi = j(j + 1)\hbar^2\psi \qquad j = \frac{1}{2}, \frac{3}{2}, \frac{5}{2}, \ldots \qquad (22\text{-}8)$$

These angular momenta would in turn combine to form the total angular momentum of the whole system, $\mathbf{J} = \Sigma\, \mathbf{J}_i$. This possibility is referred to as *j–j coupling*.

Another possibility is that all the individual spins add up to a definite total spin such that

$$\mathbf{S}^2\psi = S(S + 1)\hbar^2\psi \qquad (22\text{-}9)$$

where $S = 0, 1, 2, 3, \ldots$ for Z even and $S = \frac{1}{2}, \frac{3}{2}, \frac{5}{2}, \ldots$ for Z odd, and where

$$\mathbf{S} \equiv \sum_{i=1}^{Z} \mathbf{S}_i \qquad (22\text{-}10)$$

Furthermore, all the individual orbital momenta simultaneously add up to a definite value for the system as a whole,

$$L^2\psi = L(L+1)\hbar^2\psi \qquad (22\text{--}11)$$

where $L = 0, 1, 2,, \ldots$ and

$$\mathbf{L} \equiv \sum_{i=1}^{Z} \mathbf{L}_i \qquad (22\text{--}12)$$

Then finally **L** and **S** add up to the total angular momentum vector (operator), $\mathbf{J} = \mathbf{L} + \mathbf{S}$. This possibility is known as $L\text{--}S$ *coupling* or Russell-Saunders coupling.

The combination of angular momenta in quantum mechanics is a very difficult subject and involves a rather complicated operator algebra. The difficulty stems in part from the fact that, although the magnitude $|\mathbf{L}|$ of an angular momentum vector is $[l(l+1)]^{1/2}\hbar$ (Eq. 20–29 and Fig. 20–10), the maximum value of any component of **L** (say $\mathbf{L}_z$) is $l\hbar$. A simpler model, called the *vector model*, in which angular momenta are treated as ordinary vectors, is often helpful in visualizing the real quantum mechanical situation. In this model the length of an angular momentum vector $|\mathbf{L}|$ is taken to be $l\hbar$ rather than $[l(l+1)]^{1/2}\hbar$, and similarly for J and S. If used with caution the vector model can often lead very simply to the correct quantum mechanical results. Within this model $j\text{--}j$ coupling may be illustrated as in Fig. 22–2, where $\mathbf{L}_1$ and $\mathbf{S}_1$ add up to $\mathbf{j}_1$, etc., and where the $\mathbf{j}_i$'s add up to the total **J**. In Fig. 22–3 an $L\text{--}S$ coupling scheme is sketched, with $\mathbf{L} = \mathbf{L}_1 + \mathbf{L}_2 + \mathbf{L}_3$, $\mathbf{S} = \mathbf{S}_1 + \mathbf{S}_2 + \mathbf{S}_3$, and $\mathbf{J} = \mathbf{L} + \mathbf{S}$. The $j\text{--}j$ coupling and $L\text{--}S$ coupling schemes are quite distinct ways of adding up the vector angular momenta, which lead to different results. Which of the two ways is the best approximation to the truth depends on the details of the interactions between the particles; usually the choice between them is made empirically, by comparing their predictions with experiment.

In using the vector model it is essential to obey the following rule (which can be derived from the quantum mechanical theory of angular momentum operators). When any two angular momentum vectors are

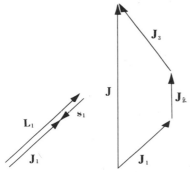

Fig. 22–2. j–j *coupling.*

added together they may be parallel, in which case the magnitude of the sum is the sum of their magnitudes; or they may be antiparallel, when the magnitude of the sum is the difference of their magnitudes. The only other possibilities for the vector sum are the values in between these two extreme values which differ from them by an integral multiple of $\hbar$. Thus for example in j–j coupling, if $l = 1$, j could be either $3/2$ or $1/2$, since s is always equal to $1/2$; likewise if $l = 2$, then j could be $5/2$ or $3/2$. In L–S coupling, if $l_1 = 2$ and $l_2 = 3$, then L could be 5, 4, 3, 2, or 1; if l_1 and l_2 are both 1, the possibilities for L are 2, 1, or 0. With two spins, the only possibilities for S are 1 (parallel) or 0 (antiparallel), because s_1 and s_2 are always $1/2$. Then if for example $L = 2$ and $S = 1$, the value of J could be 3, 2, or 1. The rule of vector addition makes it clear that in general, with L and S given, J cannot exceed the maximum value $L + S$ or be less than $|L - S|$. (See Fig. 22–4.) It can also assume any intermediate value which differs from the extremes by an integer. In explaining the rules for combining angular momenta we have used the vector model in order to make the operations more graphic. The rules could also be interpreted simply as laws for combining *quantum numbers*, and that is how they are derived in the actual quantum mechanical theory. It is because we are really dealing with quantum numbers that the restriction of the sums to integral or half-integral values arises.

In general the wave function ψ of the system is not an *exact* eigenfunction of either L^2, S^2, or the individual J_i^2, although it is always an eigenfunction of the total J^2. Even if the j–j coupling or the L–S coupling is only approximately valid, however, it may still be of great utility in classifying the quantum mechanical state of a many-electron system. Actually the L–S coupling is prevalent in most atomic systems (especially systems with low Z); i.e., we can view the total orbital angular momentum and the total spin as being separately quantized. Their respective quantum numbers L and S as well as J can be deduced from the atomic spectrum (Chapter 23). These quantum numbers furnish a great deal of information about *the system as a whole*, which is often of more interest than the knowledge of the l values of the individual electrons.

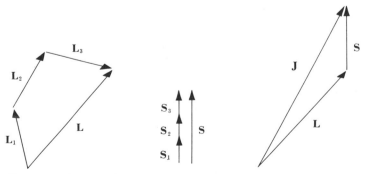

Fig. 22–3. L–S coupling.

Whenever possible one likes to specify the state of an atomic system by giving the electron configuration (n and l of each electron) as well as the L, S, and J values (assuming L–S coupling). We denote the L values by the same code used for the individual l's, but capitalize the letters. Thus, the $L = 0, 1, 2, 3, 4$, and 5 states are respectively labeled S, P, D, F, G, and H states. The total spin quantum number S is given in terms of its "multiplicity," $2S + 1$, which indicates how many different eigenvalues m_s one of its components, say S_z, can take on. The "multiplicity" is written as a superscript on the left-hand side of the letter denoting the L value, while J is written as a subscript on the right-hand side. The symbol $^2P_{1/2}$ for example indicates a "doublet P one-half" state, with $2S + 1 = 2$ (or $S = \frac{1}{2}$), $L = 1$, and $J = \frac{1}{2}$. Similarly $^3D_2$ denotes a "triplet D two" state with $S = 1$, $L = 2$, and $J = 2$. These designations of the L, S, and J values are often called "term symbols." The electron configurations as well as the term symbols for the ground states and the ionization potentials of all the elements are given in Table 22–2.

Determining the L, S, and J values for a heavy (large Z) element might at first seem to be a hopeless task. Fortunately, however, the lowest energy values of a system always correspond to rather small angular momenta. Thus every atom consisting entirely of closed shells, i.e., the noble gases He, Ne, A, Kr, Xe, and Rn; and also others with closed subshells such as the alkaline earths Be, Mg, Ca, Sr, Ba, and Ra with two s-electrons outside a noble gas core; as well as Zn, Pd, Cd, Yb, and Hg, all have a spherically symmetric electron configuration with $L = 0$ and pairs of individual spins canceling each other for no total spin, $S = 0$. With J then necessarily zero, all of these atoms are in an $^1S_0$ state. The alkali metals have noble gas cores with $L_{core} = 0$ and $S_{core} = 0$ plus a single electron outside with $l = 0$ and $s = \frac{1}{2}$ for a total $L = 0$, $S = \frac{1}{2}$, and hence $J = \frac{1}{2}$. The term symbol for all the alkali metals in the ground state is therefore $^2S_{1/2}$. The largest known ground state values of S, L, and J for atomic systems are $S = 4$, $L = 8$, and $J = 17\frac{1}{2}$, respectively (not for the same atom). One never gets up to higher values, because with each closed subshell one essentially starts over again from $S = L = J = 0$.

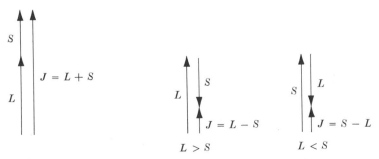

Fig. 22–4. Maximum J = L + S, minimum J = |L − S|.

TABLE 22–1   The Periodic Table of the Elements

H							He										
Li	Be	B	C	N	O	F	Ne										
Na	Mg	Al	Si	P	S	Cl	A										
K	Ca							Sc	Ti	V	Cr	Mn	Fe	Co	Ni	Cu	Zn
		Ga	Ge	As	Se	Br	Kr										
Rb	Sr							Y	Zr	Nb	Mo	Tc	Ru	Rh	Pd	Ag	Cd
		In	Sn	Sb	Te	I	Xe										
Cs	Ba						La										
	Ce	Pr	Nd	Pm	Sm	Eu	Gd	Tb	Dy	Ho	Er	Tm	Yb	Lu			
								Hf	Ta	W	Re	Os	Ir	Pt	Au	Hg	
		Tl	Pb	Bi	Po	At	Rn										
Fr	Ra						Ac										
	Th	Pa	U	Np	Pu	Am	Cm	Bk	Cf	E	Fm	Mv	No	Lw			

TABLE 22–2   Electron Configuration and Ionization Potentials

Element	Atomic number Z	First ionization potential in volts	Configuration										Ground state term
			$1s$	$2s$	$2p$	$3s$	$3p$	$3d$	$4s$	$4p$	$4d$	$4f$	
H	1	13.595	1										$^2S_{1/2}$
He	2	24.580	2										$^1S_0$
Li	3	5.390	2	1									$^2S_{1/2}$
Be	4	9.320	2	2									$^1S_0$
B	5	8.296	2	2	1								$^2P_{1/2}$
C	6	11.264	2	2	2								$^3P_0$
N	7	14.54	2	2	3								$^4S_{3/2}$
O	8	13.614	2	2	4								$^3P_2$
F	9	17.418	2	2	5								$^2P_{3/2}$
Ne	10	21.559	2	2	6								$^1S_0$
Na	11	5.138				1							$^2S_{1/2}$
Mg	12	7.644		Neon		2							$^1S_0$
Al	13	5.984		configuration		2	1						$^2P_{1/2}$
Si	14	8.149				2	2						$^3P_0$
P	15	10.55				2	3						$^4S_{3/2}$
S	16	10.357		10 electron		2	4						$^3P_2$
Cl	17	13.01		core		2	5						$^2P_{3/2}$
A	18	15.755				2	6						$^1S_0$

TABLE 22-2   Electron Configuration and Ionization Potentials—Continued

Element	Atomic number Z	First ionization potential in volts	4d	4f	5s	5p	5d	5f	5g	6s	6p	6d	6f	6g	6h	Ground state term
K	19	4.339								1						$^2S_{1/2}$
Ca	20	6.111								2						$^1S_0$
Sc	21	6.538							1	2						$^2D_{3/2}$
Ti	22	6.818							2	2						$^3F_2$
V	23	6.743							3	2						$^4F_{3/2}$
Cr	24	6.763							5	1						$^7S_3$
Mn	25	7.432			Argon				5	2						$^6S_{5/2}$
Fe	26	7.90			configuration				6	2						$^5D_4$
Co	27	7.862							7	2						$^4F_{9/2}$
Ni	28	7.633							8	2						$^3F_4$
Cu	29	7.724			18 electron				10	1						$^2S_{1/2}$
Zn	30	9.391			core				10	2						$^1S_0$
Ga	31	6.00							10	2	1					$^2P_{1/2}$
Ge	32	7.88							10	2	2					$^3P_0$
As	33	9.81							10	2	3					$^4S_{3/2}$
Se	34	9.75							10	2	4					$^3P_2$
Br	35	11.84							10	2	5					$^2P_{3/2}$
Kr	36	13.996							10	2	6					$^1S_0$
Rb	37	4.176			1											$^2S_{1/2}$
Sr	38	5.692			2											$^1S_0$
Y	39	6.5	1	Krypton	2											$^2D_{3/2}$
Zr	40	6.95	2	configuration	2											$^3F_2$
Nb	41	6.77	4		1											$^6D_{1/2}$
Mo	42	7.10	5		1											$^7S_3$
Tc	43	7.28	6	36 electron	1											$^6S_{5/2}$
Ru	44	7.364	7	core	1											$^5F_5$
Rh	45	7.46	8		1											$^4F_{9/2}$
Pd	46	8.33	10													$^1S_0$
Ag	47	7.574			1											$^2S_{1/2}$
Cd	48	8.991	Palladium		2											$^1S_0$
In	49	5.785	configuration		2	1										$^2P_{1/2}$
Sn	50	7.342			2	2										$^3P_0$
Sb	51	8.639			2	3										$^4S_{3/2}$
Te	52	9.01	46 electron		2	4										$^3P_2$
I	53	10.454	core		2	5										$^2P_{3/2}$
Xe	54	12.127			2	6										$^1S_0$

TABLE 22–2   Electron Configuration and Ionization Potentials—Continued

Element	Atomic number Z	First ionization potential in volts	Configuration (core shells)	4f	5s	5p	5d	5f	5g	6s	6p	6d	6f	6g	6h	7s	7p	Ground state term
Cs	55	3.893	Xenon configuration							1								$^2S_{1/2}$
Ba	56	5.210	54 electron core							2								$^1S_0$
La	57	5.61			2	6	1			2								$^2D_{3/2}$
Ce	58	6.91		1	2	6	1			2								$^3H_4$
Pr	59	5.76		2	2	6	1			2								$^4I_{9/2}$
Nd	60	6.31		3	2	6	1			2								$^5I_4$
Pm	61	—		4	2	6	1			2								$^6H_{5/2}$
Sm	62	5.6		5	2	6	1			2								$^7F_0$
Eu	63	5.67	Shells	6	2	6	1			2								$^8S_{7/2}$
Gd	64	6.16	1s to 4d	7	2	6	1			2								$^9D_2$
Tb	65	6.74	contain	8	2	6	1			2								$^6H_{15/2}$
Dy	66	6.82	46 electrons	9	2	6	1			2								$^5I_8$
Ho	67	—		10	2	6	1			2								$^4I_{15/2}$
Er	68	—		11	2	6	1			2								$^3H_6$
Tm	69	—		13	2	6	0			2								$^2F_{7/2}$
Yb	70	6.2		14	2	6	0			2								$^1S_0$
Lu	71	5.0		14	2	6	1			2								$^3D_{5/2}$
Hf	72	7					2			2								$^3F_2$
Ta	73	7.88					3			2								$^4F_{3/2}$
W	74	7.98	Shells				4			2								$^5D_0$
Re	75	7.87	1s to 5p				5			2								$^6S_{5/2}$
Os	76	8.7	contain				6			2								$^5D_4$
Ir	77	9	68 electrons				7			2								$^4F_{9/2}$
Pt	78	9.0					9			1								$^3D_3$
Au	79	9.22					10			1								$^2S_{1/2}$
Hg	80	10.43								2								$^1S_0$
Tl	81	6.106								2	1							$^2P_{1/2}$
Pb	82	7.415	Shells							2	2							$^3P_0$
Bi	83	7.287	1s to 5d							2	3							$^4S_{3/2}$
Po	84	8.43	contain							2	4							$^3P_2$
At	85	9.5	78 electrons							2	5							$^2P_{3/2}$
Rn	86	10.746								2	6							$^1S_0$
Fr	87	4.0	Radon configuration													1		$^2S_{1/2}$
Ra	88	5.277	86 electron core													2		$^1S_0$

TABLE 22–2   Electron Configuration and Ionization Potentials—Continued

Element	Atomic number Z	First ionization potential in volts	5s	5p	5d	5f	5g	6s	6p	6d	6f	6g	6h	7s	7p	Ground state term
Ac	89							2	6	1				2		$^2D_{3/2}$
Th	90					1		2	6	1				2		$^3F_2$
Pa	91					2		2	6	1				2		$^4K_{11/2}$
U	92	4				3		2	6	1				2		$^5L_6$
Np	93				Shells	4		2	6	1				2		$^6L_{11/2}$
Pu	94				1s to 5d	5		2	6	1				2		$^7F_0$
Am	95				contain	6		2	6	1				2		$^8S_{7/2}$
Cm	96				78 electrons	7		2	6	1				2		$^9D_2$
Bk	97					8		2	6	1				2		$^8H_{17/2}$
Cf	98					9		2	6	1				2		$^5I_8$

The ionization potentials are obtained from *Circular 467*, "Atomic Energy Levels," National Bureau of Standards.

PROBLEMS

22–1. What does it mean to say that an electron configuration is

$$1s^2 2s^2 2p^6 3s^2?$$

What atom has this configuration?

22–2. Give the S, L, and J values for the terms $^1S_0$, $^2S_{1/2}$, $^1P_1$, $^3P_2$, $^3F_4$, $^5D_1$, $^1D_2$, $^6F_{9/2}$.

22–3. Give all the possible terms (L–S coupling) with the configurations:

(a) $2p3p$
(b) $4d5p$

22–4. Repeat Prob. 22–3 for the configuration $3s3p4p$.

22–5. Consider a three-electron system in the one-electron approximation. Write the three-electron wave function in terms of one-electron wave functions in such a way that the wave function is anti-symmetric under the interchange of any two electrons.

22–6. With $L = 3$ and $S = 1$, what are the possible term symbols?

22–7. With $L = 2$ and $S = 4$, what are the possible term symbols?

22–8. Copy Fig. 22–1 and draw little circles to represent the electrons in the various levels. Number the electrons in the order in which they are added (Table 22–2). Do this up through the krypton configuration.

22–9.   Two electrons have orbital angular momenta equal to $l_1 = 1$ and $l_2 = 3$. What are the possible values of L? of S? For each L, S combination find the possible values of J.

22–10.   Two electrons have $l_1 = 1$ and $l_2 = 3$, respectively. Assume j–j coupling. What are the possible values of j_1 and j_2? For each j_1, j_2 combination find the possible values of J. Compare the last result with Prob. 22–9.

REFERENCES

F. K. Richtmyer, E. H. Kennard, and T. Lauritsen, *Introduction to Modern Physics* (McGraw-Hill, 1955, 5th ed.), Ch. 7.

R. B. Leighton, *Principles of Modern Physics* (McGraw-Hill, 1959), Ch. 7.

M. Born, *Atomic Physics* (Hafner, 1951, 5th ed.), Ch. 6.

W. Heitler, *Elementary Wave Mechanics* (Oxford, 1946), Ch. 5, 7.

G. Herzberg, *Atomic Spectra and Atomic Structure* (Dover, 1944), Ch. 3.

23/atomic spectra

As in the case of hydrogen atoms, a photon of energy $h\nu = E_2 - E_1$ is emitted from a many-electron atom when it undergoes a transition from a state of higher energy E_2 to one of lower energy E_1. Since the level scheme is much more complicated in a large Z atom than in hydrogen, a very confused spectrum results in general. Nevertheless it is possible to deduce a consistent energy level scheme which explains the bewildering array of lines that one observes. It is clear that the electrons in the outermost shells are the ones most easily excited, while the electrons in the tightly bound inner shells are much harder to perturb. Since the energy differences between the normally unoccupied higher energy levels correspond to photons in the visible and infrared range, while those between the closed shell levels fall in the ultraviolet and x-ray region, it is safe to say that the optical spectra are caused by transitions of the electrons normally in the outermost shell. We can, therefore, forget about the inner shells in our discussion of the optical spectra. This represents a considerable simplification, especially in treating the alkali spectra, which result from transitions involving only the single electron outside the noble gas core.

X-ray spectra result from electronic transitions of just the same kind, except that inner shell electrons are involved. That is, the energy of an inner shell electron increases or decreases with the simultaneous absorption or emission of a photon. Since the energy differences (photon energies) are large in the x-ray region, small magnetic effects are relatively unimportant. Some of the complexity of optical spectra is therefore absent in the main features of x-ray spectra. We shall begin our discussion with the optical spectra, and we must start with a description of the hitherto neglected magnetic effects, especially the so-called "spin-orbit" energy. The L–S coupling will be assumed to apply, so that it is meaningful to consider the total orbital angular momentum of all *the electrons and the total spin angular momentum of all the electrons. The vector sum of these two is the total electronic angular momentum of the atom, and we shall find that it influences the energy of the atom to some extent.*

23-1 THE SPIN-ORBIT SPLITTING

The spin-orbit energy means that the energy of the atom is affected by an interaction between the spin angular momentum S and the orbital angular momentum L. The interaction is relatively small in most cases, so that the energy levels are to a first approximation given by the electron configuration as previously assumed. But in the presence of the interaction, for a given L and S, the energy depends to some extent on how the vectors are added together—i.e., on the value of J. The reason for such an interaction is best seen intuitively by considering the classical Bohr model of the hydrogen atom.

An orbiting electric charge constitutes a current loop, and as such it produces a magnetic field like that of a magnetic dipole. This magnetic "dipole moment" interacts with another magnetic field in just the same way that a permanent magnet tends to align itself with an applied field. Thus the orbiting electron generates a *magnetic moment*, which is proportional to the orbital angular momentum L. Similarly, a spinning electric charge possesses an intrinsic magnetic moment μ, which is proportional to the intrinsic spin angular momentum S. That the magnetic moment associated with the electron spin should interact with the magnetic moment associated with the orbital motion can be seen by imagining oneself stationed on the electron and orbiting around the nucleus with it. From this point of view, one sees the charged nucleus orbiting around the electron, thus giving rise to a magnetic field at the position of the electron. It is this field with which the intrinsic spin magnetic moment μ of the electron interacts. The interaction depends on the relative directions of L and S, and therefore on $L \cdot S$.

Quantum mechanically, the analogous situation is described by saying that the L and S vector operators are not quite independent of each other as implied up to now. There is a magnetic field associated with the orbital motion of the electrons (proportional to L) which interacts with the magnetic dipole moment of the spinning electrons (proportional to S), resulting in a term of the form $L \cdot S$ in the expression for the total energy operator of the system. There is in addition a relativistic correction to the energy of the same $L \cdot S$ form, and so we may combine these two effects into a "spin-orbit" energy operator,

$$H_{LS} = \frac{A}{\hbar^2} L \cdot S \tag{23-1}$$

where A is a positive constant. For a given L and S several energy levels may be possible, an "LS multiplet," with the individual levels characterized by different eigenvalues of $L \cdot S$.

We may note first that it is consistent with the L–S coupling scheme to assume that the quantum numbers L and S have definite values given and that the energy levels should depend strongly on them. One of these levels may then be split into sublevels, the LS multiplet, depending on the relative orientation of **L** and **S**—i.e., on J. Second, we apparently have to deal with an entirely new operator in **L·S**, and we might expect that the calculation of its eigenvalues would be a formidable job. Actually, however, a little algebraic manipulation of operators which have already been considered will lead immediately to the eigenvalues of **L·S**.

Since

$$\mathbf{J}^2 = (\mathbf{L} + \mathbf{S})^2 = \mathbf{L}^2 + \mathbf{S}^2 + 2\mathbf{L}\cdot\mathbf{S}$$

it follows that

$$\mathbf{L}\cdot\mathbf{S} = \tfrac{1}{2}[\mathbf{J}^2 - \mathbf{L}^2 - \mathbf{S}^2]$$

With the wave function of the system an eigenfunction simultaneously of $\mathbf{J}^2$, $\mathbf{L}^2$, and $\mathbf{S}^2$ (L–S coupling), we see that it must also be an eigenfunction of **L·S**, with the eigenvalue (Eqs. 22–6, 22–9, and 22–11)

$$\tfrac{1}{2}\hbar^2[J(J + 1) - L(L + 1) - S(S + 1)]$$

As a result the spin-orbit energy is equal to

$$E_{LS} = \frac{A}{2}\,[J(J + 1) - L(L + 1) - S(S + 1)] \qquad (23\text{–}2)$$

For a given L and S the spin-orbit energy is a function of J only and the energy levels in the LS multiplet are consequently those characterized by the allowed values of J: $J = |L\text{–}S|, |L\text{–}S| + 1, \ldots, L + S$. For $S < L$ there will clearly be $2S + 1$ possible J values, and for $L < S$, $2L + 1$ possibilities. Since the constant A is small (especially for Z small) the energy levels in an LS multiplet are close together, whereas states of the system with different L quantum numbers can have very different energies, as can those of different total spins S. Transitions from one LS multiplet to another will therefore give rise to many spectral lines only slightly separated from one another. It was this *fine structure* in the spectra that led to the discovery of the electron spin.

23-2 ALKALI SPECTRA

The alkali atoms have an electron configuration consisting of $Z - 1$ electrons in inner closed shells and a single outer valence electron. The outer electron sees the nuclear charge Ze shielded by the spherically symmetric charge distribution of the $(Z - 1)$ closed shell electrons for a net charge of e, so that we would expect the energy levels and the spectra to resemble those of the hydrogen atom. This is especially true for the levels corresponding to large orbital angular momenta, in which case the outer electron wave function does not penetrate the closed shells appreciably.

For the low L values ($L = 0, 1$) the shielding is not nearly so complete and consequently the effective nuclear charge is larger than e.

Since the closed shells always have $L = 0$ and $S = 0$, the total spin of the alkali electrons is simply the spin of the single electron outside the noble gas core. Therefore S is equal to $\frac{1}{2}$, and the multiplicity of the LS multiplet is $2S + 1 = 2$ for all $L > \frac{1}{2}$, i.e., $L = 1, 2, 3, \ldots$; and $2L + 1 = 1$ for $L = 0$. With all but the $L = 0$ levels split in two by the spin-orbit coupling, we get an energy level scheme as shown for Na in Fig. 23–1(a). (The splitting of the doublets is much exaggerated there, in order to make it visible.) The hydrogen levels are shown in this figure for comparison. Note that as expected the high L value sodium levels agree best with those of hydrogen. For small L the energy is lowered, because of the enhanced attraction when the electron penetrates close to the nucleus.

The most probable electron transitions are those which change L by 1, $|\Delta L| = 1$, and which do not change S, $\Delta S = 0$. J may change by $+ 1$, 0, or $- 1$, but $J = 0$ to $J = 0$ transitions cannot occur. These are called *allowed* transitions. The *selection rules*, $|\Delta L| = 1$, $\Delta S = 0$, and $|\Delta J| = 0$ or 1, can be derived from the full quantum mechanical theory and have the effect of greatly limiting the number of observable spectral lines. When the angular momentum of the atom changes in a transition, the law of conservation of total angular momentum tells us that the emitted photon must itself carry angular momentum. An example of allowed transitions is the series labeled sharp, principal, diffuse, and fundamental in Fig. 23–1(a). The names go back to the early days of spectroscopy and their first letters S, P, D, and F were used to label the electron states prior to the transition, i.e., the $L = 0, 1, 2$, and 3 states, respectively. The most prominent lines in the sodium spectrum are the yellow lines in the first principal series doublet, which come from the transitions $3p\ ^2P_{1/2} \to 3s\ ^2S_{1/2}$ and $3p\ ^2P_{3/2} \to 3s\ ^2S_{1/2}$. The wave lengths are 5896 Å and 5890 Å, respectively.

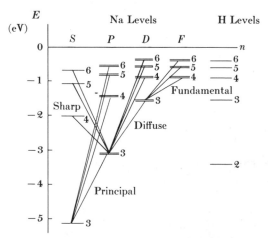

Fig. 23–1(a). The energy levels of the sodium atom.

We get two lines in the $3p$ to $3s$ transition because of the spin-orbit splitting. For the S-states, $E_{LS} = 0$, while for the $^2P_{1/2}$ state we have $J = \frac{1}{2}$, $L = 1$, and $S = \frac{1}{2}$, and by Eq. 23-2,

$$E_{LS} = A\frac{1}{2}[\frac{1}{2}(\frac{1}{2} + 1) - 1(1 + 1) - \frac{1}{2}(\frac{1}{2} + 1)] = -A$$

For the $^2P_{3/2}$ state we have $J = \frac{3}{2}$ and

$$E_{LS} = A\frac{1}{2}[\frac{3}{2}(\frac{3}{2} + 1) - 1(1 + 1) - \frac{1}{2}(\frac{1}{2} + 1)] = \frac{1}{2}A$$

The photons in the principal series doublets therefore differ in energy by $\frac{3}{2} A$. From the measured energy level difference we can clearly determine the value of the constant A.

The details of the more complicated spectra observed when there are several electrons in the outer shell are too involved to go into here. We will, however, briefly examine the spectrum resulting from 2 electrons outside a closed shell.

23-3 TWO-ELECTRON SPECTRA

With 2 electrons outside closed shells, the total spin can be either $S = 0$ (singlet) with the spins antiparallel or $S = 1$ (triplet) with the spins parallel. Since a transition changing S is improbable, we get two practically independent spectra, one resulting from transitions within the group of singlet ($S = 0$) states, the other from transitions among the triplet ($S = 1$) states. The former ($S = 0$) spectrum shows no spin-orbit splitting, since with $S = 0$ the L–S multiplicity is $2S + 1 = 1$.

As an example of a two-electron spectrum, we will consider the spectrum of zinc. Zinc has $Z = 30$. The first 28 electrons fill the $n = 1$, $n = 2$, and $n = 3$ shells. These closed shells have a total $S = 0$ and $L = 0$. We can therefore forget about them in the following discussion. The remaining 2 electrons are in the $n = 4$ level. In the ground state of zinc these two electrons are both in the $4s$ level (i.e., with $l_1 = 0$, $l_2 = 0$) and with their spins opposed to form an $S = 0$, $L = 0$ state ($^1S_0$ term). The full designation is $1s^2 2s^2 2p^6 3s^2 3p^6 3d^{10} 4s^2$ $^1S_0$, often abbreviated $4s^2$ $^1S_0$ (see Table 22-2).

The zinc atom can be excited by having one of the $4s$ electrons go into

Fig. 23-1(b). The emission spectrum of sodium. Wave lengths of lines in the principal series are shown. [Courtesy of G. Herzberg, Atomic Spectra and Atomic Structure *(Dover, New York, 1944).]*

a higher energy level, say the $4p(L = 1)$ or $5s(L = 0)$ levels. The radiations emitted in the allowed transitions,

$$4s5s\ ^3S_1 \rightarrow 4s4p\ ^3P_0$$
$$\rightarrow 4s4p\ ^3P_1$$
$$\rightarrow 4s4p\ ^3P_2$$

all fall in the visible region (in fact between 4000 and 5000 Å) and are therefore a prominent feature of the zinc spectrum. The three transitions are all from an $L = 0$, $S = 1$ to an $L = 1$, $S = 1$ state. (The $^3S_1$ level has no spin-orbit splitting since $E_{LS} = 0$ with $L = 0$.) In the absence of the spin-orbit interaction the 3 lines would therefore coincide. Since $L = 1$ and $S = 1$, J can take on the values $0(^3P_0)$, $1(^3P_1)$, or $2(^3P_2)$. With the spin-orbit energy given by Eq. 23–2,

$$E_{LS} = A\tfrac{1}{2}[J(J + 1) - L(L + 1) - S(S + 1)]$$
$$= A\tfrac{1}{2}[J(J + 1) - 4]$$

we have

$$E_{LS} = A(-2) \text{ for } J = 0$$
$$= A(-1) \text{ for } J = 1$$
$$= A(+1) \text{ for } J = 2$$

The level separation should therefore be in the ratio of 2:1, as in Fig. 23–2. Experimentally the ratio is 2.05:1, which indicates that the L–S coupling is only approximately valid.

Calcium also has two electrons outside closed shells (Fig. 23–3(a)). In deducing the optical spectrum to be expected from this diagram, you should bear in mind that all the strong lines arise from electronic transitions which do not change S and which change L by 1 and J by 0 or 1.

As the atomic number Z of the element increases, two effects occur: first, the spin-orbit interaction becomes progressively stronger; and

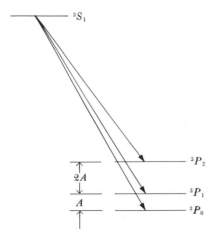

Fig. 23–2. $^3S \rightarrow {}^3P$ transitions.

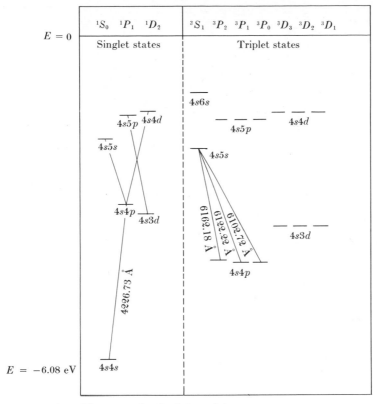

Fig. 23–3(a). The energy levels of the calcium atom.

second, the $L\text{–}S$ coupling assumption becomes a less valid approximation. Both of these effects are in evidence in Table 23–1, which shows the
wave lengths of some triplets derived from a transition $(n+1)\,^3S_1 \rightarrow n\,^3P_{0,1,2}$.
Although the levels are proportional to inverse wave lengths, it is immediately apparent from the wave lengths themselves that the separation increases with increasing Z. Furthermore the theoretical ratio of 2:1 (with
$L\text{–}S$ coupling) is a fairly good approximation for Ca and Zn, but for Hg it
is almost useless. For lighter elements the splitting is smaller. For Mg, we
could infer from the 6 Å splitting of the Na doublet that the lines of the

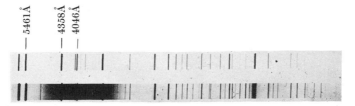

*Fig. 23–3(b). The emission spectrum of mercury. The three lines labeled with their
wave lengths constitute a prominent spin-orbit triplet. [Courtesy of G. Herzberg,* Atomic
Spectra and Atomic Structure *(Dover, New York, 1944).]*

TABLE 23-1

Element	Z	n	Wave lengths (Å)		
Ca	20	4	6103	6122	6162
Zn	30	4	4680	4722	4810
Hg	80	6	4046	4358	5461

triplet ought to be separated by a few Angstroms. In Be the splitting is a fraction of an Angstrom; and in He it is so small that for a long time the closer pair of the triplet could not be resolved, experimentally.

23-4   X-RAYS

In 1895 the German physicist Röntgen discovered a penetrating radiation, which he called x-rays, emanating from a high voltage, low density gas discharge tube. He found that the source of the radiation was that area of the glass wall struck by the "cathode rays" (electrons). We now understand that the high energy electrons from the cathode knocked electrons out of the normally filled inner shells of the atoms in the glass wall, and that the resulting electronic transitions in the atom gave rise to the x-ray photons observed by Röntgen. Since Röntgen's discovery predated Bohr's atomic theory by 18 years, however, he was unable to interpret the origin of x-rays in these terms.

The x-ray spectroscopists, like their colleagues working in the optical region, introduced their own distinctive notation for the spectral lines that they observed. This notation has survived and should therefore be learned. The observed spectral lines were grouped into series, the two most prominent of which were named the K-series and the L-series. The terms K-radiation and L-radiation were first introduced by the Swedish physicist Barkla (1908), but it was the British physicist Moseley (1913) who made the first systematic study of the frequencies of the K- and L-lines as a function of the atomic number Z of the element from which the x-rays were emitted. The K-radiation actually results when an electron falls from a less tightly bound shell into the innermost ($n = 1$) shell. The K-lines therefore correspond to the most energetic x-rays. Similarly the L-radiation is produced when an electron falls into the $n = 2$ shell. The K and L x-ray series are in other words respectively the Lyman and Balmer series of an atom with a large atomic number. To x-ray spectroscopists, the $n = 1$ shell is known as the K-shell, and the $n = 2$ shell as the L-shell. Successive shells are called the M-, N-, O-shells and so on in alphabetic order.

The diffraction of x-rays by crystals was discussed in Chapter 13. Working with a potassium ferrocyanide crystal spectrometer, Moseley found that the frequency of the K_α-line (an electron falling from the L-shell to the K-shell) as a function of Z was given by

$$h\nu_{K_\alpha} = 13.6 \text{ eV} \left(Z - 1 \right)^2 \left(\frac{1}{1^2} - \frac{1}{2^2} \right) \qquad (23\text{--}3)$$

With one electron removed from the K-shell, an L-shell electron sees the nucleus shielded by the single remaining K-shell electron for an effective nuclear charge of $(Z - 1)e$. With this effective charge it follows from Eq. 21–17 that the energy difference between an $n = 2$ and an $n = 1$ state should be precisely the K_α x-ray energy found by Moseley, Eq. 23–3.

To get an idea of the wave length involved, let us consider the K_α x-ray from molybdenum $(Z = 42)$. Molybdenum is one of the elements commonly used in practical x-ray tubes. From Eq. 23–3 we obtain

$$\lambda_{K_\alpha} = c/\nu_{K_\alpha} = \frac{4}{3} \frac{hc}{(42 - 1)^2 \times 13.6 \text{ eV} \times 1.6 \times 10^{-12} \text{ erg/eV}}$$
$$= 0.72 \times 10^{-8} \text{ cm}$$

or

$$\lambda_{K_\alpha} = 0.72 \text{ Å}$$

For elements about halfway up the periodic table we see that the K_α x-rays have wave lengths somewhat less than one Ångstrom. The K_β ($n = 3$ to $n = 1$ transition) and K_γ ($n = 4$ to $n = 1$ transition) x-rays will have higher energies and therefore wave lengths even shorter than the K_α-line.

The L-rays which result when one of the L-electrons has been removed, will of course be less energetic and have longer wave lengths than the K-rays. When an electron goes from the third shell (the M-shell) to the L-shell, it sees the nucleus screened by the 9 remaining electrons in the K- and L-shells. We would expect the effective nuclear charge to be $(Z - 9)e$ in this case. Actually the screening is only about 82 percent effective, so that the L_α x-ray energies are best given by

$$h\nu_{L_\alpha} = 13.6 \text{ eV} \left(Z - 7.4 \right)^2 \left(\frac{1}{2^2} - \frac{1}{3^2} \right) \qquad (23\text{--}4)$$

With 10 electrons in the K- and L-shells when full, this would predict an M-shell energy of about 13.6 eV $(Z - 8.2)^2 \, 1/3^2$.

Other series of x-ray lines with still smaller energies, or longer wave lengths, also occur. The M-series results when an electron is missing in the M-shell, the N-series is caused by a vacancy in the N-shell, and so forth. A simplified energy level diagram for a many-electron atom identifying the transitions giving rise to the several series of x-ray lines may be found in Fig. 23–4. It is clear that the most energetic series, the K-series, will in general be accompanied by the less energetic L-, M-, and N-series, since a K_α transition leads to a vacancy in the L-shell, which, if filled through an L_α transition, in turn leads to a vacancy in the M-shell, and so on down the line. In our discussion (and in Fig. 23–4) we have ignored the fact that the L-, M-, N-, and higher shells in turn consist of subshells. In an L-shell it makes some difference in the resulting L x-ray lines whether the missing electron was a $2s$ or a $2p$ electron. In addition there is the fine structure due

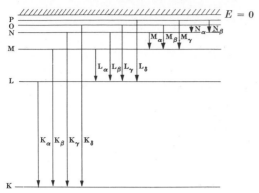

Fig. 23–4. The x-ray series.

to the spin-orbit interaction, discussed in Section 23–1. The main features of the discrete x-ray spectrum, however, may be understood in terms of the simplified picture given in Fig. 23–4.

23–5   X-RAY ABSORPTION

Perhaps the most important practical characteristic of x-rays is their ability to penetrate through macroscopic distances in optically opaque materials. This is the basis for their great utility in medicine, in industry, and in other important areas of human endeavor. Clearly, however, some absorption does take place. It is precisely the difference in the x-ray absorption in bone tissue versus soft tissue that is helpful in diagnosing a bone fracture.

The absorption of photons in matter was discussed in Section 17–3. We showed there that the intensity I of a beam of photons as a function of the distance x that the beam travels through an absorptive medium is given by Eq. 17–14,

$$I = I_0 e^{-\mu x}$$

The parameter μ, called the absorption coefficient, is very much a function of the kind of material used as well as of the wave length of the x-rays. X-ray absorption occurs primarily through the photoelectric emission of inner electrons. (See Fig. 17–7.) Pair production (Section 17–2) can only take place for energies above 1 MeV, whereas the x-ray region extends roughly from 1 to 100 keV. For low atomic numbers Compton scattering plays an important role, however. For Al, for example, Compton scattering is more important than the photoelectric absorption for x-rays of energies higher than about 50 keV.

The absorption coefficient μ can be measured by interposing varying thicknesses of the absorbing material between an incoming beam and a detector. The result of a typical experiment measuring μ as a function of the x-ray frequency ν is illustrated in Fig. 23–5. One finds, starting with

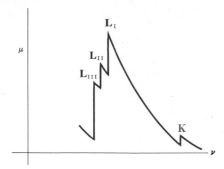

Fig. 23–5. The K and L x-ray absorption edges.

high frequency, that the absorption coefficient increases as the frequency decreases until one reaches the *K absorption edge*, marked K in Fig. 23–5. Here there is a sudden drop in μ. At this point the x-ray photons no longer have enough energy to knock an electron out of the K-shell; i.e., x-ray absorption through photoelectric emission of K-electrons ceases, and consequently μ drops. The residual absorption is due mainly to the photoelectric emission of L-electrons, which increases as ν is decreased further. The absorption coefficient increases until the frequency is reduced to the L absorption edge (really the L_I, L_{II}, and L_{III} absorption edges), at which point the L-electron photoelectric absorption also ceases, leading once again to an abrupt drop in μ. For still lower frequencies the x-ray absorption is due to the photoelectric emission of M-electrons. The fact that there are three absorption edges L_I, L_{II}, and L_{III} very close together, and in the expected frequency range of the L-series, shows that the L-shell really consists of three subshells. This is caused by the difference in the screening of the 2*s* versus 2*p* electrons and the spin-orbit splitting of the energy level of the latter.

The measured frequencies corresponding to the x-ray absorption edges give the binding energies of the tightly bound inner electrons in a many-electron atom. Such x-ray absorption measurements, along with the observed x-ray emission spectra, therefore yield valuable information about the electronic structure of atoms.

PROBLEMS

23–1.   In Fig. 23–1 write the electron configuration (the outer electron will do) and the term symbol corresponding to each of the levels.

23–2.   Comparing the Na and H levels in Fig. 23–1, we see that when the outer electron is in one of the $L \geq 2$ excited states, the effective nuclear charge is very close to $(Z - 10)e$ or e. Calculate the effective nuclear charge seen by the electron in its $3s\ ^2S_{1/2}$ ground state. (The ionization potential is given in Table 22–2.)

23–3.   Knowing the wave length of the $3p\ ^2P_{1/2} \rightarrow 3s\ ^2S_{1/2}$ transition in Na to be 5896 Å, calculate the effective nuclear charge seen by the outer electron in the $3p\ ^2P_{1/2}$ state. (See Prob. 23–2.)

23–4.   Why is there no $4s4s\ ^3S_1$ state in Fig. 23–3(a)?

23–5.   Copy Fig. 23–3(a) and draw in all the allowed transitions.

23–6.   Draw a ^3F and a ^3D multiplet with the correct relative spacings within each multiplet. Label each energy level with the appropriate J value. Indicate with arrows all the allowed $^3F \rightarrow {}^3D$ transitions.

23–7.   Repeat Prob. 23–6 for the $^4D \rightarrow {}^4P$ transitions and the $^4P \rightarrow {}^4S$ transitions.

23–8.   Look up the spectral lines of Mg in the *Handbook of Chemistry and Physics.* Try to find several triplets, and check how well the theoretical $2:1$ ratio (with L–S coupling) for the level separation holds, assuming that the transition is actually $^3S \rightarrow {}^3P$.

23–9.   Calculate the wave lengths of the K_α, K_β and the L_α, L_β x-rays from lead.

23–10.   What nucleus would have a K_α-line of roughly the same wave length as the L_α-line from lead?

23–11.   The K absorption edge of a well-known metal is found to be at a wave length of 1.377 Å. Calculate the K energy level. What metal is it? Estimate the wave length of the K_α-line and the approximate location of the L absorption edges.

REFERENCES

G. Herzberg, *Atomic Spectra and Atomic Structure* (Dover, 1944), Ch. 1, 2.

H. E. White, *Introduction to Atomic Spectra* (McGraw-Hill, 1934), Ch. 12, 14.

R. C. Johnson, *Atomic Spectra* (Methuen, 1950, 2nd ed.).

F. K. Richtmyer, E. H. Kennard, and T. Lauritsen, *Introduction to Modern Physics* (McGraw-Hill, 1955, 5th ed.), Ch. 7, 8.

R. B. Leighton, *Principles of Modern Physics* (McGraw-Hill, 1959), Ch. 8, 12.

G. L. Clark, *Applied X-Rays* (McGraw-Hill, 1955, 4th ed.).

A. H. Compton and S. K. Allison, *X-Rays in Theory and Experiment* (Van Nostrand, 1935, 2nd ed.).

24/molecular binding

Quantum mechanics has had a spectacular success in explaining the structure of isolated atoms. It leads to precise agreement with experimental measurements in the simplest cases; and even in complicated atoms, where mathematical difficulties obstruct exact solutions, suitable approximations furnish a qualitative understanding and the basis for numerical calculations. We now wish to extend this analysis to still more complex problems, involving aggregates of atoms in molecules and solids, which underlie the fields of chemistry, solid state physics, and materials science. Such aggregations of atoms are the forms in which one usually encounters matter in everyday life, and consequently they are of immense technological importance. This problem has already been approached in Chapter 14 by assuming that the atoms were entities which interacted with each other through certain hypothetical force laws. The present approach is more fundamental, in that one assumes a collection of nuclei and electrons, and tries to calculate the electron wave functions and energy levels in the field of all the nuclei. Rather than displacing the previous approach, however, this calculation supplements it (even justifies it), and may indeed be interpreted as the fundamental theoretical explanation of those interatomic force laws which previously were introduced in a semi-empirical way. Basically, the reason why the atoms usually retain their identity even in this more fundamental description is that most of the electrons are bound in the atom (except for the lightest atoms) with energies of thousands of electron volts (Section 23–4), whereas the binding energies of molecules and solids are only of the order of a few electron volts. Thus most of the electrons may still be regarded as tightly bound to a single nucleus, constituting an atom or ion, and only the outer, most loosely bound electrons will suffer serious modification of their wave functions when the atoms are brought close together. It is just this modification which may lead to a lower total energy, and hence binding, when the nuclei (or ions) are in close proximity.

24–1   THE H_2^+ MOLECULAR ION

When more than one nucleus is present, we have to consider the motion of electrons in a *multi-center force field*, in contrast to the single center force field of an isolated atom with only one nucleus. It will be expedient in this problem to use the same strategy as for the treatment of atoms—namely to begin with the simplest conceivable case (in that instance, the hydrogen atom), and then to proceed to more complicated cases involving many electrons. The simplest case may again be chosen to involve only a single electron, and this problem turns out to admit an exact analytic solution. Having calculated the *one-electron energy states*, the desired many-electron problem can be approached in a first order approximation by simply loading the required number of electrons into the already calculated one-electron states. In doing so, the Pauli principle will again be seen to have an overwhelming role in the first order approximation. A second order, although still very important, effect is the electrostatic repulsion between the several electrons. With these considerations, we shall find that the most important properties of materials can be understood, at least in a qualitative way. It should be obvious that with 10 atoms in a molecule or 10^{23} atoms in a solid, a precise quantitative calculation will demand great cleverness in making approximations or very powerful methods of numerical computation, or usually both. As the capability of computing machinery develops, the exploitation of the latter approach is destined to increase.

The simplest possible molecular system is the singly ionized hydrogen molecule, i.e., the hydrogen molecular ion H_2^+. The hydrogen molecule H_2 which has lost one of its electrons consists of a single electron moving in the electrostatic field of two protons (Fig. 24–1). Since the protons are very much heavier than the electron, they will move much more slowly; therefore as a first approximation we may assume that the two protons are at rest and discuss the motion of the electron around them, just as we did for the H atom. We shall assume that the protons are separated by a distance R and try to estimate the energy of the electron in the field of the protons which are fixed at this distance. Then afterward R may be treated as a variable parameter, and we can describe the energy of the whole system as a function of the separation R of the two nuclei. This energy will turn out to have a minimum at a certain value of R, so that the nuclei may be *bound*, with this equilibrium separation. The discussion of the electron energy states can thus predict the binding of the whole system.

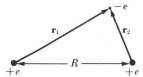

Fig. 24–1. Model of the H_2^+ molecular ion.

The problem of a particle which is attracted to two force centers by an inverse square law force, like that of a single force center, can be solved exactly if the equations are expressed in a suitable coordinate system (for a single force center, spherical coordinates; for two force centers, "spheroidal" coordinates). Both the classical equations of motion and the quantum mechanical Schrödinger equation can be solved in this way, but the solutions are more complicated than for the hydrogen atom. All the essential features of the solution can be found, however, by an approximate consideration of the electron wave function. The exact Schrödinger equation for the electron (excluding, for the time being, the mutual repulsive energy of the two fixed nuclei) is

$$\left[-\frac{\hbar^2}{2m} \nabla^2 - \frac{e^2}{r_1} - \frac{e^2}{r_2} \right]\psi = E\psi \qquad (24\text{--}1)$$

where r_1 and r_2 are the distances of the electron from the two nuclei (Fig. 24–1).

When R is very large, near nucleus 1 the term e^2/r_2 is negligible, and so in this vicinity the wave function will look just like the H atom wave function; conversely, near nucleus 2 the term e^2/r_1 is negligible, and there also the wave function is the same as for the H atom (Fig. 24–2(a)). The only difference is in the normalization constant, since the probability is $\frac{1}{2}$ to be near either nucleus. This situation really corresponds to having one H atom and one H$^+$ ion, separated from each other, without specifying which is the atom and which the ion. On the other hand, if R were zero, the problem would be just the same as the He$^+$ ion problem (nuclear charge $+2e$), with its corresponding wave function (Fig. 24–2(c)). At close but not zero distance, we can at least imagine approximately what the wave function looks

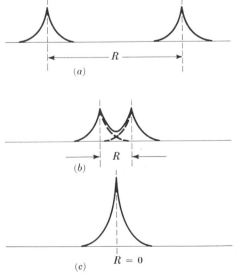

(a)

(b)

(c) $R = 0$

Fig. 24–2. Ground state wave function for $H_2{}^+$.

like, by adding together the two H atom wave functions (Fig. 24–2(b)). These cases are illustrated here for *the ground state.*

Now the *electron energy levels* can also be obtained by the same argument —exactly in the two extreme cases of R large or zero, and approximately in the intermediate cases. For R large, the energy is just the H atom energy, Eq. 21–17,

$$E = -\,e^2/2a_0 = -\,13.6 \text{ eV}$$

in the ground state. (Although the electron wave function is distributed over both nuclei, the electron will always be *observed* near one nucleus or the other, never halfway in between. Thus, the measured energy is just that of the H atom when the other nucleus is far away.) For $R = 0$, it is the He+ ion energy, which with $Z = 2$ is 4 times larger,

$$E = -\,2e^2/a_0 = -\,54.4 \text{ eV}$$

in the ground state. The transition between these values, as a function of R, will occur mainly when the two H atom wave functions begin to overlap appreciably, that is, at a distance of the order of a_0 in the ground state. This energy is shown as a dashed line in Fig. 24–3, as a function of the parameter $R;$ it includes the kinetic energy of the electron, and its potential energy of interaction with the two nuclei (the zero of energy being when the electron is "at rest" infinitely far from the two nuclei).

In addition, there is the energy of the nuclei; since they are assumed to be (nearly) at rest, this is just their potential energy of *coulomb repulsion,*

$$V = e^2/R$$

also shown as a dashed line in Fig. 24–3. The *total energy* of the whole system is now the sum of the electron energy and nuclear repulsion energy (the two dashed curves), and it is plotted as the solid curve. (The zero of

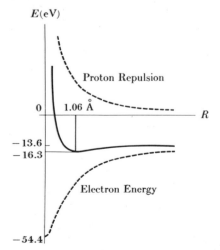

Fig. 24–3. Energy of the $H_2{}^+$ system in the ground state.

total energy in this graph is where the electron and two protons are all infinitely far from each other.) The curve of total energy has a minimum, which corresponds to a stable bound state of the system. Clearly the equilibrium separation will be of the order of a_0 ($=0.53$ Å) and the binding energy of the order of several electron volts. The actual values are 1.06 Å and 16.3 eV. If the electron were recombined with one of the protons, the ionization energy of 13.6 eV would be regained. Therefore the energy to dissociate H_2^+ into H and H^+ is $(16.3 - 13.6) = 2.7$ eV (actually 2.65 eV), which is usually referred to as the *binding energy*.

24-2   THE H_2 MOLECULE AND HOMOPOLAR BINDING

With this beginning, the neutral *hydrogen molecule* H_2 can be described by putting a second electron into the ground state. Because the second electron is assigned the same wave function as the first, the Pauli principle demands that the two electrons should have their *spins antiparallel.* (Also, because of the Pauli principle, a third electron would have to go into an excited state, so that H_2^- could be expected to be a considerably less tightly bound system.) If the mutual electrostatic repulsion of the two electrons is neglected, the curve representing the electronic energy of the two electrons would be lowered (more negative) by a factor of 2. When this function is added to the nuclear repulsion energy to give the total energy of the system, the equilibrium separation of the nuclei will be smaller and the binding energy will be about twice as great as for H_2. The experimental values are 0.742 Å and 31.9 eV. This 31.9 eV is the energy to separate all the electrons and protons to infinity; the energy to separate two H atoms to infinity, 4.72 eV, is smaller by twice the ionization potential of H. These experimental values indicate a somewhat larger separation and smaller binding than would be obtained from the calculation described. This discrepancy is a result of the mutual repulsion of the two electrons, which was neglected; when included it modifies the wave functions and increases the electronic energy (i.e., makes it less negative), and a careful (but still approximate) calculation gives good agreement with the experimental values.

The binding of two H atoms into the H_2 molecule is the simplest example of the *homopolar bond*, or *covalent bond*, which occurs between identical atoms. The essential feature of the H atom which makes it susceptible to bond formation (*reactive*, in chemical terminology) is its *unpaired electron.* When two atoms approach each other, the Pauli principle allows the unpaired electrons from each atom to pair up (with antiparallel spins) in the ground state wave function, which has its energy lowered in the combined system. The system He_2 is not stable because 2 electrons could go into the ground state, but the next two would have to go into an excited state. (When only one electron is in the excited state, the energy is not too high—He_2^+ is stable.) The molecule Li_2 is stable (2.67 Å, 1.03 eV), however, since the $2s$ electron of Li plays just the same role as the $1s$ electron of H; the only difference is that in Li the s electron moves in the field of the tightly bound He-like ion core Li^+ instead of moving in the field of the single proton. That is the reason for the larger separation of Li_2. The bond forming electrons are those which lie outside of closed shells, and this is why these are called "*valence electrons.*"

24–3   IONIC BINDING, POLYATOMIC MOLECULES

When it comes to unlike atoms, the electron charge density (wave function) need not be concentrated equally around the two nuclei, as it must (by symmetry) for two identical nuclei. For example, the molecule of hydro-fluoric acid HF is stable (0.92 Å, ≤ 6.4 eV), although the binding energy is not known exactly. The electrons are concentrated around the F nucleus (charge $+7e$) in preference to the H nucleus ($+e$). In fact, an alternative way to consider this system is to take the electron from the 1s state of the H atom and put it into the one unoccupied 2p state of the F atom. The result-ing proton H^+ and Ne-like F^- are attracted to each other electrostatically, and form a molecule via the *ionic bond*, or *heteropolar bond*, which was dis-cussed before in Chapter 14. The LiF molecule is similar, in that the He-like Li^+ is attracted to the Ne-like F^- by an electrostatic force, and re-pelled at closer distance by an ion core repulsion of the same kind as acts between noble gas atoms (and prevents the formation of stable He_2 or HeNe molecules).

Returning to the case of NaCl, which was treated in Section 14–2, the work which has to be done in order to separate the Na^+ and Cl^- ions was calculated to be 5.1 eV (experimentally 4.9 eV). It costs 3.8 eV more (the *electron affinity*) to remove the electron from Cl^-, but 5.1 eV is regained (the ionization energy) when the electron is returned to the Na^+. Thus the energy needed to dissociate NaCl into Na + Cl is (Fig. 24–4)

$$4.9 + 3.8 - 5.1 = 3.6 \text{ eV}$$

The properties of the systems mentioned so far are summarized in Table 24–1.

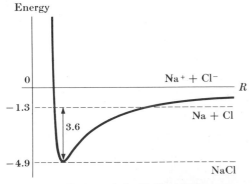

Fig. 24–4. Energy of the NaCl system.

The molecules H_2O (water) and NH_3 (ammonia) could also be thought of as bonded ionically by completing a Ne-like closed shell of the anion (N^{---} or O^{--}), using the electrons contributed by the H atoms. With CH_4 (methane), however, one wonders whether the H atom electrons are donated to the C to complete the Ne-like shell, or whether the four H electrons pair up individually with the two $2s$ and two $2p$ electrons of the C to form four covalent bonds like the bond in H_2. In fact, the latter approach is the more useful, but the lesson we should learn from this case is that both the ionic bond and the covalent bond are idealizations (except for identical atoms), and actual molecules may come in between these two extreme descriptions. They differ in the *charge distribution* in the molecule—uniform for the covalent bond, but with an excess multiple of $+e$ or $-e$ on the cation and anion, respectively, in the ionic bond. It does not require very much sophistication to appreciate that the charge distribution determined by the electron wave functions in actual molecules may be somewhere *intermediate* between these extremes, and that is indeed the case.

In both the covalent bond and the ionic bond, the importance of electrons outside the closed shells is paramount. Until 1962, it was thought that *only* these electrons could be involved in the formation of chemical compounds. With the discovery of XeF_4 (and subsequently other stable compounds of Xe and Kr), however, it has been realized that the ionization potential (or oxidation potential, in chemical terms) of the heavier noble gases is small enough that they can react with strong oxidizing agents (in the chemical sense of atoms which have a large electron affinity) like F. Nevertheless, with these intriguing exceptions, it remains true that nearly all chemical interactions between atoms involve primarily the electrons which are outside of completed shells.

It is sometimes stated that the bonding forces between atoms (especially covalent forces, but also the repulsive component in the ionic bond) can be understood only in terms of quantum mechanical concepts like "resonance" or "exchange." This is true in a sense, but there is a theorem (called the Hellmann-Feynman theorem) which dispels some of the mystery by stating that in a certain sense the forces that hold molecules together are nothing

TABLE 24–1

Molecule	Internuclear Distance ($\overset{\circ}{A}$)	Binding Energy (eV)
$H_2{}^+$	1.06	2.65
H_2	0.74	4.72
$He_2{}^+$	1.08	3.1
He_2	Unstable	Unstable
Li_2	2.67	1.03
HF	0.92	≤ 6.4
LiF	—	≤ 6.6
NaCl	2.51	3.58

but classical *electrostatic forces*. The gist of the theorem is that the force be-tween the nuclei in a molecule can be correctly calculated from the electro-static repulsion between the nuclei and the electrostatic attraction of the electrons on the nuclei. Thus, given the distribution of the electrons, the calculation of the internuclear (binding) force, or energy, is purely a classi-cal electrostatic problem. The problem of determining the electron distribu-tion, of course, is where quantum mechanics is indispensable, but once the electron charge distribution is determined by the electron wave functions, the remaining problem is classical. The theorem shows, for example, that what leads to binding in the H_2^+ system is the large amplitude of the ground state electron wave function in the region between the two nuclei (Fig. 24–2(b)). The nuclei are attracted inward toward this concentration of negative charge between them, and they have a stable configuration where this attraction just balances their mutual repulsion.

24–4 EXCITED STATES

We have so far discussed only the ground state of the molecule, where it spends most of its time. There are also excited states, however, and transi-tions between the various states account for the emission and absorption spectra of molecules, just as in the case of single atoms. Following the same procedure as before, we begin with the simplest possible system in order to consider the first excited state of a diatomic molecule. Surprisingly, this state, like the ground state of the molecule, is also derived from the *ground* state of the individual separated atoms. Let us again consider the system H_2^+. When R is very large, instead of the wave function considered pre-viously (Fig. 24–2), we could use the wave function shown in Fig. 24–5(a). This also describes a situation in which the electron would, with equal

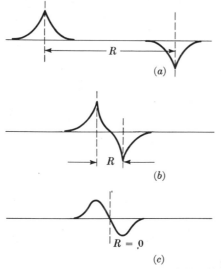

Fig. 24–5. First excited state wave function for H_2^+.

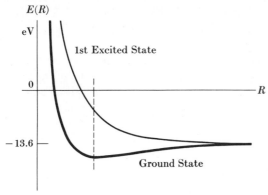

Fig. 24–6. Energy of H_2^+ in the lowest two states.

probability, be observed in the lowest energy state of one or the other of the H atoms: the probability distribution $|\psi|^2$ is just the same as for the previous wave function, and so is the corresponding energy level.

When the nuclei are brought closer together, however, the new wave function, and corresponding energy level, differs significantly from the real *molecular* ground state wave function considered before. This one has a *node* between the nuclei, as the other did not, and it therefore, as we have seen in general (Section 20–6), corresponds to a higher energy state. Indeed, when $R = 0$, this state must go into one of the states of He$^+$; this state must in fact be the $2p$ state, since the wave function has a single node at the origin (Fig. 24–5(c)).

By an argument similar to the one used for the ground state, the energy of the excited state is -13.6 eV for R very large. This time the energy for $R = 0$, however, in the $2p$ state of He$^+$, is also -13.6 eV ($Z = 2$, $n = 2$, in Eq. 21–17). Although the energy decreases slightly at intermediate values of R, the decrease is not enough to give a minimum when the coulomb repulsion of the two protons is added, and so this first excited state is an *unbound state* of the molecular ion (Fig. 24–6). (Most other molecules have some *bound* excited states.) An electronic excitation of the molecular ion will lead to *dissociation*. The reason why this state has higher energy can also be understood from the wave function, using the Hellmann-Feynman theorem: because of the node in ψ, the electron charge density $-e\,|\psi|^2$ is very small in the region between the nuclei, and so the nuclei are not strongly attracted toward the center by the negative electron charge. This situation is in contrast to the ground state, where there *is* a concentration of negative charge between the nuclei (Fig. 24–7).

(a)   (b)

Fig. 24–7. Electron charge density in H_2^+ for (a) the ground state and (b) the first excited state.

24-5   MOLECULAR SPECTRA

Transitions between the various states of molecules account for their emission and absorption spectra, just as in the case of an isolated atom. Even in a diatomic molecule, however, the energy levels cannot be classified according to their total angular momentum, as proved so advantageous in an atom. Classically, the angular momentum of the electron is not conserved in the two-force-center problem, since it does not give rise to a central force (Section 3-5). Quantum mechanically, this means that the energy eigenfunctions (i.e., the stable states) of the molecule are not eigenfunctions of the operator L^2, and so the angular momentum does not have a definite value in the stable states. In a diatomic molecule, however, because of the rotational symmetry about the axis through the two nuclei (taken as the z-axis), there is no torque about this axis, and so the z-component of angular momentum *is* conserved. This means that the stable states *are* eigenfunctions of L_z, and the z-component of angular momentum has the definite values $m\hbar$, with $m = 0, 1, 2, \ldots$ In the molecular context, $m\hbar$ is customarily denoted $\lambda\hbar$ instead. The states with $\lambda = 0, 1, 2, \ldots$ are designated σ, π, δ, $\ldots$, by analogy with the s, p, d, $\ldots$ designation for atomic states. The two states of Fig. 24-6 both happen to be σ states.

There is another respect in which molecular energy levels differ from atomic ones. In the molecule, the two *nuclei* can move relative to each other, and the quantization of this motion gives rise to new structure in the energy level scheme. (In both the molecular and atomic case we ignore the translational kinetic energy of the entire system, since this free-particle energy is not quantized.) The nuclear motion can be separated into two parts: in a bound state, like the ground state of all stable molecules (Fig. 24-4), the nuclei can vibrate about the equilibrium configuration at the minimum of the energy curve as a function of internuclear distance. In addition, the entire molecule can rotate freely about its center of mass. These two motions are both quantized, giving further energy levels, and leading to rather complex molecular spectra. To a good approximation we may treat them separately, even though there is really some coupling between them.

The molecular *vibration* about the equilibrium configuration has already been considered in Sections 4-4 and 14-5. There we found that for not too large energies of vibration (relative to the dissociation energy D), the motion was approximately simple harmonic, with a frequency $\nu_0 \approx 10^{13}$ sec^{-1} calculated for NaCl. Quantum mechanically, the oscillator can vibrate with only certain discrete energies; these energy levels, quoted in Eq. 18-25 and Section 20-6, are

$$E_n = (n + \tfrac{1}{2})h\nu_0 \tag{24-2}$$

Thus, for example in the NaCl molecule, the vibrational energy levels are separated by

$$h\nu_0 \cong 6.6 \times 10^{-27} \times 10^{13}/1.6 \times 10^{-12} = 0.04 \text{ eV}$$

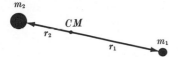

Fig. 24-8. Model of a diatomic molecule.

Since dissociation energies are typically at least 1 eV, there are usually more than about 20 vibrational levels in the potential well. (See Fig. 24–9.)

The *rotation* about the center of mass is described with the aid of the moment of inertia I. From Fig. 24–8,

$$I = m_1 r_1{}^2 + m_2 r_2{}^2$$

It is not difficult to show (Prob. 24–8) that this is equivalent to

$$I = mr^2 \qquad (24\text{–}3)$$

where m is the reduced mass (Eq. 3–35) and $r = r_1 + r_2$ is the separation of the two nuclei in the diatomic molecule. Then the rotational energy is related to the angular momentum of rotation L by

$$E = L^2/2I \qquad (24\text{–}4)$$

Quantum mechanically, the *operator* L^2 has the eigenvalues

$$L_l{}^2 = l(l + 1)\hbar^2$$

according to Eq. 20–29, so that the energy levels (eigenvalues) are

$$E_l = \frac{\hbar^2}{2I} l(l + 1) \qquad (24\text{–}5)$$

Note that here the particle described by the wave function on which L^2 operates is a nucleus, rather than an electron. Nevertheless L^2 has exactly

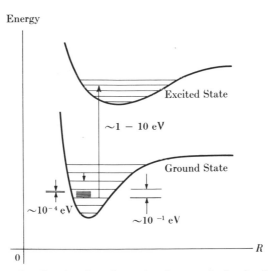

Fig. 24–9. Electronic, vibrational, and rotational energy levels of a diatomic molecule.

the same eigenvalues; the mass of the particle enters only into the *energy* eigenvalues, through I.

The rotational levels of Eq. 24–5 are not equally spaced. The separation of the levels is

$$E_l - E_{l-1} = (\hbar^2/I)l \qquad (24\text{–}6)$$

Again using values appropriate to the NaCl molecule (Section 4–4), $I = md_0^2 = 14 \times 1.66 \times 10^{-24}(2.5 \times 10^{-8})^2 = 1.45 \times 10^{-38}$ g-cm^2, $\hbar^2/I = 1.054^2 \times 10^{-54}/1.45 \times 10^{-38} \times 1.6 \times 10^{-12} \cong 5 \times 10^{-5}$ eV. The lower rotational levels are therefore much more closely spaced than the vibrational levels. If there are l_0 rotational levels between each pair of vibrational levels, their average spacing will be about $(\hbar^2/I) \, \tfrac{1}{2} \, l_0$, according to Eq. 24–6. Then, with $h\nu_0 = 0.04$ eV,

$$l_0 \cong \frac{4 \times 10^{-2}}{5 \times 10^{-5}l_0/2} \qquad l_0^2 \cong 1600 \qquad l_0 \cong 40$$

The typical overall energy level scheme is sketched in Fig. 24–9 for a diatomic molecule which has an excited electron state that still gives binding of the two nuclei. The curvature of the excited state energy as a function of nuclear separation, and the position of its minimum, need not be the same as for the ground state of the electrons. The atoms may well be more loosely bound in the excited state, giving a shallower and broader potential well with its minimum at a larger separation. (Indeed, in the case we considered in detail, H_2^+, the excited state was not a bound state at all.) Therefore the vibrational levels in general have different spacings in the ground and excited states, and likewise the rotational levels (since d_0 is different). No attempt has been made to represent all the rotational levels in Fig. 24–9.

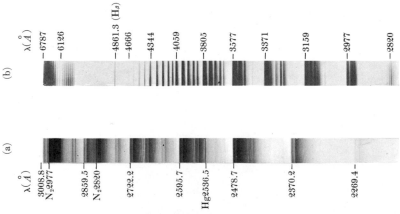

Fig. 24–10.   Band spectrum emitted by air. [Courtesy of G. Herzberg, Spectra of Diatomic Molecules (Van Nostrand, Princeton, N. J., 1950, 2nd ed.).]

The molecular spectra which result from transitions between these states are of three kinds:

1) The electronic state changes, as well as the vibrational and rotational states. The electronic transition occurs so rapidly that the nuclei do not have time to move very much, and so the arrow representing the transition is drawn vertically in Fig. 24–9. The separation of the states being a few eV, the absorption (or emission) lies in or near the visible spectrum. Since so many vibrational and rotational sublevels are available for the initial and final states, these spectra have a very complex structure. The lines generally appear in bands, and so these are called *band spectra*.

2) The vibrational and rotational state changes, but there is no electronic excitation. The energy change in this case was found to be about 0.04 eV, and the emitted or absorbed photon has the same energy,

$$h\nu \approx 0.04 \text{ eV}$$

The corresponding wave length is

$$\lambda = c/\nu \cong 3 \times 10^{-3} \text{ cm} = 30\mu$$

These transitions appear as an infrared spectrum and are well adapted to give experimental information about the vibrational frequency and equilibrium separation in the molecule.

3) Only the rotational state changes. For these transitions $h\nu \approx 10^{-4} - 10^{-3}$ eV, so that

$$\lambda \approx 1 \text{ cm} - 1 \text{ mm}$$

These wave lengths are in the microwave region, and the transitions are usually studied with microwave absorption spectroscopy.

If the excited state is not a bound state (Fig. 24–6), then transitions to this state lead to dissociation of the molecule. Since the "vibrational" levels in the excited state go over into the continuum of translational levels for the free atoms when the state is not bound, the resulting spectrum is a continuous spectrum. The appearance of a continuum in the absorption spectrum of a molecule is therefore experimental evidence of photochemical dissociation of the molecule.

PROBLEMS

24–1.   The energy of the H_2^+ system is -16.3 eV at the equilibrium nuclear separation of 1.06 Å. (See Fig. 24–3.) Calculate the contribution of the coulomb repulsion of the nuclei and then the contribution of the electron energy.

24–2.   Compute the ionization energy of molecular hydrogen, $H_2 \rightarrow H_2^+ + e^-$ (*Hint:* Consider $H_2 \rightarrow 2H^+ + e^- + e^- \rightarrow H_2^+ + e^-$.) Is molecular hydrogen more or less difficult to ionize than atomic hydrogen?

24–3.   What is the energy required for

$$Li_2 \rightarrow 2\ Li^+ + 2e^-?$$

(Look up the ionization energy of Li in Table 22–2.) What is the coulomb repulsion energy of two Li^+ ions at the molecular equilibrium separation of 2.67 Å?

24–4.   The molecular ions He_2^+ and H_2^- both have 3 electrons. Which would you expect to be more stable? Why?

24–5.   The He atom and the H^- ion both have 2 electrons. An energy of 24 eV is required to remove the first electron from He, and 54 eV to remove the second one. The energy required to remove the first electron from H^- is only 0.8 eV, compared with 13.6 eV required to remove the second one. Give a qualitative explanation of the fact that the ratio is much larger for He (about $\frac{1}{2}$) than it is for H^- (only about $\frac{1}{20}$).

24–6.   The electron affinity of H is 0.754 eV. (See Prob. 24–5.) From the ionization energy of Li and the coulomb attraction of Li^+ and H^- at the equilibrium separation of 1.60 Å, estimate the binding energy of lithium hydride, LiH. (Neglect the ion core repulsion energy.)

24–7.   Ethane and propane have the chemical formulas C_2H_6 and C_3H_8, respectively. Assuming these molecules are formed by covalent bonds, predict their structural formulas. (*Hint:* The structural formula of methane CH_4

is represented as H—C—H.)
$$\begin{array}{c} H \\ | \\ H—C—H \\ | \\ H \end{array}$$

24–8.   Prove that the moment of inertia of a diatomic molecule is given by Eq. 24–3.

24–9.   The vibrational frequency of the NaCl molecule is $1.14 \times 10^{13}\ sec^{-1}$ (Section 14–5). Compute the zero-point energy. (This energy is included in the binding energy tabulated in Table 24–1.)

24–10.   The H_2 molecule absorbs infrared light of wave length 2.3μ when the vibrational state changes by $\Delta n = 1$ (with no change in the electronic or rotational state). What is the zero-point energy?

24–11.   Compute the difference in separation of the vibrational energy levels for the molecules H_2 and HD, where D is deuterium, the heavy isotope of hydrogen with twice the atomic mass. Which molecule would have the greater binding energy?

24–12.   In Fig. 24–9, when an electron is excited the potential well is shown as having a smaller curvature and greater equilibrium separation. Give a qualitative justification for such an effect. Why would the separation between levels be smaller for the vibrational states? for the rotational states?

24–13.   Compute the smallest rotational energy level separation of H_2 (in eV). To what wave length separation (in Å) would this energy separation correspond for light in the visible region of the spectrum ($\sim$5000 Å)?

REFERENCES

J. C. Slater, *Quantum Theory of Molecules and Solids* (McGraw-Hill, 1963), Vol. I,
  Ch. 1.

R. B. Leighton, *Principles of Modern Physics* (McGraw-Hill, 1959), Ch. 9.

M. Born, *Atomic Physics Atomic Physics* (Hafner., 1951, 5th ed.), Ch. 9.

W. Heitler, *Elementary Wave Mechanics* (Oxford, 1946), Ch. 8, 9.

G. Herzberg, *Spectra of Diatomic Molecules* (Van Nostrand Co., 1950).

25/electron band theory of solids

Quantum mechanics has been very successful in explaining the properties of molecules, as we have seen in the last chapter. It has been equally successful in calculations of the properties of solids, even though this fact may at first seem surprising: since a macroscopic solid ordinarily contains some 10^{23} times as many particles as a molecule, one might have some anxiety that the problem would be about 10^{23} times harder to solve. It is not, however, and in fact it may even be easier than the problem of a fairly complicated molecule. The reason lies in the periodicity of the crystal structure (Chapter 13) and the practically infinite extent of the crystal. The complexity of the description consequently is essentially that of the unit cell, and we can achieve about the same level of rigor in our discussion as in the case of molecules.

The approach we shall follow is the same as that which we adopted in the case of atoms and then of molecules. Namely, we shall first consider the one-electron states in the field of all the nuclei or ion cores. Then we shall treat the real many-electron problem by simply loading all the electrons into the one-electron states previously obtained, paying attention to the Pauli principle. This procedure amounts to ignoring the mutual electrostatic interaction of the electrons among themselves. If this interaction were also taken into account, the electron energy levels would be rearranged somewhat, but nevertheless the basic description of the energy levels (in terms of the so-called energy-band scheme) will suffice. The general features of the energy-level scheme can be extrapolated from the energy levels of a diatomic molecule, which have already been described in Chapter 24.

25–1   ORIGIN OF ELECTRON ENERGY BANDS

The general problem of a single electron in the field of more than two force centers (nuclei or ions) is sufficiently difficult that a rigorous analytical solution has never been obtained. Approximate solutions can be derived, but the mathematical method for deriving them (perturbation theory) is fairly complicated and we have not considered it. Therefore we shall give a qualitative discussion of the way in which we should expect the electron energy levels to be arranged. This discussion can take off from our detailed description of the energy levels of a diatomic molecule (Section 24–4).

   For the purpose of understanding the electronic structure of solids, the important feature to notice about the energy diagram (Fig. 24–6) for a diatomic system is that when the two atoms are very far apart, the ground state energy level is *degenerate* (and likewise the excited states). (See Fig. 25–1.) But when the atoms are brought closer together, this two-fold degeneracy is *removed*, by the mutual interaction of the atoms, which perturbs the wave functions and the energy levels. (See Fig. 25 2.) The originally degenerate level is *split* into two levels, whose separation increases as the two atoms interact more strongly at closer distance. (Each of these levels still has a two-fold degeneracy, corresponding to the two spin states.) If now there were three atoms, all very far apart, the ground state would have a three-fold degeneracy. This degeneracy would be removed by the mutual interaction of the atoms if they were brought closer together.

   Similarly, N atoms, all far apart, have an N-fold degenerate level which is split up when they approach each other. (See Fig. 25–3.) The addition of each new atom adds one more energy level to the energy level scheme. The addition of a new atom does not, however, increase the maximum spread in the set of energy levels significantly, provided that the separation of any pair of atoms (the nearest neighbor distance) is kept about constant. The

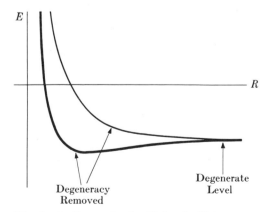

Fig. 25–1. Energy level splitting in $H_2{}^+$.

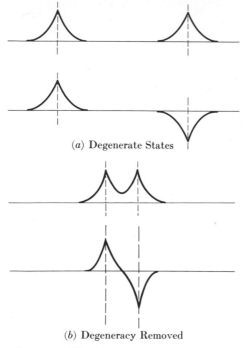

(a) Degenerate States

(b) Degeneracy Removed

Fig. 25–2. Wave functions for the two states in Fig. 25–1.

reason is that the overlap of the wave functions associated with any pair of individual atoms does not increase when a new atom is added, and it is this overlap that introduces the shift of the energy levels. If now we assume that the separation R is fixed at the equilibrium separation of the atoms in the crystal, d, we can draw an energy level diagram for the electron in a solid (Fig. 25–4) which is analogous to that for an electron in an atom (Fig. 18–3).

In a *solid* the number N of atoms may be of the order of 10^{23}. Since the spreading of the set of (originally degenerate) levels is at most a few elec-

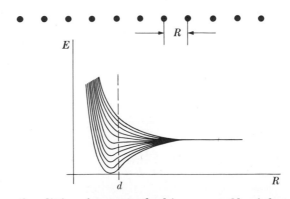

Fig. 25–3. Schematic splitting of an energy level in an assembly of eleven atoms.

Fig. 25–4. Energy level diagram corresponding to the interatomic separation d *in Fig. 25-3.*

tron volts, the separation in energy between neighboring levels is not more than about 10^{-22} eV. These levels are so close together that for all practical purposes they form a *continuous energy band* of levels. Even at the lowest temperature which has ever been obtained experimentally—about 10^{-5} deg—kT is about 10^{-9} eV, so that kT is always more than 10^{13} times larger than the separation of the levels. Therefore, the essential feature of the electron energy levels in a solid is that they form quasi-continuous bands of levels, whose real discreteness never becomes apparent at any attainable temperature.

Although the discreteness of the levels in an energy band is never important from the standpoint of the separation between levels, there is nevertheless a finite (though very large) number of levels in the band, of the order of N, the number of atoms in the solid. The lowest level can hold two electrons with spins antiparallel, the next level two more, and so on. Only two electrons can be put in each level (one in each spin state) because of the *Pauli principle*. The total number of electrons which must be put into these energy levels is also of the order of N, and so some significant fraction of the levels will be filled with electrons and the remainder empty. For example, in the collection of N hydrogen atoms we have considered, there would be N levels in the band (deriving from the $1s$ states of the H atom) and N electrons to put into the levels (1 electron from each atom). Since the band could hold $2N$ electrons altogether, it would be only half full. On the other hand, in a similar collection of N He atoms, the corresponding band would be fully occupied, because each atom brings 2 electrons.

25-2 CLASSIFICATION INTO METALS AND INSULATORS

In a collection of heavier atoms, the bands which derive from the higher atomic levels must also be considered. There will be a band of N levels from the $1s$ states, a band of N levels from the $2s$ states, a band of $3N$ levels from the (3-fold degenerate) $2p$ states, etc. The occupation of the bands is determined by the occupation of the levels in the isolated neutral atom. Those bands which derive from *closed shells* in the isolated atom will always be *fully occupied* in the solid. The bands derived from the valence electron states may or may not be completely full.

As in the case of a molecule, the bonding comes almost entirely from electrons outside of closed shells. Therefore the bands corresponding to the *unclosed* shells will be several electron volts wide, because the electron wave functions overlap appreciably. The bands derived from the inner shells, however, will be much narrower, because the inner shell wave functions are less extended, and so do not overlap very much at a separation of the atoms which is determined by the overlap of the outer shell wave functions. (See Fig. 25-5.) The corresponding energy level scheme consists of wide and narrow bands (Fig. 25-6).

The extent to which the states in an energy band are occupied by electrons has a very profound effect on the properties of the solid. As we shall see in the next chapter, if the band is completely full, the material is an insulator or semiconductor, whereas if it is only partly full, it is a metal. Unfortunately, it is not possible to predict these properties from the simple considerations we have adduced, because the spreading of the valence electron bands becomes very complicated for the heavier atoms. Even for an atom no heavier than Be ($Z = 4$), our prediction would go wrong: in the Be atom there are 2 electrons in the $2s$ states (and two electrons in the $1s$ states), so that the band derived from the $2s$ states should be full and Be should be an insulator. Nevertheless, Be is a metal, because its band derived from the $2p$ states overlaps with the $2s$ band, effectively forming a single band, which is not full.

The prediction would even be wrong for H, although in this case the correct answer could be anticipated: according to the example described above, the $1s$ band of a collection of H atoms would be only half full, and solid hydrogen should be a metal. The trouble here is that *two* H atoms form a very stable molecule; only very weak forces between these stable molecular units operate to form the condensed phase of hydrogen (boiling point 20°K). Most other cases of homopolar forces are similar, in that stable molecules are formed, giving a gas at ordinary temperatures because the intermolecular forces are very weak. The Group IV elements C (diamond), Si, Ge are exceptional because their four valence electrons can form four covalent bonds; these four bonds per atom can hold the atoms together in a stable *3-dimensional* structure (the diamond structure), an impossibility if there can be only one bond per atom as for H.

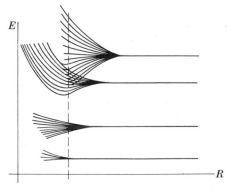

Fig. 25–5. Splitting of levels corresponding to inner and outer shells.

Fig. 25–6. Energy bands associated with Fig. 25–5.

Our simple band picture really gives an unambiguous differentiation between insulators and metals only for the elements which are noble gases (e.g., He, an insulator) or alkali metals (e.g., Li, a metal), where there is either a closed p shell (or $1s$ shell) or single s electron outside it. Among compounds, it correctly predicts that ionic crystals are insulators—for example in LiF the band derived from the fluorine $2p$ states is completely full and the lithium $2s$ band is completely empty. In a loose sense, it has thereby done a pretty good job of prediction, since most of the other elements either form covalent gas molecules or else they are metals or semiconductors (semiconductors being "insulators" with a very narrow gap between the filled valence band and next higher empty band). This qualitative success stems from the tendency of the valence bands to overlap in the heavier elements in a complicated way. (The most serious misses are boron and diamond, both insulators.)

To make calculations which give quantitative agreement with experimental information on particular band structures is exceedingly difficult (as are the experiments also), but considerable progress has already been made in this direction. In any case, the qualitative picture derived from quantum mechanics, in which the electron energy levels lie in *allowed bands* of levels, separated by *forbidden gaps* in which there are no allowed levels, has been extremely fruitful in leading to an understanding of the electronic properties of solids. Some of these properties will be considered in the next chapter.

25–3 ELECTRON WAVE FUNCTIONS AND EFFECTIVE MASS

Those properties of solids which depend on the motion or excitation of electrons, notably the electrical conductivity of metals and semiconductors, can only be understood on the basis of the quantum mechanical picture of the electron energy levels which was developed in the last section. The inner shell electronic structure of the atoms is not very much modified by the state of aggregation (the corresponding energy bands being very narrow), so that the atoms actually preserve much of their individuality. Phenomena involving these inner electrons (e.g., x-ray emission and absorption) are essentially the same as when the atoms are isolated in a gas.

The electronic behavior which is characteristic of the condensed state of the matter depends on the electrons in the outer valence shell, whose wave functions are strongly perturbed by neighboring atoms, leading to relatively wide energy bands in the solid. Henceforth our attention will be limited to the electrons occupying states in the upper, wide energy bands.

In order to analyze the electronic behavior in more quantitative detail, it is essential to have definite (preferably analytic) expressions for the electron wave functions corresponding to the energy states in the upper energy bands. As has been emphasized, the *atomic wave functions*, still appropriate for the inner electrons, are not much good for the outer electrons. The original atomic wave functions would be strongly overlapping at the close interatomic distance involved, and they are very severely modified. In fact, as in the case of the H_2 molecule (Fig. 25–2), instead of being concentrated around the individual nuclei, the wave functions are smeared over all the nuclei (Fig. 25–7). In any given state, the probability of finding the electron almost anywhere in the solid is large. This means that the electron would be able to move more or less freely through the solid.

This circumstance suggests a very simple choice of wave functions which we might hope would lead to useful results for these electrons: the electron wave functions could be approximated by *plane waves*,

$$\psi = e^{i\mathbf{K}\cdot\mathbf{r}} \tag{25–1}$$

(See Fig. 25–8.) These plane waves correspond to a description of *free electrons* in the solid (Section 20–4), each having a definite constant momentum given by Eq. 20–9,

$$\mathbf{p} = \hbar\mathbf{\kappa} \tag{25–2}$$

The approximation of free electrons amounts to assuming that the electron potential energy is constant throughout the crystal. That is, we ignore the real periodic variation due to the charge of the ion cores consisting of the nuclei plus inner shell electrons. It is admittedly a crude approximation, and much of current solid state theory is directed toward devising superior wave functions. What is surprising is that the free electron approximation furnishes an essential understanding of the effects we will be concerned with.

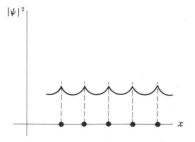

Fig. 25–7. Schematic electron density in a crystal.

The choice of wave functions which has been adopted determines the distribution of energy levels in the band. For a free electron, according to Eq. 20–7,

$$E = p^2/2m = (\hbar^2/2m)\kappa^2 = E(\kappa) \qquad (25\text{–}3)$$

Each different value of κ determines a different wave function, or two different states (since two spin directions are possible). This relation between E and κ implies that the *zero of energy* is at the bottom of the energy band. It is different from the convention adopted for the atomic states (zero at infinity), but the choice of zero is arbitrary, and the present one will now be adhered to for the time being.

The description in terms of $E(\kappa)$ actually suggests a somewhat more general description, in which we can relax slightly the assumption of absolutely free electrons. If the real periodic potential were taken into account to a better approximation, the plane wave functions $\exp (i\kappa \cdot \mathbf{r})$ could be modified by a weakly varying (instead of constant) amplitude, and $E(\kappa)$ would be slightly different from the free electron quadratic dependence on κ. Nevertheless, one could expand the real $E(\kappa)$ in a power series,

$$E(\kappa) = c_1\kappa^2 + c_2\kappa^4 + \ . \ . \ .$$

In this series, the constant term is missing because we chose $E - 0$ for $\kappa = 0$; all the odd powers of κ are missing because $E(\kappa) = E(-\kappa)$, the energy being independent of the direction of motion of the electron. Therefore, keeping only the first term of the power series,

$$E = (\hbar^2/2m^*)\kappa^2 \qquad (25\text{–}4)$$

where we have written $c_1 \equiv (\hbar^2/2m^*)$. The coefficient c_1 is written in this form, in terms of the new constant m^*, in order to bring out the similarity between Eqs. 25–4 and 25–3. Since m^* occurs in place of the electron mass m in Eq. 25–3, it is called the "effective mass" of the electron.

The constant m^*, the effective mass of the electron, could be calculated after the improved wave functions were determined. Alternatively, m^* can be accepted as an adjustable parameter in the theory, and the value, for a particular material, obtained from one experiment can be used to make predictions about other experiments. (To take a positive view of the situation, the experimental value of m^* can be said to furnish insight into the band structure of the solid.) With this additional flexibility, afforded by

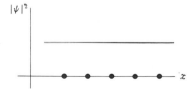

Fig. 25–8. Electron density in the free electron (plane wave) approximation.

adjusting the electron mass to take account of forces actually acting, the "free" electron theory gives a fairly consistent picture of most electronic phenomena. From the above approximate relation, Eq. 25–4, the effective mass of the electron is usually *defined* by

$$m^* \equiv \frac{\hbar^2}{d^2E/d\kappa^2} \qquad (25\text{–}5)$$

When this approximation is made, the electrons are said to be "quasi-free" electrons, meaning that they behave *as if* they were free.

25–4   THE DENSITY OF STATES AND FERMI ENERGY

The relation between E and κ determines in detail how the energy levels are arranged in the energy band. As has been pointed out, the discrete levels in the band are so close together that for most purposes E can be treated as a continuous variable. Nevertheless, it is necessary to know how many states there actually are in any particular energy interval, say between E and $E + dE$. This number will be proportional to dE (for dE small enough) but dependent on E; it may be written

$$S(E)\, dE$$

where $S(E)$ is called the *density of states*. The density of states is a function of energy which gives the number of states per unit energy interval, and its values are very large numbers if the units of energy are electron volts. Since each value of κ specifies two states, with opposite spins, from the relation $E(\kappa)$ for the quasi-free electrons one can find the corresponding density of states; the result is

$$S(E) = \frac{V}{2\pi^2}\left(\frac{2m^*}{\hbar^2}\right)^{3/2}\sqrt{E} \qquad (25\text{–}6)$$

where V is the total volume of the solid. The density of states is proportional to the volume, as should be expected, and it depends on E parabolically.

In order to derive the above expression for $S(E)$, Eq. 25–6, it is necessary to modify temporarily our assumption that the electrons are strictly quasi-free, even though this is the most convenient assumption for other purposes. They are not totally free, because they are confined to the solid, like a particle in a box. (The energy of the bound electron states in the solid is less than zero, if the energy zero is taken at infinity.) The discreteness of the energy levels results, in the quasi-free electron picture, when the boundary conditions are satisfied at the surface of the solid. The wave functions which satisfy the boundary conditions, namely those which vanish at the boundary (Section 20–5), are the functions sin κx, with κ given by one of the values $n\pi/L$ (Eq. 20–11). These wave functions are like standing waves (Section 16–3). The free-electron wave functions exp $i\kappa x$, on the other hand, are like travelling waves (Section 16–2), exp $i(\omega t + \kappa x)$, as may be seen when they are multiplied by the time dependent factor exp $i\omega t$. The wave functions that must be used for the present argument, which satisfy the boundary conditions, are *standing waves* sin κx, rather than travelling waves exp $i\kappa x$, and the use of the latter amounts to assuming the material is effectively infinite in extent, so that surface effects can be ignored. Here, however, it is just the finite dimension which leads to the discrete levels (and to the appearance of the volume V in $S(E)$), and so the *standing waves* must be counted.

If we assume the "box" is a cube of side L, then, as for the one dimensional box where L must be an integral number of half wave lengths, one must require, as in Eq. 20–11, that

$$\kappa_x = (\pi/L)\, n_x \qquad n_x = 1, 2, 3, \ldots$$

and similarly for the y- and z-dimensions, since electron waves can exist in those directions too. That is, in a unit interval of κ_x, there are just (L/π) integers, and twice that number of states (allowing for two spin directions). To count the number of states between κ and $\kappa + d\kappa$ in three dimensions, we need to multiply $(L/\pi)^3$ times the corresponding volume element of κ-space (which, since $p_x = \hbar\kappa_x$, etc., is the same as momentum space or velocity space, except for a change of scale on the coordinate axes). The volume element of a spherical shell in κ-space is $4\pi\kappa^2 d\kappa$. (See Fig. 25–9.) Since only positive values of κ_x, κ_y, κ_z occur, only one octant is wanted, so the volume of the spherical shell must be divided by 8. Then the number of states between κ and $\kappa + d\kappa$ is

$$\text{no.} = 2\left(\frac{L}{\pi}\right)^3 \frac{4\pi\kappa^2 d\kappa}{8} \qquad (25\text{–}7)$$

To reiterate, the factor 2 is for the two spin directions; the factor $(L/\pi)^3$ is the density of distinct wave functions in κ-space; and the remaining factor is the volume of κ-space between κ and $\kappa + d\kappa$.

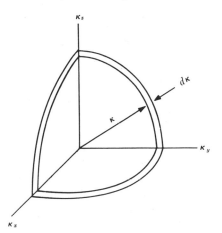

Fig. 25–9

Now, using the relation, from Eq. 25–4, for quasi-free electrons,

$$E = (\hbar^2/2m^*)\kappa^2 \tag{25-4}$$

we calculate the interval dE corresponding to $d\kappa$:

$$dE = (\hbar^2/2m^*)\, 2\kappa d\kappa \tag{25-8}$$

Finally, the number of states given by Eq. 25–7 is converted to $S(E)dE$ by substitution of Eqs. 25–4 and 25–8. The result is Eq. 25–6,

$$S(E) = \frac{V}{2\pi^2}\left(\frac{2m^*}{\hbar^2}\right)^{3/2}\sqrt{E} \tag{25-6}$$

where $V = L^3$. Although the density of states is derived for standing waves and henceforth we shall use travelling waves, no serious inconsistency is introduced, because the assumption of plane waves is only a rather rough approximation anyway. Notice from Eq. 25–6 that when m^* is large, the density of states is also large. A large value of m^*/m results from a big departure from the free-electron wave function—i.e., a strong interaction of the electron with the ion cores, or a small overlap of the individual atoms, with the same number of states squeezed into a correspondingly narrow band.

As a first application of our derived density of states function, and as a preliminary check on the reasonableness of the plane wave approximation, we may calculate the highest energy of an electron if N electrons are in the N lowest states of the band (taking into account the Pauli principle). This energy E_F, called the *Fermi energy* in metals, where the band is not completely full, results by requiring that the total number of states below $E = E_F$ should equal N:

$$\int_0^{E_F} S(E)dE = N \tag{25-9}$$

(Cf. Fig. 25–10.) Carrying out the integration and solving for E_F,

$$E_F = \frac{\hbar^2}{2m^*}(3\pi^2N/V)^{2/3} \tag{25-10}$$

The energy E_F is the (kinetic) energy of the most energetic electron when the entire solid is in its ground state—i.e., all the electrons are in the lowest possible 1-electron states consistent with the Pauli principle. (We shall see

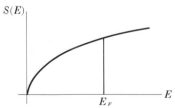

Fig. 25–10. *Density of states for free electrons.*

in the next chapter that this would imply that the solid is at the absolute zero of temperature.)

Notice that the Fermi energy depends only on the *density of electrons* N/V, or the number of electrons per unit volume, so that it is independent of the size of the particular piece of material. It can be calculated from the number of atoms per unit volume, if the number of valence electrons per atom is known. For example, for metals with a single s electron (the alkali metals and Cu, Ag, and Au), N/V equals the number of atoms per unit volume, and one finds values of E_F in the range of about 2 to 7 eV. For these metals, the valence electrons are essentially free, and therefore m^*/m is approximately 1. On the other hand, the transition metals have an incomplete $3d$ shell, and these inner shell electrons, with only slight interaction and with states in a correspondingly narrow band, have effective masses for which m^*/m is greater than 10. The main point is that the quasi-free electron theory leads to a band of occupied levels whose width is consistent with the band picture which had been derived qualitatively from the atomic states (Section 25-1). Another way of saying the same thing is that the quasi-free electrons can be fit into the experimental valence bands without having to assume that the effective mass m^* is too different from the free electron mass m.

25-5 OPTICAL ABSORPTION

Having described the general features of the energy level schemes to be expected in solids, we may discuss transitions between the levels, just as we did previously for isolated atoms (Chapter 23) and for molecules (Section 24-5). An upward transition can be caused by the absorption of a photon, leading to an excitation of the electronic state of the solid, or a downward transition can result in emission of a photon. As in the case of atoms and molecules, the optical spectrum which is observed can be used to infer the positions of the energy levels. In solids, however, and particularly in metals, the optical properties are not the sole source of information about the energy levels, and other kinds of properties are very significant (Chapter 26). We shall concern ourselves in this section mainly with optical absorption, even though light emission from solids is involved in the important phenomenon of luminescence. In particular, the absorption spectrum derived from the band theory will explain the fact, mentioned in Section 17-3, that some solids are transparent to visible light.

Since it is a familiar fact that metals are opaque, whereas many insulators are transparent, let us develop further the distinction made in Section 25-2 between metals and insulators. Let us define the *valence band* as the highest energy band in the solid which is occupied by any electrons when the solid is in its ground state. The levels in the valence band in the solid will usually be derived from the valence electron levels in the ground state of the isolated atom. We also define the *conduction band* as the lowest energy band in the solid which contains any empty levels when the solid is in its ground

Fig. 25–11

state. The valence band and conduction band could be the same band, if there is a band which is only partly full. They could also be different, if one band is completely full and the other is completely empty, and in this case the material is an *insulator*. If two bands overlap in energy, they will be considered as a single band in this discussion. Thus, for example, in Be, where the $2s$ and $2p$ bands overlap, the combined band is only partly full, so that Be is not an insulator but a metal. This difference between a metal and an insulator is illustrated schematically in Fig. 25–11.

Now it is immediately obvious how an insulator can be transparent. The smallest energy change involved in any possible electronic transition results when an electron with the largest possible energy (at the top of the valence band) is excited to the lowest empty state (at the bottom of the conduction band.) (See Fig. 25–12.) The energy $h\nu$ of the absorbed photon will be the same, according to conservation of energy, so that

$$h\nu = E_G = hc/\lambda$$

E_G being the width of the forbidden energy gap. Thus, if $E_G \geq 3$ eV, no photon of smaller energy ($\lambda \geq 4000$ Å) can be absorbed, and the material is transparent in the visible region. On the other hand, higher energy photons (shorter wave length light) *can* be absorbed, so that all materials become opaque in the ultraviolet region (Fig. 25–13). For example, in diamond, corundum (Al_2O_3), the alkali halides, and the alkali earth oxides,

$$E_G \approx 5 - 10 \text{ eV}$$

and single crystals of all these substances are transparent. They are transparent for the same reason that air, for example, is transparent. In O_2 and

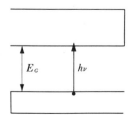

Fig. 25–12. *Photon absorption in an insulator.*

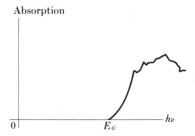

Fig. 25–13. *Absorption spectrum for an insulator.*

N_2 molecules, the lowest electronically excited state is more than 3 eV above the ground state, and so the molecule cannot absorb visible light.

Other materials are opaque because E_G is smaller. In "semiconductors" (Chapter 26), $E_G \leq 1.5$ eV. These materials are therefore opaque to visible light, although they are transparent to infrared light. For example Si ($E_G = 1.2$ eV) looks black and shiny, but it is transparent to wave lengths longer than 10,000 Å. Metals are opaque to all wave lengths, because $E_G = 0$, and an electron can find a vacant excited state no matter how small the available energy.

In insulators and semiconductors, the presence of lattice defects (Chapter 15) is often important in modifying the absorption spectrum, since the peculiar electron wave functions in their immediate vicinity introduce extra energy levels, which very often fall somewhere in the forbidden gap between the top of the valence band and the bottom of the conduction band (Fig. 25–14). Excitation of an electron in one of these isolated levels can therefore occur with longer wave length light, leading to an absorption peak at $h\nu = E_I$ (Fig. 25–15). For example, ruby is corundum (Al_2O_3) which contains a fraction of a percent of Cr ions as an impurity. The absorption peak of the Cr in the green gives ruby its red color, in contrast to the transparent pure corundum. Other colored gems are similar; for example, sapphires are also corundum, containing other impurities. Even lattice vacancies can give rise to such absorption peaks. In the alkali halides, a halogen vacancy which has trapped an electron produces F-centers, which give the salt a characteristic color. (The "F" comes from the German "Farbzentrum," which means "color center.") Studies of such optical absorption peaks have yielded much information about practically important defects in solids.

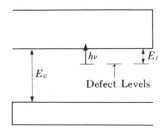

Fig. 25–14. *Absorption by defect electrons.*

Absorption

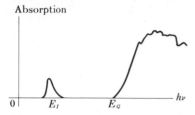

0 E_I E_G $h\nu$

Fig. 25-15.   Defect absorption spectrum.

The absorption cross section for these isolated atomic centers is usually of the order of the geometric cross section of the atom, i.e., about 10^{-16} cm². (Cf. Section 17–3.) Thus it takes only a small concentration of them to give an appreciable depth of color. For example, 10^{16} cm⁻³ (or about 1 part per million) would give an absorption constant (Eq. 17–14) of 1 cm⁻¹. Since the absorption peaks are rather wide, a very high concentration simply makes the material look opaque.

PROBLEMS

25–1.   Determine the approximate size of a metal particle for which the energy level separation in an energy band might be significant. (*Hint:* Find the number of atoms for which the energy difference would be equal to kT at 1°K.)

25–2.   Discuss the binding of H_2S and ZnS, both in molecular and solid form. (Look up the properties of these compounds in the *Handbook of Chemistry and Physics.*)

25–3.   Compute the Fermi energy for Cu, assuming there is one quasi-free electron per atom, for which $m^*/m = 1$.

25–4.   The energy gap in Ge is about 0.75 eV. At what wave length would Ge begin to absorb light?

25–5.   In NaCl, the F-center energy level is 2.65 eV below the conduction band. What wave length does it absorb? What color is NaCl containing F centers?

25–6.   Suppose an As atom is a substitutional impurity in Ge. If one of the 5 As valence electrons were removed, the remaining 4 could form covalent bonds with the Ge, and the 1 extra would be free, except that it would be attracted to the As⁺ ion. (Such an impurity is called a "donor.") In its lowest energy state, it would be in the ground state of this hydrogen-like system, where the coulomb attraction is modified by the dielectric constant of the Ge. The distance of this state below the conduction band E_I (cf. Fig. 25–12) is the ionization energy of the hydrogen-like system. Calculate E_I and the corresponding wave length, assuming a dielectric constant of 16.

25–7.   The x-ray emission spectrum of light elements ("soft" x-rays) can give information about the spread of occupied energy levels in a solid. For example, in Na ($Z = 11$), the width of the K_β-radiation peak depends on the width of occupied conduction band levels (Fermi energy). Calculate the approximate energy of this transition (Section 23-4), and the relative width of the emission line.

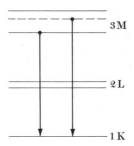

25-8. Assuming that the absorption cross section for visible light in a metal is 10^{-16} cm², and that there are 10^{22} atoms cm⁻³, what is the absorption coefficient? If a thin film of the metal were evaporated onto glass, how thick would the film have to be in order to absorb 50% of the incident light?

REFERENCES

R. L. Sproull, *Modern Physics* (John Wiley & Sons, 1956), Ch. 8.

C. Kittel, *Introduction to Solid State Physics* (John Wiley & Sons, 1956, 2nd ed.), Ch. 10.

A. J. Dekker, *Solid State Physics* (Prentice-Hall, 1957), Ch. 15.

26/electronic properties of solids

Having studied the allowed states of the valence electrons in a solid, we are now prepared to calculate some of the properties of the material which depend on them. In this chapter we shall see that the electron wave functions and energy levels which were discussed in the preceding chapter can provide a simple explanation of many of these properties.

Previously (Chapters 14 and 15) we derived some aspects of solid behavior from a treatment of the interacting atoms of the material—for example, the elastic constants, specific heat, thermal expansion, diffusion, etc. This treatment could be essentially classical, except near absolute zero of temperature, since the atoms or ions are relatively heavy. We have just seen that this possibility arises because the atoms as a whole preserve some of their individuality in the solid, inasmuch as the inner shell electron wave functions do not overlap appreciably and are little modified. Those properties which depend on the motion or excitation of electrons, however, notably the electrical conductivity of metals and semiconductors, involve the outer shell electrons of the atoms, whose states lie in the valence and conduction bands of the solid, and they can be understood only on the basis of quantum mechanics. Here we shall be concerned with some electronic thermal properties, transport processes, and other effects which depend on the outer electrons. This theory has been most highly developed for crystalline solids, but much of our simplified version would also apply approximately to amorphous solids or even liquids.

26-1 THERMAL EQUILIBRIUM DISTRIBUTION OF THE ELECTRONS

In Chapter 25 we considered all the allowed energy levels of the electrons, but for the most part we assumed that the solid was in its ground state. This lowest possible energy state consisted in fully occupying the N lowest energy one-electron states with the N electrons, in accordance with the Pauli principle which forbids more than one electron per state. This situation would actually obtain at absolute zero of temperature; but now we want to admit the possibility of thermal excitation of the electrons. Many of the characteristic electronic properties of solids depend on the thermal excitation; obviously thermal properties like the specific heat do.

In order to orient ourselves in the problem of computing the thermal equilibrium distribution of the electrons over their allowed energy levels, we might think of the assembly of quasi-free electrons as a *gas* of electrons enclosed in a "container," which is the boundaries of the solid. From this point of view, the problem of calculating the specific heat, for example, is the same as for a gas of atoms: the average energy of the electron gas must be calculated, using a weighted average, with the weighting factor for each state given by the *Boltzmann factor*. The Boltzmann factor $\exp(-E/kT)$ gives the probability that a system is in a state of energy E. The result for the quantum mechanical electron gas turns out to be quite different from that for the classical gas of atoms, in that the law of equipartition of energy does not hold. The failure of this classical law stems from two features of the quantum mechanical electron: the absolute identity of any two electrons (which cannot be distinguished by any observational means) and, even more importantly, the applicability of the Pauli principle.

For the statistical calculation of the distribution of the electrons over the quantum mechanical states, let us begin by considering the discrete energy eigenvalues

$$E_1, E_2, E_3, \ldots, E_n, \ldots$$

even though these may be so closely spaced that we will later want to treat them quasi-continuously. In this enumeration, degenerate eigenvalues are assumed to be listed separately, so that some of the energies may have the same numerical value. We have already agreed to simplify the many-electron problem by neglecting the electrostatic interaction (coulomb repulsion) between the electrons, and so these one-electron energy states are used for each electron, just as if all the other electrons were absent. In this approximation, a straightforward application of the Boltzmann principle would give

$$f(E_n) = Ae^{-E_n/kT} \tag{26-1}$$

for the probability that an electron has the energy E_n (A being a normalization constant). The average number of electrons with energy E_n would correspondingly be $Nf(E_n)$, where N is the total number of electrons in the gas:

$$\bar{N}_n = Nf(E_n) \tag{26-2}$$

Unfortunately, this straightforward result cannot be correct, because it violates the Pauli principle: the lower the temperature T, the more rapidly the exponential distribution falls off (Fig. 26–1), and in the limit $T = 0$, the probability to be in any state with $E_n > 0$ would be 0. Therefore, all the electrons would have to be in the lowest state ($E_n = 0$), in contradiction to the Pauli principle, which allows only one electron in the lowest state (two in the lowest spin-degenerate energy level).

What is wrong is not the Boltzmann distribution, but our treatment of the electrons as completely independent particles. Even though no forces are assumed to be acting between the electrons, so that any given electron does not "know" that the others are present and is adequately described by the one-electron wave function, nevertheless the Pauli principle introduces a *correlation* between the electrons. If there were forces acting between the electrons, the probability that a given electron is in a certain state would be dependent on the states of the other electrons. Although the Pauli principle is not a "force," it still prescribes a correlation, in that, if one electron occupies a certain state, no other electron is allowed to occupy that state. The remedy which must be adopted is the same as that which was briefly mentioned (Section 9–8) in the case of a gas of strongly interacting atoms (e.g., a liquid): in the Boltzmann distribution we must consider the energy of the whole system, rather than of a single particle, so that the "interaction" can be taken into account. In other words, we must consider a many-particle distribution function rather than a single-particle distribution function.

The energy of the *system of electrons* is specified by stating the numbers

$$N_1, N_2, \ldots, N_n, \ldots$$

of electrons in each of the states E_n (still ignoring the real coulomb repulsion); these numbers are called the *occupation numbers* of the states. The total energy of the whole gas of electrons is then

$$U = N_1 E_1 + N_2 E_2 + \cdots + N_n E_n + \cdots \qquad (26\text{–}3)$$

and the many-particle Boltzmann distribution can be correctly applied to give the probability

$$f(U) = A e^{-U/kT} \qquad (26\text{–}4)$$

that the system has the energy U.

In order to revert to the conceptually simpler description in terms of individual electrons, we may now compute the average occupation number

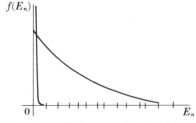

Fig. 26–1. Boltzmann distribution at high and low temperatures.

$\bar{N}_n$ of the state with energy E_n, using the correct Boltzmann distribution in the usual way:

$$\bar{N}_n = \Sigma N_n f(U) = \frac{\Sigma N_n e^{-U/kT}}{\Sigma e^{-U/kT}} \qquad (26\text{--}5)$$

This equation gives the number of electrons to be expected in each of the one-electron states with energy E_n. The sum Σ is to be taken over all possible occupation numbers (appearing in U as in Eq. 26–3), subject to two restrictions,

$$N_1 + N_2 + \cdots + N_n + \cdots = N$$
$$(26\text{--}6)$$
$$N_1, N_2, \ldots, N_n, \ldots = 0 \text{ or } 1$$

The first restriction states that all the occupation numbers add up to the total number of electrons; the second expresses the Pauli principle, which permits only the occupation numbers 0 or 1.

The sum in Eq. 26–5, of course, contains an enormous number of terms, but by using some tricks the result can be reduced to a relatively simple form (after considerable calculation):

$$\bar{N}_n = \frac{1}{e^{(E_n - E_F)/kT} + 1} \qquad (26\text{--}7)$$

As will be shown, E_F is a normalizing constant, and is the same as the Fermi energy, Eq. 25–10. We could also write Eq. 26–7 as a 1-electron distribution function (cf. Eq. 26–2)

$$\bar{N}_n = f_F(E_n) \qquad (26\text{--}8)$$

with

$$f_F(E_n) = \frac{1}{e^{(E_n - EF)/kT} + 1} \qquad (26\text{--}9)$$

The function f_F is called the *Fermi-Dirac distribution function*, and it is the correct 1-electron distribution function. Equation 26–8 shows that if the Fermi-Dirac distribution Eq. 26–9 is used instead of the Boltzmann distribution Eq. 26–1, the electrons can be treated as truly independent. The Pauli principle is automatically contained in the distribution function. Henceforth we shall always use the 1-electron Fermi-Dirac distribution function for the electrons rather than the many-electron Boltzmann distribution, from which it is derived.

Incidentally, the Pauli principle is not the only nonclassical feature of the above argument. Even if the restrictions given by Eq. 26–6 are dropped, the result is still not the classical one-particle distribution, but the *Bose-Einstein distribution function*

$$f_B(E_n) = \frac{1}{e^{(E_n - EB)/kT} - 1} \qquad (26\text{--}10)$$

(E_B a normalization constant). This function must be used for quantum particles with integral spin which do not obey the Pauli principle. For example, it would describe the *photon gas* mentioned in connection with cavity radiation (Section 18–4). We shall have no occasion to use it here, but its difference from the classical distribution (even without the Pauli principle) points up the importance of a more general aspect of the quantum mechanical many-particle problem: namely, the particles are absolutely *indistinguishable* from each other, in the sense that no experiment could be devised to put a label on a particle. It is never meaningful to say, for example, here is electron A and there is electron B—only that here there is one electron and there there is one electron. This assumption of complete indistinguishability was tacitly introduced when the states of the system were described merely by the occupation numbers of the states; if we conceive of interchanging two of the electrons, that gives not a different state (as it would in a classical counting of the states) but the *same* state.

26-2   THE FERMI-DIRAC DISTRIBUTION

Returning to the Fermi distribution, Eq. 26–9, we may now investigate some of its properties as the correct one-particle distribution function for particles which obey the Pauli principle. First, at $T = 0$, it predicts that all states for which $E_n - E_F > 0$ are occupied with probability zero (since f_F has $e^{+\infty}$ in the denominator), and all states with $E_n - E_F < 0$ are occupied with probability one (since $e^{-\infty} = 0$ is in the denominator). (See Fig. 26–2.) The Pauli principle is therefore satisfied by choosing E_F so that there are enough states with $E_n < E_F$ to contain all the electrons; in this sense E_F is the normalization constant, and it depends on the arrangement of the states (or their density, in the continuum approximation). It also agrees with the definition of Eq. 25–9, as we shall see in more detail below. Since in the remainder of this chapter, we shall be discussing only the application of the Fermi distribution to electrons in solids, we may drop the subscript on f_F, and also replace the discrete energies E_n by a continuous variable E, writing

$$f(E) = \frac{1}{e^{(E-E_F)/kT} + 1} \tag{26–11}$$

At temperatures $T > 0$, the corners of the distribution are rounded off, as shown in Fig. 26–3. Obviously $f = \frac{1}{2}$ for $E = E_F$, since $e^0 = 1$; it is not

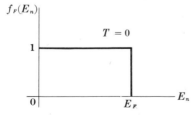

Fig. 26–2. Fermi-Dirac distribution at absolute zero.

difficult to show that the function is symmetric with respect to this point. (See Prob. 26–1.) The width of the energy interval over which f effectively falls from 1 to 0 is something of the order of kT, since in this interval the exponential in the denominator changes by a factor of $e = 2.72 \ldots$

The distribution function is used to calculate the number of electrons $dN(E)$, which actually have energies in a certain energy interval between E and $E + dE$, as follows. According to the definition of the density of states $S(E)$, Eq. 25–6, the number of allowed states in the interval is $S(E)dE$. The probability that these states are occupied by electrons is $f(E)$. Therefore

$$dN(E) = f(E)S(E)dE \qquad (26\text{–}12)$$

The normalization condition (from which E_F is calculated) is

$$N = \int_0^N dN(E) = \int_0^\infty f(E)S(E)dE \qquad (26\text{–}13)$$

We have already used this condition to obtain E_F at $T = 0$ in the case of a *metal*: for $T = 0$,

$$f(E) = \begin{cases} 1 \text{ for } E < E_F \\ 0 \text{ for } E > E_F \end{cases}$$

as in Fig. 26–2. Therefore the integral in Eq. 26–13 reduces to Eq. 25–9:

$$N = \int_0^{E_F} S(E)dE$$

Using the quasi-free electron expression for $S(E)$, Eq. 25–6, we calculated E_F from this result,

$$N = \frac{V}{3\pi^2}\left(\frac{2m^*}{\hbar^2}\right)^{3/2} E_F^{3/2} \qquad (26\text{–}14)$$

as in Eq. 25–10. At higher temperatures, if $S(E)$ were constant in the vicinity of E_F, then E_F would be independent of temperature because of the symmetry of f about E_F. Since $S(E)$ generally varies slightly over the range of about kT in which $f(E)$ falls from 1 to 0, E_F is somewhat temperature dependent. This temperature dependence however is small (much less than that of the normalization constant in the classical Maxwell distribution of Eq. 9–14), and we shall ignore it. In an *insulator*, with a valence band

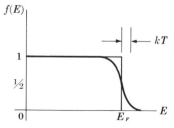

Fig. 26–3. *Fermi-Dirac distribution at* T > 0.

which is fully occupied at $T = 0$, similar considerations apply, although E_F will be seen later (Section 26–3) to lie near the middle of the forbidden gap (Fig. 25–11) between the valence band and the next higher unoccupied band, the conduction band.

26–3 THERMAL EXCITATION OF THE ELECTRONS

The thermal properties of the electrons depend on the numbers of electrons which are *thermally excited* to higher energy states, and the motive for introducing the Fermi distribution was to be able to calculate these numbers.

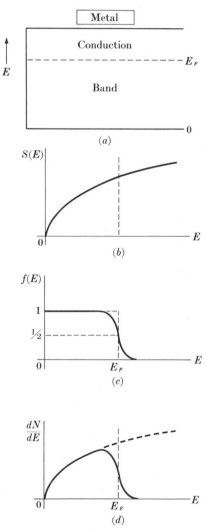

Fig. 26–4. *Electron density in a metal* dN/dE, *as the product of the density of states* S(E) *times the distribution function* (*occupation probability*) f(E).

The excited electrons in a *metal* are in a range $\Delta E \approx kT$ above E_F. (Cf. Fig. 26–3.) Their number ΔN can be found from $dN = fSdE$ (Eq. 26–12) by letting $dN = \Delta N$, $dE = \Delta E \approx kT$:

$$\Delta N \approx S(E_F)kT \qquad (26\text{–}15)$$

since $f(E_F)$ is of the order of 1 (actually $f(E_F) = \frac{1}{2}$). This number can be expressed more usefully if we notice from Eqs. 26–14 and 25–6 that

$$N = \frac{V}{3\pi^2}\left(\frac{2m^*}{\hbar^2}\right)^{3/2} E_F^{3/2} = \tfrac{2}{3}E_F S(E_F) \qquad (26\text{–}16)$$

Then the relative number of excited electrons in the metal is given by combining Eqs. 26–15 and 26–16:

$$\frac{\Delta N}{N} \approx \frac{kT}{E_F} \qquad (26\text{–}17)$$

From this expression, one sees that the number of electrons which are excited is rather small. It is of the order of 1% at room temperature, since $kT \cong 0.02$ eV and $E_F \cong 2$ eV, in a typical case.

In an *insulator*, on the other hand, the number is very much smaller still. If we assume as in Fig. 26–5(b) that the density of states near the top of the valence band also has a parabolic shape (as will be justified later) with the same curvature, then E_F must lie in the middle of the *forbidden gap*, in order for the number of electrons removed from valence band states to equal the number added to conduction band states (recalling the symmetry of f). (See Fig. 26–5(d).) At the bottom of the conduction band, $E - E_F \gg kT$, and so from Eq. 26–11,

$$f(E) \approx e^{-(E-E_F)/kT} = (e^{E_F/kT})e^{-E/kT}$$

i.e., the Fermi distribution is approximately the same as the Boltzmann distribution. For $E - E_F = E_G/2$, where E_G is the width of the forbidden gap, we have at the bottom of the conduction band

$$f \approx e^{-E_G/2kT}$$

instead of $f \approx 1$ as for a metal. Still the distribution function falls by $1/e$ in an interval kT, and so ΔE should again be taken as about kT. The density of states function should also be evaluated at kT, since it starts from 0 at the bottom of the band. Then $dN = fSdE$ becomes

$$\Delta N \approx e^{-E_G/2kT}S(kT)kT \qquad (26\text{–}18)$$

In order to compare this result with Eq. 26–17 for a metal, we may again use $N \approx E_F S(E_F)$ from Eq. 26–16, even though it strictly applies to the metal, and note that $S(kT)/S(E_F) = (kT/E_F)^{1/2}$:

$$\frac{\Delta N}{N} \approx \left(\frac{kT}{E_F}\right)^{3/2} e^{-E_G/2kT} \qquad (26\text{–}19)$$

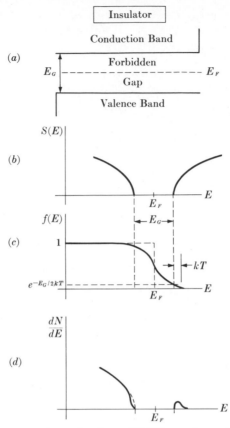

Fig. 26–5. *Electron density in an insulator* dN/dE, *as the product of the density of states* S(E) *times the distribution function* f(E).

This number is smaller than for a metal partly because the density of states is smaller near the bottom of the conduction band than at the Fermi energy in the metal, but mainly because of the factor $\exp(-E_G/2kT)$. For $E_G = 5$ eV, near room temperature this factor would be

$$e^{-100} = 10^{-43}$$

giving an entirely negligible number of excited electrons. If E_G is considerably less than 5 eV (perhaps 1 eV or less), the number, although still small, is significant in some respects, and the material is a *semiconductor* rather than an insulator. Semiconductors, which will be discussed in more detail later, are poor insulators, or moderately good conductors.

26–4   ELECTRONIC SPECIFIC HEAT

As a first application of the theory of thermal excitation derived in the preceding section, let us estimate the electronic specific heat of a *metal*, i.e., the energy which must be supplied to the electron gas to raise its temperature

1°. Since the excited electrons are taken from states about kT below E_F and put into states about kT above E_F, the average increase of energy is about $2kT$ per electron. The total thermal energy U_T is therefore about

$$U_T \approx 2kT\,\Delta N \approx 2(kT)^2\,N/E_F$$

using Eq. 26–17. Then the heat capacity per mole (letting N be the number of free electrons in one mole of a monovalent metal) is

$$C_V = dU_T/dT \cong 4R(kT/E_F) \qquad (26\text{–}20)$$

where $R = Nk$ is the gas constant per mole.

This value is very small in comparison to the $3R$ due to the vibration of the atoms when classical equipartition (Dulong and Petit law) holds— smaller by the ratio $kT/E_F \approx 0.01$. Historically, this quantum mechanical result cleared up a long-standing mystery about why the electron specific heat was so much smaller than the classical $(3/2)R$ to be expected for a gas of free electrons. The answer is that *most* of the N electrons are prohibited from acquiring a thermal energy kT by the Pauli principle, since the states kT above are already occupied.

Although the electronic contribution to the specific heat is negligible at room temperature, at very low temperatures it becomes significant. The specific heat due to atomic vibrations also goes to zero at $T = 0$ (being proportional to T^3) for quantum mechanical reasons (Section 18–6), and near 1°K the electronic contribution becomes a measurable fraction of the total. Since the electronic specific heat is proportional to T, according to Eq. 26–20,

$$C_V = \gamma T \qquad (26\text{–}21)$$

it can be distinguished from the atomic contribution (proportional to T^3). Our estimate gave $\gamma = 4Rk/E_F$; a careful integration for the average energy gives a numerical constant 20% higher:

$$\gamma = (\pi^2/2)Rk/E_F \qquad (26\text{–}22)$$

From the measured specific heat, the Fermi energy E_F can be calculated. From it, the effective mass of the electron, m^*, can then be obtained experimentally, using Eq. 25–10. (The electronic specific heat of non-metals is unmeasurably small, because the number of excited electrons is so much smaller, according to Eq. 26–19.)

26–5 ELECTRONIC CONDUCTION

The most notable difference between metals and non-metals is in their *electrical conductivity*, and in fact this property is the basis of the empirical definition of a metal. The conductivity of a metal like copper is 10^{20} times greater than that of a good insulator such as quartz (at room temperature), and perhaps 10^6 times greater than for a typical semiconductor like germanium. This enormous range of values follows naturally from our quantum mechanical energy band picture, since the conductivity is proportional to the number of electrons in the conduction band, which may be defined generally (Section 25–5) as the lowest energy band which is not completely full (being partially full in a metal, and completely empty at $T = 0$ in an insulator).

The qualitative difference between metals and insulators can be seen as follows. When an electric field is applied, the electrons in a *metal* are accelerated in the direction opposite to the field (since their charge is negative), those which are already moving in this direction being speeded up and those moving in the other direction slowed down, and the result is a *net current* in the direction of the field. From the quantum mechanical point of view, the effect of the electric field is to induce transitions between states,

$$\kappa \to \kappa'$$

such that the momentum $\mathbf{p} = \hbar\kappa$ is incremented in the direction opposite to the electric field, becoming $\mathbf{p}' = \hbar\kappa'$. Since larger κ corresponds to higher energy, some of the electrons are shifted to slightly higher energy states and some to lower. Near $T = 0$, those at the Fermi energy are shifted into the vacant states above, and those just below move into these vacated states, and so on. Before the application of the field, the net (average) momentum was zero, since for every $\mathbf{p}$ there is also a state with $-\mathbf{p}$; after the field is applied, the electron distribution is modified to give a net momentum, which gives an electric current in response to the field.

By contrast, in an *insulator* near $T = 0$ all the states are filled (except for the vacant states in the conduction band at very much higher energy). No net transitions are possible because all the accessible states are already occupied. Therefore in an insulator it is the Pauli principle which prevents the electrons from being accelerated by the electric field. No current can flow in response to the field because all the states with equal and opposite momenta are filled and no shifting is possible. It is sometimes naively thought that a metal is a good conductor because the electrons are free and an insulator a poor one because all the electrons are tightly bound to the atoms. In our picture, however, in *both* cases the electrons have been treated as free (i.e., plane waves are used for the wave functions) and moving rapidly throughout the crystal; in the insulator no net current flows because equally many electrons are moving in each direction and the Pauli principle prohibits any change. The superiority of this latter explanation becomes apparent at temperatures $T > 0$.

At elevated temperatures, an insulator may be able to conduct an appreciable current, depending on the width of the forbidden energy gap E_G. We have already seen that at a temperature T there will be a number of excited electrons in the conduction band, $\Delta N \approx \exp(-E_G/2kT)S(kT)kT$ (Eq. 26–18), and we know the form of $S(kT)$ for quasi-free electrons (Eq. 25–6). A careful integration gives the same result, except that the numerical constant is about 10% smaller, yielding

$$\Delta N = \frac{V}{4\pi^{3/2}} \left(\frac{2m^*kT}{\hbar^2}\right)^{3/2} e^{-E_G/2kT} \qquad (26\text{-}23)$$

At room temperature, taking the volume as 1 cm³, the preexponential factor in Eq. 26–23 can be computed to be about 2×10^{19} cm^{-3} (compared with a typical value of 10^{22} atoms cm^{-3}). Thus if E_G is not too large, ΔN is small but not entirely negligible. The electrons which are in the conduction band can give an electric current, since they find plenty of vacant states. When E_G is small enough to give appreciable conductivity, the material is called a *semiconductor*. A semiconductor is distinguished from a metal by its much smaller conductivity. It is also distinguished by the strong temperature dependence of the conductivity, through the exponential factor exp $(-E_G/2kT)$, since in a metal, where all the electrons are contributing to the conduction anyway, the excitation of a few of them makes almost no difference.

Equation 26–23 is normally written in terms of the number of electrons per unit volume, and with the constants slightly rearranged:

$$\Delta N/V \equiv n = 2\left(\frac{2\pi m^*kT}{h^2}\right)^{3/2} e^{-E_G/2kT} \qquad (26\text{-}24)$$

The factor in parentheses, which has the numerical value about 10^{19} cm^{-3} near room temperature, represents the number of quantum mechanical states available to the quasi-free electron (without spin). The same factor occurs in the Saha equation, Eq. 10–3, for a free electron gas in a gaseous plasma rather than in the interior of a solid.

In a semiconductor, when some of the electrons are excited into the conduction band and there contribute to the conductivity, they leave an equal number of vacant states at the top of the valence band. Since the valence band is no longer completely filled, the electrons in it can also contribute to the conductivity, by making transitions into the emptied states. It is possible to treat these "*holes*" in the valence band like electrons with a *positive* charge. This situation is somewhat analogous to that of lattice vacancies (Chapter 15): the vacancies, which are really missing atoms, can be treated as *entities* which move through the crystal. (An important difference is that the atoms are making the jumps in the opposite direction which successively fill the vacant sites; whereas the electrons are all accelerated together, carrying the holes with them.) The electron holes, which are equally as numerous as the electrons excited to the conduction band, also give an important contribution to the conductivity (and indeed it is the presence of the two types of charge carriers which makes semiconductor transistors work). The holes can be treated as quasi-free particles of positive charge, with a parabolic shape for the density of states function near the top of the valence band.

Without going into too much detail concerning the justification for treating these empty states near the top of the valence band as positive "particles" (holes), we may note that the same approach could be taken which led to Eq. 25–4. Near the top of the valence band, the energy $E(\kappa)$ can be expanded in a power series in κ,

$$E(\kappa) = - E_G - c_1\kappa^2 + \cdot \cdot \cdot$$

Here we have assumed that $\kappa = 0$ at the top of the band, and so $E = - E_G$ for $\kappa = 0$, using the same zero of energy as previously. (If the energy at the top of the band corresponds to some value of κ other than 0, as may happen, then the power series must be expanded about that value of κ instead.) Now using the definition of effective mass given by Eq. 25–5, we see that near the band maximum, the effective mass is *negative*. In an electric field, a particle with negative charge and negative mass would accelerate in the same direction as a particle with positive charge and positive mass. In discussing the motion of these particles we may therefore pretend that both the mass and the charge are positive. The expansion coefficient c_1 could have the same numerical value at the top of the valence band as at the bottom of the conduction band, but not necessarily so, depending on the details of the periodic potential in which the electrons move. Therefore, the effective mass of the holes is not necessarily the same as that of the electrons at the bottom of the conduction band; but if it is, then the Fermi energy E_F lies at the middle of the forbidden gap, as assumed in Fig. 26–5.

26–6   ELECTRICAL AND THERMAL CONDUCTIVITY

In the preceding section, we have seen the possibility of a net transport of electrons, for example in response to an applied electric field, in a metal, or in a semiconductor at elevated temperatures. In both cases there are electrons which are free to contribute to the transport process, although the number of them is much greater in a metal than in a semiconductor. What we have not yet considered is what prevents the transport from being infinite. The answer, just as in the case of a gas of atoms (Chapter 8), is scattering of the particles. The quasi-free electron wave functions we have used up until now do not include any description of the scattering, and we shall see in the next section what kinds of crystal imperfections we have to assume in order to introduce the scattering. In fact, in this discussion we shall be able to picture the electron gas classically, for the purpose of taking the collisions into account, although of course the quantum mechanical energy bands and Fermi distribution must also be recognized. (The scattering can more rigorously be treated quantum mechanically, but we have not developed the mathematical tools for doing so, and the result is similar.) Indeed, the classical free-electron transport theory was developed (Drude, 1900) before quantum mechanics was invented, and was largely successful, except for a few discrepancies which were subsequently removed by introducing the Fermi distribution.

Let us assume that an electric field E is applied to the electron gas, so that the electrons are accelerated by the force eE. If the mean time between collisions is τ and the mean net velocity is u, then the electrons lose the momentum m^*u after each time τ. In the steady state we should equate the rate of momentum loss m^*u/τ to the rate of momentum gain eE. Then the electrons will acquire a *drift velocity*

$$u = eE\tau/m^* \qquad (26\text{-}25)$$

This drift velocity (a net average speed superimposed on the random thermal velocity) leads to a particle flux

$$J = nu$$

where n is the number of conduction electrons per unit volume. For a semiconductor this number is the number excited to the conduction band, $n = \Delta N/V$ (Eq. 26-24); for a metal it is the total number in the conduction band, $n = N/V$ (Eq. 26-14), not the number thermally excited. The electric flux (current density) is

$$j = eJ = neu \qquad (26\text{-}26)$$

Since the electrical conductivity σ is defined by

$$j = \sigma E$$

from Eqs. 26-26 and 26-25 we obtain

$$\sigma = ne^2\tau/m^* \qquad (26\text{-}27)$$

The conductivity may also be written in terms of the mean free path by making use of Eq. 8-2, $L = \bar{v}\tau$:

$$\sigma = ne^2 L/m^*\bar{v} \qquad (26\text{-}28)$$

All the quantities in Eq. 26-28 have already been investigated, except the electron mean free path L, and we must next look into it (Section 26-7).

For some purposes, it is useful to talk about the *mobility* μ, defined as the drift velocity per unit electric field:

$$\mu \equiv u/E = e\tau/m^* = eL/m^*\bar{v} \qquad (26\text{-}29)$$

(Cf. Eq. 11-11.) In terms of the mobility, from Eq. 26-26 the conductivity can be written

$$\sigma = ne\mu \qquad (26\text{-}30)$$

The usefulness of the mobility lies in the fact that it does not depend on the number of charge carriers n. It depends on the mean free path L, the mean thermal speed $\bar{v}$, and the effective mass m^*. Thus the mobility may be comparable in metals, semiconductors, and insulators, whereas n is vastly different.

Assuming that the mean free path L is comparable in metals and semiconductors, we may discuss the dependence of the mobility on $\bar{v}$ given by Eq. 26-29. In semiconductors, the kinetic energy of the thermally excited electrons at the bottom of the conduction band is about kT, whereas in metals the kinetic energy of the electrons at the Fermi level is E_F. Therefore

$$\bar{v} \cong \sqrt{kT/m^*} \quad \text{(semiconductor)} \qquad (26\text{-}31)$$

$$\bar{v} \cong \sqrt{E_F/m^*} \quad \text{(metal)} \tag{26-32}$$

Since $E_F \approx 100kT$ ordinarily, $\bar{v}$ may be some 10 times greater in a metal, giving a mobility perhaps an order of magnitude smaller than in a semiconductor. Practically, in semiconductor devices, a high mobility is desirable. The *conductivity* of semiconductors is always much smaller than that of metals, of course, because of the factor n in Eq. 26–30.

The electrons can also diffuse through the electron gas under the influence of a concentration gradient, although the diffusion is usually ambipolar (cf. Section 11–5). According to Eq. 8–29, the diffusion coefficient is approximately

$$D \cong \bar{v}L$$

In the case of a semiconductor, the mobility can also be computed from the diffusion coefficient by the Einstein relation, Eq. 10–17,

$$\mu = eD/kT \cong e\bar{v}L/kT$$

If we substitute Eq. 26–31 into this expression for μ and into Eq. 26–29, we obtain in both cases

$$\mu \cong eL/\sqrt{m^*kT}$$

The Einstein relation does *not* hold for metals, because in deriving the relation the Boltzmann distribution was used, and this applies to conduction electrons only in semiconductors or plasmas where the density of the electron gas is very low.

Under the influence of a temperature gradient, the flux of the electrons through the electron gas will give a *thermal conductivity* which can be estimated from Eq. 8–15, calculated for a gas of atoms,

$$\kappa \cong \rho c \bar{v} L$$

The quantity ρc represents the heat capacity per unit volume. We have computed the heat capacity per mole in Eq. 26–20 for the electrons in a metal, but the heat capacity per unit volume is obtained immediately by replacing the number of electrons per mole N with the number per unit volume n. Then

$$\kappa \cong n \frac{k^2 T}{E_F} \bar{v} L \tag{26-33}$$

For metals, this gives an important, in fact the principal, contribution to the thermal conductivity. For semiconductors, the effect is less dominant, because of the smallness of ρc. In insulators the electronic thermal conductivity is completely negligible, compared to the heat conducted by the vibrations of the atoms.

It is interesting to make a comparison between the electrical conductivity and the thermal conductivity due to the conduction electrons in a metal. Using Eq. 26–32 to eliminate E_F, Eq. 26–33 becomes

$$\kappa \cong nk^2 TL/m^*\bar{v} \tag{26-34}$$

On comparison with Eq. 26–28, we find

$$\kappa/\sigma \cong (k/e)^2 T$$

If all the averages are calculated by accurate integrations, a numerical constant appears,

$$\kappa/\sigma = (\pi^2/3)(k/e)^2 T \qquad (26\text{–}35)$$

This relation is known as the *Wiedemann-Franz ratio*. It is remarkable that it is completely independent of all properties of the particular metal. Furthermore it is in fairly close agreement with the experimental values, except at very low temperatures where other complications lead to its failure. Thus the electrical and thermal conductivities are approximately proportional to each other in all metals.

26–7   ELECTRON MEAN FREE PATH

In order to make any numerical estimates of the electrical conductivities to be expected theoretically, we must consider the mean free path. The quantum mechanical scattering calculation which leads to the mean free path is rather difficult, and we shall not be able to treat it at all. We might therefore simply adopt the empirical point of view, that measured conductivities can give us experimental values of the mean free path, by the use of Eq. 26–28. Much more physical insight will be gained, on the other hand, by trying to make some estimate, however crude, of the mean free path values to be expected theoretically.

It might be thought at first that the mean free path would be very short for electrons in a solid, inasmuch as the scattering cross section σ_s of an atom for an electron is of the order of the square of the atomic diameter, as stated in Section 19–2. For Cu, for example, the radius of the Cu^+ ion core is about 1 Å, giving an area of about 3×10^{-16} cm^2. According to Eq. 8–3, the mean free path is $L = 1/n_s\sigma_s$, where n_s is the number of scatterers (atoms) per cm^3. Since this number is of the order of 8×10^{22} cm^{-3} in Cu, the mean free path should apparently be of the order of 4×10^{-8} cm $= 4$ Å, or about 2 atom diameters. (In this section, where we have to discuss the scattering cross section, we shall represent it by σ_s, in order to avoid confusion with the conductivity σ.) This result follows from the dense packing of the atoms in a solid. Such a short mean free path would really vitiate the picture we have developed, in which the quasi-free electrons were only occasionally scattered by collisions. Fortunately, however, it is incorrect. The main interaction between the conduction electrons and the atoms (or ion cores) of the lattice has already been taken into account (Section 25–3) by the effective mass m^*. The only interactions which actually lead to scattering are *deviations* from the perfectly regular lattice potential.

Thus, for example, impurities, vacancies, or interstitials, representing a perturbation of the regular potential, exhibit cross sections of the order of 10^{-15} cm^2. Since they are normally present in concentrations of only a fraction of a percent, say 10^{-3}, or about 10^{20} cm^{-3}, they may give a mean free path of the order of 10^{-5} cm $= 1000$ Å. A more important perturbation of the ideal periodicity at normal temperatures is the thermal vibration amplitude. Very roughly, we might suppose that if the area of the atom at rest does not contribute to the cross section, it would be only the additional area due to the vibration of the atom which would cause scattering. As a measure of this area, we may take the mean square displacement $\overline{x^2}$ of the vibrational motion about the equilibrium position of the atom. In Chapter 14 (Prob. 14–12), we found that the amplitude of vibration was only a few percent of the interatomic distance—or atomic diameter—and so its square is only perhaps 10^{-3} times the area of the atom. Thus the cross section for thermal scattering may be only of the order of 10^{-18} cm^2. On the other hand, all 10^{23} atoms/cm^3 are contributing to the scattering, not just the impurity

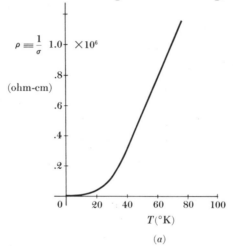

(a)

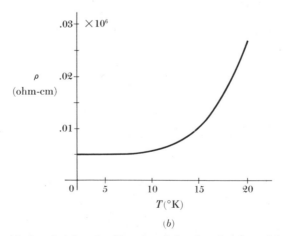

(b)

Fig. 26–6. *Electrical resistivity of sodium metal showing the effect of thermal scattering at high temperature and impurity scattering at low temperature.*

atoms. The thermal scattering therefore also leads to a mean free path which is of the order of 1000 Å. In fact, according to the equipartition law (Section 14–6),

$$\tfrac{1}{2}K\overline{x^2} = \tfrac{1}{2}kT$$

Since $\overline{x^2} \propto \sigma_s \propto 1/L$, the mean free path is inversely proportional to T at high temperature, where the thermal scattering predominates; and it is independent of T at low temperature, where the impurity scattering is dominant.

The temperature dependence of the conductivity may now be inferred from Eq. 26–28. In a metal, n and $\bar{v}$ (Eq. 26–32) are nearly independent of T, and so the temperature dependence enters only through the mean free path L. Thus at high temperature the conductivity is inversely proportional to temperature, or the resistivity is proportional to temperature; at low temperature it levels off at a value determined by imperfections (Fig. 26–6). In a semiconductor, on the other hand, n (Eq. 26–24) and $\bar{v}$ (Eq. 26–31) both depend on T, and so does L. According to Eq. 26–29, the mobility varies like $T^{-3/2}$, when thermal scattering predominates, as is usually the case. The principal temperature dependence of the conductivity arises in Eq. 26–30 not from the mobility but from the exponential temperature dependence of n. (See Fig. 26–7.)

It is important to note that the semiconductor behavior we have described is characteristic of a *pure* (or "intrinsic") semiconductor, containing equal numbers of conduction electrons and holes. When impurities are present, they may dominate the conductivity behavior (in a way which is somewhat analogous to electrolytic conduction in an ionic crystal containing impurities). If the impurities are dominant, the temperature characteristic is no longer exponential, but at sufficiently low temperatures the number of conduction electrons or holes is approximately constant. Although this "extrinsic" behavior is always of great practical importance in semiconductor devices, we shall not go into it here.

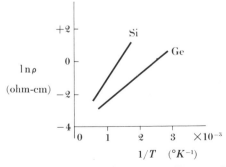

Fig. 26–7. *Electrical resistivity of the semiconductors silicon and germanium showing the exponential behavior in the intrinsic range.*

PROBLEMS

26-1.   Let $\delta \equiv E - E_F$ be the distance from the Fermi energy. Show that according to Eq. 26–11, $f(E_F + \delta) = 1 - f(E_F - \delta)$.

26-2.   In the Fermi distribution, let $\delta = E - E_F$. Calculate f for $\delta = 2kT$, $4kT$, $10kT$.

26-3.   Suppose a certain two-electron system has only 3 allowed energy levels, which are equally spaced. (Ignore spin, so that the levels are non-degenerate.)
(a) Enumerate the 3 possible states of this system, in terms of the occupation numbers.
(b) Using Eqs. 26–5 and 26–6, write expressions for $\bar{N}_0$, $\bar{N}_1$, $\bar{N}_2$.
(c) Evaluate these expressions for $T = 0°K$ and $T \to \infty$.

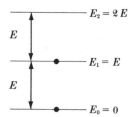

26-4.   Using the Fermi distribution (and density of states), prove that the *average* energy of the electrons in the conduction band of a metal at $0°K$ is $\bar{E} = (3/5) E_F$.

26-5.   If the Fermi energy for cobalt is $E_F = 1.1$ eV, approximately what fraction of the conduction band electrons are in excited states at the melting point?

26-6.   For Na, Cu, and Ag, the electronic heat capacity coefficient γ is 4.3, 1.8, and 1.6×10^{-4} cal/mole-deg², respectively.
(a) Calculate E_F from γ.
(b) Calculate m^*/m from E_F.

26-7.   Suppose that the effective mass of holes m_h^* is considerably greater than that of the electrons m_e^* (as is often the case). Where would E_F lie near $T = 0$, relative to the middle of the forbidden gap?

26-8.   Assume that a copper wire of cross section 10^{-2} cm² is carrying a current of 1 amp. For Cu, there are $n = 8 \times 10^{22}$ conduction electrons/cm³.
(a) What is the current density j in the wire?
(b) What is the electron flux per unit area J?
(c) What is the electron drift velocity u?

26-9.   Look up the resistivity of copper near room temperature.
(a) Calculate the mobility μ.
(b) Calculate the mean time between collisions τ, assuming $m^*/m = 1.5$.
(c) Calculate the mean free path, L, assuming $E_F = 7.0$ eV.

26-10.   Calculate the electronic thermal conductivity of copper, using the Wiedemann-Franz ratio and the experimental electrical conductivity. Compare this with the experimental thermal conductivity (from the *Handbook of*

Chemistry and Physics); what fraction of the thermal conductivity is due to the electrons?

26–11. The electron mean free path in Na metal near room temperature is 350 Å.
  (a) If this mean free path is due to thermal scattering (i.e., scattering by the thermal vibrations of the atoms), what is the effective cross section?
  (b) What concentration of impurities or lattice defects would give the same mean free path, if their cross section was 10^{-15} cm²?

REFERENCES

R. L. Sproull, *Modern Physics* (John Wiley & Sons, 1956), Ch. 9.

C. Kittel, *Introduction to Solid State Physics* (John Wiley & Sons, 1956, 2nd ed.), Ch. 10.

A. J. Dekker, *Solid State Physics* (Prentice-Hall, 1957), Ch. 12.

D. A. Wright, *Semiconductors* (Methuen, 1955, 2nd ed.).

V

NUCLEAR PARTICLES

In our discussion of atoms, molecules, and solids, we have only been concerned with their electronic structures. We have been content to treat the nuclei as massive and positively charged "points" of essentially no extension. This is quite legitimate for the study of atomic phenomena. Now, however, we propose to take another step away from our ordinary macroscopic world to delve into the actual internal structure of our "point" nuclei. This is a giant step indeed! Whereas typical atomic distances are measured in Ångstroms ($1\mathring{A} \equiv 10^{-8}$ cm), nuclear distances are 10^{-5} times as large and are measured in fermis ($1 f \equiv 10^{-13}$ cm). Similarly we step up in energy from a few eV in the atomic case to nuclear energies measured in MeV (10^{6} eV). Numerically speaking it is clear that we are talking about a completely different regime, making extrapolations from the atomic regime highly dangerous.

Everything we know about the nucleus is of course based on experimental results. Thus information about nuclear energy levels can be obtained by measuring the energies of photons (γ-rays) emitted by an excited nucleus. The nuclear situation is here quite analogous to the atomic one, but since the nuclear photon energies are much higher than those emitted in atomic transitions, their measurement presents special problems. Although the results of many nuclear experiments will be discussed in the ensuing chapters, there will be little or no mention of how nuclear measurements are actually carried out. Measurement techniques are best learned in the laboratory, and it is expected that the students reading this book will have the opportunity to make some nuclear measurements. Furthermore, the measurement process in a nuclear experiment is essentially of a non-nuclear nature. A typical experiment involves the acceleration of a charged particle by electromagnetic means and the detection and counting of the end products of a nuclear collision through their electromagnetic interaction with the measuring apparatus. The details of the measurements are therefore more likely to involve the physics of solids (e.g., scintillation counters), of ionized gases (e.g., Geiger counters), or the chemistry of photography (nuclear emulsions) than the physics of nuclei. For these reasons, and to keep the nuclear part of the book from getting too long, our discussion will be limited largely to a theoretical *description of the properties and the structure of the nucleus. This description, it is important to remember, is firmly based on nuclear measurements, which have been carried out with skill and ingenuity by a great many nuclear experimenters.*

In going from macroscopic physics to atomic physics we found it necessary to abandon classical mechanics in favor of quantum mechanics. We might well ask whether we must now give up quantum mechanics in favor of a new "nuclear mechanics." Fortunately such a drastic step has not proved necessary. It is true that our quantum theory has to be extended in many ways, but the basic ideas of quantum mechanics carry over perfectly well from atomic to nuclear physics. We find for instance that nuclear energies and angular momenta are quantized and that the basic nuclear constituents, the neutrons and the protons, obey the Pauli exclusion principle. One might hope, therefore, to proceed much as in atomic physics: first to solve the two-body problem (the analog to the hydrogen atom), secondly to use the two-body wave functions to construct approximate wave functions and find approximate energy levels for the many-body nuclei.

In a way we are better off in nuclear physics than in solid state physics, where we encounter systems of $\sim 10^{23}$ particles. The heaviest naturally occurring nucleus, uranium, contains only 238 particles. In other respects, however, the nuclear systems are much more difficult to treat than atoms, molecules, and solids. The basic force law or "interaction" involved in atomic systems is electromagnetic in nature and well known from macroscopic physics. To obtain the hydrogen atom energy levels we simply inserted the coulomb potential between the electron and the proton into the Schrödinger equation, which we then proceeded to solve. The nuclear force does not extend over macroscopic distances, not even over atomic distances. As a result the nuclear force is not nearly as well known as the electromagnetic force. We do know three things: The nuclear force is very strongly attractive at distances of the order of 10^{-13} cm. This can be deduced from the fact that nuclei with up to 92 positively charged and hence mutually repelling protons are held within a radius of $\sim 10^{-12}$ cm. Secondly, the nuclear force has a very short range. Experiments in which protons are scattered off protons show that the interparticle force is simply the coulomb force until the protons get within 10^{-12} cm–10^{-13} cm of each other. Thirdly, the nuclear force between two nuclear particles is not simply a function of their separation, but depends in a complicated way on their relative spin orientations, on the angles between the spin directions and the direction from one particle to another, and even on the relative particle velocities.

With the two-body nuclear force imperfectly understood, it is clear that we are seriously handicapped in any basic approach to the many-body nuclear problem. Furthermore, we lack the simplifying feature of a single strong force center, which turned out to be so helpful in our discussion of many-electron atoms, where to a first approximation we ignored the forces between the electrons. Our approach to the many-body nuclei will therefore necessarily be phenomenological in nature. We will find that some fairly simple models of the nuclei can "explain" many of the observed features in a qualitative way. Before we go any further, however, we will briefly discuss some of the basic properties of nuclei, which any fundamental theory would have to encompass.

27/basic properties of nuclei

Our study of the atomic nucleus begins with a description of the nucleus in terms of its constituents, and a discussion of the basic nuclear parameters of mass, size, charge, and spin.

27-1 NUCLEAR CONSTITUENTS

It is the aim of the scientist to understand all observed phenomena in terms of a few basic concepts. In spite of many problems and temporary setbacks, this quest for understanding has been remarkably successful. One of the most important early advances was the recognition that all matter in its seemingly infinite variety of forms is built up of atoms of different elements, the number of different elements being quite small (< 100).

A premature step toward further simplification was taken as early as 1816 when Prout suggested that all atomic weights were integral multiples of the atomic weight of hydrogen and that all the heavier elements were in fact combinations of hydrogen atoms. Prout's hypothesis fell into disfavor, however, when some atomic weights were found not to be even approximate multiples of the hydrogen weight.

With the discovery of the electron, a negatively charged particle much lighter than even the lightest element, as a part of the neutral atom, it became clear that the bulk of the mass was positively charged. Rutherford's scattering experiments (1911) established that the mass and the positive charge were concentrated in an exceedingly small nucleus with a diameter $\lesssim 10^{-12}$ cm. (See Chapters 5 and 6.) Since the atomic diameter is of the order of 10^{-8} cm, the volume of the nucleus takes up only a fraction $\lesssim (10^{-12}/10^{-8})^3 = 10^{-12}$ of the atomic volume.

Rutherford's fundamental discovery may be considered the birth of nuclear physics. Following the discovery of the nucleus, efforts were made to explain the nuclei of the heavy elements as composites of hydrogen nuclei and electrons, the latter being needed to give the correct charge to mass ratio. Support for this hypothesis was obtained from the observed emission of electrons ("β-particles") from radioactive nuclei. The α-particles (helium nuclei) also emitted from radioactive nuclei could be understood as a combination of 4 hydrogen nuclei (called *protons*) and 2 electrons.

The electron-proton model of the nucleus nevertheless met with insurmountable difficulties. One of these may be understood in terms of the uncertainty principle (Chapter 19). An electron confined to the nuclear volume ($\Delta x \approx 10^{-12}$ cm) would have a minimum kinetic energy of the order of 100 MeV (Prob. 19-7), much greater than any reasonable coulomb binding energy. Furthermore, the most energetic electrons emitted by nuclei in β-decays have energies of about 4 MeV. It seems unlikely therefore that the nucleus can contain free electrons. This dilemma was resolved with the discovery of the neutron, a neutral particle with a mass approximately equal to that of the proton.

Since the discovery of the neutron in 1932 (Chadwick), which is discussed in Chapter 31, our view of the constitution of the nucleus has remained essentially unchanged: the nucleus is a closely packed structure built up of neutrons and protons. The proton is simply the nucleus of the hydrogen atom with a charge $+e$ equal in magnitude and opposite in sign to the charge of the electron, with a mass M_p equal to $1836m_e$ (m_e = electron mass), and with a spin quantum number equal to $\frac{1}{2}$. The neutron has no electric charge, but is in other respects very similar to the proton with a mass M_n equal to $1839m_e$ and a spin of $\frac{1}{2}$. Both the neutrons and the protons are found to obey the Pauli exclusion principle (Chapter 22). Because of the many similarities between the neutron and the proton a common name, *nucleon*, has been introduced to denote either nuclear constituent.

The nucleons in a nucleus do not form a rigid lattice like the atoms in a crystal, but rather a fluid structure with the nucleons free to move around like molecules in a liquid. The analogy to a fluid is exploited in the *liquid drop model* of the nucleus (Chapter 29), which is capable of explaining in qualitative terms many of the observed nuclear properties.

The number of protons in the nucleus is called the *atomic number* and is usually designated by the letter Z. The total nuclear charge is then equal to

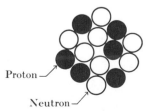

Proton

Neutron

Fig. 27–1. A nucleus is a close packed, fluid structure of neutrons and protons.

Ze, and the neutral atom will have Z electrons surrounding the nucleus. Since the chemical properties depend only on the electron structure, the atomic number Z specifies the chemical element. The total number of nucleons, called the *mass number*, is denoted by the symbol A. It follows that the number of neutrons N is equal to $A - Z$,

$$N = A - Z \tag{27-1}$$

Nuclei with the same atomic number Z but different mass numbers A are referred to as *isotopes*. Most elements have more than one stable isotope (Section 27–2). Nuclei with equal N but different Z are known as *isotones,* and nuclei with equal A, but different Z and N, are called *isobars*.

Since the atomic number Z is known if the symbol for the chemical element, call it X, is given (Table 22–2), the nucleus is identified completely by writing the mass number A as a superscript, X^A. Thus the unstable hydrogen isotope, tritium ($Z = 1$, $A = 3$) is denoted by the symbol H^3. Sometimes the Z and N numbers are given explicitly on the left side of the chemical symbol, $^N_Z X^A$, although this is not really necessary. Tritium would then be identified by $^2_1 H^3$.

The successful explanation of the structure of the 100 or so known chemical elements in terms of but three kinds of particles, neutrons and protons in a small nucleus surrounded by electrons, represents a great simplification in basic concepts. The nature of the force which holds the nucleons together, however, is still imperfectly understood (Chapter 28).

27–2   STABLE NUCLEI

One might think that, since the nuclear force is strongly attractive, stable nuclei of any atomic number Z and neutron number N would exist. Such is not the case. A plot of the N and Z values of the stable nuclei is given in Fig. 27–2. The heaviest stable nucleus is the bismuth isotope Bi^{209} with $Z = 83$ and $N = 126$. However, since the unstable isotopes U^{238}, U^{235}, and Th^{232} decay very slowly, these heavier elements and their decay products are still naturally present on Earth. They represent the undecayed residue of the heavier elements present when the solar system was formed about 5×10^9 years ago.

Twenty elements have only a single stable isotope and eight others have single isotopes with a relative abundance greater than 99%. Most elements, however, have several stable isotopes. Tin has the greatest number, ten, while xenon has nine. It is this mixture of isotopes that leads to atomic weights that are not even approximate multiples of the hydrogen atomic weight (Prout's downfall). There are no stable nuclei with $Z = 43$ or 61; with $N = 19, 35, 39, 45, 61, 89, 115,$ or 123; nor with $A = 5$ or 8. With these exceptions all Z values from 1 to 83, all N values from 0 to 126, and all mass numbers A from 1 to 209 correspond to stable nuclei.

The relative terrestrial isotopic abundances of the stable and the very long lived unstable nuclei are given in Table 27–1.

The reason nuclei other than those in Fig. 27-2 are unstable can be understood in terms of (a) the coulomb repulsion of the protons, (b) the "saturation" of nuclear forces, and (c) the Pauli exclusion principle, which favors $Z \approx N$. The fact that positively charged particles repel each other needs no further elaboration. What is meant by saturation of nuclear forces will become clear as we discuss the variations of the binding energy and the nuclear size with the mass number A (Sections 27-3 and 27-4). The near equality of Z and N for the stable nuclei (especially the light nuclei) can best be understood in terms of a shell model or single-particle model of the nucleus (Chapter 29) analogous to the electronic shell model of the atom. Since the neutrons and protons obey the Pauli exclusion principle, they fill up "shells" in the nuclear potential well. Thus in the lowest energy level one can put two protons (spin up, spin down) and two neutrons. This situation is energetically favored over a four neutron system where two of the neutrons would have to go into the next higher energy level. Since neutrons can turn into protons and vice versa through the processes of β-decay (the emission of an electron from a nucleus) and electron capture (Chapter 30), nu-

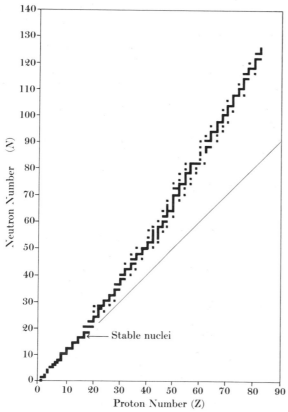

Fig. 27-2. *The stable nuclei.*

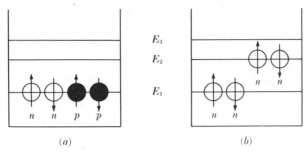

Fig. 27–3. *The lowest energy configuration of* (a) *two protons and two neutrons and* (b) *four neutrons in a nuclear potential.*

clei off the stable Z-N curve (Fig. 27–2) will adjust their Z/N ratio through these processes until a stable isobar is reached. For heavy nuclei the coulomb repulsion between the protons makes it energetically favorable to have $Z < N$. A compromise is reached between the tendency of the Pauli principle towards $Z \approx N$ and of the coulomb repulsion towards $Z \approx 0$. Thus the stable lead isotopes have $Z = 82$ and $N = 124, 125,$ and 126. The instability of nuclei with $A > 209$ to α-decay (the emission of a helium nucleus) results from the coulomb repulsion of the protons and will be discussed in Chapter 30.

27–3 NUCLEAR BINDING ENERGIES

The atomic masses of the stable isotopes have been measured with great precision. The masses are determined from data obtained with mass spectrometers as well as from the energy release in nuclear reactions and decays. The atomic masses are commonly given in terms of atomic mass units (amu). There are unfortunately three different scales of atomic mass units in use. One is based on the mass of the $_6C^{12}$ isotope. In this scheme 1 amu $\equiv$ $\frac{1}{12} \times$ (atomic weight of C^{12}). It is expected that this standard will be universally adopted since it is more convenient for mass measurements with mass spectrometers. Our table of atomic masses, Table 27–1 (at the end of this chapter), is based on the C^{12} standard. An alternative definition is 1 amu $\equiv$ $\frac{1}{16}$ (atomic weight of O^{16}). Most tables in older books are based on the O^{16} standard. There is also a chemical scale in which 1 amu $\equiv$ $\frac{1}{16}$ (atomic weight of the naturally occurring mixture of oxygen isotopes).

The *binding energy*, B, of the nucleus is defined as the energy that must be applied to the nucleus in order to break it up into its constituent particles. This definition is completely analogous to the one used previously for atoms, molecules, and solids. After the breakup the total energy of the system is just the rest energy of the nucleons, $ZM_pc^2 + NM_nc^2$, where M_p and M_n are the proton and neutron masses, respectively. Before the breakup the total energy is the rest energy of the nucleus, M_Nc^2. The binding energy is therefore equal to

$$B = (-M_N + ZM_p + NM_n)c^2$$

Adding the mass of Z electrons to M_N we obtain the atomic mass, $M_{Z,A} = M_N + Zm_e$, if we ignore the very small binding energy of the electrons.

The expression for the nuclear binding energy may now be rewritten in terms of the atomic masses:

$$B = (-M_N - Zm_e + Z(M_p + m_e) + NM_n)c^2$$

or

$$B = (-M_{Z,A} + ZM_H + NM_n)c^2 \qquad (27\text{-}2)$$

Here $M_H = M_p + m_e$ is the atomic mass of hydrogen. Since the amu is related to MeV by

$$1\,\text{amu}(C^{12}) = 931.441\,\text{MeV}/c^2$$

we find that the binding energy may be expressed as follows:

$$B = 931.441\,\text{MeV}\,[Z \times 1.0078252 + N \times 1.0086654 - M_{Z,A}] \qquad (27\text{-}3)$$

where it is understood that $M_{Z,A}$ is to be given in amu(C^{12}). If we define the *mass deficit*, ΔM, as the *decrease* in total mass when a number of protons, neutrons, and electrons combine to form an atom, we see that the binding energy B and the mass deficit are very simply related,

$$B = \Delta M c^2$$

The binding energy per nucleon B/A is an important nuclear parameter. In Fig. 27–3 we have plotted B/A as a function of A for the stable nuclei. The most striking thing about this plot is the near constancy of B/A; $B/A \approx 8$ MeV for all but a small number of the lightest nuclei. The constancy of B/A implies that the nuclear forces "saturate." This implication will be discussed more fully in the next section. The slow decrease in B/A for large A results from the increased effect of the coulomb repulsion for the

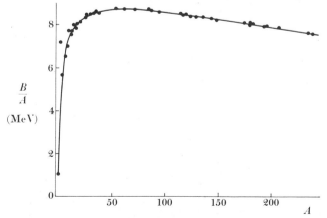

Fig. 27–4. The binding energy per nucleon of the stable nuclei as a function of mass number.

heavy nuclei. (See Chapter 29.) The binding energy of the nuclei is seen to be enormous,

$$B \approx 8\,\mathrm{MeV} \times A \qquad (27\text{--}4)$$

When even a small fraction of this energy is released, e.g., in the fission of uranium nuclei or the fusion of light nuclei, one finds (Chapter 30) that the nuclear energy yield per pound of "fuel" is incomparably greater than the yield of chemical energy from more ordinary fuels.

27-4 THE SIZE OF NUCLEI

The nuclear dimensions have been determined primarily through scattering of fast neutrons and very fast electrons. It was quickly established that the density of nuclear matter varies very little from one nucleus to the next, i.e., that the nuclear volume is proportional to A, the number of nucleons in the nucleus. The nuclear radius R may then be expressed by the formula

$$R = r_0 A^{1/3} \qquad r_0 = \mathrm{const} \qquad (27\text{--}5)$$

The value one obtains for r_0 depends to a small extent on the method of measurement. The neutron scattering experiments give $r_0 \approx 1.3 - 1.4$ f, while the electron scattering experiments yield values in the range $1.2 - 1.3$ f. Actually the two methods do not measure quite the same thing. The electron scattering gives a measure of the nuclear electric charge distribution, i.e., the proton density distribution, while the neutron scattering measures the extent of the nuclear potential. The slight discrepancy should not alarm us, therefore.

Another method for determining r_0 is available for the heavy $(A > 209)$ α-emitters. From the energies of the α-particles and the lifetimes of the decay, the nuclear radius can be calculated. The values for r_0 obtained this way vary somewhat from one nucleus to the next, but the average value is about 1.4 f. Overall we will choose

$$r_0 = 1.3\ \mathrm{f} \qquad (27\text{--}6)$$

or

$$R = 1.3 A^{1/3}\ \mathrm{f} \qquad (27\text{--}7)$$

as the best value for the average nuclear radius. With this choice the nuclear radii are seen to vary from ~ 1.3 f for $A = 1$ to $1.3\sqrt[3]{238}$ f ≈ 8 f for U^{238}.

27-5 SATURATION OF NUCLEAR FORCES

The constant density of nuclear matter gives rise to the picture of a nucleus consisting of "hard sphere" or billiard ball nucleons. Again the analogy with a fluid comes to mind. (See the discussion of the liquid-drop model in Chapter 29.) If we add two cups of water together, the density of the water is essentially unchanged. Furthermore, the binding energy or "heat of condensation" for water is proportional to the volume (i.e., twice as much heat boils away twice as much water). This is precisely the result we arrived at for nuclei (Section 27–3), $B/A \cong$ const, or since the mass number A is proportional to the volume $\frac{4\pi}{3} R^3$, Eq. 27–5, $B/$volume $\cong$ const.

In a liquid these properties (constant density, and binding energy proportional to volume) are attributed to the saturation of the bonds, which permits the atoms to interact strongly with only a small number of neighbors rather than with all the atoms in the liquid. The analogous nuclear properties, Eqs. 27–4 and 27–5, are referred to as the saturation properties of nuclear matter. The observed dependence of the nuclear binding energy on the mass number can now be understood if we assume that each nucleon does not interact with all the other nucleons, but only with a few of the neighbors. This in turn implies that the nuclear forces must have a very *short range*, specifically it must be shorter than the radius $1.3A^{1/3}$ f for all but the very lightest nuclei, i.e., of the order of 1 to 2 f. That the nuclear forces saturate quickly may be seen from the fact that already with helium, $A = 4$, the binding energy per nucleon is 7.07 MeV, or close to the saturation value. (Note, however, the large irregularity in B/A for small A, Fig. 27–3.)

Long-range forces, such as gravitational and electrostatic forces, do not saturate. Thus each proton in the nucleus interacts electrically with every other proton, i.e., with $Z - 1$ other protons. The number of interacting pairs is equal to $Z(Z - 1)/2$, and the coulomb energy should be proportional to this quantity, or approximately to Z^2 for $Z \gg 1$. The repulsive coulomb energy per proton is therefore not constant, but increases linearly with Z. The relative importance of coulomb force repulsion to nuclear force attraction will then increase with Z, which explains the decrease in B/A for heavy nuclei, Fig. 27–3. We shall find (Chapter 29) that the dependence of the nuclear masses and binding energies on A and Z can be understood remarkably well in terms of the simple liquid-drop model of the nucleus, provided we allow for the coulomb energy and the decrease in binding at the surface of the nucleus.

27–6 ELECTRICAL AND MAGNETIC PROPERTIES OF THE NUCLEI

The charge of the nucleus is of course equal to Ze, since each proton carries a charge equal to $+ e$ while the neutrons are neutral. It is found that the nuclear charge distribution is not quite spherically symmetrical. A measure of the departure from spherical symmetry is the so-called *quadrupole moment* of the nucleus. Its precise definition will not concern us here; suffice it to say that if the charge distribution is uniform throughout an ellipsoid of rotation with a semi-axis a along the axis of symmetry and semi-axis b perpendicular to the axis, then the quadrupole moment Q is

$$Q = \tfrac{2}{5}Ze(a^2 - b^2)$$

A positive Q corresponds to prolate or cigar-like spheroids $(a > b)$, negative Q to oblate or pancake-like spheroids $(a < b)$, while a sphere $(a = b)$ has $Q = 0$. The existence of a non-vanishing quadrupole moment for the deuteron (Chapter 28) establishes beyond question the fact that the neutron-proton force is *non-central*, which is indeed a seriously complicating feature of the nuclear force.

Many nuclei also possess a magnetic dipole moment as though they were tiny bar magnets. Nuclear magnetic moments are measured in units of nuclear magnetons,

$$1 \text{ nuclear magneton} = e\hbar/2M_pc = 0.505 \times 10^{-23} \text{ erg/gauss}$$

The direction of the magnetic moment is always given with respect to the direction of the angular momentum of the nucleus. With these conventions the magnetic moment of the proton is

$$\mu_p = +2.793$$

while that of the neutron is

$$\mu_n = -1.913$$

The minus sign in the moment of the neutron indicates that it points in a direction opposite to that of the neutron spin. One finds (Chapter 29) that nucleons pair off in the nucleus, leading to a pairwise cancellation of spins and magnetic moments. Thus it is an experimental fact that all nuclei with Z even and N even have zero angular momentum and zero magnetic moment. All odd A nuclei, however, must have either Z or N odd. One might think that the angular momentum and the magnetic moment of the whole nucleus would be due to the one odd nucleon. This is a basic assumption of the single-particle model of the nucleus (Chapter 29) and on the whole a fairly good one.

TABLE 27–1   Nuclear Properties

Symbol	Atomic number (Z)	Mass number (A)	Relative abundance (%)	Atomic mass excess $M - A$ (10^{-3} amu(C^{12}))	Binding energy B (MeV)
n	0	1		8.6654	. . .
H	1	1	99.9849–99.9861	7.8252	. . .
D	1	2	0.0139–0.0151	14.1022	2.225
T	1	3		16.0494	8.482
He	2	3	$\sim 10^{-5}$–10^{-4}	16.0299	7.718
		4	~ 100	2.6036	28.295
Li	3	6	7.52	15.126	31.991
		7	92.48	16.005	39.244
Be	4	9	100	12.186	58.161

TABLE 27-1   Nuclear Properties—Continued

Symbol	Atomic number (Z)	Mass number (A)	Relative abundance (%)	Atomic mass excess M − A (10⁻³ amu(C¹²))	Binding energy B (MeV)
B	5	10	18.45– 19.64	12.939	64.749
		11	80.36– 81.55	9.305	76.205
C	6	12	98.892	0	92.161
		13	1.108	3.354	97.108
N	7	14	99.634	3.074	104.66
		15	0.366	0.108	115.49
O	8	16	99.759	− 5.085	127.62
		17	0.037	− 0.867	131.76
		18	0.204	− 0.840	139.81
F	9	19	100	− 1.595	147.80
Ne	10	20	90.92	− 7.560	160.64
		21	0.257	− 6.151	167.40
		22	8.82	− 8.616	177.77
Na	11	23	100	− 10.227	186.56
Mg	12	24	78.70	− 14.955	198.25
		25	10.13	− 14.160	205.58
		26	11.17	− 17.409	216.68
Al	13	27	100	− 18.465	224.95
Si	14	28	92.21	− 23.073	236.53
		29	4.70	− 23.509	245.01
		30	3.09	− 26.239	255.62
P	15	31	100	− 26.237	262.91
S	16	32	95.0	− 27.926	271.77
		33	0.760	− 28.540	280.42
		34	4.22	− 32.136	291.84
		36	0.014	− 32.909	308.70
Cl	17	35	75.529	− 31.146	298.20
		37	24.471	− 34.104	317.10
Ar		36	0.337	− 32.452	306.71
		38	0.063	− 37.276	327.34
		40	99.600	− 37.616	343.80
K	19	39	93.10	− 36.29	333.7
		40	0.012	− 35.99	341.5
		41	6.88	− 38.16	351.6
Ca	20	40	96.97	− 37.41	342.0
		42	0.64	− 41.37	361.9
		43	0.145	− 41.22	369.8
		44	2.06	− 44.51	380.9
		46	0.003	− 46.31	398.8
		48	0.185	− 47.64	416.1
Sc	21	45	100	− 44.08	387.8
Ti	22	46	7.93	− 47.37	398.2

TABLE 27-1   Nuclear Properties—Continued

Sym- bol	Atomic number (Z)	Mass number (A)	Relative abundance (%)	Atomic mass excess M − A (10^{-3} amu(C^{12}))	Binding energy B (MeV)
		47	7.28	− 48.24	407.1
		48	73.94	− 52.05	418.7
		49	5.38	− 52.13	426.8
		50	5.34	− 55.21	437.8
V	23	50	0.24	− 52.84	434.8
		51	99.76	− 56.02	445.8
Cr	24	50	4.31	− 53.95	435.0
		52	83.76	− 59.49	456.3
		53	9.55	− 59.35	464.3
		54	2.38	− 61.12	474.0
Mn	25	55	100	− 61.95	482.1
Fe	26	54	5.82	− 60.38	471.7
		56	91.66	− 65.07	492.3
		57	2.19	− 64.61	499.9
		58	0.33	− 66.73	509.9
Co	27	59	100	− 66.81	517.3
Ni	28	58	67.88	− 64.66	506.5
		60	26.23	− 69.22	526.8
		61	1.19	− 68.95	534.6
		62	3.66	− 71.66	545.3
		64	1.08	− 72.04	561.8
Cu	29	63	69.1	− 70.41	551.4
		65	30.9	− 72.21	569.2
Zn	30	64	48.89	− 70.86	559.1
		66	27.81	− 73.95	578.1
		67	4.11	− 72.85	585.2
		68	18.56	− 75.14	595.4
		70	0.62	− 74.65	611.1
Ga	31	69	60.4	− 74.32	601.9
		71	39.6	− 75.16	618.8
Ge	32	70	20.52	− 75.72	610.5
		72	27.43	− 78.26	629.0
		73	7.76	− 76.64	635.6
		74	36.54	− 78.85	645.7
		76	7.76	− 78.64	661.6
As	33	75	100	− 78.42	652.6
Se	34	74	0.87	− 77.49	650.9
		76	9.02	− 80.77	662.0
		77	7.58	− 80.07	669.5
		78	23.52	− 82.65	679.9
		80	49.82	− 83.49	696.9
		82	9.19	− 83.34	712.9
Br	35	79	50.54	− 81.65	686.3
		81	49.46	− 83.66	704.3

TABLE 27–1   Nuclear Properties—Continued

Symbol	Atomic number (Z)	Mass number (A)	Relative abundance (%)	Atomic mass excess M − A (10⁻³ amu(C¹²))	Binding energy B (MeV)
Kr	36	78	0.354	− 79.63	675.6
		80	2.27	− 83.61	695.4
		82	11.56	− 86.52	714.3
		83	11.55	− 85.87	721.7
		84	56.90	− 88.50	732.2
		86	17.37	− 89.38	749.2
Rb	37	85	72.15	− 88.29	739.3
		87 ·	27.85	− 90.82	757.8
Sr	38	84	0.56	− 86.62	728.9
		86	9.86	− 90.74	748.9
		87 ·	7.02	− 91.11	757.3
		88	82.56	− 94.39	768.5
Y	39	89	100	− 94.57	775.9
Zr	40	90	51.46	− 95.68	784.2
		91	11.23	− 94.75	791.4
		92	17.11	− 95.41	800.1
		94	17.40	− 93.86	814.8
		96	2.80	− 91.80	829.1
Nb	41	93	100	− 93.98	806.1
Mo	42	92	15.84	− 93.71	797.0
		94	9.04	− 95.26	814.6
		95	15.72	− 94.28	821.7
		96	16.53	− 95.45	830.9
		97	9.46	− 94.25	837.8
		98	23.78	− 94.49	846.1
		100	9.63	− 92.43	860.4
Ru	44	96	5.51	− 92.40	826.5
		98	1.87	− 94.50	844.6
		99	12.72	− 93.92	852.1
		100	12.62	− 96.98	863.0
		101	17.07	− 95.88	870.1
		102	31.61	− 96.28	878.5
		104	18.58	− 94.47	893.0
Rh	45	103	100	− 95.20	884.8
Pd	46	102	0.96	− 95.06	875.8
		104	10.97	− 96.44	893.2
		105	22.23	− 95.36	900.3
		106	27.33	− 96.80	909.7
		108	26.71	− 96.08	925.2
		110	11.81	− 95.50	940.8
Ag	47	107	51.35	− 95.03	915.4
		109	48.65	− 95.30	931.8
Cd	48	106	1.215	− 94.05	905.6
		108	0.875	− 96.00	923.6

TABLE 27–1   Nuclear Properties—Continued

Sym-bol	Atomic number (Z)	Mass number (A)	Relative abundance (%)	Atomic mass excess M − A (10⁻³ amu(C¹²))	Binding energy B (MeV)
		110	12.39	− 97.03	940.7
		111	12.75	− 95.85	947.6
		112	24.07	− 97.16	956.9
		113 ·	12.26	− 95.39	963.3
		114	28.86	− 96.43	972.4
		116	7.58	− 94.99	987.2
In	49	113 ·	4.28	− 95.72	962.9
		115 ·	95.72	− 95.93	979.2
Sn	50	112	0.96	− 95.06	953.4
		114	0.66	− 97.04	971.4
		115 ·	0.35	− 96.47	978.9
		116	14.30	− 97.89	988.3
		117	7.61	− 96.94	995.5
		118	24.03	− 98.21	1004.8
		119	8.58	− 96.61	1011.3
		120	32.85	− 97.87	1020.6
		122	4.72	− 96.59	1035.5
		124	5.94	− 94.76	1050.0
Sb	51	121	57.25	− 96.25	1026.4
		123 ·	42.75	− 95.85	1042.1
Te	52	120	0.089	− 95.49	1016.8
		122	2.46	− 97.00	1034.4
		123 ·	0.87	− 95.82	1041.3
		124	4.61	− 97.24	1050.7
		125	6.99	− 95.58	1057.2
		126	18.71	− 96.76	1066.4
		128	31.79	− 95.29	1081.2
		130	34.49	− 93.30	1095.5
I	53	127	100	− 95.65	1072.7
Xe	54	124	0.096	− 93.88	1046.0
		126	0.090	− 95.83	1064.0
		128	1.919	− 96.46	1080.7
		129	26.44	− 95.22	1087.6
		130	4.08	− 96.49	1096.9
		131	21.18	− 94.91	1103.5
		132	26.89	− 95.84	1112.4
		134	10.44	− 94.60	1127.4
		136	8.87	− 92.78	1141.9
Cs	55	133	100	− 94.91	1118.8
Ba	56	130	0.101	− 93.75	1092.8
		132	0.097	− 94.88	1110.0
		134	2.42	− 95.69	1126.9
		135	6.59	− 94.43	1133.8
		136	7.81	− 95.64	1143.0

TABLE 27-1   Nuclear Properties—Continued

Symbol	Atomic number (Z)	Mass number (A)	Relative abundance (%)	Atomic mass excess M − A (10⁻³ amu(C¹²))	Binding energy B (MeV)
		137	11.32	− 94.44	1149.9
		138	71.66	− 94.99	1158.5
La	57	138	0.089	− 93.19	1156.0
		139	99.911	− 93.94	1164.8
Ce	58	136	0.193	− 92.90	1138.9
		138	0.250	− 94.28	1156.3
		140	88.48	− 94.72	1172.8
		142	11.07	− 90.96	1185.5
Pr	59	141	100	− 92.61	1178.1
Nd	60	142	27.11	− 92.52	1185.4
		143	12.17	− 90.38	1191.4
		144	23.85	− 90.10	1199.2
		145	8.30	− 87.84	1205.2
		146	17.22	− 87.31	1212.8
Sm	62	144	3.09	− 88.35	1196.0
		147	14.97	− 85.38	1217.5
		148	11.24	− 85.44	1225.6
		149	13.83	− 83.07	1231.5
		150	7.44	− 82.99	1239.5
		152	26.72	− 80.51	1253.3
		154	22.71	− 77.99	1267.1
Eu	63	151	47.82	− 80.37	1244.3
		153	52.18	− 79.14	1259.3
Gd	64	152	0.20	− 80.47	1251.7
		154	2.15	− 79.28	1266.8
		155	14.73	− 77.41	1273.1
		156	20.47	− 77.90	1281.6
		157	15.68	− 76.06	1288.0
		158	24.87	− 75.90	1295.9
		160	21.90	− 72.88	1309.2
Tb	65	159	100	− 75.05	1302.4
Dy	66	156	0.0524	− 76.24	1278.5
		158	0.0902	− 76.04	1294.4
		160	2.294	− 75.17	1309.8
		161	18.88	− 73.40	1316.2
		162	25.53	− 73.53	1324.4
		163	24.97	− 71.63	1330.7
		164	28.18	− 71.17	1338.3
Ho	67	165	100	− 69.70	1344.3
Er	68	162	0.136	− 71.22	1320.7
		164	1.56	− 70.71	1336.6
		166	33.41	− 69.60	1351.5
		167	22.94	− 67.95	1358.0
		168	27.07	− 67.62	1365.8

TABLE 27-1   Nuclear Properties—Continued

Sym- bol	Atomic number (Z)	Mass number (A)	Relative abundance (%)	Atomic mass excess $M - A$ $(10^{-3}$ amu(C^{12}))	Binding energy B (MeV)
		170	14.88	− 64.49	1379.0
Tm	69	169	100	− 65.65	1371.2
Yb	70	168	0.135	− 66.10	1362.8
		170	3.03	− 65.12	1378.0
		171	14.31	− 63.54	1384.6
		172	21.82	− 63.44	1392.6
		173	16.13	− 61.70	1399.0
		174	31.84	− 60.98	1406.4
		176	12.73	− 57.26	1419.1
Lu	71	175	97.40	− 59.11	1412.0
		176	2.60	− 57.26	1418.3
Hf	72	174	0.18	− 59.74	1403.7
		176	5.20	− 58.35	1418.6
		177	18.50	− 56.52	1424.9
		178	27.14	− 56.13	1432.6
		179	13.75	− 53.98	1438.7
		180	35.24	− 53.19	1446.0
Ta	73	181	100	− 52.02	1452.2
W	74	180	0.135	− 53.02	1444.3
		182	26.41	− 51.73	1459.3
		183	14.40	− 49.71	1465.5
		184	30.64	− 49.01	1472.9
		186	28.41	− 45.66	1485.9
Re	75	185	37.07	− 46.98	1478.3
		187 ·	62.93	− 44.04	1491.7
Os	76	184	0.018	− 47.44	1469.8
		186	1.59	− 46.06	1484.7
		187 ·	1.64	− 44.04	1490.9
		188	13.3	− 44.03	1498.9
		189	16.1	− 41.75	1504.9
		190	26.4	− 41.40	1512.6
		192	41.0	− 38.59	1526.2
Ir	77	191	37.3	− 39.15	1517.8
		193	62.7	− 36.72	1531.7
Pt	78	190	0.0127	− 40.05	1509.8
		192	0.78	− 38.57	1524.6
		194	32.9	− 37.19	1539.4
		195	33.8	− 35.18	1545.6
		196	25.3	− 35.02	1553.6
		198	7.21	− 32.47	1567.3
Au	79	197	100	− 33.45	1559.4
Hg	80	196	0.146	− 34.18	1551.2
		198	10.02	− 33.23	1566.5
		199	16.84	− 31.74	1573.2

TABLE 27-1   Nuclear Properties—Continued

Symbol	Atomic number (Z)	Mass number (A)	Relative abundance (%)	Atomic mass excess M — A (10⁻³ amu(C¹²))	Binding energy B (MeV)
		200	23.13	− 31.66	1581.2
		201	13.22	− 29.69	1587.4
		202	29.80	− 29.37	1595.2
		204	6.85	− 26.52	1608.6
Tl	81	203	29.50	− 27.67	1600.9
		205	70.50	− 25.54	1615.0
Pb	82	204	1.48	− 26.93	1607.5
		206	23.6	− 25.54	1622.3
		207	22.6	− 24.10	1629.0
		208	52.3	− 23.36	1636.4
Bi	83	209	100	− 19.58	1640.2
Th	90	232	100	38.21	1766.5
U	92	234	0.0056	40.90	1778.6
		235	0.7205	43.93	1783.8
		238	99.2739	50.76	1801.7

Sources: G. H. Fuller, "Relative Isotopic Abundances," Table V, Nuclear Data Tables, U.S. Atomic Energy Commission (1959).

König, Mattauch, and Wapstra, "1961 Nuclidic Mass Table," *Nuclear Physics* **31**, 18 (1962).

PROBLEMS

27–1.   What is the nuclear radius of
(a) Fe^{56}?
(b) Pb^{208}?

27–2.   Is it possible for a heavier isobar to have more binding energy B than a lighter isobar? Explain.

27–3.   Using Eq. 27–3 calculate the binding energy B and the binding energy per nucleon B/A for
(a) O^{16}
(b) Fe^{56}
(c) U^{238}

27–4. Lu^{175} has a very large electric quadrupole moment equal to the proton charge e times 5.6×10^{-24} cm². If the charge is uniformly distributed throughout an ellipsoid of rotation, estimate the difference $a - b$ between the semi-major and semi-minor axes of the nucleus. Sketch the shape of this nucleus.

27–5.   From the table of atomic masses, calculate the binding energy of the last proton in O^{16}, F^{19}, Mg^{24}, Na^{23}, and Bi^{209}, and the last neutron in O^{17}, Ne^{22}, Ne^{21}, and Pb^{208}. Compare the results with the average binding energy per nucleon. Compare results for even and odd A.

27–6.   Consider C^{12} and O^{16} as bound systems consisting of 3 and 4 α-particles, respectively. What are the binding energies of the 3α and 4α systems?

27–7.   Plot the number of stable nuclei as a function of the atomic number Z. Where do the maxima occur?

27–8.   Repeat Prob. 27–7 for the neutron number $N = A - Z$.

27–9.   What nucleus has a radius twice as large as $_{13}Al^{27}$?

REFERENCES

I. Kaplan, *Nuclear Physics* (Addison-Wesley, 1963, 2nd ed.), Ch. 8, 9.

R. D. Evans, *The Atomic Nucleus* (McGraw-Hill, 1955), Ch. 2, 4, 5.

W. E. Burcham, *Nuclear Physics* (McGraw-Hill, 1963), Ch. 10, 11.

L. R. B. Elton, *Introductory Nuclear Theory* (Pitman, London, 1959), Ch. 1, 2.

28/the nuclear force

As in the case of atomic physics, we begin our study of nuclear structure with the two-particle system. With the two-nucleon system we might hope to learn something about the nature of the nuclear force free of the mathematical complexities inherent in a many-particle situation.

28–1 THE TWO-NUCLEON SYSTEM

Only one bound two-nucleon system has been observed, the *deuteron*, consisting of one proton and one neutron. The deuteron has an atomic number Z equal to one and is therefore a hydrogen isotope. There is no bound state of the two-proton or the two-neutron systems. It would seem, therefore, that the neutron-proton force is different (more strongly attractive) from the neutron-neutron and the proton-proton forces. This would also explain why stable nuclei tend to have roughly equal numbers of neutrons and protons. To a physicist who seeks simplicity and unity in nature, this is not a very appealing situation, however. Since the neutron and proton are so much alike (equal spins and practically equal masses), we might hope that the *nuclear* force between any pair of nucleons would be the same. The neutrons and protons would then only differ in their *electromagnetic* properties. The coulomb repulsion between two protons might perhaps explain the absence of a stable di-proton, but the instability of the two-neutron system cannot be understood this way. We shall find, nevertheless, that the concept of a common attractive *nucleon-nucleon force* is applicable.

The reason for the instability of the di-proton and the di-neutron turns out to be quite subtle and involves the Pauli exclusion principle, which applies to neutrons and protons as well as electrons. The nucleon-nucleon force depends on the relative orientation of the nucleon spins. With each nucleon having a spin quantum number s equal to $\frac{1}{2}$, the two-nucleon system can be in a triplet state of total spin S equal to 1 (spins parallel) or in a singlet state with S equal to 0 (spins antiparallel). Nucleons with parallel spins are found to be more strongly attracted than nucleons with antiparallel spins. The most direct evidence for this is the fact that all deuterons are found to be in the spin triplet state, i.e., with the neutron and proton spins parallel. Since no bound excited state of the deuteron has ever been observed, we must conclude that none of the neutron-proton spin singlet states, $S = 0$, are bound.

In the case of the di-neutron or the di-proton both nucleons are of the same kind and the Pauli principle does not permit the particles to have the same set of quantum numbers. Because of the complete spatial symmetry between, say, the two neutrons in the $l = 0$ ground state of the di-neutron, the only way the particles can differ is in their spin orientations, i.e., in their values of m_s. In the ground state of the di-neutron and of the di-proton one particle must have $m_s = +\frac{1}{2}$ and the other $m_s = -\frac{1}{2}$ for a total spin equal to zero. The neutron-proton system is not restricted in this way, since the two particles involved here are distinguishable. (See Sections 22–1 and 22–2.) If we now assert quite generally that the two-nucleon system can be bound in the triplet ($S = 1$) state, but that there is no bound two-nucleon singlet ($S = 0$) state, we can explain the stability of the deuteron and the instability of the di-neutron and the di-proton without assuming an inherent difference in the nature of the neutron-neutron, neutron-proton, and proton-proton nuclear force fields. The fact that there is no bound singlet state does not necessarily mean that the nucleon-nucleon force is repulsive when the spins are antiparallel, but only that the "singlet potential well" is not deep enough to hold the nucleons together (Fig. 28–1).

From the preceding paragraph it is clear that any information obtained from a study of the deuteron pertains to the two-nucleon "triplet potential" only. Information about the "singlet potential" can be gained from nucleon-nucleon scattering experiments, because two unbound colliding nucleons *can* interact through the singlet potential.

The deuteron is known to have a ground state binding energy of 2.225 MeV, or 1.11 MeV per nucleon, a small binding energy compared to the nucleons in an average nucleus (Section 27–3). The deuteron spin quantum number S as well as the total angular momentum quantum number J equals unity, $S = J = 1$. In the case of the hydrogen atom the observed spec-

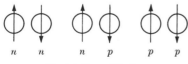

n   n   n   p   p   p

Singlet Force Weaker

(a)

n   p

Triplet Force Stronger

(b)

Fig. 28–1

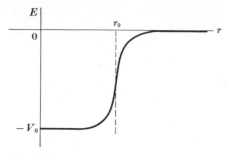

Fig. 28–2

trum made it possible to deduce the energy levels of a large number of excited states. We are not fortunate enough to have such detailed information regarding the deuteron; there are no bound excited states at all. The knowledge of the ground state energy level is not nearly sufficient to determine the shape of the two-nucleon triplet potential. Let us assume, however, that it is a central attractive potential well, $V(r)$, with a fairly definite range r_0 and depth V_0 as illustrated in Fig. 28–2. A number of different potential forms have been suggested, e.g., a "square well," a gaussian well $V \propto e^{-(r/r_0)^2}$, an exponential well $V \propto e^{-r/r_0}$, and the Yukawa potential $V \propto e^{-r/r_0}/r$. Of these only the Yukawa potential has any basis in fundamental theory (Chapter 31). The others are chosen for their mathematical simplicity. Unfortunately *all* of these potentials can satisfactorily explain the deuteron binding energy and the results of low energy ($\lesssim 10$ MeV) neutron-proton scattering experiments, while they all fail to account for the high energy scattering data. The experimental data do not suffice, in other words, to give us the detailed shape of the potential, but merely its rough range r_0 and depth V_0. Even this information is very useful, however, and in the next three sections we will indicate how r_0 and V_0 can be determined.

28–2   THE SQUARE WELL POTENTIAL

Since the square well potential is the easiest one to treat mathematically, we shall adopt this potential as the basis for our analysis of the neutron-proton system. We assume that (Fig. 28–3),

$$V = -V_0 \qquad \text{for} \qquad r \leq r_0$$
$$ = 0 \qquad \text{for} \qquad r > r_0 \qquad\qquad (28\text{–}1)$$

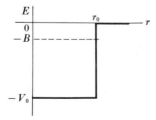

Fig. 28–3. The "square well" nucleon-nucleon potential.

Let us ignore the small mass difference between the neutron and the proton and set both masses equal to M. The reduced mass, m, is then equal to (Chapter 3)

$$m = \frac{M^2}{M + M} = \frac{1}{2}M \qquad (28\text{--}2)$$

We recall that a two-body problem can be reduced (Chapter 3) to the problem of a single particle with the reduced mass moving in a central force field, where the central force is just the interparticle force. Proceeding as with the hydrogen atom we arrive at a Schrödinger equation for the neutron-proton system analogous to Eq. 21–4:

$$-\frac{\hbar^2}{2m}\frac{1}{r^2}\frac{d}{dr}r^2\frac{dR}{dr} + \left[\frac{l(l+1)\hbar^2}{2mr^2} + V(r)\right]R = ER \qquad (28\text{--}3)$$

Here we must insert the expression for $V(r)$ given by Eq. 28–1 rather than the $-Ze^2/r$ potential used in Eq. 21–4, and the reduced mass, Eq. 28–2, appropriate for the deuteron. With an argument similar to the one given in Section 21–1, we find again that the ground state of the bound system must be an $l = 0$ state. The low energy scattering (Section 28–3) also takes place in the $l = 0$ state. Setting $l = 0$, the Schrödinger equation, Eq. 28–3, becomes

$$-\frac{\hbar^2}{M}\frac{1}{r^2}\frac{d}{dr}r^2\frac{dR}{dr} + (V - E)R = 0 \qquad (28\text{--}4)$$

This equation can be simplified further by introducing the function $u(r)$, defined by

$$u(r) \equiv rR \qquad (28\text{--}5)$$

Substituting u/r for R in Eq. 28–4 leads to the equation

$$u'' + \frac{M}{\hbar^2}(E - V)u = 0 \qquad (28\text{--}6)$$

which we will solve for the square well potential with E both negative and positive.

Case 1: $\qquad\qquad\qquad E < 0$

With E negative, the system is bound with a binding energy $-E$, which we denote by B,

$$B \equiv -E$$

If we now define the constants α^2 and β^2 by

$$\alpha^2 \equiv \frac{M}{\hbar^2}(V_0 - B) \qquad (28\text{--}7)$$

and

$$\beta^2 \equiv \frac{M}{\hbar^2} B \qquad (28\text{--}8)$$

Eq. 28–6, with V given by Eq. 28–1, can be written as

$$u'' + \alpha^2 u = 0 \qquad \text{for} \qquad r \leq r_0 \tag{28–9}$$

and

$$u'' - \beta^2 u = 0 \qquad \text{for} \qquad r > r_0 \tag{28–10}$$

We can write down the solutions immediately,

$$u = A_1 \sin \alpha r + B_1 \cos \alpha r, \qquad r \leq r_0$$

and

$$u = A_2 e^{-\beta r} + B_2 e^{+\beta r}, \qquad r > r_0$$

If we require the wave function, $R \equiv u/r$, to be finite everywhere, we must set $B_1 = 0$, or else R blows up at the origin, and $B_2 = 0$, or R blows up as $r \to \infty$. The solutions to Eqs. 28–9 and 28–10 must therefore be restricted to

$$u = A_1 \sin \alpha r, \qquad r \leq r_0 \tag{28–11}$$

and

$$u = A_2 e^{-\beta r}, \qquad r > r_0 \tag{28–12}$$

If we can determine the constants A_1 and A_2 we will have the correct solution for u (and R) for all values of r. A relation between A_1 and A_2 is obtained by noting that u'' is finite since u and V are both finite, Eq. 28–6, which in turn requires u' and u to be continuous. The requirement that u and u' be continuous at $r = r_0$ leads to the equations

$$u(r_0) = A_1 \sin \alpha r_0 = A_2 e^{-\beta r_0} \tag{28–13}$$

and

$$u'(r_0) = \alpha A_1 \cos \alpha r_0 = -\beta A_2 e^{-\beta r_0} \tag{28–14}$$

With A_2 expressed in terms of A_1 by Eq. 28–13, A_1 itself can be determined from the normalization integral for the wave function, Eq. 20–23. The value of A_1 will not concern us here, however. Instead we divide Eq. 28–14 by Eq. 28–13 to obtain the relation

$$\alpha \cot \alpha r_0 = -\beta \tag{28–15}$$

or by Eqs. 28–7 and 28–8 the relation

$$\sqrt{V_0 - B} \cot \left[r_0 \sqrt{M(V_0 - B)}/\hbar \right] = -\sqrt{B} \tag{28–16}$$

between the unknown parameters r_0 and V_0 of the square well potential·

In Chapter 20 we found for a one dimensional potential well that the ground state always corresponded to a wave function with no nodes. The argument used there carries over to the three dimensional case: the more nodes, the more rapidly the wave function curves and the larger the kinetic energy becomes. With the ground state solution, Eqs. 28–11 and 28–12, having no nodes, $u(r)$ will take the form indicated in Fig. 28–4. In order to match a decaying exponential curve $e^{-\beta r}$ to $\sin \alpha r$ at $r = r_0$, $\sin \alpha r$ must have passed through its first maximum ($\alpha r = \pi/2$) and be on its

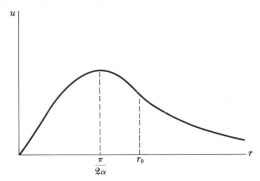

Fig. 28–4. *The ground state deuteron wave function.*

way down again at $r = r_0$. It follows that for the ground state solution αr_0 lies in the second quadrant,

$$\frac{\pi}{2} < \alpha r_0 < \pi \qquad (28\text{--}17)$$

as drawn in Fig. 28–4. The relation between r_0 and V_0 obtained from Eq. 28–15 or Eq. 28–16, and satisfying the restriction imposed by Eq. 28–17, is plotted in Fig. 28–5 for $B = 2.225$ MeV, the known binding energy of the deuteron. (Since the equations are transcendental, they must be solved numerically.) For r_0 equal to 1 fermi, this plot yields a potential well depth of 118 MeV, while for $r_0 = 2$ f we find $V_0 = 36.6$ MeV. The latter range, $r_0 = 2 \times 10^{-13}$ cm, is found to be a reasonable value for the nucleon-nucleon triplet potential. (See Section 28–3.)

Case 2: $E > 0$

To distinguish clearly the unbound case from the bound one, we now introduce the new symbols γ and κ for the wave numbers corresponding to $r \leq r_0$ and $r > r_0$, respectively:

$$\gamma^2 \equiv \frac{M}{\hbar^2} (E + V_0) \qquad (28\text{--}18)$$

$$\kappa^2 \equiv \frac{M}{\hbar^2} E \qquad (28\text{--}19)$$

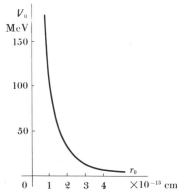

Fig. 28–5. *The variation of the depth of the deuteron potential with its range.*

Eq. 28–6 then becomes

$$u'' + \gamma^2 u = 0 \tag{28-20}$$

for $r \leq r_0$ and

$$u'' + \kappa^2 u = 0 \tag{28-21}$$

for $r > r_0$. The solution to Eq. 28–20 is

$$u = C_1 \sin \gamma r, \qquad r \leq r_0 \tag{28-22}$$

where the $\cos \gamma r$ solution has been dropped to keep $R \equiv u/r$ finite at the origin. The general solution for $r > r_0$ may be written as a sum of a $\sin \kappa r$ and a $\cos \kappa r$ term, or equally well as

$$u = C_2 \sin (\kappa r + \delta), \qquad r > r_0 \tag{28-23}$$

As in the bound case, Eqs. 28–13 and 28–14, we must require that u and u' be continuous at $r = r_0$. With the solutions for u given by Eqs. 28–22 and 28–23, this requirement leads to the relations

$$C_1 \sin \gamma r_0 = C_2 \sin (\kappa r_0 + \delta) \tag{28-24}$$

and

$$\gamma C_1 \cos \gamma r_0 = \kappa C_2 \cos (\kappa r_0 + \delta) \tag{28-25}$$

Dividing Eq. 28–25 by Eq. 28–24, the constants C_1 and C_2 drop out, and we are left with the relation

$$\gamma \cot \gamma r_0 = \kappa \cot (\kappa r_0 + \delta) \tag{28-26}$$

which is the unbound ($E > 0$) analog to the result, Eq. 28–15, for the bound case.

For a known energy E, Eq. 28–26 relates the parameters r_0, V_0, and δ. Since we shall find (Section 28–3) that at low energies the total scattering cross section σ is equal to

$$\sigma = \frac{4\pi}{\kappa^2} \sin^2 \delta \tag{28-27}$$

the parameter δ, called the *phase shift*, can be determined from scattering experiments. Equation 28–26 then contains only two unknown parameters, r_0 and V_0, as does Eq. 28–15. From the two equations relating r_0 and V_0 one might hope to arrive at a unique determination of the range r_0 and depth V_0 of the neutron-proton potential consistent with the known deuteron binding energy and the low energy neutron-proton scattering cross section.

28–3   NEUTRON-PROTON SCATTERING

All that we can learn from the *bound* neutron-proton system is embodied in Fig. 28–5, which gives the relation between the range and the depth of the neutron-proton potential with the spins parallel, $S = 1$. For further information on the neutron-proton force we must study the *unbound* states, i.e., perform neutron-proton scattering experiments. In Chapter 6 we calculated the scattering cross sections for the $\frac{1}{r}$ potential and the hard sphere potential based on classical mechanics. Our approach here will be a little different. First of all we must use quantum mechanics. Secondly we will try to use a measured cross section to determine an unknown potential.

In a neutron-proton scattering experiment a uni-directional beam of neutrons is aimed at a hydrogen- (or proton-) rich target, and the number of scattered neutrons is measured as a function of the scattering angle. Actually for low energies all angles are equally probable in the center of mass system. This can be seen by the following qualitative classical argument.

If the neutron is to be scattered by the proton, it must pass close enough to the proton to feel its force, i.e., the impact parameter b must be smaller than the range of the potential r_0, $b < r_0$. If the incoming neutron has a velocity $\mathbf{v}$ and the proton (in the target) is at rest, the angular momentum, $L = Mbv$, must be smaller than Mr_0v for scattering to take place (Fig. 28-6),

$$L < Mr_0v$$

For non-relativistic speeds, $v = \sqrt{2E/M}$, this condition becomes

$$L < \sqrt{2ME}\, r_0 \qquad (28\text{-}28)$$

(Within a factor of two the same result is obtained in the center of mass system.)

Although our argument has been based on classical mechanics, a similar, but less absolute, result is obtained quantum mechanically. (In the quantum mechanical theory there is a small but non-zero probability of finding a particle with large L close to the origin, since the wave functions for $l \geq 1$, though small close to the origin, vanish strictly only at $r = 0$.) We have found, however, that angular momentum is quantized (Eq. 20-29),

$$L = \sqrt{l(l+1)}\hbar \qquad l = 0, 1, 2, 3 \ldots$$

Thus we may rewrite Eq. 28-28,

$$\sqrt{l(l+1)}\hbar < \sqrt{2ME}\, r_0$$

from which it follows that for

$$E \leq \hbar^2/Mr_0^2 \qquad \text{we have} \qquad l < 1 \qquad (28\text{-}29)$$

But $l < 1$ implies $l = 0$, since angular momentum is quantized for the particle of reduced mass in the center of mass system. For energies below the limit given by Eq. 28-29, therefore, scattering takes place predominantly in the $l = 0$ state (S-state), which has a spherically symmetric wave

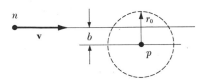

Fig. 28-6. *An incident neutron about to be scattered by a proton.*

function. For $r_0 = 2$ f this energy is equal to 20 MeV. For energies below about 20 MeV, therefore, the wave function of the scattered particle is spherically symmetric (Fig. 28–7) in the center of mass system. An incoming low energy particle (neutron) with $l \geq 1$ will usually not be scattered at all, because it does not get close enough to the scattering center (proton) to interact with it. The wave function that describes a low energy particle in a scattering process would therefore be expected to be a superposition of a *plane wave* (Eq. 20–9), representing the incoming free particle, and a *spherical wave* (Eq. 16–21), the latter giving the probability that the incoming particle is scattered. Let us see if we can find a solution to the Schrödinger equation which is of this type. (See Fig. 28–7.)

At distances from the origin larger than the range of the potential r_0, the particle is free, $V(r) = 0$, and the Schrödinger equation takes the form, Eq. 20–22,

$$\nabla^2 \psi + \kappa^2 \psi = 0 \tag{28–30}$$

where

$$\kappa^2 \equiv \sqrt{2mE}/\hbar = \sqrt{ME}/\hbar$$

This is just the Helmholtz equation, Eq. 16–18. Plane wave and spherical wave solutions to this equation were obtained in Chapter 16, Eqs. 16–19 and 16–21. Since the equation is linear, a sum of these solutions is also a solution, so that we may write

$$\psi = D\left(e^{i\kappa z} + f\frac{e^{i\kappa r}}{r}\right) \tag{28–31}$$

as the solution to the Schrödinger equation for $r > r_0$. Here we have taken the direction of the incoming beam of particles to be the z-direction. D is a normalization constant and the constant f (the *scattering amplitude*) gives a measure of the magnitude of the scattered wave. It is our aim to relate f to the experimentally determined scattering cross section on the one hand, and to the parameters of the potential on the other.

The relation between the scattering cross section σ and the factor f in Eq. 28–31 is readily established. Since σ is the effective "target area" presented to the incoming particle (Chapter 6), it also represents the *probability* that a particle incident on a unit area centered on the target is scattered (Fig. 28–8). In terms of Fig. 28–9 this means that σ represents the probability that a particle in unit volume A should later find itself in the spherical shell of volume B rather than in unit volume C. Since $|\psi|^2$ represents the

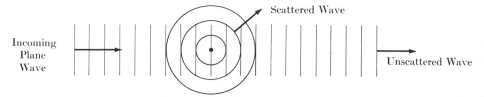

Fig. 28–7. A wave mechanical picture of a scattering event.

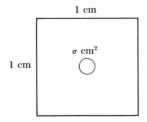

Fig. 28–8

probability per unit volume, the probability that the particle is in volume
A is $|De^{i\kappa z}|^2 \times 1 = |D|^2$ (see Eq. 28–31), while the probability that it is in
volume B is

$$|Dfe^{i\kappa r}/r|^2 \, 4\pi r^2 \times 1 = 4\pi \, |D|^2 \, |f|^2$$

Since σ is the ratio of these probabilities, we find

$$\sigma = 4\pi \, |D|^2 \, |f|^2/|D|^2 = 4\pi \, |f|^2 \qquad (28\text{–}32)$$

Next we shall try to relate the factor f in Eq. 28–31 to the parameters r_0
and V_0 of the square well potential. (See Section 28–2.) We have argued that
only the incoming particles in the $l = 0$ state are scattered at low energies.
The plane wave $e^{i\kappa z}$, however, represents any free particle travelling in the
z-direction no matter what its impact parameter b or its angular momentum
might be. In fact $e^{i\kappa z}$ is not an eigenfunction of the square of the angular
momentum operator L^2, but can be written as an infinite sum of eigenfunctions of L^2 corresponding to all possible l values. We state without proof the
following mathematical result:

$$e^{i\kappa z} = \frac{\sin \kappa r}{\kappa r} + \sum_{l=1}^{\infty} \psi_l(r, \theta) \qquad (28\text{–}33)$$

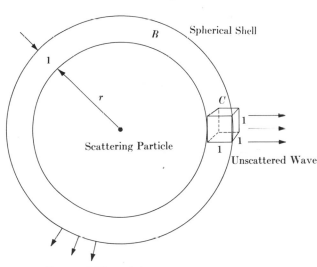
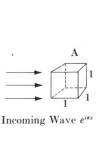

Incoming Wave $e^{i\kappa z}$

Scattering Particle

Unscattered Wave

Scattered Wave $e^{i\kappa r/r}$

Fig. 28–9

where the "partial waves" ψ_l satisfy the eigenvalue equation

$$L^2\psi_l = l(l+1)\hbar^2\psi_l$$

as well as the Schrödinger equation. The first term in Eq. 28–33 is spherically symmetric and therefore an $l = 0$ solution. The spherically symmetric ($l = 0$) part of the entire wave function for $r > r_0$ (Eq. 28–31) is then given by

$$\psi_0 = D\left[\frac{\sin \kappa r}{\kappa r} + f\frac{e^{i\kappa r}}{r}\right] \qquad (28\text{–}34)$$

where the first term represents the $l = 0$ part of the incoming plane wave and the second term is the scattered wave.

We have already found the general form of the $l = 0$ solution for $r > r_0$ (i.e., for $V = 0$), however. This solution is given in Eq. 28–23, where $u \equiv r\psi_0$. To show that the function in Eq. 28–34 can be written in the form given in Eq. 28–23, we equate the two expressions for $u \equiv r\psi_0$:

$$C_2 \sin(\kappa r + \delta) = D\left[\frac{1}{\kappa}\sin \kappa r + fe^{i\kappa r}\right]$$

$$C_2 \frac{1}{2i}[e^{i(\kappa r + \delta)} - e^{-i(\kappa r + \delta)}] = D\left[\frac{1}{2i\kappa}(e^{i\kappa r} - e^{-i\kappa r}) + fe^{i\kappa r}\right]$$

or

$$e^{i\kappa r}\left[\frac{1}{2i}C_2e^{i\delta} - D\frac{1}{2i\kappa} - Df\right] + e^{-i\kappa r}\left[D\frac{1}{2i\kappa} - C_2\frac{1}{2i}e^{-i\delta}\right] = 0$$

This last equation can only be satisfied for all r's if the coefficients of the $e^{i\kappa r}$ and $e^{-i\kappa r}$ terms vanish independently. Setting the coefficient multiplying $e^{-i\kappa r}$ equal to zero, we find

$$C_2 = D\frac{1}{\kappa}e^{i\delta}$$

which, when substituted in the coefficient to the $e^{i\kappa r}$ term, yields

$$f = \frac{1}{2i\kappa}(e^{2i\delta} - 1)$$

or

$$f = \frac{1}{\kappa}e^{i\delta}\sin \delta \qquad (28\text{–}35)$$

This proves that $r\psi_0$ as given in Eq. 28–34 can be written in the form of Eq. 28–23, with a phase shift δ given in terms of f by Eq. 28–35. Combining Eqs. 28–32 and 28–35, we find that the total scattering cross section can be given in terms of the phase shift δ by the simple relation

$$\sigma = \frac{4\pi}{\kappa^2}\sin^2 \delta \qquad (28\text{–}27)$$

a result that we have already quoted in Section 28–2.

So far we have discussed the solution to the Schrödinger equation for $r > r_0$. For $r \leq r_0$ the wave function will certainly not look like the free particle solution, Eq. 28–31. We can argue that the "partial waves" ψ_l (Eq. 28–33) for $l \geq 1$ are unaffected by the potential, however, since we have found that a low energy particle with $l \geq 1$ rarely gets close enough to the origin to see the potential. What one finds is that the ψ_l's for $l \geq 1$ essentially vanish for $r \leq r_0$, or that the total wave function is predominantly an $l = 0$ solution of the Schrödinger equation for $r \leq r_0$. We should therefore solve the Schrödinger equation for $l = 0$ and $r \leq r_0$ and match this solution at $r = r_0$ to the $l = 0$ wave for $r > r_0$, Eq. 28–34 or Eq. 28–23. But this has already been done in Section 28–2. The solution for $r \leq r_0$ is given by Eq. 28–22, and the result of matching the solutions at $r = r_0$ by Eq. 28–26. After some trigonometric manipulations, Eq. 28–26 can be solved for $\sin \delta$ explicitly (Prob. 28–4). The result, after substituting in Eq. 28–27, is

$$\sigma = \frac{4\pi}{\kappa^2}\sin^2 \delta = \frac{4\pi}{\kappa^2}\frac{\sin^2 \kappa r_0 \, (\kappa \cot \kappa r_0 - \gamma \cot \gamma r_0)^2}{\kappa^2 + \gamma^2 \cot^2 \gamma r_0} \qquad (28\text{–}36)$$

We have now succeeded in expressing the total scattering cross section σ in terms of the energy E (through κ and γ), the depth of the potential V_0 (through γ), and its range r_0. In the limit of low energies, $E \to 0$ or $\kappa \to 0$, the expression given in Eq. 28–36 simplifies considerably to (Prob. 28–5)

$$\sigma(E = 0) = 4\pi r_0^2 \left[1 - \frac{\tan \gamma r_0}{\gamma r_0} \right]^2 \qquad (28\text{–}37)$$

If σ is measured for a given energy E, Eq. 28–36 gives us a second relation between r_0 and V_0, which in conjunction with Eq. 28–16 or Fig. 28–5 might lead to a unique determination of the range and the depth of the potential. There is one complication, however. Since the deuteron is in an $S = 1$ state, Eq. 28–16 and Fig. 28–5 refer to the parameters of the triplet potential only. The neutron-proton system in a scattering process, on the other hand, can be in either an $S = 1(m_s + 1, 0, \text{or} - 1)$ or an $S = 0$ $(m_s = 0)$ state. Each of the four possible combinations of S and m_s are equally probable, that is, the triplet encounter is three times as probable as singlet encounter. If we denote the scattering cross section for the triplet state by σ_t and that for the singlet state by σ_s, the experimentally determined cross section is actually

$$\sigma = \tfrac{3}{4}\sigma_t + \tfrac{1}{4}\sigma_s$$

By measuring σ at many energies ($\lesssim 20$ MeV), however, it is possible to determine the two parameters V_0 and r_0 for both the singlet and the triplet potentials. Good agreement is obtained with all the low energy scattering data if we take

$$r_{0_t} \approx 2.0 \text{ f and } V_{0_t} \approx 36 \text{ MeV} \qquad (28\text{–}34)$$

for the triplet state and

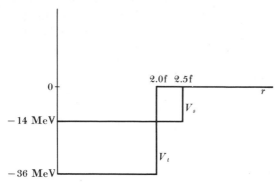

Fig. 28–10. *The two-nucleon singlet and triplet potentials.*

$$r_{0_s} \approx 2.5 \text{ f and } V_{0_s} \approx 14 \text{ MeV} \qquad (28\text{--}35)$$

for the singlet state.

This singlet potential well is not quite deep enough for a bound state. Even at the top of the well the kinetic energy (14 MeV) is not large enough to curve the sinusoidal wave function enough to reach its first maximum ($\alpha r = \pi/2$) before r reaches r_0. An exponentially decaying wave function can therefore not be matched to it for $r \geq r_0$, as is necessary for a bound state, Eq. 28–12 and Fig. 28–4.

A proton-proton scattering process is somewhat harder to analyze than neutron-proton scattering. This is because the protons interact through the repulsive coulomb force as well as with the nuclear force. When the nuclear potential is abstracted, however, the proton-proton singlet potential is found to agree well with the corresponding neutron-proton potential, Eq. 28–35. Proton-proton low energy ($l = 0$) scattering can only take place in the singlet state (spins opposed) because of the Pauli exclusion principle. Neutron-neutron scattering data can be obtained indirectly from neutron-deuteron scattering experiments (there is no pure neutron target), but are not precise enough to determine the neutron-neutron potential parameters with much accuracy. The data, however, do not disagree with the supposition that the neutron-neutron singlet potential is equal to the neutron-proton and proton-proton singlet potentials.

In summary we can say that the hypothesis of the *charge independence* of nuclear forces receives considerable support from the low energy nucleon-nucleon scattering experiments.

28–4   THE NUCLEAR FORCE PROBLEM

We have found that the nucleon-nucleon force is strong, attractive, and has a range of about 2×10^{-13} cm. The force is spin dependent, being more strongly attractive in the parallel spin (triplet) state. However, this is not the complete story. The departure from spherical symmetry, as evidenced by the fact that the deuteron possesses a nonzero quadrupole moment, shows that the potential is not entirely central, as assumed up to now. The potential actually depends on the orientation of the spin vector to the relative interparticle position vector. As a result the ground state of the deuteron is not entirely an $l = 0$ state. One finds that there is about a 4% probability of observing it in an $l = 2$ state.

There is also some evidence for a "repulsive core" in the nucleon-nucleon potential as indicated in Fig. 28–11. There is no way of distinguishing between the potentials in Figs. 28–3 and 28–11 from the low energy scattering data.

The repulsive core would help to explain the *saturation of nuclear forces*. We have seen (Chapter 27) that the neutrons and protons seem to be packed in the nucleus like hard spheres with the nuclear radius proportional to $A^{1/3}$, and that the binding energy per nucleon is roughly constant (independent of A). One can show that a potential like the one given in Fig. 28–3 would lead to a collapse of the nucleus until each nucleon is within the force range of every other nucleon. This would lead to a nuclear radius of about 2 f independent of A and a binding energy per nucleon that would increase with A, both results in disagreement with the observed facts. A repulsive core on the other hand would keep the nucleons apart and lead to an increase of the radius with $A^{1/3}$. This in turn would mean that each nucleon could only interact with a fixed small number of neighboring nucleons within its force range, resulting in a constant binding energy per nucleon independent of A. With a repulsive core, Fig. 28–11, the inter-nucleon force is similar in form to the inter-atomic force, Fig. 14–2. This similarity is the basis for the "liquid-drop" model (Chapter 29) of the nucleus.

In explaining the saturation of nuclear forces, we should also mention the *exchange* nature of the nuclear force. When the neutron was discovered (1932), Heisenberg suggested that when a neutron interacts with a proton the charge jumps from the proton to the neutron, thereby changing the neutron into a proton and the proton into a neutron. Other possibilities were also suggested, such as the exchange of spins but not charge. Exchange forces have the property of being attractive or repulsive depending on the *state* of the two nucleons with respect to each other. (Why this is so cannot readily be understood at a non-mathematical level.) Since the Pauli principle ensures that the nucleons in a heavy nucleus occupy a variety of states, some nucleons would repel each other while others would be attracted. The repulsive forces would tend to prevent the collapse of the nucleus, although it is doubtful whether the exchange forces alone are sufficient to explain the observed "saturation." It seems clear now that the nuclear force is a mixture of non-exchange or ordinary forces and exchange forces, but the exact combination of the terms is still in question.

The presence of exchange forces does not affect our discussion of the low energy nucleon-nucleon interaction in Sections 28–2 and 28–3, since this discussion was restricted to interactions in the $l = 0$ state. What the exchange force permits is for the potential to be quite different in other l states.

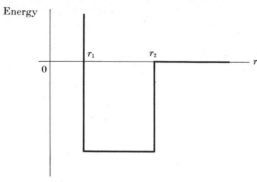

Energy

r_1 r_2

0 r

Fig. 28–11. A potential well with a "hard core."

When Heisenberg made his suggestion of an exchange force, it was not clear how the exchange really took place. Now we know that π-mesons, and at very short distances heavier mesons as well (Chapter 31), shuttle back and forth between the interacting nucleons. The situation is reminiscent of the covalent binding effected by the electrons in the H_2 *molecule* (Chapter 24), but here the forces are nuclear, not electromagnetic. The ordinary nuclear forces involve neutral π-mesons only, while the exchange forces act through charged as well as neutral mesons. Further discussion of the role of the π-mesons in transmitting the nuclear force is left for the chapter on elementary particles (Chapter 31).

Finally we should mention the problems that have been raised by the high energy nucleon-nucleon scattering data. The low energy data do not give detailed information about the shape of the nuclear potential, merely its rough range and depth. With the shorter wave lengths, $\lambda = h/p$, at higher energies, one would hope to be able to see the finer details of the potential form. A wealth of experimental data is now available. There is direct evidence for strong exchange forces, and some evidence for a repulsive core, Fig. 28–11. Strong non-central forces must be present. There is also evidence for a nuclear spin-orbit interaction (see Chapter 23), i.e., a term of the form $\mathbf{L}\cdot\mathbf{S}$ in the potential. Such a term is non-central as well as velocity dependent. We will find additional evidence for the spin-orbit term when we discuss the nuclear shell structure (Chapter 29).

In summary we can say that, although a great deal is known about the nature of the nuclear force, our knowledge is far from complete. It is not possible, therefore, to develop a rigorous theory of nuclear structure based on our present knowledge of the two-body nucleon-nucleon force.

PROBLEMS

28–1.   Calculate the depth V_0 of the square well potential from Eq. 28–16 if the range r_0 is 1.8×10^{-13} cm and B is the deuteron binding energy.

28-2. With the range of the deuteron triplet potential equal to 2×10^{-13} cm, how deep would the well have to be for the deuteron to have an excited bound triplet state?

28-3. Roughly how high would the energy of a nucleon in the $l = 4$ state have to be for it to be readily scattered by another nucleon at rest?

28-4. Derive Eq. 28-36.

28-5. Derive Eq. 28-37.

28-6. The two-nucleon singlet potential has a range of about 2.5×10^{-13} cm and a depth of about 14 MeV. How much deeper would it have to be to allow a bound state?

28-7. Calculate the nucleon-nucleon scattering cross section in the limit of low energies, $E \rightarrow 0$, for the triplet potential ($r_0 = 2.0$ f, $V_0 = 36$ MeV) and the singlet potential ($r_0 = 2.5$ f, $V_0 = 14$ MeV). What cross section would be measured experimentally?

28-8. Calculate the cross section for nucleon-nucleon scattering in the triplet state ($r_0 = 2.0$ f, $V_0 = 36$ MeV) for $E = 5$ MeV.

REFERENCES

W. E. Burcham, *Nuclear Physics* (McGraw-Hill, 1963), Ch. 18.

I. Kaplan, *Nuclear Physics* (Addison-Wesley, 1963, 2nd ed.), Ch. 17.

L. R. B. Elton, *Introductory Nuclear Theory* (Pitman, London, 1959), Ch. 3, 4.

29 / the structure of nuclei

In studying a many-nucleon nucleus we are faced with two major problems. One of these is our incomplete knowledge of the force field between two nucleons (Chapter 28). The second problem is a mathematical one: the inherent complexity of any many-body system.

The latter problem is not a difficulty unique to the nucleus, but arises in any system consisting of a large number of particles. The nuclear many-body problem is particularly complex, however, because of the lack of simplifying features. In a macroscopic volume of gas the number of particles is so large that statistical methods (Part II) give good results, in a crystalline solid the regularity of the particle arrangement can be exploited, and in the many-electron atom there is a single strong force center. A nucleus possesses none of these advantages. The number of nucleons is too small for a statistical treatment to be reliable, and no force center is stronger than any other. Because of these difficulties nuclear physicists have been forced to work with simple models which incorporate some, but certainly not all, of the features of the real nucleus.

The modes of nuclear behavior can generally be divided into two broad categories: (a) those primarily due to the action of a single particle in the nucleus and (b) those in which the collective behavior of all the particles plays a role. Nuclear phenomena that fall in the first category can best be studied within an independent particle model, also called the shell model (Section 29–2), while those in the latter category can only be understood within a model which emphasizes the collective motion of the particles, such as the liquid drop model, which is discussed in the following section.

Much more elaborate models incorporating both collective and independent particle features have been concocted, but the simpler models will serve our limited purpose, which is to demonstrate that such models can yield a great deal of insight into the behavior of real nuclei.

29-1   THE LIQUID DROP MODEL

The liquid drop model will be employed to arrive at the "semi-empirical mass formula" and to discuss the collective excitation and fission of heavy nuclei.

In our discussion of the saturation of nuclear forces in Chapter 27 the analogy to a liquid was pointed out. In a liquid drop the binding energy (heat of condensation) is largely proportional to the volume or the number of particles in the drop. For a nucleus this would be a term B_1, called the *volume energy*, proportional to A,

$$B_1 = a_1 A \tag{29-1}$$

This term actually overestimates the binding energy somewhat, since the nucleons at the surface interact with fewer neighbors and thus are less tightly bound than those completely surrounded by nucleons. The number of particles at the surface is proportional to the surface area, or to $A^{2/3}$, since the radius is proportional to $A^{1/3}$. Thus we should add a negative correction proportional to $- A^{2/3}$ to the binding energy,

$$B_2 = - a_2 A^{2/3} \tag{29-2}$$

the so-called *surface energy*, analogous to the surface tension in a liquid.

Another important correction to the volume energy arises from the coulomb repulsion of the protons. The coulomb force lessens the binding and, as discussed in Chapter 27, it is proportional to the number of interacting pairs, $Z(Z - 1)/2 \approx Z^2/2$ for Z large, and inversely proportional to the nuclear radius R or to $A^{1/3}$,

$$B_3 = - a_3 Z^2 A^{-1/3} \tag{29-3}$$

To improve on the formula $B = B_1 + B_2 + B_3$ for the binding energy of the nuclei, we must actually go beyond the liquid drop model and take into account the effect of the Pauli principle on the individual particles. As discussed in Chapter 27 and again in the next section, the Pauli principle ensures that the nuclei with roughly equal numbers of neutrons and protons have the largest binding energy, other things being equal. A departure from $Z \approx N$ decreases the binding. A detailed study of the effect shows that this *symmetry energy* should take the form

$$B_4 = - a_4 (\tfrac{1}{2}A - Z)^2/A \tag{29-4}$$

The terms discussed up to this point are all continuous functions of the atomic and mass numbers Z and A (or Z and N). Experimentally one finds, however, that the variation of the binding energy with Z is not quite smooth (Fig. 27-3), but depends significantly on whether Z is even or odd. The same result is found in the variation of B with N. Nuclei with even Z and even N are most stable and most abundant, while those with odd A (either Z or N odd) are intermediate with respect to stability, and those with both Z and N odd are most unstable and least abundant. (See Table 27–1 and Fig. 27–2.) This feature can also be understood in terms of the Pauli principle and single particle energy levels in the nucleus. A *pairing energy* term, B_5, of the form

$$B_5 = \begin{cases} + f(A) & A \text{ even}, Z \text{ odd (and therefore } N \text{ odd)} \\ 0 & A \text{ odd} \\ - f(A) & A \text{ even}, Z \text{ even} \end{cases} \quad (29\text{--}5)$$

is therefore added to the others. The various constants a_1, a_2, a_3, a_4, and the function $f(A)$, are then adjusted for the best fit with the experimentally known binding energies. Several slightly different sets of constants have been obtained, depending on the precise nature of the fit. One set, computed by A. E. S. Green, leads to the formula

$$B = 15.753\,A - 17.804\,A^{2/3} - 0.7103\,\frac{Z^2}{A^{1/3}}$$
$$- 94.77\,\frac{(\tfrac{1}{2}A - Z)^2}{A} - B_5 \text{ MeV} \quad (29\text{--}6)$$

where in B_5 $f(A)$ is taken to be

$$f(A) = 33.6\,A^{-3/4} \text{ MeV} \quad (29\text{--}7)$$

By Eq. 27–2, the mass of an atom is then represented by

$$M = Z\,M_H + (A - Z)M_n - B/c^2 \quad (29\text{--}8)$$

where B is given in terms of A and Z by Eq. 29–6. A mass formula of this kind was first discussed by the German physicist Carl von Weizsäcker.

With these rather simple considerations one is able to obtain agreement with the experimental binding energies of all the heavy and intermediate nuclei ($A \gtrsim 15$) to an accuracy of better than 1 per cent. The agreement with the experimental atomic masses is very much better, since the dominant terms in Eq. 29–8 are the first two terms, while the deviations occur in the relatively small B/c^2 term.

With a formula for the masses of the nuclei, we are now in a position to discuss their relative stability. In particular we can study the stability properties of isobars, i.e., nuclei with a common mass number A. Let us start by considering odd A nuclei in which case B_5 vanishes. With A constant, the mass M is only a function of Z. This function is seen, Eq. 29–6, to be a polynomial in Z of second degree, or a parabola, Fig. 29–1. The parabolic mass curve for $A = $ constant has a minimum, which can be found by setting $\partial M / \partial Z$ equal to zero. The isobar closest to this minimum must have the smallest mass and therefore the lowest total energy $E = Mc^2$. There will normally be only one stable isobar (A odd), since we shall find that nuclei can change their Z-number keeping A constant through the process of β-decay, in which an electron or a positron is emitted (Chapter 30). Only in rare cases, e.g., $A = 113$ and $A = 123$, are two isobars with odd A equally close to the minimum of the parabola and thus both stable. With the mass formula given in Eq. 29–8, the A and Z values of the minimum mass isobars agree very well with the curve of the stable nuclei, Fig. 27–2.

With A even, B_5 is no longer zero, but equals $+f(A)$ for Z odd and $-f(A)$ for Z even, with $f(A)$ given by Eq. 29–7. With A constant, $f(A)$ is also constant. For a given even A we must therefore add a constant to the mass parabola for Z odd and subtract a constant when Z is even. For A even, the masses of the odd Z isobars will therefore lie on a separate parabola elevated by a constant amount with respect to the even Z mass parabola, Fig. 29–2. This explains the absence of stable even A, odd Z nuclei for $A > 14$, and why even A nuclei often have several stable isobars (Table 27–1), such as those labeled a, b, and c in Fig. 29–2. These atoms all have masses below the isobars whose proton numbers Z differ from them by one. Since the process of β-decay (Chapter 30) can only change Z by one, they are stable; i.e., it is impossible for a in Fig. 29–2 to decay into b even though the mass of b is smaller than the mass of a.

We have seen that the Z and A values of the stable isobars can be understood in terms of our simple mass formula. Why, beyond a certain value of A, even the "stablest" isobars are unstable with respect to α-decay will be discussed more fully in the next chapter. For any given Z/A ratio, however, we see that the volume binding energy is proportional to A while the coulomb term is proportional to $A^{5/3}$. For large A, therefore, the coulomb repulsion gets relatively more important, thereby lessening the binding energy per nucleon. A more stable configuration is then reached by breaking the nucleus up into smaller pieces through such processes as α-decay or nuclear fission.

Other features of the nucleus that can be understood in terms of the liquid drop model are the modes of "collective excitation" of the nucleus. The system of nucleons in a given nucleus can be excited above its ground state energy in many ways. Some modes of excitation involve essentially all the nucleons, and can be characterized as elastic vibrations, surface oscilla-

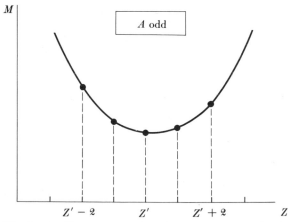

Fig. 29–1. *The mass as a function of atomic number for odd A isobars.*

tions, or as a rotation of the whole nucleus. The latter motion has already been treated quantum mechanically in the section on molecular spectra, Section 24–5. The energy levels are (Eq. 24–5)

$$E_l = \frac{\hbar^2}{2I} l(l + 1)$$

where I is the moment of inertia and l the orbital angular momentum quantum number associated with the rotation. From the existence of an electric quadrupole moment, we know that the nucleus deviates from a perfectly spherical shape. Calculations of the rotational energy levels of slightly deformed nuclei (from a sphere) give very good agreement with observed excitation energies. Rotational series are easily identified because the energy levels have the very simple dependence of $l(l + 1)$ on the integral angular momentum quantum number l.

The energy levels corresponding to surface vibrations can also be calculated, although we shall not do so here. In general the vibrational excitations are of higher energies (several MeV) than the rotational energy levels. The lowest energy vibrational mode is the one illustrated in Fig. 29–3, where the nucleus periodically assumes an ellipsoidal shape. When the sphere is deformed at a constant density, the only terms in the mass for-

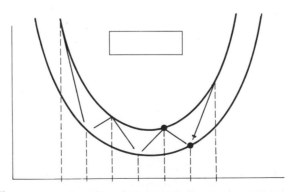

Fig. 29–2. The mass as a function of atomic number for even A isobars.

Fig. 29–3. Oscillation of a "liquid drop" nucleus.

mula, Eqs. 29–6 and 29–8, that change are the surface and coulomb terms. With the volume remaining constant, any deformation away from the spherical shape increases the surface and thereby the surface term contribution to the total mass, Eq. 29–8. With an ellipsoidal shape the protons are on the average farther apart than in the case of the sphere, leading to a decrease in the coulomb energy contribution to the mass. If the *increase* in the surface term is larger than the *decrease* in the coulomb term, the total energy (or mass) of the system increases, i.e., energy must be *added* to the nucleus to deform it. Such a nucleus is stable. If energy is added to the nucleus to deform it slightly, it can oscillate stably as indicated in Fig. 29–3. If, on the other hand, the decrease in the coulomb term is larger than the increase in the surface term (coulomb repulsion stronger than the surface tension), the nucleus can spontaneously deform with no addition of energy until it breaks in two. This is the process of *fission* (Fig. 29–4), which will be discussed more fully in Chapter 30. Fission will occur spontaneously when the change in the coulomb term $|\Delta B_3|$ exceeds the change in the surface term $|\Delta B_2|$, $|\Delta B_3|/|\Delta B_2| > 1$. A careful calculation of B_2 and B_3 (Eqs. 29–2, 29–3, and 29–6) in an ellipsoidal geometry shows that $|\Delta B_3|/|\Delta B_2|$ is equal to $\dfrac{a_3 Z^2}{2a_2 A}$, which exceeds unity for $Z^2/A \gtrsim 50$, or, along the curve of stable nuclei, for $Z \sim 140$, $A \lesssim 390$. Actually a nucleus is unstable to α-decay long before this point ($Z > 83$), and we shall see (Chapter 30) that even fission can be induced for much smaller mass numbers by adding a modest amount of energy to the nucleus.

We should finally mention the importance of the liquid drop model in understanding the idea of a *compound nucleus* in nuclear reactions, an idea which will also be explored further in Chapter 30.

29–2 THE SHELL MODEL

The success of the liquid drop model in explaining the main features of the binding energy of the nuclei as a function of A and Z should not blind us to its limitations. Whereas the liquid drop model predicts a generally smooth variation of all nuclear properties with A and Z, experiments show

Fig. 29–4. Fission of a nucleus.

a very irregular departure from the smooth curves (Fig. 27–3). Particularly interesting are the marked discontinuities at certain special proton or neutron numbers, namely for N or Z equal to 2, 8, 20, 28, 50, 82, and 126. These numbers have become known as the *magic numbers* of nuclear physics. Nuclei with N or Z "magic" are found to be particularly stable, i.e., their binding energies are greater or their masses smaller than the ones predicted by Eq. 29–6. In atomic physics we found that especially stable electron configurations (large ionization potentials) were associated with closed shells or subshells. It is tempting to infer the same association in the case of nuclei.

The closed shell effects at the magic N- and Z-numbers show up in many different ways. First of all there are more stable isotopes with magic Z-numbers and more stable isotones with magic N-numbers than with neighboring Z- and N-numbers. Thus Sn with $Z = 50$ has the largest number of stable isotopes of any element, namely ten, with N ranging from 62 to 74. Similarly we find seven stable isotones with $N = 82$ (from Xe^{136} to Sm^{144}) compared to three with $N = 80$ and two with $N = 84$ (Fig. 27–2; Table 27–1). We also find that the natural abundance of nuclei with magic N- or Z-numbers is higher than the abundance of neighboring non-magic nuclei.

Further evidence is obtained from nuclear reactions or decays. Thus nuclei with magic N-numbers have especially low neutron absorption cross sections, while nuclei with one less neutron (N equal to a magic number minus one) readily absorb a neutron to fill the shell. One also finds that when a nucleus gets rid of a single neutron outside a closed shell through the process of β-decay, the energy release is especially large. Such is the case when $_{18}^{21}Ar^{39}$ decays by transforming the 21st neutron into the 19th proton.

Evidence for the closed shell structure with $N = 126$ and $Z = 82$ is obtained from the energy release in α-decay (Chapter 30). All nuclei with $N > 126$ are unstable with respect to α-decay, while there are two stable isotones, bismuth and lead, with N equal to 126. In fact all the four α-radioactive series (Chapter 30) end in stable nuclei in the vicinity of $N = 126$ and $Z = 82$, $_{83}^{126}Bi^{209}$, $_{82}^{126}Pb^{208}$, $_{82}^{125}Pb^{207}$, and $_{82}^{124}Pb^{206}$.

In spite of the evidence for a shell structure in the nuclei, there are good reasons why one might have serious doubts about its validity. The electronic shell structure in an atom was deduced through a *single particle approximation*, in which the electron was assumed to move independently in the dominant force field of the nucleus. The weaker effect of the other electrons was only considered through a reduction of the effective nuclear charge (the screening effect).

In a nucleus there is no dominant central potential like the one in the atom. If we are to consider the nucleons as moving independently in a common potential, this must really be an *average* potential arising from the interaction of the nucleons with one another. Does it make sense to consider a nucleon as moving freely through the nucleus in a smooth common potential due to all the other nucleons? At first thought the answer seems to be no.

The nucleon-nucleon forces are of short range and are very strong (Chapter 28). One might therefore expect a wildly fluctuating potential, and moreover expect that a nucleon would interact violently with its neighbors as it moves through the nucleus. Such a state of affairs would not be consistent with the picture of all the nucleons moving independently in a common potential well.

Actually the Pauli principle removes the paradox, at least in part. If there is to be an interaction of two nucleons in the interior of the "nuclear matter," one nucleon will have to impart energy and momentum to the other, thereby changing the quantum mechanical state of both particles. If there is an exchange of energy, one particle would lose energy, i.e., go down into a lower energy level. With all the lower energy levels already occupied, the Pauli principle forbids such a collision. A nucleon meeting a neighbor would like to give it a push, but often finds nowhere to push it. This is a rather oversimplified picture, and it is not surprising that the shell structure of the nuclei should be less pronounced than the atomic shell structure. Nevertheless, it justifies the independent particle picture in a qualitative way.

Let us now turn to the task of explaining why the closed shells occur at the mentioned magic neutron and proton numbers. Since the nucleons are confined within the nuclear radius $R \approx 1.3 \times A^{1/3}$ f, we should consider the common nuclear potential well to have the range R. The detailed shape of the potential is hard to guess. Potentials frequently used because of their mathematical simplicity are the finite spherical well potential, Fig. 29–5(a),

$$V = -V_0, r \leq R \qquad V = 0, r > R$$

and the finite harmonic oscillator potential, Fig. 29–5(b),

$$V = -V_0 + \tfrac{1}{2}Kr^2, r \leq R \qquad V = 0, r > R$$

Even simpler are the infinite wells:

$$V = -V_0, r \leq R \qquad V = \infty, r > R$$

or

$$V = -V_0 + \tfrac{1}{2}Kr^2 \qquad \text{for all } r$$

If the Schrödinger equation is solved for the infinite spherical well the ordering of the lowest energy levels is found to be as follows: $1s$, $2p$, $3d$, $2s$,

Fig. 29–5. (a) *Square well and* (b) *harmonic oscillator approximations to the nuclear potential.*

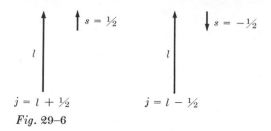

$j = l + \frac{1}{2}$ $j = l - \frac{1}{2}$

Fig. 29–6

$4f$, $3p$, $5g$, $4d$, $6h$, $3s$, $5f$, $7i$, $4p$ . . . , where the letters s, p, d, f, g . . . stand for $l = 0, 1, 2, 3, 4$, etc., while the numbers stand for the principal quantum number n or the number of nodes in the radial part $R(r)$ of the wave function plus $(l + 1)$ (Chapter 21). Since the number of identical particles in each level is limited by the Pauli principle to $2(2l + 1)$ (Section 22–4), the number of particles in these low levels are respectively 2, 6, 10, 2, 14, 6, 18, 10, 22, 2, 14, 26, and 6, for closed shells at proton or neutron numbers equal to 2, 8, 18, 20, 34, 40, 58, 68, 90, 92, 106, 132, and 138. Of these numbers only 2, 8, and 20 are observed to be "magic," i.e., correspond to closed shells, while such numbers as 50, 82, and 126 are conspicuously absent.

With the infinite harmonic oscillator potential, the $1s$ level is again lowest, followed by $2p$; and then by $2s$ and $3d$ at the same energy; $3p$ and $4f$ together; $3s$, $4d$, and $5g$ together; and $4p$, $5f$, and $6h$ also at the same energy. With these groupings the closed shells occur with 2, 8, 20, 40, 70, and 112 particles. Once again the magic numbers 2, 8, and 20 appear while others like 50, 82, and 126 do not.

With other potentials one gets a further slight reshuffling of the order in which the lower energy levels appear, but no amount of reshuffling can produce all the magic numbers. What has been ignored up to this point is the strong coupling between the spin and orbital angular momenta of the individual nucleons.

A nucleon with $l \geq 1$ can have its spin $s = \frac{1}{2}$ parallel to or antiparallel to its orbital angular momentum, for a total angular momentum j equal to $l + \frac{1}{2}$ or $l - \frac{1}{2}$, Fig. 29–6. In nuclei it is found that the individual j's rather than the total L and S are approximate constants of the motion (j-j coupling rather than L-S coupling, Chapter 22). One finds that the Hamiltonian operator for each nucleon contains a spin-orbit term of the form

$$- \beta \mathbf{L}_i \cdot \mathbf{S}_i = - \frac{\beta}{2} [\mathbf{J}_i{}^2 - \mathbf{L}_i{}^2 - \mathbf{S}_i{}^2]$$

where β is a positive constant. This term gives rise to a spin-orbit energy (Eq. 23–2) equal to

$$E_{ls} = - \frac{\beta}{2} \hbar^2 [j(j + 1) - l(l + 1) - s(s + 1)] \qquad (29\text{–}9)$$

Note that these are the j, l, and s values for a single nucleon rather than for the whole system. With $j = l + \frac{1}{2}$ this energy becomes

$$E_{ls} = -\frac{\beta}{2}\hbar^2\left[\left(l+\frac{1}{2}\right)\left(l+\frac{3}{2}\right) - l(l+1) - \frac{1}{2}\left(\frac{3}{2}\right)\right]$$

$$= -\frac{\beta}{2}\hbar^2 l \tag{29-10}$$

and for $j = l - \frac{1}{2}, l \geq 1$,

$$E_{ls} = -\frac{\beta}{2}\hbar^2\left[\left(l-\frac{1}{2}\right)\left(l+\frac{1}{2}\right) - l(l+1) - \frac{1}{2}\left(\frac{3}{2}\right)\right]$$

$$= +\frac{\beta}{2}\hbar^2[l+1] \tag{29-11}$$

The energy is therefore lowered for the spin parallel to the orbital angular momentum, $j = l + \frac{1}{2}$, and raised for the spin antiparallel to the angular momentum, $j = l - \frac{1}{2}$. For $l = 0$ there is no spin-orbit splitting, since with $l = 0$, $s = \frac{1}{2}$, and $j = \frac{1}{2}$, $E_{ls} = 0$, Eq. 29–9. All energy levels corresponding to l not zero, however, will be split in two with $j = l + \frac{1}{2}$ and $l - \frac{1}{2}$, respectively, and with the magnitude of the splitting proportional to $2l + 1$, Eqs. 29–10 and 29–11. A level of a given j has room for $2j + 1$ nucleons of each kind (not $2(2j + 1)$ since the direction of the spin is now fixed). Thus the $2p$ level, which in the absence of a spin-orbit energy would contain $2(2 \times 1 + 1) = 6$ particles, is now split into two levels corresponding to $j = l + \frac{1}{2} = \frac{3}{2}$ with $2 \times \frac{3}{2} + 1 = 4$ particles, and $j = l - \frac{1}{2} = \frac{1}{2}$ with $2 \times \frac{1}{2} + 1 = 2$ particles, respectively. Proceeding in this fashion we can indeed find a level scheme with closed shells for 2, 8, 20, 28, 50, 82, and 126 particles in agreement with the observed facts. (See Fig. 29–7.) The closed shells occur where the energy gaps between adjacent levels are particularly large. The importance of the spin-orbit term in the shell structure of the nuclei was first recognized independently by Mrs. Mayer in the United States and by Haxel, Jensen, and Suess in Germany.

We might add that there is independent evidence from scattering of nucleons off nuclei for a spin-orbit coupling of the same sign and the same magnitude as that found with the shell model.

For closed shell nuclei (e.g., O^{16}), as with the electron configurations of the noble gases, we predict that the total angular momentum should vanish. This is indeed found to be the case. Similarly for nuclei with a single nucleon outside closed shells, we expect that the total angular momentum of the nucleus should be due to the angular momentum of this single nucleon, $J = j$. Thus $_{83}^{126}\text{Bi}^{209}$ has a closed shell of neutrons and a single proton outside the $Z = 82$ closed shell configuration. The magic number 82 (Fig. 29–7) results from the splitting of the $6h$ level into its $j = 11\frac{1}{2}$ and $j = 9\frac{1}{2}$ sublevels. With the $j = 11\frac{1}{2}$ level filled, the 83rd proton should go into the $j = 9\frac{1}{2}$ level (Fig. 29–7). The total angular momentum quantum number of Bi^{209} is indeed found to be $9\frac{1}{2}$. Similarly $_{20}^{21}\text{Ca}^{41}$ has one neutron outside closed shells of 20 neutrons and protons. Ca^{41} has a total nuclear angular momentum of $7\frac{1}{2}$ in agreement with the level scheme in Fig. 29–7. Further support comes from $_{21}^{28}\text{Sc}^{49}$ and $_{8}^{9}\text{O}^{17}$, which have angular momenta of $7\frac{1}{2}$ and $5\frac{1}{2}$, respectively.

How the angular momenta of the nucleons add up when a shell is only partially filled presents a more difficult problem. It is an experimental fact, however, that all nuclei with an even number of neutrons and an even number of protons have angular momenta equal to zero. One is tempted to conclude that when a single nucleon is added to such an even neutron, even proton configuration, the angular momentum of the entire nucleus is due to the single odd nucleon, $J = j$. This assumption, called the *single-particle* model, has proved remarkably successful. For $A \leq 140$ almost all

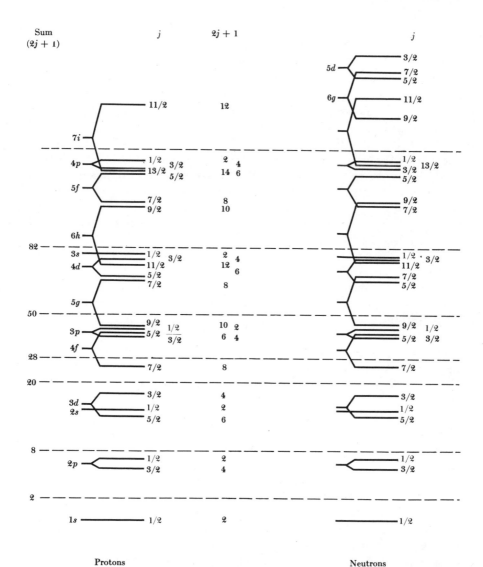

Fig. 29–7. The ordering of the proton and neutron energy levels in a nucleus, based on the shell model with spin-orbit coupling.

nuclear angular momenta can be explained with the single-particle picture and the level scheme given in Fig. 29–7. The relative ordering of the levels, however, is to a certain extent a function of how many particles occupy the levels, as in the case of the atomic electron levels. For $A > 140$ the single-particle model works best near the magic numbers 82 and 126.

As examples let us consider the three nuclei $_{21}^{24}\text{Sc}^{45}$, $_{42}^{55}\text{Mo}^{97}$, and, $_{62}^{87}\text{Sm}^{149}$. In the first of these, the 21st proton should go in the $j = \frac{7}{2}$ branch of the $4f$ level, in the second the 55th neutron into the $j = \frac{5}{2}$ branch of the $4d$ level, and in the third example with 5 neutrons outside the $N = 82$ closed shell structure, the odd 87th neutron should be in the $j = \frac{7}{2}$ branch of the $5f$ level, Fig. 29–7. The total angular momenta J of these nuclei are indeed $\frac{7}{2}$, $\frac{5}{2}$, and $\frac{7}{2}$, respectively.

It should be emphasized that the assumption of like nucleons (e.g., neutrons) outside closed shells pairing off so as to cancel their angular momenta is far from obvious. One would have to prove that among all the possible angular momentum states, this is the one of lowest energy. Such energy calculations have been carried out, proving the single-particle assumption to be valid for most nuclei. The combination of angular momenta in a nucleus is therefore much simpler than in the electronic system surrounding it. A half-filled electron shell with an even number of electrons will in general have a nonzero angular momentum (Table 22–2). That the rules in the nucleus should differ from those in the electron system is not surprising, since in the nucleus we are dealing with forces that are completely different.

A further confirmation of the single-particle model and the energy level scheme given in Fig. 29–7 is obtained by calculating the expected magnetic moments of nuclei of odd A. The agreement is not quite as good as in the case of the angular momenta. Angular momenta are quantized, and predictions are either exactly right or off by a whole unit of $\hbar$. With the single-particle model they are usually right. The magnetic moment is not quantized, however, and the predictions of the model are only approximately correct. On the other hand, it can be shown that the comparison of calculated and measured magnetic moments yields the l as well as the j quantum number of the odd nucleon for a direct confirmation of the shell model level scheme (Fig. 29–7). In contrast a measurement of J (the total angular momentum of the nucleus) yields only j (the angular momentum of the odd nucleon), but cannot determine whether l is equal to $j + \frac{1}{2}$ or $j - \frac{1}{2}$.

So far we have only discussed the predictions of the shell model with regard to the ground states of nuclei. We would expect, however, that it would be possible to excite a nucleus by having a nucleon go up into one of the unoccupied energy levels. Such a mode of excitation would involve giving the excitation energy to a single nucleon and is therefore very different from the collective modes of excitation (vibration, rotation) considered in Section 29–1, where the excitation energy is shared among all the nucleons. Predominantly single-particle excitations of this kind have definitely been identified. The de-excitation of the nucleus is usually achieved through the emission of a photon or γ-ray, in complete analogy to the electronic transitions in an atom. The photon energy in a nuclear transition, however, is typically measured in MeV.

One particularly striking success of the shell model is its correct prediction of the N- and Z-number regions in which *isomers* are found. An isomer is simply a nucleus in an excited state with a very long half-life (hours, days, or years) compared to most excited nuclear states, which last only 10^{-6} to 10^{-13} sec. Transitions involving large changes in the angular momentum of a system are known to be very improbable (Chapter 23), and it had long been realized that the isomers owed their long life to the fact that the angular momenta of the isomeric state and the ground state are very different. Experimentally one finds that the isomers occur mainly in the following separate groups, called the "islands of isomerism,"

(a) $39 \leq (N \text{ or } Z) \leq 49$ (b) $63 \leq (N \text{ or } Z) \leq 81$ (c) $91 \leq N \leq 125$

The presence of isomers in these regions can be understood immediately from the level scheme in Fig. 29–7. We see that the "outermost" neutron or proton in the group (a) nuclei is found in an energy region where the $5g(j = \frac{9}{2})$ and $3p(j = \frac{1}{2})$ levels lie very close together. Thus yttrium, $_{39}\text{Y}^{89}$, with the 39th proton in a $p_{1/2}$ state, has an excited $g_{9/2}$ state, while the indium isotopes $_{49}\text{In}^{113}$ and $_{49}\text{In}^{115}$ have the levels inverted, with $g_{9/2}$ ground states and $p_{1/2}$ excited states. In this first island alone there are more than thirty known isomers.

The group (b) isomers can similarly be understood through the proximity of the high angular momentum $g_{7/2}$ and $h_{11/2}$ energy levels to those of the $s_{1/2}$ and $d_{3/2}$ states, while most of the group (c) isomers arise from the proximity of the $i_{13/2}$ and the $p_{1/2}$ levels (Fig. 29–7).

In summary we can say that there are a number of nuclear properties that essentially originate through individual particle effects and that can be understood at least approximately within the shell model. On the other hand there are collective effects that can best be understood within a model that emphasizes the collective motion of all the nucleons, such as the liquid drop model. We have discussed examples of both single-particle excitations and collective modes of excitation in a nucleus. The emission of a gamma ray (photon) from a nucleus can therefore be either a single particle or a collective effect. Fission, on the other hand, is clearly a collective process (Section 29–1), while β-decay involves the change of a single neutron into a proton or vice versa. Then there are a number of effects, such as α-decay, that involve principally a cluster of particles, more than a single nucleon but certainly not all of them. These intermediate cases are perhaps the hardest to treat analytically. What is remarkable, however, is not that the nuclear problems are hard, but that the simple models we have introduced in this chapter are as successful as they have proved to be.

PROBLEMS

29-1.   Use the formula Eq. 29-6 to calculate the total binding energies of Al^{27}, Cu^{63}, Xe^{130}, and U^{238}. Compare with the actual binding energies given in Table 27-1.

29-2.   Repeat Prob. 29-1 for O^{16}, Ca^{40}, Sn^{120}, and Pb^{208}. Discuss the differences between the results of Prob. 29-1 and 29-2.

29-3.   Plot the volume energy $B1$, the surface energy $B2$, and the coulomb energy B_3 as functions of A. For B_3 choose the Z-values corresponding to the most stable isobar and pick A-values about 25 units apart. What can you conclude from this plot?

29-4.   Instantaneous fission will occur if $2a_2A/a_3Z^2$ is less than unity. Calculate this ratio for $_{92}U^{238}$ and $_8O^{16}$.

29-5.   The nucleus $_{92}U^{235}$ decays into the fission fragments $_{36}Kr^{90}$ and $_{56}Ba^{144}$ plus a neutron. Use the mass formula to estimate the total energy released in the fission reaction. Compare this energy to the coulomb energy between the two (spherical) fission fragments when they are just touching.

29-6.   Plot the curve in Fig. 29-1 for $A = 73$ based on the mass formula, Eqs. 29-6 and 29-8. Which isobar do you predict to be stable? Check your result against Table 27-1. Estimate the energy release in the β-decays of the two neighboring isobars.

29-7.   Plot the curves in Fig. 29-2 from the mass formula, Eqs. 29-6 and 29-8, for $A = 64$. From Table 27-1, mark the actual values for Ni^{64} and Zn^{64}. Explain why Cu^{64} can decay by emitting either an electron or a positron. Estimate the energy release in the β^-- and the β^+-decays of Cu^{64}.

29-8.   Assume that the moment of inertia of a nucleus of mass M and average radius R is $I = (2/5)MR^2$. With a mass number A equal to 125 estimate the energy (in MeV) of a γ-ray emitted in a transition from a rotational energy level with $l = 2$ to one with $l = 0$.

29-9.   Using the mass formula, Eqs. 29-6 and 29-8, investigate the stability of U^{235} against emission of (a) an α-particle, (b) a proton, and (c) a neutron (i.e., calculate the energy release if any).

29-10. Based on the shell model and the energy level scheme in Fig. 29-7 give the l and j values of all the nucleons in (a) $_1H^3$, (b) $_6C^{12}$, (c) $_6C^{13}$, and (d) $_{17}Cl^{35}$. What total angular momenta J do you predict for these nuclei?

29-11. From the mass formula calculate the binding energies of the last proton in Bi^{209} and in Pb^{206} and of the last neutron in Pb^{208} and in Pb^{207}. Compare with the actual values obtained from Table 27-1 and interpret the results in terms of the shell model.

REFERENCES

I. Kaplan, *Nuclear Physics* (Addison-Wesley, 1963, 2nd ed.), Ch. 17.

W. E. Burcham, *Nuclear Physics* (McGraw-Hill, 1963), Ch. 9, 12.

L. R. B. Elton, *Introductory Nuclear Theory* (Pitman, London, 1959), Ch. 5.

30/radioactive decay and nuclear reactions

Since nuclei are built up of smaller constituents, the nucleons, it is not surprising that they can be transformed in various ways. We could easily imagine two colliding nuclei forming a compound nucleus (*a "liquid drop" consisting of the two original nuclei*), *which could then break up into two, three, or more nuclei, subject, however, to the laws of conservation of total charge, energy, and momentum. Since the number of different possible reactions of this kind is exceedingly large, we cannot hope to study them all. Instead we select a few nuclear transformations that are particularly important and consider these in some detail.*

Nuclear transformations can conveniently be divided into two groups. An induced nuclear reaction *is the result of introducing energy in one way or another into the nucleus. The energy may be carried by a γ-ray, a neutron, a second nucleus, or by any other particle. This is the only way a stable nucleus can be transformed. The unstable nuclei, however, may change spontaneously. Spontaneous nuclear reactions are usually referred to as* radioactive transformations. *We will consider these first and come back to the induced reactions later in this chapter.*

30–1 RADIOACTIVITY

Radioactivity was first observed in uranium by Becquerel in 1896. The existence of an atomic nucleus had not yet been established, but in retrospect we recognize Becquerel's discovery as the earliest recorded nuclear effect.

If we assume that the nuclei of a radioactive material have a constant probability per unit time, λ, of spontaneously decaying, the probability, $d\Pi$, of a nucleus decaying in the time interval dt will equal

$$d\Pi = \lambda \, dt$$

If there are N nuclei present, we would expect $Nd\Pi = N\lambda \, dt$ to decay in the time dt. The change in the number of nuclei, dN, is therefore equal to

$$dN = - N\lambda \, dt \qquad (30\text{–}1)$$

which can be integrated to yield N as a function of time:

$$N = N_0 e^{-\lambda t} \qquad (30\text{–}2)$$

Here N_0 is the number of nuclei present at $t = 0$. Experimentally one observes that the number of radioactive decays per unit time does indeed decay exponentially in time in agreement with Eqs. 30–1 and 30–2. (See Fig. 30–1.)

The time τ it takes for half of the nuclei in a radioactive sample to disintegrate is called the *half-life*. The relation between the half-life τ and the decay constant λ is easily established by substituting $N = N_0/2$ and $t = \tau$ in Eq. 30–2, $\frac{1}{2} = e^{-\lambda \tau}$, or

$$\tau = \frac{\ln 2}{\lambda} = \frac{0.693}{\lambda} \qquad (30\text{–}3)$$

The values of τ for different nuclei vary from less than 10^{-13} sec to more than 10^{10} years.

Often the situation is more complex than indicated in Eqs. 30–1 and 30–2. Nuclei of type a may decay into nuclei of type b, which in turn decay into type c and so on. The result is a *radioactive chain* with the numbers of nuclei of each type varying with time in a complicated way depending on the decay constants and the original abundance of the different kinds of nuclei.

Even when the decay products are stable, it often happens that two or more radioactive species are mixed together, e.g., a mixture of unstable nuclei in the ground state and the same nuclei in isomeric states (Section 29–2). The observed radioactivity is then the sum of the separate activities. If the various activities have different half-lives, they can usually be distinguished and the half-life of each determined. An illustration is given in Fig. 30–4, which shows the decays of Ag^{110} and In^{116} isomers. The mathematical analysis of these more complicated situations will be omitted here.

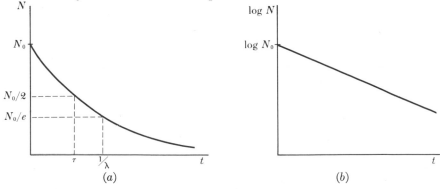

Fig. 30–1. *The number of radioactive nuclei, N, as a function of time.*

Radioactivity is usually measured in *curies*, where 1 curie is defined as 3.70×10^{10} decays per second. A millicurie is 10^{-3} curie.

It was early established that three different kinds of radiations were emitted in radioactive decays. These were called α-, β-, and γ-rays and subsequently identified as He^4 nuclei, electrons, and photons, respectively. Later it was found that positively charged electrons or *positrons* (Chapter 31) were also sometimes emitted, making it necessary to distinguish between β^--(electron) and β^+-(positron) decays. We will now discuss these different emissions in reverse alphabetical order.

30-2 GAMMA DECAY

In gamma decay neither the mass number A nor the atomic number Z is altered. A gamma ray is simply a photon emitted during the transition of an excited nucleus to a lower energy state. As discussed in the preceding chapter, this may be a collective de-excitation or the transition of a single nucleon from one nuclear shell to another. In principle, gamma decay is very similar to the emission of visible light or x-rays from an atom. The energy of a γ-ray, however, is usually much higher, often in the MeV range. By measuring the energies of the γ-rays emitted by excited nuclei, it is possible to construct detailed nuclear-energy-level diagrams. A complete nuclear theory should be able to predict the position of these levels. Such a theory does not exist at this time, but many of the observed energy levels can be understood qualitatively in terms of either the shell model or a collective model of the nucleus (Chapter 29).

The half-life for an allowed gamma decay is expected on theoretical grounds to be about 10^{-14} sec, or too fast to be measured. Highly forbidden decays with large changes in the angular momentum of the nucleus can have much longer half-lives. As mentioned in the previous chapter, the half-life of isomers can sometimes be measured in minutes, hours, or days. Most gamma decay half-lives, however, are very short. The reason γ-rays are still observed to emanate from naturally occurring radioactive materials is not because the gamma decay has a long half-life, but because an α-decay or a β-decay often leaves the resulting nucleus in an excited state. The deexcitation of this nucleus gives rise to the γ-ray. An example of gamma rays accompanying a β-decay is given in Fig. 30-2 and also in Fig. 30–4.

Another way in which a nucleus can get rid of excess energy is by trans-

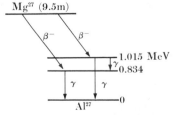

Fig. 30–2. The β- decay of Mg^{27}.

ferring this energy to one of the inner atomic electrons (usually in the K-shell), which as a result is expelled from the atom. This process, which competes with the gamma decay, is called *internal conversion*.

30-3 BETA DECAY

We shall now discuss some of the ways in which a nucleus can change its atomic number by one unit while the mass number remains unchanged, i.e., the change of a nucleus into one of its isobars. Historically, the first of these processes to be observed was the β^--decay, in which a neutron in the nucleus changes into a proton (which remains in the nucleus) with the simultaneous creation of an electron (or β^--particle). Examples are given in Figs. 30–2 and 30–4. If a nucleus at rest, symbolized by $_ZX^A$, β^--decays into a "daughter" nucleus $_{Z+1}X^A$ and an electron e^-, the electron and the daughter nucleus must have momenta of equal magnitude, p, and opposite direction in order that momentum be conserved. The conservation of total energy then demands that

$$\sqrt{p^2c^2 + m_e^2c^4} + \frac{p^2}{2M_{Z+1,A}} + M_{Z+1,\,A}c^2 = M_{Z,A}c^2 \qquad (30\text{--}4)$$

where m_e is the mass of the electron, $M_{Z,A}$ the mass of the mother nucleus, and $M_{Z+1,\,A}$ the mass of the daughter nucleus. Because of its large mass the latter is always nonrelativistic. Equation 30–4 yields a unique value for p^2 and hence for the kinetic energy of the electron. In other words, the electrons in the beta decay should all emerge with the same energy E_0 (Fig. 30–3(a)). This is a general result of any decay process with but two products. The observed electron energy spectrum, however, looks more like Fig. 30–3(b), an energy spectrum typical of more than two decay products.

With three or more products the total energy of the decay can be shared among the particles in such a way that the electron can acquire any kinetic energy from zero up to a maximum value as shown in Fig. 30–3(b). This led to Pauli's suggestion (1930), further developed by Fermi, that another particle was emitted in addition to the electron in β-decay. This particle,

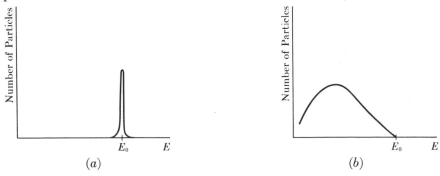

Fig. 30–3. *Typical energy distributions with* (a) *two decay products and* (b) *more than two decay products.*

which must be neutral to conserve electric charge, was dubbed the *neutrino*. It is now actually called the *antineutrino*, the symbol for which is $\bar{\nu}$,

$$_{z}X^{A} \rightarrow _{z+1}X^{A} + e^{-} + \bar{\nu}$$

Since this particle interacts very weakly with other particles, it is difficult to detect (Section 31–2). It was not observed to react with matter in any way until 1956, when it was "seen" in the "inverse β-decay" (Chapter 31),

$$\text{antineutrino} + \text{proton} \rightarrow \text{positron} + \text{neutron}$$

The neutrino has a spin equal to $\frac{1}{2}$. Its rest mass is known to be less than $0.0005m$ and thought to be equal to zero. This is deduced from the fact that the maximum energy E_0 of the electron spectrum (Fig. 30–3(b)) is equal to the energy predicted by Eq. 30–4 for a neutrino energy (including rest energy) equal to zero.

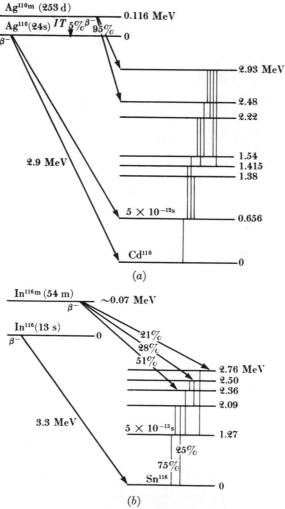

Fig. 30–4. *The β- and γ- decays of* (a) *silver and* (b) *indium isomers.*

The β^--decay is the process by which a nucleus too rich in neutrons approaches its stable isobar (Fig. 27–2). Beta decays often accompany α-decays (Tables 30–1 to 30–4) in the natural chains of radioactivity among the heavy unstable nuclei, $A > 209$. In an α-decay a helium nucleus is expelled, thereby reducing Z by 2 and N by 2. With $N > Z$ α-decay therefore *increases* the N/Z ratio, leading to an imbalance alleviated through β-decay.

The β^+-decay or *positron decay* was first observed in 1934 by Curie and Joliot, when they studied the reaction

$$_{13}\text{Al}^{27} + {}_2\text{He}^4 \rightarrow {}_{15}\text{P}^{30} + {}_0n^1$$

The nucleus $_{15}\text{P}^{30}$ is radioactive and decays as follows:

$$_{15}\text{P}^{30} \rightarrow {}_{14}\text{Si}^{30} + e^+ + \nu$$

The positron is the positive electron discussed in Chapter 17 and in more detail in Chapter 31. The process of β^+-decay is one of the reactions by which a nucleus too rich in protons approaches its stable isobar. Another is the process of *electron capture*, often called K-capture since the electron captured by the nucleus usually comes from the K-shell of the atom.

$$_Z\text{X}^A + e^- \rightarrow {}_{Z-1}\text{X}^A + \nu$$

The stability of a nucleus to β-decay and K-capture can be understood in a qualitative way from the semi-empirical mass formula as discussed in Section 29–1. (See also Figs. 29–1 and 29–2.)

30–4   ALPHA DECAY

Having discussed γ-decay, which changes neither A nor Z, and β-decay, which changes Z but not A, we now turn to α-decay, which changes both, reducing Z by 2 and A by 4. While β^+- and β^--decays get rid of excess positive or negative charge, α-decay gets rid of excess mass as well as charge, Fig. 30–5. In α-decay there are only two decay products, the α-particle itself and the daughter nucleus,

$$_Z\text{X}^A \rightarrow {}_{Z-2}\text{X}^{A-4} + {}_2\text{He}^4$$

The α-particles in a given decay process will therefore all emerge with the same kinetic energy E_α (Section 30–3 and Fig. 30–3(a)). Since the energy released in the decay is about 10^3 times smaller than the α-particle rest energy (≈ 4 GeV), the α-particles are always nonrelativistic. The energy conservation equation (the analog of Eq. 30–4) may then be written

$$\frac{p^2}{2M_\alpha} + \frac{p^2}{2M_{Z-2,A-4}} + M_\alpha c^2 + M_{Z-2,A-4}c^2 = M_{Z,A}c^2$$

or

$$E_\alpha = p^2/2M_\alpha = (1 + M_\alpha/M_{Z-2, A-4})^{-1}(M_{Z, A} - M_{Z-2, A-4} - M_\alpha)c^2 \quad (30\text{–}5)$$

Observed α-particle energies vary in a quite limited range from 3.99 MeV in the decay of $_{90}\text{Th}^{232}$ (half-life 1.39×10^{10} years) to 8.78 MeV in the

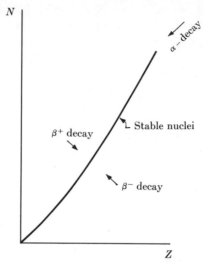

Fig. 30–5. *The regions of α-, β⁻-, and β⁺- decay relative to the stable nuclei.*

decay of   Po²¹² (half-life 3 × 10⁻⁷ sec), while as indicated the half-lives vary enormously. By comparing the α-particle energies and the decay half-lives in the four radioactive series, Tables 30–1 to 30–4, we see that there is a reciprocal relationship between energy and half-life.

We can understand this relationship qualitatively in terms of a quantum mechanical "tunneling" through a potential barrier. Consider the motion of the α-particle in the potential of the daughter nucleus. Outside the range of nuclear forces, $r > 1.3A^{1/3}$ fermi, the potential is a repulsive coulomb potential $V \propto r^{-1}$. At shorter distances the strong attractive nuclear forces take over, and we get a total potential somewhat as drawn in Fig. 30–6. If we choose the potential to be zero at infinite separation, the energy of the α-particle, $E\alpha$, must be positive and of the order of 4 to 9

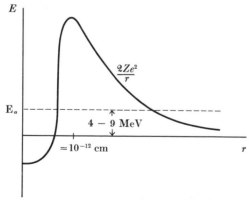

Fig. 30–6. *The relative potential energy of an α-particle and a heavy nucleus as a function of their separation.*

TABLE 30–1.   Uranium Series

Nuclide	Common Name	Particle Emitted	Half-life	E(MeV)
$_{92}U^{238}$	Uranium I	α	4.51×10^9 yr	4.18
$_{90}Th^{234}$	Uranium X$_1$	β	24.1 days	0.19, 0.10
$_{91}Pa^{234}$	Uranium X$_2$	β	1.18 min	2.31
$_{91}Pa^{234}$	Uranium Z	β	6.66 hr	0.5
$_{92}U^{234}$	Uranium II	α	2.50×10^5 yr	4.76
$_{90}Th^{230}$	Ionium	α	8.0×10^4 yr	4.68, 4.61
$_{88}Ra^{226}$	Radium	α	1620 yr	4.78, 4.59
$_{86}Em^{222}$	Radon	α	3.825 days	5.48
$_{84}Po^{218}$	Radium A	α	3.05 min	6.00
$_{82}Pb^{214}$	Radium B	β	26.8 min	0.7
$_{83}Bi^{214}$	Radium C	β α	197.7 min	β 1.6, 3.17
				α 5.5–10.5
$_{84}Po^{214}$	Radium C′	α	1.6×10^{-4} sec	7.68
$_{81}Tl^{210}$	Radium C″	β	1.32 min	1.9
$_{82}Pb^{210}$	Radium D	β	20 yr	0.02
$_{83}Bi^{210}$	Radium E	β	5.0 days	1.17
$_{84}Po^{210}$	Polonium	α	138 days	5.30
$_{82}Pb^{206}$	Radium G	stable		

SOURCE: *Chart of the Nuclides*, 5th ed. (1956), The General Electric Company.

TABLE 30–2.   Actinium Series

Nuclide	Common Name	Particle Emitted	Half-life	E(MeV)
$_{92}U^{235}$	Actinouranium	α	7.1×10^8 yr	4.40, 4.58
$_{90}Th^{231}$	Uranium Y	β	25.6 hr	0.09, 0.30, 0.22
$_{91}Pa^{231}$	Protoactinium	α	3.4×10^4 yr	5.0, 4.63–5.05
$_{89}Ac^{227}$	Actinium	β	22 yr	0.046
$_{90}Th^{227}$	Radioactinium	α	18.2 days	5.97, 5.65–6.03
$_{88}Ra^{223}$	Actinium X	α	11.6 days	5.70–5.68
$_{86}Em^{219}$	Actinon	α	3.92 sec	6.82, 6.56
$_{84}Po^{215}$	Actinium A	α	1.8×10^{-3} sec	7.36
$_{82}Pb^{211}$	Actinium B	β	36.1 min	1.4, 0.5
$_{83}Bi^{211}$	Actinium C	α β	2.15 min	α 6.62, 6.27
				β 0.35
$_{81}Tl^{207}$	Actinium C″	β	4.78 min	1.45
$_{84}Po^{211}$	Actinium C′	α	0.52 sec	7.43
$_{82}Pb^{207}$	Actinium D	stable		

SOURCE: *Chart of the Nuclides*, 5th ed. (1956), The General Electric Company.
There is also branching at actinium and the Ac A.

TABLE 30-3.   Thorium Series

Nuclide	Common Name	Particle Emitted	Half-life	E(MeV)
$_{90}Th^{232}$	Thorium	α	1.39×10^{10} yr	3.99, 3.93
$_{88}Ra^{228}$	Mesothorium$_1$	β	6.7 yr	<0.02
$_{89}Ac^{228}$	Mesothorium$_2$	β	6.13 hr	1.11, 0.45–2.18
$_{90}Th^{228}$	Radiothorium	α	1.90 yr	5.42, 5.34
$_{88}Ra^{224}$	Thorium X	α	3.64 days	5.68, 5.44
$_{86}Em^{220}$	Thoron	α	52 sec	6.28, 5.75
$_{84}Po^{216}$	Thorium A	α	0.16 sec	6.77
$_{82}Pb^{212}$	Thorium B	β	10.64 hr	0.34, 0.58
$_{83}Bi^{212}$	Thorium C	β α	60.5 min	β 2.25 α 6.05, 6.09
$_{80}Po^{212}$	Thorium C'	α	3×10^{-7} sec	8.78
$_{81}Tl^{208}$	Thorium C''	β	3.1 min	1.79, 1.28
$_{82}Pb^{208}$	Thorium D	stable		

SOURCE: *Chart of the Nuclides,* 5th ed. (1956), The General Electric Company.
Branching also occurs at Th A.

MeV, since this is the observed range of energies of the emerging particles in α-decay. If E_α were negative, the α-particle would be absolutely bound in the nuclear potential well with a wave function ψ as indicated in Fig. 30–7(a). With E_α positive the wave function (Fig. 30–7(b)) is not completely zero even after falling off exponentially through the potential barrier. (See Chapter 20.) There is a finite though small probability of finding the

TABLE 30–4.   Neptunium Series

Nuclide	Particle Emitted	Half-life	E(MeV)
$_{93}Np^{237}$	α	2.2×10^6 yr	4.79, 4.52–4.87
$_{91}Pa^{233}$	β	27.4 days	0.26, 0.14, 0.57
$_{92}U^{233}$	α	1.62×10^5 yr	4.82, 4.78, 4.73
$_{90}Th^{229}$	α	7300 yr	4.85, 4.94, 5.02
$_{88}Ra^{225}$	β	14.8 days	0.32
$_{89}Ac^{225}$	α	10 days	5.80
$_{87}Fr^{221}$	α	4.8 min	6.30, 6.07
$_{85}At^{217}$	α	1.8×10^{-2} sec	7.02
$_{83}Bi^{213}$	β α	47 min	β 1.39 α 5.90
$_{84}Po^{213}$	α	4.0×10^{-6} sec	8.34
$_{81}Tl^{209}$	β	2.2 min	1.8, 2.3
$_{82}Pb^{209}$	β	3.3 hr	0.62
$_{83}Bi^{209}$	stable		

SOURCE: *Chart of the Nuclides,* 5th ed. (1956), The General Electric Company.

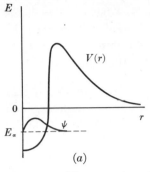 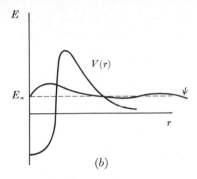

(a)   (b)

Fig. 30–7. *The wave functions of an α-particle moving in the potential of a heavy nucleus with* (a) *energy less than zero and* (b) *energy greater than zero.*

α-particle outside the nucleus; i.e., the particle can escape by tunneling through the potential hilltop. If we idealize the situation and consider a square barrier (Fig. 30–8) of a height V_0 and a width d, the wave function inside the barrier (Chapter 20) takes the form

$$\psi \propto e^{-\sqrt{2M\alpha(V_0 - E\alpha)}\; x/\hbar}$$

The ratio of the wave function at b to that at a is therefore

$$\frac{\psi(b)}{\psi(a)} = e^{-\sqrt{2M\alpha(V_0 - E\alpha)}\; d/\hbar} \qquad (30\text{–}6)$$

The square of this ratio should be a measure of the probability of finding the particle at b rather than at a; i.e., the probability of penetration. If the probability is small, say 10^{-15}, the effect of doubling d or quadrupling $V_0 - E_\alpha$ is enormous; indeed it changes the probability to 10^{-30}. It is clear, therefore, that a small decrease in the α-particle energy E_α, say from 7 MeV to 5 MeV, which in the "real" potential (Fig. 30–6) both increases the effective height $V_0 - E_\alpha$ and the effective width d of the barrier, can increase the half-life by many orders of magnitude. The enormous differences in the observed half-lives (Tables 30–1 to 30–4) with modest differences in decay energies can therefore be understood in terms of the α-decay as a quantum mechanical tunneling process.

The α-particle does not really exist as an independent particle in the

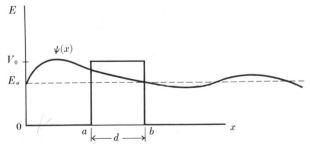

Fig. 30–8. *Wave mechanical tunneling through a potential barrier.*

interior of the nucleus, but there is known to be a correlating of nucleons into α-particle clusters at the surface of the nucleus, and it is here that the penetration, if any, of the barrier must take place. Our crude model cannot be expected to give more than a qualitative understanding of α-decay in any event.

By comparing the masses of nuclei (Table 27–1), we find that E_α as given by Eq. 30–5 should be positive for nuclei with mass numbers much below $A \approx 208$, where the natural radioactive series (Tables 30–1 to 30–4) end. For these nuclei, however, E_α is so small, $E_\alpha < 4$ MeV, and the tunneling probability so slight that for all practical purposes the nuclei are stable (Prob. 30–6).

30–5 FISSION

The process of fission, in which a nucleus divides into two nearly equal fragments, has already been discussed in terms of the liquid drop model (Chapter 29). But fission may also be viewed as an "α-decay" in which the α-particle has been replaced by a particle some 25 times heavier. In comparing α-decay and fission as tunneling processes, it is clear from Eq. 30–6 that the larger mass of the fission fragment tends to lessen the probability of the fission process. On the other hand the energy release is much larger in fission than in α-decay. This may be deduced from Fig. 27–3, which shows that the binding energy per nucleon, B/A, is considerably larger for $A \approx 120$ than for $A \approx 240$. The difference is mainly caused by the coulomb force term (Eq. 29–3), which increases with $Z^2 A^{-1/3}$, or with $A^{5/3}$ for a fixed Z/A ratio. The coulomb term is therefore $2^{5/3} \approx 3.2$ times bigger, or 1.6 times bigger per nucleon, for a nucleus with mass number A than for one with mass number $A/2$. Since the coulomb energy is an "anti-binding" term, this leads to less binding per nucleon for the very heavy nuclei. In the fission of a nucleus of atomic number Z, mass number A, and mass $M_{Z,A}$ into two equal fragments of atomic number $Z/2$, mass number $A/2$, and mass $M_{Z/2,A/2}$, the energy release E_f is equal to

$$E_f = (M_{Z,A} - 2M_{Z/2,A/2})c^2 \tag{30–7}$$

An estimate of this energy for a typical fission reaction may be obtained by using the mass formula, Eqs. 29–8 and 29–6. The first two terms in Eq. 29–8 drop out in forming the difference $M_{Z,A} - 2M_{Z/2,A/2}$. The fission energy E_f is therefore obtained by subtracting the binding energy before the fission reaction from the total binding energy of the two fission fragments. From Fig. 27–3 we see that $B/A \approx 8.4$ MeV for $A \approx 120$, and $B/A \approx 7.6$ MeV for $A \approx 240$. In the fission of an $A \approx 240$ nucleus the energy release is therefore

$$E_f \approx (8.4 - 7.6) \times 240 \text{ MeV} \approx 200 \text{ MeV}$$

This energy is to be compared with the 4 to 9 MeV released in an α-decay.

If we draw the potential energy of one fission fragment as a function of its separation from the other, we obtain a curve, Fig. 30–9, analogous to that of an α-particle in the field of the daughter nucleus (Fig. 30–6). The fission fragment, like the α-particle, has a potential barrier to penetrate. This follows from the discussion in Section 29–1, where we found that small deformations from the spherical shape *increase* the total energy of a nucleus for $A \lesssim 390$ (surface tension > coulomb repulsion). In comparing the tunneling probability of a fission fragment and an α-particle, the fission fragment has the advantage of a larger energy release, but the disadvantage of a larger mass (note the dependence on mass in Eq. 30–6). On balance, fission cannot compete with α-decay for any of the heavy nuclei listed in Tables 30–1 to 30–4. Fission does not occur spontaneously, therefore, but it can be *induced* through the addition of a modest amount of energy to a heavy nucleus.

Three important heavy nuclei, $_{92}U^{235}$, $_{92}U^{233}$, and $_{94}Pu^{239}$, have the property of undergoing fission quite readily upon the absorption of a *slow neutron*, i.e., a neutron of negligible kinetic energy. In falling into the nucleus, the slow neutron reduces its potential energy by an amount equal to its binding to the nucleus (a few MeV). This energy reappears as added agitation of the nucleus and often this additional kinetic energy is enough to cause fission. That slow neutrons can trigger the fission of these nuclei is important, since the probability of a nucleus capturing a slow neutron is much larger than the probability of capturing a fast one. A slow neutron spends more time in the vicinity of a given nucleus than does a fast one, and so has more time to be absorbed; it also has less excess energy to get rid of. In an average fission process 2 or 3 neutrons "boil" off. If one or more of these can be slowed down and captured to trigger new fission events, the process of fission can be sustained. The nearly simultaneous fission of a large mass of heavy nuclei in such a *chain reaction* was first achieved by Fermi and co-workers in 1942.

In fission, as in all decays of unstable systems, we are converting rest energy into kinetic energy. The 200 MeV released in a fission is less than 0.1 percent of the total rest energy, but in the fission of a macroscopic quantity of "fissionable material," the total energy release is still enormous. The utilization of this energy in nuclear reactors and in uranium bombs

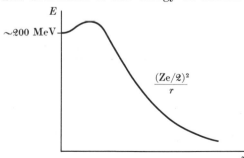

Fig. 30–9. The relative potential energy of two fission fragments as a function of their separation.

is well known. The details of these applications will not be discussed here. Only a few words about the source of our fissionable materials: as is evident from Tables 30–1 to 30–4, all naturally occurring nuclei heavier than $A = 209$ owe their existence to the three long-lived nuclei $_{92}U^{238}(4.5 \times 10^9$ yr), $_{92}U^{235}(7.1 \times 10^8$ yr), and $_{90}Th^{232}(1.39 \times 10^{10}$ yr). These are the only heavy nuclei ($A > 209$) that occur in any quantity on Earth and the only possible "raw material" for our nuclear fuel. Only $_{92}U^{235}$ is usable as it stands, i.e., fissionable upon absorbing a slow neutron, but the relative abundance of this isotope is only 0.7 per cent. Although the very abundant $_{92}U^{238}$ and $_{90}Th^{232}$ cannot be used as fission fuel directly, they can be transformed through the absorption of a neutron followed by two β^--decays into the fissionable nuclei $_{94}Pu^{239}$ and $_{92}U^{233}$, respectively. It may therefore be possible to burn all of our heavy nuclei in fission reactors. This could be done if with the neutrons from a $_{92}U^{235}$ reactor more nuclear fuel is made from $_{90}Th^{232}$ and $_{92}U^{238}$ than is consumed in the reactor. This has indeed been achieved in so-called "breeder" reactors.

30–6   FUSION

Let us return for a moment to Fig. 27–3, from which it is clear that the average nucleon binding energy is greatest for nuclei of mass number A equal to about 50. Both the lighter and the heavier are less tightly bound. Energy will therefore be released in the *fusion* of light nuclei as well as in the fission of heavy ones. Indeed the fusion of hydrogen into helium is known to be the main source of energy in the stars, including our sun.

Unlike the fission of uranium, which is usually triggered by the capture of a neutral particle, fusion can only be achieved by bringing two positively charged particles within a few fermis of each other against their coulomb repulsion. At a distance of 2×10^{-13} cm, two protons have a coulomb potential energy of 0.72 MeV. Since this energy increases with the square of the atomic number Z, it becomes increasingly difficult to fuse nuclei as they get heavier. The fusion of hydrogen is the most important fusion process as well as the one most easily achieved.

The principal cycle that fuses hydrogen into helium in the sun is now believed to be the *proton-proton chain*. This is a three-step process:

$$H^1 + H^1 \rightarrow H^2 + e^+ + \nu + 0.42 \text{ MeV}$$

$$H^1 + H^2 \rightarrow He^3 + \gamma + 5.5 \text{ MeV}$$

$$He^3 + He^3 \rightarrow He^4 + 2H^1 + 12.8 \text{ MeV}$$

The net result is

$$4H^1 \rightarrow He^4 + 2e^+ + 2\gamma + 2\nu + 26.7 \text{ MeV}$$

(About 0.5 MeV is carried off by the neutrinos.) The estimated temperature in the interior of the sun is about 2×10^7 °K for an average kinetic energy, $\frac{3}{2}kT$, of about 1 keV. This energy is not nearly enough to "hurdle" the coulomb barrier. Some of the protons in the energy distribution will have much higher energy, however, and these particles in the high-energy tail of the distribution fuse more readily. Besides, it is possible to tunnel in through the coulomb barrier in fusion, as well as tunnel out in α-decay. The fusion rate in the sun is actually quite slow, with about 10^{-11} of the sun burning per year.

The fusion reaction is also of great interest because of the promise it holds for a cheap and abundant source of power here on Earth. The proton-proton chain is not very promising because the first reaction in the chain is exceedingly slow. On Earth we do not have to fuse protons, however, since deuterons are readily available. Heavy water constitutes about 1 part in 5000 of ordinary seawater, and can be extracted very cheaply. This makes possible fusion reactions of the following types:

$$H^2 + H^2 \rightarrow He^3 + n + 3.25 \text{ MeV}$$
$$H^2 + H^2 \rightarrow H^3 + H^1 + 4.0 \text{ MeV}$$
$$H^3 + H^2 \rightarrow He^4 + n + 17.6 \text{ MeV}$$

and

$$H^2 + He^3 \rightarrow He^4 + H^1 + 18.3 \text{ MeV}$$

With these four reactions, it is possible to reach an over-all conversion of six deuterons as follows:

$$6H^2 \rightarrow 2He^4 + 2H^1 + 2n + 43 \text{ MeV}$$

This is a conversion of about 0.4 per cent of the deuteron rest energy into kinetic energy, a considerable increase over the fission yield. The main advantages of a fusion reactor over a fission reactor, however, lie in the cheap and abundant fuel and the absence of dangerous radioactive wastes.

The fusion of deuterons is not a very probable event. Even at the optimum energy, the particles are much more likely to collide elastically. If a high energy deuteron is not to dissipate its energy in these collisions before it has a chance to undergo fusion, the particles with which it collides must also be of high energy. With the average particle in the reacting volume at the high energy ~ 10 keV needed for appreciable fusion (tunneling in through the coulomb barrier), we find that the temperature of the reacting gas is about 10^8 °K, at which temperature (Chapter 10) the gas is of course completely ionized. The reacting material in a fusion reactor must therefore be a plasma, and we are faced with the problems of heating this plasma to the required temperature and confining it for a time sufficient for appreciable fusion to occur. The only practical way to confine plasmas seems to be with magnetic fields. The attempts made to achieve confined plasmas in devices such as the *stellarator* and the *magnetic mirror machines* were briefly discussed in Chapter 11.

30-7   OTHER REACTIONS

The number of nuclear reactions that has been studied is counted in the thousands. We will only mention a few of special interest here.

The first induced nuclear reaction ever achieved was by Rutherford in 1919. This earliest recorded reaction was

$$_2He^4 + {}_7N^{14} \rightarrow {}_8O^{17} + {}_1H^1$$

It is an example of an (α, p) or "alpha-proton reaction" (alpha in, proton out), and is usually abbreviated

$$N^{14}(\alpha, p)O^{17}$$

The first (α, n) or "alpha-neutron reaction" is particularly interesting, since it was the reaction in which the neutron was discovered by Chadwick in 1932 (Chapter 31):

$$_2He^4 + {}_4Be^9 \rightarrow {}_6C^{12} + {}_0n^1, \text{ or}$$
$$Be^9(\alpha, n)C^{12}$$

This reaction is also of practical interest, since it is one of the most common sources of neutrons.

Since neutrons have no electric charge, they are usually detected through (n, p) or (n, α) reactions in which the charged reaction products can be "seen." An example of this is a Geiger tube filled with a boron trifluoride (BF_3) gas, in which a neutron is detected through the reaction

$$B^{10}(n, \alpha)Li^7$$

The α-particle as well as the Li nucleus produce ions in the gas which trigger a discharge in the tube. Thus the neutron is detected.

Tritium is a good "fusion fuel." It can be produced most readily by bombarding lithium with neutrons (e.g., from nuclear reactors) in the (n, α) reaction,

$$_3Li^6 + {}_0n^1 \rightarrow {}_1H^3 + {}_2He^4$$

Deuteron reactions are particularly important for producing isotopes not found in nature. The (d, p) reactions form nuclei with an excess of neutrons, and (d, n) reactions form nuclei with an excess of protons.

Of special interest are the nuclei that lie above ${}_{92}U^{238}$ in the periodic table, the *transuranium elements*. These have been formed in a variety of ways; we will mention only one example,

$$_{92}U^{238} + {}_6C^{12} \rightarrow {}_{98}Cf^{244} + 6{}_0n^1$$

Other common reactions that we will merely list are the (n, p), (p, n), (p, γ), (n, γ), $(p, 2n)$, $(n, 2n)$, and $(\alpha, 2n)$ reactions. The Ag^{110} and In^{116} isomers, whose decay schemes are given in Fig. 30–4, are usually produced from Ag^{109} and In^{115} through (n, γ) reactions.

At very high energies other particles, such as π-mesons and "strange" particles, are created in reactions of the type discussed in this section. These new particles form the subject of the next and final chapter.

PROBLEMS

30–1.　We know the half-lives of U^{238} and U^{235} (Tables 30–1 and 30–2) and their present relative abundance (Table 27–1). Assuming that there were equal amounts present of the two isotopes when the Earth was formed, estimate the age of the Earth.

30–2. Calculate the fraction of the original amount of radioactive material left after 10 and after 100 half-lives.

30–3. Calculate the radioactivity (in curies) of 1 gm of radium $_{88}Ra^{226}$ (Table 30–1).

30–4. What is the activity of 1 ton of Th^{232}?

30–5. One milligram of radioactive In^{116} is produced in the reaction In^{115} (n,γ) In^{116}. Assume that the In^{116} ground state (half-life 13 sec) and the isomer (Fig. 30–4(b)) with a 54-min half-life are produced in equal amounts. Plot the resulting β^--activity (on a log scale) versus time.

30–6. Suppose that $_{60}Nd^{144}$ α-decays into $_{58}Ce^{140}$. Calculate the energy of the α-particle. From Table 30–3 plot the α-particle energy versus the log of the half-life for the thorium series. Extrapolate the curve to estimate the half-life of $_{60}Nd^{144}$.

30–7. From Table 27–1 calculate the maximum electron energy in the β^--decay of H^3 (also denoted by T for tritium).

30–8. Calculate the Q (see Chapter 6) of the following reactions: $B^{10}(n,\alpha)Li^7$, $Be^9(\alpha,n)C^{12}$, $N^{14}(\alpha,p)O^{17}$, $Cl^{35}(p,\alpha)S^{32}$. For each reaction calculate the minimum energy of the incoming particle (the threshold energy) that will permit the reaction to occur. At threshold the reaction products move together if Q is positive.

30–9. The minimum proton energy needed (the threshold energy) for the reaction $_{29}Cu^{65}$ (p,n) $_{30}Zn^{65}$ is 2.16 MeV. Calculate the Q of the reaction (see Section 6–2), and the mass of $_{30}Zn^{65}$. How would you expect $_{30}Zn^{65}$ to decay?

30–10. In the fusion of two oxygen isotopes $_8O^{16} + {}_8O^{17} \rightarrow {}_{16}S^{32} + n$, calculate the total energy released and compare it to the coulomb energy between the oxygen nuclei when they are just touching.

30–11. O^{14} decays to an excited state of N^{14} with the emission of a positron. The maximum kinetic energy of the positrons is observed to be 1.81 MeV and the γ-ray emitted when N^{14} decays to its ground state has an energy of 2.31 MeV. Calculate the mass of O^{14} from the known (Table 27–1) mass of N^{14}.

REFERENCES

I. Kaplan, *Nuclear Physics* (Addison-Wesley, 1963, 2nd ed.), Ch. 10–16, 19.

W. E. Burcham, *Nuclear Physics* (McGraw-Hill, 1963), Ch. 13–16.

H. Semat, *Introduction to Atomic and Nuclear Physics* (Holt, Rinehart and Winston, 1962, 4th ed.), Ch. 11–14.

31/elementary particles

Much of the history of physics can be characterized as a probing away from the world of everyday human experience inward and downward to the microscopic world. In the 20th century this probing has reached the world of elementary particles, a world in which distances are typically measured in fermis (10^{-13} cm). In his search for the deepest substructure of matter the scientist has continually been guided and stimulated by his faith in the underlying simplicity and symmetry of nature.

The idea that matter is constituted of elementary particles is now generally accepted, although on further examination the particles turn out to be less "elementary" than hoped for at first. An elementary particle should not be thought of as a tiny billiard ball. It is merely the smallest known entity to which we can assign definite numbers for mass, spin, electric charge, and certain other more mysterious properties to be defined later. One might ask in what sense the particles making up a large molecule are more "elementary" than, say, the grains of sand making up a beach. There is a fundamental difference here between the elementary particles and the grains of sand (aside from the difference in size). All the electrons in a molecule (and indeed in the universe as far as we know) are identical particles, whereas on close examination no two grains of sand on a beach have ever been found to be exactly alike. It is a source of great wonder that nature in its myriad of forms should be made up of a few groups of precisely identical objects. This is not to say that the elementary particles themselves have no internal structure. Indeed, the electric charge distributions in the proton and the neutron have been a subject of intensive study in recent years. The internal structure of the elementary particles will undoubtedly receive increasing attention in the years ahead, and whether the presently known particles will themselves be understood in terms of still more elementary entities is an open question.

To the physicist the discovery of a new elementary particle is an exciting event. Although we cannot hope to recapture the drama and the excitement of their discovery in this brief discussion, it seems proper to introduce the elementary particles in their historical context.

31-1 THE DISCOVERY OF THE PARTICLES

The corpuscular nature of matter is far from self-evident. Thus the possibility that electricity is a continuous homogeneous fluid was seriously considered and not excluded until the existence of the first elementary particle, the *electron*, was established through J. J. Thompson's measurement of its charge to mass ratio in 1897. In view of the size of present-day equipment in particle physics, it is interesting to note that Thompson's entire apparatus, in which he measured the deflections of cathode rays (electrons) in electric and magnetic fields, was about a foot long.

The next particle to be "discovered" was the *photon*. As discussed in Chapters 17 and 18, the corpuscular nature of light was established through the work of Planck (1900) and Einstein (1905). Until the 1930s, however, the photon was not regarded as a "true" elementary particle on a par with, say, the electron. The photons have no mass, always travel with the speed of light in every reference frame, and they can freely appear and disappear (i.e., they are emitted and absorbed). "Real" particles—it was thought—existed forever. With the advance of the quantum theory, however, the difference between a photon and a massive particle narrowed. In particular, one found that massive particles could also be created and annihilated. The photon is now considered an elementary particle in good standing.

A major step forward was taken in 1911 when Rutherford's scattering experiments (Chapters 5 and 6) established the existence of the atomic nucleus. The famous Rutherford picture of the nuclear atom, and the work by Bohr which quickly followed, revolutionized atomic physics. In the present context, however, we merely wish to point out that the existence of a positively charged atomic nucleus implies the existence of the *proton*, since the proton is simply the nucleus of the hydrogen atom.

For some twenty years the proton, the electron, and the photon, which we shall denote by the symbols p, e^-, and γ, respectively, were the only known particles. The properties of these and more recently discovered particles are summarized in Table 31–1. Although the period 1911–31 was a quiet one in particle physics, it was as we have seen a period of tremendous progress in atomic physics and quantum theory. The quietude in particle physics was broken in 1932 with the discovery of the *neutron n* by J. Chadwick and the positive electron or *positron e^+* by C. D. Anderson.

The penetrating neutral radiation given off in the reaction

$$_4\text{Be}^9 + {}_2\text{He}^4 \rightarrow {}_6\text{C}^{12} + n$$

had been assumed by earlier workers to consist of gamma rays. Chadwick aimed the radiation at targets containing hydrogen and nitrogen, respectively. By measuring the velocities of the protons and the nitrogen nuclei knocked out of the targets by the neutrons, he was able to determine their mass to be approximately that of the proton. The properties of the neutron are summarized in Table 31–1. As we have discussed in the preceding four chapters, the discovery of the neutron marked the real beginning of modern nuclear physics. It was now possible to understand the constitution of all the elements in terms of the *nucleons* (protons and neutrons) and the electrons. Perhaps it would have been nice if we could have ended our story here, since most of the recently discovered particles added confusion rather than understanding to the picture.

The positron was discovered by Anderson with the help of a *cloud chamber*, an ingenious instrument for making tracks of charged particles visible, invented by C. T. R. Wilson. Charged particles knock electrons out of atoms as they pass through matter, forming a trail of ions. The cloud chamber is the first of a line of clever schemes for making this local ionization visible. In a cloud chamber the charged particle leaves a visible track of droplets condensing on the ions in a supersaturated gas. In a *nuclear emulsion* the charged particle activates the silver bromide grains in the emulsion to form a "latent image," which is developed by proper chemical treatment into the pure silver grains of the final photograph. A more recent and very useful discovery, made by D. Glaser in 1952, is that particle tracks can be made visible through the formation of gas bubbles in a liquid in which the pressure has suddenly been reduced below that at which the liquid boils. This discovery led to the *bubble chamber*. Finally we should mention the *spark chamber*, first used in its modern form by T. Cranshaw and J. deBeer. It consists of a series of parallel plates in a gas. When a high voltage is applied between adjacent plates, sparks occur along the path of ionizing particles, and these sparks can be photographed.

Anderson exposed a cloud chamber to *cosmic rays*, high energy particles impinging on Earth from space. One of his photographs revealed a particle that looked precisely like an electron, but which curved in the opposite direction in the applied magnetic field. (The density of droplets is characteristic of each particle; that is how an electron can be recognized.) Subsequent experiments have shown the positron to have exactly the same mass, the same spin, and a charge equal in magnitude and opposite in sign to that of the electron. The positron was actually predicted a few years earlier by the relativistic quantum theory of the electron formulated by P. A. M. Dirac. Dirac's equation is invariant under a symmetry operation called "charge conjugation" (Section 31–3), and as a consequence it has solutions corresponding to the ordinary particle (the electron) as well as the "charge conjugate particle" or the *antiparticle* (the positron). Which is called the particle and which the antiparticle is a matter of convention. The convention is that the ordinary matter in our part of the universe is made up of particles, but this does not exclude the possibility of "antimatter" made up of antiparticles elsewhere. The most startling prediction and the most brilliant success of the Dirac theory is the prediction of the complete *annihilation* of an electron and a positron with the entire rest energy of the two particles converted into radiant energy (or photons) and the inverse process of the *creation* of an electron-positron pair from a photon (pair production, Chapter 17). The success of Dirac's theory for the electron soon led to the speculation that every particle might have an antiparticle partner and that any particle, no matter how massive, could be created and annihilated. Of particular interest was the possible existence of anti-nucleons. After the construction of the six billion electron volt proton accelerator, the Bevatron, of sufficient energy to create these heavy anti-particles, the question was settled with the discovery of the *antiproton* $\bar{p}$ in 1955 and the *antineutron* $\bar{n}$ in 1956.

It is difficult to attach a definite date to the "discovery" of the *neutrino*. Its existence was suggested by Pauli in 1930 to save the law of conservation of energy in beta decay (Chapter 30). Soon it was found to be the savior of the momentum and angular momentum conservation laws as well. Pauli's suggestion preceded the discovery of the neutron and he viewed the neutrino as well as the electron as existing inside the nucleus prior to the beta decay. With the advent of the neutron, the presence of electrons inside the nucleus was no longer necessary to account for the mass number A's being larger than the atomic number Z. Fermi (1934) took advantage of this in constructing a theory for the beta decay process in which the electron and the neutrino were created at the moment of the decay in the same way that a photon is created in gamma decay or in atomic de-excitation. Fermi's theory has proved very successful; its main features are still accepted today. The processes of creation and annihilation of particles are now thought to govern all of the basic interactions in nature.

To conserve angular momentum in beta decay it was necessary to assign a spin quantum number of $\frac{1}{2}$ to the neutrino. The neutrino, like the electron, proton, and neutron, is therefore subject to the Pauli exclusion principle (Section 22–3). The mass of the neutrino is thought to be exactly zero and is known experimentally to be less than one thousandth of the electron mass.

The conventions regarding which neutrino is the particle and which the antiparticle have changed since 1934. The particle emitted in β-decay is now called the *antineutrino*, $\bar{\nu}$,

$$n \rightarrow p + e^- + \bar{\nu}$$

while the particle emitted in β^+-decay is called the *neutrino*, ν,

$$p \rightarrow n + e^+ + \nu$$

Because of their weak interaction with other particles, the neutrinos are exceedingly difficult to observe directly. Not until 1956 was this task accomplished. The neutrinos discussed here, which are born in association with electrons, are now often indicated with the subscript e, ν_e and $\bar{\nu}_e$, to distinguish them from another distinct pair of neutrinos, ν_μ and $\bar{\nu}_\mu$, associated with the *muon*, μ.

We will discuss the *muon* and the *pion*, π (also called the π-meson) together. Although they are very different particles, the histories of their discoveries are much intertwined.

In 1935 the Japanese theoretical physicist Yukawa suggested that the strong force between nucleons was mediated by a nuclear force field in the same way that the force between charged particles is mediated by the electromagnetic field between them. The nuclear force field, like the electromagnetic force field, would be expected to be quantized. If the nuclear field quanta, like the electromagnetic quanta or photons, had no rest mass, Yukawa showed that the nuclear potential should have an infinite range, falling off with distance as r^{-1} in analogy with the coulomb potential. A field quantum of rest mass m, however, led to a potential of the form $r^{-1}e^{-rmc/\hbar}$, which has a range of the order of $\hbar/mc$, the "Compton wave length" of the field quantum. With a nuclear force range of the order of 2 fermis,

$$2 \times 10^{-13} \text{ cm} \approx \hbar/mc$$

we obtain

$$m \approx 200m_e$$

where m_e is the mass of the electron. Because the expected mass was intermediate between that of the electron and the nucleons, the particle was dubbed the *meson*.

We can understand Yukawa's result in a crude way from the uncertainty principle,

$$\Delta E \, \Delta t \gtrsim \hbar$$

In a time Δt the energy of a nucleon will be uncertain by at least $\Delta E = \hbar/\Delta t$, and its mass M uncertain by $\Delta M = \Delta E/c^2 = \hbar/c^2\Delta t$. If ΔM is as large as the mass m of the meson, $\Delta M = m$, we cannot know whether the system consists of a nucleon or a nucleon and a meson. This uncertainty in the mass, however, only lasts for a short time,

$$\Delta t = \hbar/\Delta E = \hbar/mc^2$$

during which time the meson, if it existed at all, must have been emitted and reabsorbed. For $m \approx 200m_e$ this time is exceedingly short,

$$\Delta t \approx 10^{-23} \text{ sec}$$

This is the time it takes a particle travelling with the speed of light to travel a nuclear distance. It is therefore a natural unit of time on the nuclear scale. In this time Δt the meson can travel no further than

$$c \, \Delta t = \hbar/mc$$

or a distance equal to its Compton wave length. According to Yukawa's ideas, then, the nucleon, even when isolated from all other particles, may constantly emit and reabsorb field quanta or mesons. The nucleon is surrounded by a "meson cloud" out to a distance of the order of $\hbar/mc$. If, as Yukawa assumed, the mesons could carry electric charge, the proton might for brief moments exist as a neutron and a positively charged meson and the neutron as a proton surrounded by a negatively charged meson. This view is supported by recent high energy electron-nucleon scattering experiments, which reveal that the neutron has a net positive charge out to a radius of about 0.6 f and a net negative charge outside this radius. The mesons in the "cloud," which have only a momentary existence chained to the nucleon, are called *virtual* mesons. They are not real observable particles, because energy conservation prevents their escape from an isolated nucleon. When a second nucleon comes within the meson cloud, i.e., within a distance $\hbar/mc$ of the first nucleon, however, a meson emitted by one of the nucleons has time to travel to the other before energy conservation demands its disappearance. This way a meson can transmit momentum, angular momentum, energy, and even charge from one nucleon to another; the nucleons *interact* through an exchange of mesons.

In 1937, two years after Yukawa published his meson theory, Neddermeyer and Anderson, and also Street and Stevenson, independently reported finding a cosmic ray particle with a rest mass of the order predicted by Yukawa. The particle was immediately hailed as Yukawa's nuclear field quantum, but further work showed that something was very wrong. Since the Yukawa particle is assumed to transmit nuclear forces, it must interact strongly with nuclei. As a consequence it should be quickly absorbed in passing through matter. The particle discovered in 1937, now known as the *muon*, μ, was found to penetrate matter easily and thus to interact weakly with nuclei. It was demonstrated in 1947 that the forces transmitted by the muon were weaker than the strong nuclear forces by a factor of at least 10^{13}.

The resolution of this dilemma came the same year (1947) through the discovery of the π-meson or *pion* by C. F. Powell and his group. The pions are found to interact strongly with nuclei and are identified with Yukawa's mesons. (Actually Yukawa only discussed the charged pions, π^+ and π^-. The neutral pion π^0 was first predicted in 1939 by N. Kemmer.) The masses of π^- and its antiparticle π^+ are $273.1m_e$, while the neutral π^0, which like the photon is its own antiparticle, has a mass of $264.3m_e$. The charged pions decay predominantly into muons and neutrinos with a measured mean life of 2.55×10^{-8} sec,

$$\pi^+ \longrightarrow \mu^+ + \nu_\mu$$
$$\pi^- \longrightarrow \mu^- + \bar{\nu}_\mu$$

while the neutral pion π^0 decays into 2 photons with a mean life of about 2×10^{-16} sec,

$$\pi^0 \longrightarrow 2\gamma$$

The pions have no spin; $s = 0$.

The muon remains somewhat of a mystery. It seems to be identical to the electron in all its properties except for the difference caused by its much larger mass, $m_\mu = 206.8 m_e$. The origin of the large mass of this "heavy electron" and the reason for the existence of this "unnecessary" particle are among the many intriguing unsolved problems of elementary particle physics.

It is conventional to regard the μ^- as the "particle" and μ^+ as the "antiparticle" in analogy with the electron convention. (There is no neutral muon.) The muon is unstable and decays into an electron and a pair of neutrinos,

$$\mu^+ \rightarrow e^+ + \nu_e + \bar{\nu}_\mu$$
$$\mu^- \rightarrow e^- + \bar{\nu}_e + \nu_\mu$$

with a mean life of 2.21×10^{-6} sec. The fact that the muon's neutrino ν_μ differs from the electron's neutrino ν_e was established in 1962 by a Columbia University group. In this experiment neutrinos ν_μ and $\bar{\nu}_\mu$ arising from the decays of π^+ and π^- were captured by nucleons in the reactions

$$\bar{\nu}_\mu + p \rightarrow n + \mu^+$$
$$\nu_\mu + n \rightarrow p + \mu^-$$

Some of the muons created in these reactions were observed in a spark chamber. The chamber was shielded by 44 feet of iron from the battleship Missouri to keep out all particles other than the desired neutrinos. Some 3×10^{17} protons were accelerated to 15 GeV to produce enough pions for an estimated 10^{14} neutrinos (pion decay products) to pass through the chamber. The difficulty of the experiment is illustrated by the fact that only twenty-nine of these 10^{14} neutrinos were observed to produce muons. If the muon neutrino ν_μ and the electron neutrino ν_e were identical, we would expect that electrons and positrons would be created along with the muons in reactions such as

$$\bar{\nu}_e + p \rightarrow n + e^+$$

Indeed, it was through this reaction that the electron antineutrino arising from beta decay was first observed by C. Cowan and F. Reines in 1956. Not a single event of this kind was observed with the muon neutrinos originating in pion decays, however, and we must conclude that ν_e and ν_μ are two different particles. We may regard the existence of a distinct muon neutrino as another piece in the "muon puzzle." The electron and the muon together with their respective neutrinos make up the family of particles known as the *leptons*, from the Greek meaning "light weight."

The elementary particle situation as known in 1947 was reasonably simple. Electrons and nucleons were necessary to build the nuclear atom, and photons and pions were needed to transmit the electromagnetic and nuclear forces, respectively. The existence of antiparticles seemed like a pleasant aspect of symmetry in nature. Only the muons and the neutrinos appeared to have no place in the scheme of things, but their presence did not clutter the landscape unduly. Since that time, however, a host of new and unexpected particles has been discovered. Collectively these were named the *"strange particles."* From 1947 to 1953 the only source of sufficient energy to produce these heavy unstable particles was the cosmic radiation. The number of cosmic strange particles was few and far between, and progress was slow until 1953, when the first particle accelerator of sufficient energy to produce strange particles in the laboratory went into operation (the 3-GeV cosmotron at Brookhaven). By 1956, when the situation began to clear a bit, a total of 16 new "elementary" particles had either been discovered or were firmly expected to exist. (Some of the antiparticles had not yet been observed.) The strange particles fell into two main groups, the two *K-mesons* or *kaons* with their antiparticles and the six *hyperons* and their antiparticles. The K-mesons like the π-mesons have spin zero and are known to play a role in the transmission of the strong nuclear forces at very short distances. Because of the large energy needed to create a K-meson, the range of the kaon potential (≈ 0.3 f) is much shorter even than the pion (or Yukawa) potential. There are four K-mesons in all, the positively charged K^+ and the neutral K^0 with their antiparticles K^- and $\overline{K}^0$. (The K^0 and the $\overline{K}^0$ are quite distinct particles.)

The hyperons may be thought of as heavy and "strange" nucleons. Along with the nucleons they make up a group of eight particles known as *baryons*, from the Greek meaning "heavy weight." The hyperons come in 3 groups or *charge multiplets*. The least heavy hyperon is the neutral Λ^0 (lambda), which stands alone. Next comes a charge triplet Σ^+, Σ^0, and Σ^- (sigma), and finally the heavy "cascade" particle doublet Ξ^0 and Ξ^- (xi). All these hyperons have a spin of $\frac{1}{2}$ and thus obey the Pauli exclusion principle.

The mass, charge, spin, and mean life of all the elementary particles observed (or expected and since observed) by the middle 1950s are given in Table 31-1. We have also included in this table the distinct muon neutrino (established in 1962) and the *graviton*, the hypothetical quantum of the gravitational field, as well as the recently discovered η^0-meson and Ω^--hyperon.

The important decay modes of the elementary particles and their relative probabilities are listed in Table 31-2. The decay modes of the antiparticles are obtained by replacing all the decay products by their antiparticles. The decay of the neutral K-meson is particularly fascinating since the K^0 (or $\overline{K}^0$) behaves as though it were a mixture of two other particles, dubbed K_1^0 and K_2^0, which decay at different rates.

The era of the "strange particles" (the 1950s) has been followed by the era of the *"resonances"* (the 1960s). The so-called resonances are elementary particles which are so short-lived ($\sim 10^{-22}$ sec) that they may not deserve to be called particles at all. Grouped with the resonances, however, there will be an occasional long-lived particle, such as the newly discovered Ω^-. This particle has a mean life of about 10^{-10} sec, and thus deserves the name particle every bit as much as the others listed in Table 31-1. Special interest was attached to this particle since it was predicted as the sole long-

TABLE 31-1. The Elementary Particles

Particle	Symbol	Mass (in units of m_e)	Charge	Spin	Mean Life (seconds)	Antiparticle
Graviton (?)	g	0	0	2	stable	g itself
Photon	γ	0	0	1	stable	γ itself
Leptons:						
Neutrinos	ν_e	0	0	½	stable	$\bar\nu_e$ (Antineutrinos)
	ν_μ	0	0	½	stable	$\bar\nu_\mu$
Electron	e^-	1	$-e$	½	stable	e^+ (Positron)
Mu minus	μ^-	206.77 ± 0.02	$-e$	½	$(2.212 ± 0.001) × 10^{-6}$	μ^+ (Mu plus)
Mesons:						
Pi zero	π^0	264.2 ± 0.1	0	0	$(2.2 ± 0.8) × 10^{-16}$	π^0 itself
Pi plus	π^+	273.2 ± 0.1	$+e$	0	$(2.55 ± 0.03) × 10^{-8}$	π^- (Pi minus)
K plus	K^+	966.6 ± 0.4	$+e$	0	$(1.224 ± 0.013) × 10^{-8}$	K^- (K minus)
K zero	K^0	974 ± 1	0	0	K_1^0: $(1.00 ± 0.04) × 10^{-10}$ K_2^0: $(6.1 ± 1.4) × 10^{-8}$	$\bar K^0$ (K zero-bar)
Eta	η^0	1072 ± 2	0	0	$\sim 10^{-18}$ (?)	η^0 itself
Baryons:						
Proton	p	1836.12 ± 0.02	$+e$	½	stable	$\bar p$ (Antiproton)
Neutron	n	1838.65 ± 0.02	0	½	$(1.01 ± 0.03) × 10^3$	$\bar n$ (Antineutron)
Lambda	Λ^0	2182.8 ± 0.3	0	½	$(2.51 ± 0.09) × 10^{-10}$	$\bar\Lambda^0$ (Antilambda)
Sigma plus	Σ^+	2327.7 ± 0.4	$+e$	½	$(0.81 ± 0.06) × 10^{-10}$	$\bar\Sigma^-$ (Antisigma minus)
Sigma zero	Σ^0	2331.8 ± 1.0	0	½	less than $10^{-11} \sim (10^{-19}?)$	$\bar\Sigma^0$ (Antisigma zero)
Sigma minus	Σ^-	2340.5 ± 0.6	$-e$	½	$(1.61 ± 0.10) × 10^{-10}$	$\bar\Sigma^+$ (Antisigma plus)
Xi zero	Ξ^0	2565 ± 8	0	½	approximately 10^{-10}	$\bar\Xi^0$ (Antixi zero)
Xi minus	Ξ^-	2580 ± 2	$-e$	½	$(1.3 ± 0.4) × 10^{-10}$	$\bar\Xi^+$ (Antixi plus)
Omega minus	Ω^-	3300 ± 20	$-e$	3/2 (?)	$\sim 10^{-10}$	$\bar\Omega^+$ (Antiomega plus)

lived member of a group of 10 resonances by a symmetry scheme known as the *eight-fold way*. Our knowledge of the resonances is still fragmentary, but as their number (counting the different charge states and the anti-resonances) approaches 100 it becomes increasingly clear that the particles in Table 31–1 only represent the beginning of the story. The resonances

TABLE 31–2. Decay Modes of the Unstable Particles

Decay Reaction	Relative Probability(%)
$\mu^+ \rightarrow e^+ + \nu + \bar{\nu}$	100
$\pi^0 \rightarrow 2\gamma$	99
$\rightarrow \gamma + e^+ + e^-$	1
$\pi^+ \rightarrow \mu^+ + \nu$	99.99
$\rightarrow e^+ + \nu$	0.01
$K^+ \rightarrow \mu^+ + \nu$	64
$\rightarrow \pi^+ + \pi^0$	19
$\rightarrow 2\pi^+ + \pi^-$	6
$\rightarrow \pi^0 + e^+ + \nu$	5
$\rightarrow \pi^0 + \mu^+ + \nu$	5
$\rightarrow \pi^+ + 2\pi^0$	2
$K_1^0 \rightarrow \pi^+ + \pi^-$	67
$\rightarrow 2\pi^0$	33
$K_2^0 \rightarrow \pi^+ + e^- + \bar{\nu} \left.\begin{array}{c}\\\\\end{array}\right\}$ $\rightarrow \pi^- + e^+ + \nu$	48
$\rightarrow \pi^+ + \mu^- + \bar{\nu} \left.\begin{array}{c}\\\\\end{array}\right\}$ $\rightarrow \pi^- + \mu^+ + \nu$	38
$\rightarrow \pi^+ + \pi^- + \pi^0 \left.\begin{array}{c}\\\\\end{array}\right\}$ $\rightarrow 3\pi^0$	14
$\eta^0 \rightarrow 2\gamma$	$\sim$35
$\rightarrow 3\pi^0$	$\sim$30
$\rightarrow \pi^+ + \pi^- + \pi^0$	$\sim$30
$\rightarrow \pi^+ + \pi^- + \gamma$	$\sim$5
$n \rightarrow p + e^- + \bar{\nu}$	100
$\Lambda^0 \rightarrow p + \pi^-$	67
$\rightarrow n + \pi^0$	33
$\Sigma^+ \rightarrow p + \pi^0$	50
$\rightarrow n + \pi^+$	50
$\Sigma^0 \rightarrow \Lambda^0 + \gamma$	100
$\Sigma^- \rightarrow n + \pi^-$	100
$\Xi^0 \rightarrow \Lambda^0 + \pi^0$	$\sim$100
$\Xi^- \rightarrow \Lambda^0 + \pi^-$	$\sim$100
$\Omega^- \rightarrow \Lambda^0 + K^-$	?
$\rightarrow \Xi^0 + \pi^-$	?
$\rightarrow \Xi^- + \pi^0$	?

Notes: (a) For the decays of antiparticles, turn all particles into antiparticles on *both* sides of the equations.
(b) The K^0's and $\bar{K}^0$'s actually produced are half K_1^0 and half K_2^0 at the instant of production, with changing fractions as they die away.

are all heavy particles which interact strongly with each other and with the longer-lived mesons and baryons, but which are not prevented by any conservation law from decaying in the very short time ($\sim 10^{-22}$ sec) characteristic of strong interactions. Since the list is still constantly being revised, there is no point in including one here. Not even the present names are likely to be permanent.

Many attempts have been made at picturing most of the particles as *"composites"* of a few "elementary" particles. An early speculation along these lines came as early as 1949 when E. Fermi and C. N. Yang suggested that the pions might be bound nucleon-antinucleon pairs. In a recent speculative treatment the number of truly elementary particles is reduced to one basic baryon and one basic lepton plus a number of mesons (not including the pions!) necessary to carry the force fields.

A different point of view, which is currently quite popular, is that all the strongly interacting particles, including mesons as well as baryons, are on an equal footing. In this picture no particle is more "elementary" than any other; they are all regarded as *states of excitation* of a single system. Attempts are being made to systematize the quantum numbers of the particles, e.g., by plotting the "mass levels" versus the angular momentum quantum numbers much as in the energy level diagrams of an atom (Figs. 21–6 and 23–1). The "Bohr theory" explaining the mass levels of the particles does not appear to be right around the corner, however. The particle problem is an exceedingly complex one. But most physicists share a deep faith in simplicity, in simple answers to seemingly complex questions, and the search goes on.

31-2 ELEMENTARY PARTICLE INTERACTIONS

We have seen (Table 31–1) that there are some 36 different elementary particles and antiparticles, not including the large number of recently discovered "resonances." Each particle is found to exert a force on every other particle, although the strength of the interaction may vary enormously. The mean free path of a low energy neutron in solid matter is measured in centimeters, while an average neutrino would travel a galactic distance through a solid wall before being absorbed in an inverse beta decay reaction. Even if we leave out the resonances there are several hundred different pairs of elementary particles to consider. The striking fact about the interactions among the elementary particles is that they all fall into one of just four very distinct classes:

1. The strong interactions.
2. The electromagnetic interactions.
3. The weak interactions.
4. The gravitational interactions.

Perhaps the most remarkable difference between these four interactions is the enormous disparity of strengths. On a scale where the strong interactions (the "nuclear glue") are assigned a strength of 1, the electromagnetic interactions would have a strength of $\sim 10^{-2}$, the weak interactions $\sim 10^{-13}$, and the gravitational interactions $\sim 10^{-38}$. Since all the particles (other than the hypothetical unobserved graviton) also interact through forces other than the gravitational one, the effect of the gravitational interaction is completely negligible at the elementary particle level.

All the baryons, mesons, and resonances interact strongly, i.e., all particles except the leptons, the photon, and the graviton. Very likely the "strong interaction" is a collection of different forces of roughly the same strengths, but since the situation remains unresolved we shall not dwell on it here. The strong interactions are responsible for the nuclear binding, the annihilation of baryon-antibaryon pairs, the production of strange particles through energetic bombardment of nucleons, and both the production and the decay of the briefly existing ($\sim 10^{-22}$ sec) resonances.

All particles except the neutrinos and the graviton experience electromagnetic interactions. This is the interaction which is responsible for all chemical and biological activity and which determines the structure of matter outside the nucleus. It is fundamental to all human activity. At the microscopic level all electromagnetic effects can be understood in terms of the emission and absorption of photons.

The weak interaction is felt by all particles except the graviton. It is the strongest force felt by the neutrinos, while all other particles can also interact electromagnetically or both electromagnetically and strongly. Since some conservation laws (Section 31–3) obeyed by the stronger forces can be violated by the weak interaction, it can mediate processes that are otherwise forbidden. Thus the weak interaction is responsible for all the decays listed in Table 31–2 with the exception of those of π^0, η^0, and Σ^0, which proceed electromagnetically. The weakly decaying particles (Table 31–1) typically have mean lives of the order of 10^{-8} to 10^{-10} sec, while the "resonances" which are broken up by the strong forces have a mean life shorter by a factor of $\sim 10^{13}$, i.e., 10^{-21}-10^{23} sec. In low energy nuclear physics the weak interaction plays a significant role only through the processes of β^-- and β^+-decay and electron capture. Whether the weak interaction is mediated by a quantized force field (the hypothetical W-mesons) is not known. Such field quanta have never been observed.

The gravitational interaction is experienced by all particles, but because of its weakness the effect of gravity is negligible in elementary particle interactions. Gravity only becomes important when the stronger forces are inoperative, such as between electrically neutral bodies separated by a macroscopic distance. It is of course the all-important force on a cosmic scale. Although many physicists are convinced that the gravitational forces are transmitted by gravitons, the quantum aspects of gravitation have so far proved unobservable.

From the preceding discussion the following rules emerge: the weaker the force, the more particles it embraces. Furthermore, any particle capable of feeling a particular force in the hierarchy will also experience all weaker interactions. The reasons for these rules are not understood.

31-3   INVARIANCE PRINCIPLES AND CONSERVATION LAWS

Conservation laws occupy a central position in modern physics. We are already familiar with a number of conservation laws (Chapter 3). In particular, we recall that an isolated system must conserve *energy, momentum, angular momentum,* and *electric charge.* In the world of elementary particles a number of other conservation laws have been discovered. Most of these are empirical rules whose existence is not understood in any deep sense. They are most welcome, however, since they impose some law and order upon the chaotic events of continual creation and annihilation in the submicroscopic world. The conservation laws severely restrict the number of possible elementary particle reactions, a number which in any case is embarrassingly large. Physicists have adopted the hypothesis that everything that *can* happen without violating a conservation law indeed *does* happen. To put it differently: when some reaction unexpectedly does not happen, one looks for a new conservation law.

To illustrate the power of conservation laws we note that the conservation of energy and electric charge ensures the absolute stability of the electron. Conservation of energy implies, of course, that a particle can only decay into particles lighter than itself. Since there are no charged particles lighter than the electron, it cannot decay.

It is an empirical fact that the number of baryons minus the number of antibaryons is strictly conserved in all reactions. If we assign a *baryon number* of $+1$ to the baryons and -1 to the antibaryons, we can say that the total baryon number is always conserved. It should be noted that some of the "resonances" also are baryons in this sense. The conservation of baryons implies the stability of the proton, since the proton is the lightest baryon. All lighter particles have a baryon number equal to zero, so the proton cannot be converted into, say, a positron and γ-rays without changing the total baryon number of the system. On the other hand the decay of the Λ^0,

$$\Lambda^0 \rightarrow p + \pi^-$$

is permitted since the baryon numbers before and after the decay are equal $(= +1)$. Similarly, the typical antiproton production reaction,

$$p + p \rightarrow p + p + p + \overline{p}$$

is allowed since the baryon number $+2$ is conserved, as is the electric charge. Another allowed reaction is the annihilation of a proton and an antiproton into pions,

$$p + \overline{p} \rightarrow \pi^+ + \pi^- + \pi^0$$

Other "family numbers" that are conserved are the *electron-family number* and the *muon-family number*. The electron family consists of the electron

e^- and its neutrino ν_e, while the muon family members are the muon μ^- and its neutrino ν_μ. Again the particles are given a family number of $+ 1$ and the antiparticles a number $- 1$. As an example consider the beta decay,

$$n \rightarrow p + e^- + \bar{\nu}_e$$

Since n and p are assigned a number equal to zero, the electron $+ 1$, and

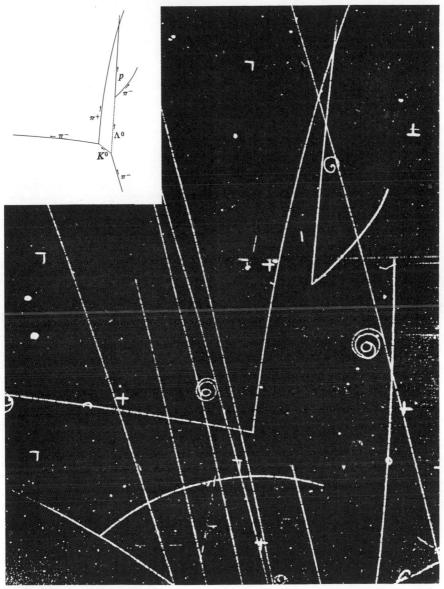

Fig. 31–1. A bubble chamber picture showing the reactions $\pi^- + \mathrm{p} \rightarrow \Lambda^0 + \mathrm{K}^0$; $\Lambda^0 \rightarrow \pi^- + \mathrm{p}$; $\mathrm{K}^0 \rightarrow \pi^- + \pi^+$. [Courtesy of Lawrence Radiation Laboratory, Berkeley, Calif.]

the antineutrino − 1, the total electron family number is conserved. In the muon decay,

$$\mu^- \rightarrow e^- + \bar{\nu}_e + \nu_\mu$$

the muon number is + 1 and the electron number 0 on both sides of the equation. Similarly in the pion decays,

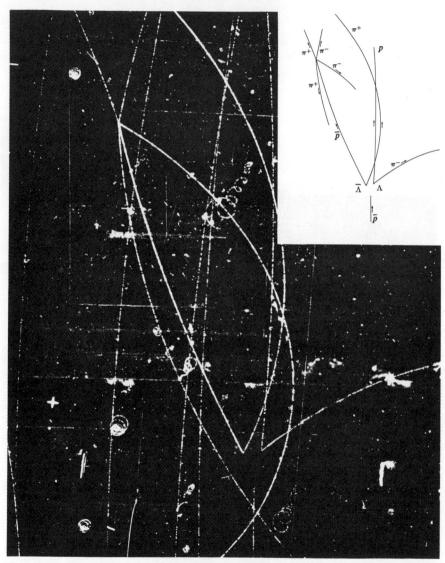

Fig. 31–2. The production and decay of a lambda-antilambda pair in a hydrogen bubble chamber. The antiproton annihilates a proton forming four pions. [Courtesy of Lawrence Radiation Laboratory, Berkeley, Calif.]

and
$$\pi^+ \rightarrow \mu^+ + \nu_\mu$$
$$\pi^- \rightarrow \mu^- + \bar{\nu}_\mu$$

the muon family number is conserved.

Before the discovery of a distinct muon neutrino (1962), μ^-, e^-, and ν were considered a single family, and one spoke of the conservation of the lepton number. The decay of a muon into an electron and a photon,

$$\mu^- \rightarrow e^- + \gamma$$

should then be allowed, and the fact that it wasn't was known as the "μ-e-γ puzzle." With the separate conservation laws of muon and electron family numbers, the puzzle is resolved, since the decay is now forbidden.

The energy, momentum, angular momentum, electric charge, and the family numbers of baryons, muons, and electrons appear to be *absolutely conserved* in all elementary particle interactions. The next conservation law that we shall discuss is a *partial conservation law*, a law obeyed by some interactions but not all.

When it became possible to produce strange particles in the laboratory (1953), it turned out that they were very easy to create. They were produced so readily in high energy collisions of "non-strange" particles (in about 10^{-22} sec) that one had to conclude that they were created in a *strong interaction*. Yet, once produced, they lived about 10^{13} times longer

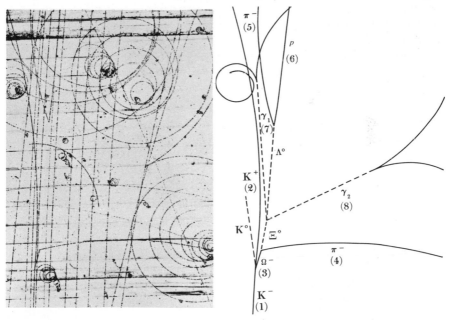

Fig. 31–3. The production and decay of an Ω^--particle. An incoming K^--meson collides with a stationary proton in the hydrogen bubble chamber with the production of a K^0-meson, a K^+-meson, and the Ω^-. [Courtesy of Brookhaven National Laboratory, Upton, Long Island, N.Y.]

than it took to produce them (Table 31–2). They were produced in strong interactions, but the apparently inverse process of decay proceeded through the weak interaction. This is what was so "strange" about the new particles. It occurred to Gell-Mann and Nishijima independently that the long life of the strange particles could be explained by a new conservation law in the same way that the conservation of electric charge explains the long life of the electron and the conservation of baryon number accounts for the stability of the proton. The new conserved quantity was called "*strangeness.*" The non-strange nucleons and pions were assigned strangeness number 0, the Λ and Σ particles $-\,1$, the $\Xi\ -\ 2$ and the K-meson $+\,1$. Of the most recent particles η^0 has a strangeness of 0 and Ω^- has $-\,3$. The antiparticles have strangeness numbers of opposite sign to those of the corresponding particles.

The Gell-Mann–Nishijima scheme has proved entirely successful. It is clear from this scheme that strange particles can only be produced from non-strange particles in pairs (or higher multiples) if strangeness is to be conserved; e.g.,

$$\pi^- + p \rightarrow \Lambda^0 + K^0$$

or

$$p + p \rightarrow \Xi^0 + p + K^0 + K^+$$

This process of "associated production" of kaons and hyperons was actually first proposed by A. Pais. The experimental evidence is now overwhelming: strangeness conserving processes and no others are observed to proceed via the strong interactions. If we examine the strange particle decays listed in Table 31–2, we see that they all (except Σ^0) violate strangeness conservation by one unit of strangeness. The mean lives of all these decays (other than Σ_0) are typical of the weak interactions, and we conclude that *strangeness is conserved by the strong and the electromagnetic interactions but may change by one unit in the weak interactions.*

Another partial conservation law is the *conservation of isotopic spin*, a law obeyed by the strong interactions but violated by both the electromagnetic and the weak interactions. When the neutron was discovered, Heisenberg suggested that the neutron and the proton should be considered different charge states of a single particle, the nucleon. The nucleon, then, is a *charge doublet*. In analogy with a spin doublet associated with a spin of $\frac{1}{2}$, the nucleon being a charge doublet was said to have an *isotopic spin* of $\frac{1}{2}$. Similarly a charge triplet like the pion has an isotopic spin of 1, in complete analogy to a spin triplet with ordinary spin equal to 1. Isotopic spin like ordinary spin is a vector, not in our ordinary space but in "isotopic spin space." Remarkably, this entity is conserved by the strong interactions, but need not be conserved by the others. Examples of violations are the decays of Λ^0 in Table 31–2. Thus Λ^0, which is a charge singlet, has isotopic spin 0, whereas its decay products have isotopic spin $\frac{1}{2}$ (the nucleon) and 1 (the pion), respectively. It is clearly impossible for spins $\frac{1}{2}$ and 1 to combine into a spin 0 state.

There is an intimate connection between the conservation laws of physics and "principles of invariance." Thus the invariance of a physical system under translation (the homogeneity of space) can be shown to imply the conservation of momentum, invariance under rotation (the isotropy of space), the conservation of angular momentum, and invariance to displacements in time (the homogeneity of time), the conservation of total energy. We shall not indulge in the mathematics needed to prove these statements rigorously here, but we can make the connection between conservation laws and principles of invariance plausible by recalling some of the results from Chapter 3: the linear momentum of a physical system is conserved in the absence of external forces (a constant external potential). But with a constant potential the system must be invariant to a spatial translation, since such a translation changes nothing. Similarly, with a potential that is a function only of the radial distance from a fixed point, a physical system must be left invariant under a rotation about this point. With such a central potential we did find the angular momentum to be conserved (Chapter 3). If the potential depends on the spatial coordinates but not on time, the system is invariant with respect to time displacements, and with such a potential (Chapter 3) we know that the total energy is conserved. It is indeed satisfying that the three powerful conservation laws of energy, momentum, and angular momentum can be founded simply upon these "obvious" statements of symmetry in space and time.

It is usually assumed, though not rigorously proved, that every conservation law is founded upon a principle of invariance, and conversely that for every principle of invariance there is "something" that is conserved. This connection is subtle and for some conservation laws the associated principles of invariance are by no means understood. Still, this connection seems worth pursuing, since a physical law anchored in a statement of symmetry in nature is likely (though not certain) to endure. Not all of the conservation laws are related to symmetries in space and time. Thus the conservation of charge follows from the invariance of the laws of physics under mathematical operations called "gauge transformations," and the conservation of isotopic spin results from invariance under rotations of the isotopic spin vector in "isotopic spin space." These statements are not likely to mean much divorced from the mathematical formulation of the theory. Suffice it to say that these conservation laws as well as the family conservation laws of baryon, muon, and electron numbers are associated with *intrinsic symmetries* of the system with no known relation to ordinary space-time.

We will now turn to three cases, time reversal, space inversion, and charge conjugation, where the principles of invariance are easier to visualize than "what is conserved."

Suppose that instead of making a displacement in time we reversed the time coordinate. Then all velocities $d\mathbf{r}/dt$ would change sign so that all motion would be reversed. The question is whether all physical processes running backwards in time would also be possible physical processes.

Newtonian mechanics is known to be invariant under time reversal. Thus the equation of motion for a particle in a potential V,

$$m \frac{d^2\mathbf{r}}{dt^2} = - \boldsymbol{\nabla} V$$

is clearly unchanged (or invariant) when t is replaced by $-t$. At the elementary particle level it is known that all strong and electromagnetic interactions are *invariant under time reversal*, and the same may be true of the weak interaction. In that case the time reverse of any real process is also a possible process. The *constraint* implied by this invariance becomes clearer if we rephrase the statement as follows: a process is forbidden unless it can also happen in the opposite order.

Next let us consider the reversal of space coordinates. Since the reversal of two coordinate axes is equivalent to a rotation of the coordinate system, and the reversal of all three coordinates equivalent to the reversal of one coordinate followed by a rotation, we need consider only the reversal of a single coordinate. Through the reversal of *one* space coordinate a physical system is converted into its *mirror image*. If a physical process is invariant under this reversal, i.e., if the mirror image of the process is also a possible process, we say that *parity* is conserved. Until 1956 it was taken for granted that parity was conserved. All macroscopic laws of physics possess this invariance. A mirror image of a normal everyday event is certainly a *possible* event. The person you see in the mirror *could* have been the real you, although if you are right-handed he is left-handed. When T. D. Lee and C. N. Yang examined the experimental basis of this invariance in 1956, they found, contrary to the generally held belief, *no* experimental evidence for right-left symmetry in the weak interactions. They suggested

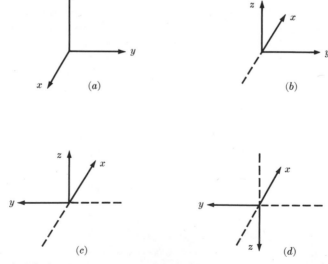

Fig. 31–4. A right-handed coordinate system with one, two, and three coordinate axes inverted.

that parity was not in fact conserved in the weak interactions and proposed an experiment to test this hypothesis. This suggestion actually grew out of a difficulty with the decay modes of the kaon (Table 31–2). The kaon could not decay into 2 pions sometimes and 3 pions other times if parity were conserved. The proposed experiment was carried out by C. S. Wu and co-workers. Radioactive Co^{60} nuclei were oriented predominantly with their spins in one direction (this required working below about 0.1°K). The electrons emitted in the process of beta decay were then surprisingly observed to come out predominantly in the direction opposed to the Co^{60} spin. The mirror image of this experiment (Fig. 31–5) shows the Co^{60} nuclei spinning in the opposite direction and the electrons coming out in the direction *along* the spin. The mirror image in other words shows a process that does *not* occur in the real world. This is the famous "breakdown of parity conservation." This breakdown is further illustrated by the discovery that the neutrino is "left-handed." The neutrino *always* has its spin pointing in a direction opposite to its direction of motion (backward), like a left-handed screw advancing. (The antineutrino is right-handed.) The mirror image of a left-handed neutrino is a right-handed neutrino (Fig. 31–6), which does not exist. The mirror image of any process involving a neutrino therefore shows an impossible process, and consequently parity conservation is violated in all neutrino reactions. Other weak interactions, such as the Λ^0-decay, $\Lambda^0 \rightarrow p + \pi^-$, are also known to violate the conservation of parity even though no neutrinos are involved. The conservation of parity is still a powerful conservation law, however, since it is strictly obeyed by the strong and the electromagnetic interactions. Only the weak interactions violate left-right symmetry.

The final symmetry operation that we shall study is *charge conjugation.* This is a very general mathematical operation on the "intrinsic spaces" of the particle which changes the signs of the electric charge, the particle family number (e.g., baryon number), and the strangeness number, but which changes nothing in ordinary space such as the orientation of the spin. The strong and the electromagnetic interactions are invariant under charge conjugation. Thus in a system of strongly interacting particles the

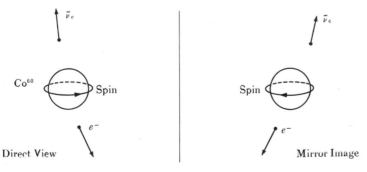

Fig. 31–5. The β-decay of Co^{60} and its mirror image.

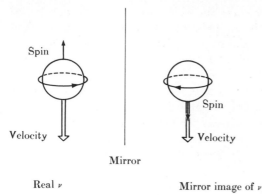

Mirror

Real ν Mirror image of ν

Fig. 31–6. A real neutrino and its mirror image.

forces and the resulting motion would remain the same if every particle was suddenly converted into its "charge conjugate" particle. The weak interactions, however, do not display this symmetry. The left-handedness of the neutrino, which violates space-inversion invariance, also violates charge-conjugation invariance. Since charge conjugation converts a left-handed neutrino into a left-handed antineutrino, which does not exist, the operation of charge conjugation converts any reaction involving a neutrino into an impossible reaction.

The combined operations of space inversion and charge conjugation will turn a left-handed neutrino into a right-handed antineutrino, a *possible* particle. Thus the real process of π^+-decay,

$$\pi^+ \longrightarrow \mu^+ + \nu_\mu$$

is converted into the real process of π^--decay

$$\pi^- \longrightarrow \mu^- + \bar{\nu}_\mu$$

by space inversion plus charge conjugation. Until the summer of 1964 it appeared that all processes mediated by the weak interaction (as well as the strong and the electromagnetic interactions) were invariant under the combined space inversion–charge conjugation operation. More recent experiments on K-meson decay, however, indicate that for the weak interaction this invariance may be only approximate. Since there are very strong theoretical reasons to suppose that the weak interaction is exactly invariant under the triple combination of time reversal, space inversion, and charge conjugation, this implies that the exact time reversal invariance of the weak interaction is now also in doubt. The issue is not completely settled, however.

We find that *the stronger the interaction the more severely it is restricted by conservation laws.* Thus the strong interactions are subject to the following twelve conservation laws or principles of invariance:

Conservation of: Energy
Momentum
Angular momentum
Electric charge
Electron-family number
Muon-family number
Baryon number

Invariance under: Combined time reversal, space inversion, and charge conjugation
Time reversal alone (and combined space inversion and charge conjugation)
Space inversion alone (and also charge conjugation alone)

Conservation of: Strangeness
Isotopic spin

Electromagnetic interactions are hemmed in by the first eleven of these laws but can violate the isotopic spin conservation law. The weak interactions obey the first eight and possibly the ninth but violate the conservation laws of parity, strangeness, and isotopic spin. Whether still more conservation laws are violated by the weakest known interaction, gravity, is an open question, since nothing is known about the gravitational interaction at the elementary particle level. It is possible, for example, that the law of baryon conservation is violated by gravity, as suggested in a theory of the universe in which matter is continuously created.

The modern view of matter has indeed taken a surprising turn. Instead of laws of certainty we find laws of chance, and instead of permanent building blocks we find a chaos of creation and annihilation, of virtual particles appearing out of nowhere only to disappear again quickly. Channeling this chaotic activity we find the conservation laws, which impose their order in the microscopic world, stabilize the electron and the proton, and make possible the highly organized structures of matter with which we are familiar in the macroscopic world. A deeper understanding of these conservation laws and the search for new symmetries in nature are among the most basic goals of modern physics.

PROBLEMS

31-1.   In the decay of a π^+-meson at rest:
(a) How much energy is carried off by the neutrino?
(b) What is the speed of the μ^+-particle?

31-2.   In the decay of a neutron at rest, $n \rightarrow p + e^- + \bar{\nu}$, what is the maximum possible energy of the electron?

31–3.   What is the energy and wave length of the photon emitted in a Σ^0-decay at rest?

31–4.   A η^0-meson decays into two photons, both of which make an angle of 30° with respect to the direction of the η^0-meson. What is the kinetic energy of the η^0? Compare the kinetic energy and the rest energy.

31–5.   Write all the decay reactions leading from a Ω^--particle into stable particles.

31–6.   In the photo-production of pions, $\gamma + p \rightarrow \pi^+ + n$, what is the minimum photon energy that will make this reaction take place? (*Hint*: At "threshold" there is no relative pion-neutron motion.)

31–7.   The first Ω^--hyperon was observed in February 1964. It was produced at Brookhaven National Laboratory with an energetic K^--beam striking protons at rest: $K^- + p \rightarrow K^+ + K^0 + \Omega^-$. What is the threshold energy for this reaction? Relativistic expressions must be used for momentum and energy.

31–8.   A π^--meson beam is directed at a hydrogen target. What is the threshold energy for the strange particle production

$$\pi^- + p \rightarrow \Lambda^0 + K^0?$$

31–9.   We wish to create a particle with a rest mass equal to 10 proton masses by aiming an energetic proton beam on a stationary proton target:

$$p + p \rightarrow p + \mathrm{x}$$

How energetic must the protons in the beam be?

31–10.   Indicate which of the following production reactions can proceed via the strong interaction (assuming that enough energy is available):

$$\pi^- + n \rightarrow K^- + \Lambda^0$$
$$\pi^+ + n \rightarrow K^+ + \Lambda^0$$
$$\pi^+ + p \rightarrow K^+ + \Sigma^+$$
$$\pi^- + n \rightarrow \Lambda^0 + K^0$$
$$\gamma + p \rightarrow n + \pi^+$$
$$\pi^- + p \rightarrow K^- + K^+$$
$$n + p \rightarrow \Lambda^0 + \Sigma^+$$

31–11.   Indicate which of the following decays are possible:

$$\Xi^- \rightarrow n + \pi^-$$
$$\Omega^- \rightarrow p + \pi^- + \pi^-$$
$$\Sigma^0 \rightarrow \Lambda^0 + e^- + e^+$$
$$\mu^- \rightarrow e^- + \bar{\nu}_e$$
$$\pi^+ \rightarrow \mu^+ + e^- + e^+$$
$$\Lambda^0 \rightarrow p + e^- + \bar{\nu}_e$$
$$\Lambda^0 \rightarrow K^- + \pi^+$$
$$K^- \rightarrow \pi^- + 3\pi^0$$
$$\pi^- \rightarrow e^- + \nu_e$$

For possible decays give the interaction by which it proceeds. For impossible decays, mention which conservation laws are violated.

REFERENCES

C. N. Yang, *Elementary Particles* (Princeton University Press, 1962).

K. W. Ford, *The World of Elementary Particles* (Blaisdell, 1963).

D. H. Frisch and A. M. Thorndike, *Elementary Particles* (Van Nostrand, 1964).

D. L. Anderson, *The Discovery of the Electron* (Van Nostrand, 1964).

appendix a/units and conversion factors

The electromagnetic force is written in a different form depending on whether the cgs or the mks system of units is to be used.

	cgs	mks
Coulomb's Law	$F = \dfrac{qq'}{r^2}$	$F = \dfrac{qq'}{4\pi\epsilon_0 r^2}$
Lorentz Force	$\mathbf{F} = q(\mathbf{E} + \dfrac{\mathbf{v}}{c} \times \mathbf{B})$	$\mathbf{F} = q(\mathbf{E} + \mathbf{v} \times \mathbf{B})$

All the other mechanical equations are the same in the two systems, except for differences arising from the introduction of the above forces. The following table lists the relations between the cgs Gaussian and the mks units.

Length	l	meter	m	10^2 cm
Mass	m	kilogram	kg	10^3 g
Time	t	second	sec	1 sec
Force	$\mathbf{F}$	newton	N	10^5 dyne
Pressure	P	newton per sq meter	N/m²	10 dyne/cm²
Energy	E	joule	J	10^7 erg
Power	P	watt	W	10^7 erg/sec
Charge*	q	coulomb	C	3×10^9 esu
Current*	I	ampere	A	3×10^9 esu/sec
Potential*	Φ	volt	V	1/300 statvolt
Electric field*	$\mathbf{E}$	volt per meter	V/m	$1/3 \times 10^4$
Conductivity*	σ	mho per meter	Ω^{-1}/m	9×10^9
Resistance*	R	ohm	Ω	$1/9 \times 10^{11}$
Capacity*	C	farad	F	9×10^{11}
Magnetic field	$\mathbf{H}$	ampere-turn per meter	A/m	$4\pi/10^3$ oersted
Magnetic induction	$\mathbf{B}$	weber per sq meter	Wb/m²	10^4 gauss
Flux	ϕ	weber	Wb	10^8 maxwell
Inductance	L	henry	H	10^9

The international standards are based on the mks units. This fact is significant only for those electrical quantities, marked by an asterisk *, in which the speed of light c occurs in the conversion factor, since these relations depend on the experimental value of c. In the above conversion table, we have assumed for convenience that the speed of light is $c = 3 \times 10^8$ m/sec. For a more accurate conversion, wherever 3 appears $(9 = 3^2)$ it should be replaced by the value 2.9979 from Appendix B. The permeability of free space μ_0 in the mks system is defined to be $\mu_0 = 4\pi/10^7$. The permittivity of free space ϵ_0 is an experimental quantity, $\epsilon_0 = 1/\mu_0 c^2$, whose value is listed in Appendix B; $1/4\pi\epsilon_0 = c^2/10^7 \cong 9 \times 10^9$ m/F.

Other units are derived from these by using prefixes that indicate a multiple or submultiple of a unit. The following table lists these prefixes (with their symbols) and the factor by which the unit is multiplied.

10^{12}	tera	T		10^{-2}	centi	c	
10^9	giga	G	(jĭ′ gȧ)	10^{-3}	milli	m	
10^6	mega	M		10^{-6}	micro	μ	
10^3	kilo	k		10^{-9}	nano	n	
10^2	hecto	h		10^{-12}	pico	p	(pē′ cȯ)
10	deka	da		10^{-15}	femto	f	
10^{-1}	deci	d		10^{-18}	atto	a	

For example, a kilometer (km) is 10^3 meters. (10^{-6} m is not called a micrometer, however, but a micron, symbol μ.) Occasionally the prefixes are combined, so that one may speak of kilomegacycles rather than gigacycles, for example.

A large number of other units, which belong neither to the cgs nor the mks system, is used for specialized purposes. Those which are used in this book are the following:

angström	Å	10^{-8} cm
astronomical unit*	au	1.49598×10^{13} cm
atmosphere	atm	1.01325×10^6 dyne/cm² ($\times 10^5$ N/m²)
atomic mass unit	amu (C¹²)	1.660×10^{-24}g
bar	bar	10^6 dyne/cm² (10^5 N/m²)
barn	barn	10^{-24} cm²
calorie (thermochemical)	cal	4.184×10^7 erg (4.184 joule)
curie	curie	3.70×10^{10} disintegrations/sec
day (mean solar)	d	8.64×10^4 sec
electron volt*	eV	1.602×10^{-12} erg ($\times 10^{-19}$ joule)
fermi	f	10^{-13} cm
foot	ft	30.48 cm
hour	h	3600 sec
light-year*	light-yr	9.46055×10^{17} cm
liter	l	10^3 cm³
micron	μ	10^{-6} m
mile	mi	1.609344 km

millimeter mercury*	mm Hg	1.333224×10^3 dyne/cm^2 ($\times 10^2$ N/m^2)
poise	p	1 dyne-sec/cm^2 (10^{-1} N sec/m^2)
torr	Torr	1 mm Hg
year (calendar)	yr	3.1536×10^7 sec

Most of these units are *defined* by the relation given. A few of them, however, marked with an asterisk *, are defined in some other terms, so that the relation given is an *experimental* one. Some of the prefixes in the preceding table are used with some of these units: e.g., μbar, kcal, GeV, mμ.

appendix b/physical constants

Avogadro's number	$N_0 = 6.023 \times 10^{23}$ mole^{-1}
Gas constant	$R = 8.314 \times 10^7$ erg/mole °K
Boltzmann constant	$k = R/N_0 = 1.381 \times 10^{-16}$ erg/°K
Standard volume of ideal gas	$V_0 = 2.241 \times 10^4$ cm^3/mole
Stefan-Boltzmann constant	$\sigma = 5.67 \times 10^{-5}$ erg/cm^2 sec °K^4
Gravitational constant	$G = 6.67 \times 10^{-8}$ dyne cm^2/g^2
Speed of light	$c = 2.9979 \times 10^{10}$ cm/sec
Permittivity of vacuum	$\epsilon_0 = 8.854 \times 10^{-12}$ farad/m
Electronic charge	$e = 4.803 \times 10^{-10}$ esu
	$= 1.602 \times 10^{-19}$ coulomb
Electron mass	$m_e = 9.109 \times 10^{-28}$ g
	$m_e c^2 = 0.5110$ MeV
Proton mass	$m_p = 1.6725 \times 10^{-24}$ g
	$m_p c^2 = 938.3$ MeV
Neutron mass	$m_n = 1.6748 \times 10^{-24}$ g
	$m_n c^2 = 939.6$ MeV
Planck constant	$h = 6.6256 \times 10^{-27}$ erg sec
	$\hbar = 1.0545 \times 10^{-27}$ erg sec
Fine structure constant	$\alpha = e^2/\hbar c = 7.297 \times 10^{-3}$
	$1/\alpha = 137.04$
Rydberg constant	$R_\infty = 1.097373 \times 10^5$ cm^{-1}
Rydberg energy	$E_R = R_\infty hc = 13.605$ eV
Bohr radius	$a_0 = \hbar^2/m_e e^2 = 5.292 \times 10^{-9}$ cm
Compton wavelength	$\lambda_c = h/m_e c = 2.426 \times 10^{-10}$ cm
Classical electron radius	$r_e = e^2/m_e c^2 = 2.818 \times 10^{-13}$ cm
Bohr magneton	$\mu_B = 9.273 \times 10^{-21}$ erg/gauss
Nuclear magneton	$\mu_N = 5.051 \times 10^{-24}$ erg/gauss

index

* Principal entries are indicated by **boldface.**